Antennas and Techniques for
Low-Band DXing

*Your guide to ham radio DXcitement
on 160, 80 and 40 meters*

John Devoldere, ON4UN

D1599525

Published by
The American Radio Radio Relay League, Inc.
225 Main Street
Newington, CT 06111-1494

Contents

Foreword

Preface

1   **Low-Band Propagation**

2   **Operating Techniques**

3   **Equipment**

4   **The New Low-Band Software**

5   **Antennas: Introduction and Definitions**

6   **The Feed Line and the Antenna**

7   **Special Receiving Antennas**

8   **Dipole Antennas**

9   **Vertical Antennas**

10 **Large Loop Antennas**

11 **Vertical Arrays**

12 **Other Arrays**

13 **Yagis and Quads for the Low Bands**

14 **Literature Review**

Index

Foreword

The ARRL is pleased to publish John Devoldere's newly updated, revised and expanded book, *Antennas and Techniques for Low-Band DXing*. Although we are calling it a 2nd edition, in fact most of the book is new. The author's antenna analyses and operating tips are based on his extensive, highly successful and never-ending on-the-air contest and DX experience.

Those who have read and profited from ON4UN's earlier work, *Low-Band DXing*, will need no incentive to delve into this book. Those who have not had the chance to put John's uncommonly practical and readable analyses to work in their stations are in for a treat.

Whether you're a seasoned operator or a relative newcomer to the low bands, if you're looking for practical ways of improving your on-the-air success (and which of us isn't!), you've come to the right place.

As with all ARRL books, we are eager to hear your comments and suggestions. A handy form has been provided at the back that will help us make the next edition even better than this one.

David Sumner, K1ZZ
Executive Vice President

Newington, Connecticut
January 1994

Preface

When I think about the major changes in Amateur Radio in the last five years I see the following areas of improvement:

◆ Tremendous growth in interest in low-band DXing, also by most of the major DXpedition operators. The low bands no longer seem to be the inevitable escape bands for when the sunspots are down.

◆ The computer invasion. Modern transceivers use a multitude of microprocessors performing all kinds of tasks. It's hard to imagine a modern radio without microprocessors built in. In addition, the availability of powerful personal computers has brought the PC into just about every shack. Typical tasks are:
- antenna modeling and antenna physical designing
- propagation forecasting
- logging and contest-logging, QSL (label) printing, award tracking, etc.
- digital voice recording/playback
- packet radio/DX clusters
- RTTY, AMTOR, PacTOR and other digital transmission modes

◆ Finally, 160 meters has now become available to amateurs in just about all countries.

I have the feeling that *Low-Band DXing*, published in 1987 by the ARRL, has contributed somewhat to the gain in popularity of DXing on the low bands. I want to thank the many readers who have written to me for their support, comments, criticisms and suggestions.

The success of the book has convinced the publisher to have me update the book. Large sections of the book were all but completely rewritten, and in the antenna section generous use was made of the latest and most powerful computer analysis and modeling tools, until recently only available on mainframe computers. The equipment review section has been updated, and the book includes a unique and new list of top-notch low-band DXers with their scores as well as equipment and antennas. The large amount of data in the literature review section has now also been made available as a dedicated computer program for more convenience. The original *Low-Band DXing* software has been completely rewritten to be a very user friendly set of tools for the low-band enthusiast.

When the original *Low-Band DXing* book was written, I had very little first-hand experience with 160-meter DXing. Since then I have made up for that shortcoming, I think. I have experienced that 160-meter propagation can be quite different from 80 meters. The same is true for 40 meters as compared to 80 meters. I am glad to be able to share some of my new experiences with the readers of this book.

For their highly appreciated advice, help and encouragement during the preparation of this book and the new software I would like to express my appreciation and sincere thanks to Ben Moeller, **OZ8BV**, Mark Demeuleneere, **ON4WW**, Pat Morel, **ON4AMI**, Klaus Owenier, **DJ4AX**, George Oliva, **K2UO**, Uli Weiss, **DJ2YA**, Guenter Schwarzbeck, **DL1BU**, Rudi Klos, **DK7PE,** Chris Kaeferlein, **DK5CZ**, Ghis Penny, **ON5NT,** Claude Van Pottelsberghe de la Potterie, **ON7TK**, always ready to help with my antenna projects, my neighbor George Van Assche who is always available for the hard antenna work, as well as all the low-band DXers who have returned the survey form and are sharing the information about their station, antennas and results with us.

My good friend Roger Vermet, **ON6WU,** who has always been a reliable source for consultation on antenna matters, did all the NEC modeling used in this book, and has been a unique source of inspiration and encouragement in all my antenna projects.

A special word of thanks goes to my neighbor farmers, who over the years have allowed me to run my Beverage antennas across the fields during winter time.

Once more I want to say that I owe a lot to my family for supporting my hobbies the way they do. I dedicate this book to them.

John Devoldere, ON4UN
February 1, 1994

LOW-BAND PROPAGATION

■ **1. TIME**

1.1. The Year

    1.1.1. MUF and FOT

    1.1.2. D-layer activity

    1.1.3. Magnetic disturbances

    1.1.4. Low-band propagation during high sunspot years

1.2. The Season

    1.2.1. Winter (15 October to 15 February in the Northern Hemisphere)

    1.2.2. Summer (15 April to 15 August in the Northern Hemisphere)

    1.2.3. Equinox Period (15 August to 15 October and 15 February to 15 April)

    1.2.4. Propagation into the Equatorial Zones

1.3. Time Of Day

    1.3.1. Daytime

    1.3.2. Night-time

    1.3.3. Dusk and dawn: twilight periods

        Definition of gray-line

        Special propagation mechanisms

        Chordal-hop or whispering-gallery propagation

        Antipodal focusing

■ **2. LOCATION**

2.1. Latitude of Your Location vs Solar Activity

2.2. Magnetic Disturbances (Aurora).

2.3. Local Atmospheric Noise.

■ **3. PROPAGATION PATHS**

3.1. Great-circle Short Path

3.2. Great-circle Long Path

    3.2.1. Long path on 160 meters

3.3 Particular Non-Great-circle Paths

    3.3.1. Propagation paths and the heterogeneous ionosphere

    3.3.2. Avoiding auroral zones

    3.3.3. Crooked polar paths in midwinter

■ **4. 160 VS 80 METERS**

■ **5. DXING TOOLS**

5.1. The Gray-line Globe

5.2. The DX Edge

5.3. The Geochron Gray-Line Map

5.4. Calculating Sunrise And Sunset Times

5.5. The Sunrise / Sunset Tables

    5.5.1. General rules for using sunrise / sunset times

    5.5.2. Remarks

5.6. Personal Computer Programs

5.7. ON4UN Propagation Programs

    1. SUNRISE-SUNSET TIMES

    2. THE DATABASE

    3. LISTING SUNRISE SUNSET TIMES

    4. GRAY-LINE PROGRAM

■ **6. THE 160-METER MYSTERY**

LOW-BAND 1 PROPAGATION

Even more than on the higher bands, it is important to understand the exact mechanisms that govern propagation on the low bands. If you know that on 160 m the opening over a 15,000 km (10,000 mile) path will occur maybe 2 days a week, and then only during a specific time of the year, and that the opening will last maybe 3 to 5 minutes, you will realize how important it is to understand how, when and why. Otherwise, you'll be looking for a needle in a haystack.

Years ago, most of the professional literature on propagation described graphical methods for determining optimum HF propagation for a given path at a given time of day. More recently, these methods have been largely replaced by numerical methods, using sophisticated computer software to predict propagation based on the latest activity data from the sun.

In the world of commercial HF broadcasting and HF point-to-point communications, the challenge consists in finding the optimum frequency or maybe the best angle of radiation (to select the right transmitting antenna) that will give the most reliable propagation, as a function of the time of day. In our hobby of low-band DXing, the problem to be solved is quite different. The challenge is to determine the best time (month, day, and hour) to realize a contact on a given (low-band) frequency, with a given antenna setup, between two specific locations.

Instead of just explaining how to use propagation tools, this chapter tells about the mechanisms that govern propagation. However, this chapter is not meant to be a study on the subject of the physics of ionospheric propagation. Rather, it is meant to explain propagation in terms that the average DXer (not a PhD!) will understand.

The 160-meter experts will yell, "There's a world of difference between propagation on 80 meters and on 160 meters." True it is, but there are numerous common points as well. Years ago, both bands were often called "those noisy, short-range bands that mostly turn useless after sunset." Although generally 80 meters will produce stronger signals over any given path at a specific time, conditions have been reported by many where long-haul DX was actually stronger on 160 than 80 meters.

I will start from some very basic observations and mechanisms to explain particular aspects of radio propagation on 80 and 160, and to a lesser degree on 40 meters. I will try to point out the major differences as we cover each of the mechanisms that determine propagation on the low bands. Basic principles of radio propagation by ionospheric refraction are described in great detail in many handbooks (Ref. 101, 103, 104 and 105), and will not be dealt with here.

In principle there are two parameters that determine and influence low-band propagation:

- TIME
- LOCATION

■ 1. TIME

With regard to propagation, time is considered not only for short durations, but also long durations. We will consider time in three aspects:

- THE YEAR
- THE SEASON
- THE TIME OF DAY.

1.1. The Year

It is well known that radio propagation by ionospheric refraction is greatly influenced by the sunspot cycle. This is simply because ionization is caused mainly by ultraviolet radiation from the sun, which in turn is highly dependent on solar activity. Sunspot activity will influence 80-meter propagation in three major areas: MUF (maximum usable frequency), D-layer activity (absorption) and the occurrence of magnetic disturbances.

1.1.1. MUF and FOT.

The MUF is the highest frequency at which reliable radio communications via ionospheric propagation can be maintained over a given path. The MUF changes with time and with specific locations on the earth, or to be more exact, with the geographic location of the ionospheric refraction points. The MUF for a given path with multiple refraction points will be equal to the lowest MUF along the path. Fig 1-1 shows a typical MUF chart. This is a typical overlay chart that is used in conjunction with a conform or Mercator projection map of the earth, Fig 1-2, in predicting propagation. From Fig 1-1, we can see that the MUF is lower during local winter and much lower at night than during the daytime. With the aid of a great-circle overlay chart, Fig 1-3, we can identify the MUF along a given great-circle path between two points. It is generally accepted that the optimum communication frequency (FOT) is about 80 to 85 percent of the MUF. On much lower frequencies, the situation is less than optimum, as the absorption in the ionosphere increases. We now have computer programs available that will accurately predict MUF and FOT for a given path and a given level of solar activity.

We have all experienced that a high sunspot number means a high MUF and good conditions on 10 and 15 meters. Higher absorption on the low-frequency bands can also be

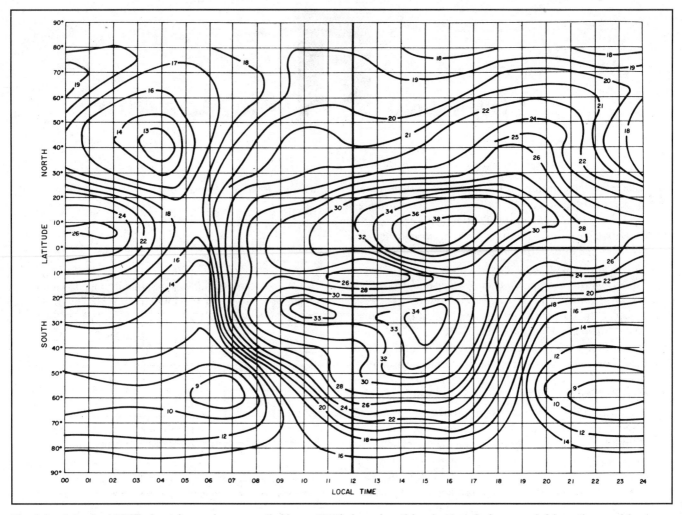

Fig 1-1—A typical MUF chart for a given month (June 1968). Imagine this chart as being overlaid on the world map of Fig 1-2. Note the lower MUF regions in the southern hemisphere, where it is winter.

expected during sunspot maxima. This in no way means that 80 and 160 are useless bands during high-sunspot years. It only means that there will be more attenuation, which for some of the most critical paths on 80 and especially 160 will mean that openings will be extremely scarce or maybe even non-existent.

The critical frequency is the highest frequency at which a signal transmitted straight up at a 90 degree elevation angle is returned to earth. The critical frequency is continuously measured in several hundred places around the world by devices called ionosondes. At frequencies higher than the critical frequency, all energy will travel through the ionosphere and be lost in space (Fig 1-4). The critical frequency varies with sunspot cycle, time of year and day, as well as geographical location. Typical values are 9 MHz at noon and 5 MHz at night. During periods with low sunspot activity the critical frequency can be as low as 2 MHz. During those times we can witness dead zones on 80 meters at night.

At frequencies slightly higher than the critical frequency, refraction will occur for a relatively high wave angle and all lower angles. As we increase the frequency, the maximum elevation angle at which we have ionospheric refraction will

become lower and lower. At 30 MHz during periods of active sunspots, such angles can be of the order of 10 degrees.

The relation between MUF and critical frequency is the wave elevation angle, where:

$$MUF = F_{crit} \times \frac{1}{\sin \alpha}$$

where α = angle of elevation

Table 1-1 gives an overview of the multiplication factor ($1/\sin \alpha$) for a number of takeoff angles (α). For the situation where the critical frequency is as low as 2 MHz it can be seen that any 3.8-MHz energy radiated at angles higher than 30 degrees will be lost in space. This is one reason for using an antenna with a low radiation angle for the low bands.

Several researchers have performed long series of measurements to ascertain the radiation angles of HF signals for a given path. Most of the work has been done between Europe and the US, and the figures obtained must be handled with care before extrapolating them to different paths and different path lengths. For a path between New Jersey and Germany, angles between 10 and 45 degrees are quoted for 80 meters by Schwarzbeck (Ref. 111).

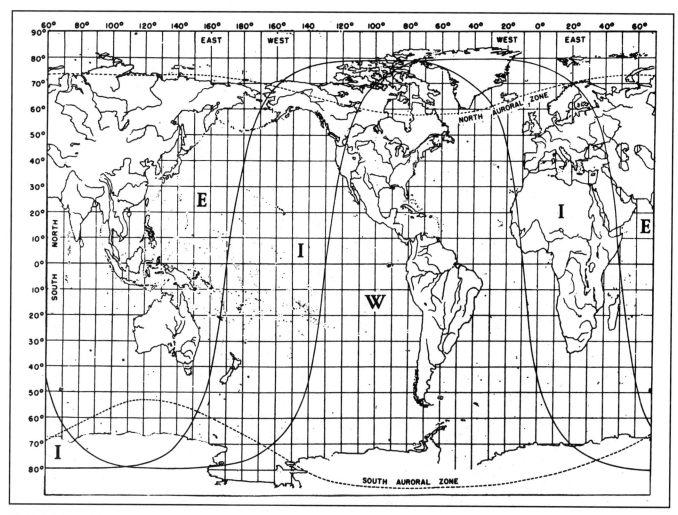

Fig 1-2—A world map made by the conform or Mercator projection. If a transparent copy of the MUF chart (Fig 1-1) is made, it can be used as an overlay on this map and shifted horizontally (to adjust local times) to find the actual situation of the MUF boundaries.

Table 1-1

Multiplication Factor for Varying Take-off Angles

α, degrees	$1/\sin\alpha$
10	5.8
20	2.9
30	2.0
40	1.6
50	1.3
60	1.2
70	1.1
80	1.0
90	1.0

1.1.2. D-layer activity.

During the day, the lowest ionospheric layer in existence is the D layer, at an altitude of 40 to 60 miles (60 to 90 km). Fig 1-5 shows how low-angle, low-frequency signals are absorbed by the D layer. The D layer absorbs signals rather than refracting them because it is much denser than the other ionospheric layers. The density of neutral, non-ionized particles, which make up the bulk of the mass in this region, is 1000 times greater in the D layer than in the E layer. For a layer to refract, the number of neutral atoms must be small enough so they do not collide frequently with free electrons. In the D layer, however, a given electron will collide with an atom about 10 million times per second. The electrons are not given the chance to refract signals, and absorption occurs instead.

The absorption level is inversely proportional to the arrival angle of the signal, so high-angle signals pass through relatively unattenuated. This is why our high-angle (low to the ground) dipoles work so well for local traffic on 80 meters. This may also be the explanation why it has often been reported that after sunrise, high angle antennas often take over from low-angle antennas for working very long (eg, long-path) distances. Around sunset, the D layer begins to dissipate; it disappears completely at night and is re-formed around sunrise.

How does the sunspot cycle affect this phenomenon? When sunspot activity is low, the formation of the D layer is slower; D layer build-up before noon is less pronounced, while the evening disintegration of the layer occurs faster. This is

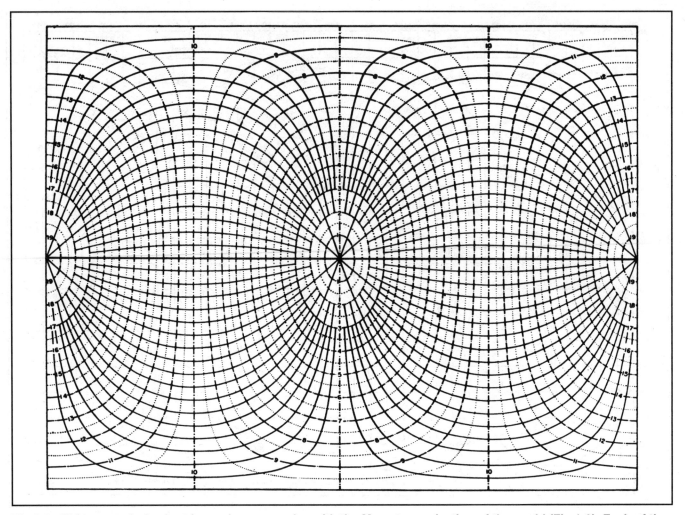

Fig 1-3—This great-circle chart is used as an overlay with the Mercator projection of the world (Fig 1-2). Each of the solid lines represents a great circle (the radial lines on a great-circle or azimuthal projection map). The dashed lines give great-circle distances in thousand kilometers.

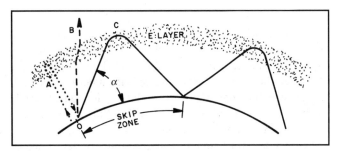

Fig 1-4—Ionospheric propagation: In case A we witness refraction of a vertically transmitted wave. This means that the frequency is below the critical frequency. In case B the angle is too high or the frequency too high and the refraction is insufficient to return the wave to earth. In case C we have the highest angle at which the refracted wave will return to earth. The higher the frequency, the lower the angle α will become. Note the "skip zone."

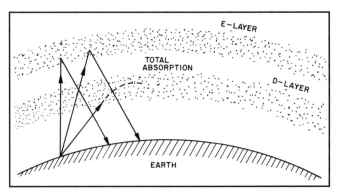

Fig 1-5—D-layer absorption. The higher-angle signals pass through the D-layer and are reflected by the layer. Low-angle signals are absorbed. This explains the need for a high-angle radiator to work short-range stations in the daytime.

because there is less ultraviolet energy from the sun to create and sustain the high ionization level of the D layer. This means, in turn, that at a sunspot minimum, absorption in the D layer will be less than at a sunspot maximum, especially around dusk and dawn.

The absorption mechanism of the D layer has been studied repeatedly during solar eclipses. Reports (Ref. 121 and 125) show that during an eclipse, D-layer attenuation is greatly reduced and propagation similar to night-time conditions occurs on short-range paths.

1.1.3. Magnetic disturbances.

Auroral activity is one of the important low-band propagation anomalies and is still largely a field of research for scientists. Amateurs living within a radius of a few thousand miles from the magnetic poles know all about the consequences of the phenomenon. The aurora phenomenon is covered in detail in Par 2.2.

1.1.4. Low-band propagation during high sunspot years.

For years it was accepted that the high-sunspot years were very unfavorable for low-band DXing, but now not everyone shares this opinion. It is true that in order to sustain a reflection mechanism (refraction, ducting etc.), there needs to be enough ionization to sustain the wave propagation. In this way the higher sun activity may be advantageous to low-band DXing as well as to DXing in general.

Until recently there was a lack of many DX signals on the low bands during the high-sunspot years. To a large degree this was attributed to the absence of DXers on those bands. The relative lack of specific interest in low-band DXing kept the run-of-the-mill DXers away from the low bands during the years that 20 meters was open day and night. Multi-band and specific low-band awards, as well as increased emphasis on low-band operating during major contests, have been very instrumental in raising the activity on the low bands all through the cycle and all through the year.

Since 1980 or so the "average" DXer has discovered the low bands and added them to the list of the higher HF bands previously considered as DX bands. Nowadays, every DXpedition includes 40, 80, and even 160-meter work in their operating schedules. At the same time the elite group of specific low-band DXers has multiplied, so that even in the middle of the summer in the high sunspot years we can often hear several stations calling CQ DX on the top band.

1.2. The Season

We all know the mechanism that originates our seasons: the declination of the sun relative to the equator. The declination reaches a maximum of 23.5 degrees around December 21 and June 21 (see Fig 1-6). This coincides with the middle of the winter propagation season and the middle of the summer propagation season. At those times the days are longest or shortest and the sun rises to the highest or lowest point at local noon in the non-equatorial zones.

On the equator, the sun will rise to its highest point at local noon twice a year, at the equinoxes around September 21 and March 21. These are the times of the year when the sun-earth axis is perpendicular to the earth axis (sun declination is zero), and when nights and days are equally long at any place on earth (equi = equal, nox = night). On December 21 and June 21, the sun is still very high at the equator (90 – 23.5 = 66.5 degrees). The maximum height of the sun at any latitude on earth is given by the expression

Height = 90 degrees – north latitude + 23.5 degrees
(with a maximum of 90 degrees)

In other words, the sun never rises higher than 23.5

degrees at the poles, and never higher than 53.5 degrees where the latitude is 60 degrees.

Because of this mechanism, it is clear that the seasonal influence of the sun on 80-meter propagation will be complementary in the northern and southern hemispheres. Any influence will be most prominent near the poles, and less pronounced in the equatorial zones (±23.5 degrees of the equator). But how do the changing seasons influence 80-meter propagation?

1. The longer the sun's rays can create and activate the D layer, the more absorption there will be during the dusk and dawn periods. During local winter, the sun will rise to a much lower apex and the rate of sunrise will be much lower. Accordingly, D-layer ionization will build up much more slowly.

2. Many thunderstorms are generated in the summer. Electrical noise (QRN) will easily mask the weaker DX signals and discourage even the most arduous DX operator. Take the north-south path (US-South America or Europe-Africa): The

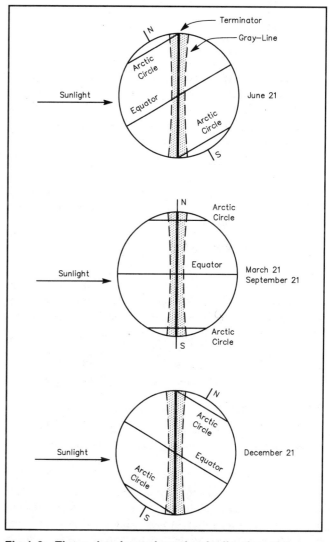

Fig 1-6—These drawings show the declination of the sun and the different positions of the terminator (solid vertical line) at different times of the year. The gray-line is represented as a zone of variable width (shaded area) to emphasize that its behavior near the poles differs from its behavior near the equator.

northern hemisphere summer may be the advantageous season, as QRN is likely to be of less intensity than the QRN during the southern hemisphere summer.

3. When the nights are longest in winter, you will have the greatest possible time for DX openings. Indeed, you must be in darkness or twilight not to suffer from excessive D-layer absorption and have acceptable conditions for long-distance propagation on the low bands.

1.2.1. Winter (15 October to 15 February in the Northern Hemisphere).

Low MUF, short days, lots of darkness, sun rising slowly, reduced D-layer activity at dusk and dawn, and no QRN from thunderstorms. This period is ideal for all stations located in the northern hemisphere during the winter. Conversely, this condition will not exist in the southern hemisphere. Therefore the winter period in the northern hemisphere is ideal for east-to-west and west-to-east propagation between two stations both located in the northern hemisphere. Typical paths are US-Europe, US-Japan, US-Asia, etc.

1.2.2. Summer (15 April to 15 August in the Northern Hemisphere).

Higher MUF, long days, faster rising sun, increased D-layer activity at dusk and dawn, and (much) QRN due to local thunderstorms. These factors create the worst conditions one can expect for east-to-west or west-to-east propagation in the northern hemisphere. What we should realize, however, is that while the large majority of amateurs may be fighting the local QRN in the northern hemisphere in summertime, our friends down under are enjoying ideal winter conditions. This means that summertime is a 100% valid time for transequatorial propagation (eg, from Europe to Southern Africa or North America to the southern part of South America).

1.2.3. Equinox Period (15 August to 15 October and 15 February to 15 April).

During these periods the ionospheric conditions are fairly similar in both the northern and the southern hemisphere: similar MUF values, days and nights approximately 12 hours long on both sides of the equator, reduced QRN etc. Clearly this is the ideal season for "oblique" transequatorial propagation, the NE-SW and NW-SE paths. Typical examples are Europe to New Zealand and West Coast US to Indian Ocean.

1.2.4. Propagation into the Equatorial Zones.

In principle, all seasons can produce good conditions for propagation from the northern or southern hemisphere into but not across the equatorial zone. The only real limiting factors are the MUF distribution along the path, and especially the amount of QRN in the equatorial zone itself. Unfortunately there is no rule of thumb to tell us everything about the electrical storm activities in these zones. From Europe we work African stations and stations in the southern part of South America on 160 mainly during the months of June, July and August. A similar situation exists between North America and the southern parts of Africa and South America.

We must conclude that it is not true that DX on the low bands can only be worked during the local winter. The equinox period is excellent for equatorial and transequatorial propagation, while in the middle of our summer (QRN being acceptably low for us), rare DX stations from down under or from the equatorial zones are commonplace. Even good east-west openings can happen in the middle of the summer, as long as there is a darkness path and the QRN level makes listening for the signals at all possible. Of course the operators on both sides must be willing to try, and not take for granted that it won't work. Over the years I have worked quite a few rare ones over an east-west path in summertime. Here are a few examples:

XYØRR (Burma) was worked on Sep 3 (1991) on 160 meters, shortly before his sunrise. After a QSO on 80-meter SSB, we moved to 160 where a 579 was exchanged. After the QSO XYØRR called CQ a few times, but nobody else came back. Those convinced that summer time is no good time for 160 meter were wrong once again. The little story to this contact is that I normally don't have a "long" Beverage up for that direction during the summer. There happened to be 2.5-m (8 ft) tall corn on the field in that direction. That day I spent a memorable couple of hours putting an insulated wire right on top of the corn field. You must try that sometime for fun!

Another striking example is what happened during the DXpedition of Rudi, DK7PE, to S21ZC in early August 1992. The first night he was on 160, I was in the middle of a local thunderstorm (S9 + 40 static crashes), and no chance for a contact. The next day, the QRN was down to S7, and a perfect QSO (579) was made over quite a long path (to be compared with a path from ST to the US East Coast, or from the west coast of Africa to California).

1.3. Time of Day

We know how the earth's rotation around its axis creates the mechanism of day and night. The transition from day to night is very abrupt in equatorial zones. The sun rises and sets very quickly; the opposite is true in the polar zones.

Let us, for convenience, subdivide the day into three periods:

1. Daytime: from after sunrise (dawn) until before sunset (dusk)
2. Night-time: from after sunset (dusk) until before sunrise (dawn)
3. Dawn/dusk: sunrise and sunset (twilight periods)

1.3.1. Daytime

After local sunrise, the D layer slowly builds up under the influence of ultraviolet radiation from the sun. Maximum D-layer ionization and activity is reached shortly after local noon. This means that from zero absorption (due to the D layer) before sunrise, the absorption will gradually increase until a maximum is reached just after local noon. The degree of absorption will in the first instance depend on the height of the sun at any given time.

For example, near the poles, such as in northern Scandinavia, the sun rises late and sets early in local winter. The consequence will be a late and slow buildup of the D layer. In the middle of the winter the sun may be just above the horizon (for regions just below the Arctic Circle, situated at $90 - 23.5 = 66.5$ degrees above the equator), or actually below the horizon all day long for locations above the Arctic Circle. It can consequently be understood that absorption due to D-layer ionization will be minimal or non-existent under these circumstances. This is why stations located in the polar regions can actually work 80-meter DX almost 24 hours a day in winter. Contacts between Finland or Sweden and the Pacific or the US West Coast are not uncommon around local noon in northern Sweden and northern Finland at that time of year.

It is obvious that this is not a good example of typical daytime conditions, as in those polar regions we never actually have typical daytime conditions in midwinter but remain in dusk and dawn periods all day long.

It has been mentioned that during typical daytime conditions, when the D-layer ionization is very intense, low-angle signals will be totally absorbed while high-angle signals will get through and be refracted in the E layer. Only at peak ionization, just after noon, may the absorption be noticeable on high-angle signals. The signal strength of local stations, received via ionospheric refraction, will dip to a minimum just after local noon. As stated before, in order to have good local coverage on 80 meters during daytime, it is essential to have an antenna with a high vertical angle of radiation. We will later see that this can very easily be obtained (for example with a low dipole).

On 160 meters, daytime propagation is essentially limited to ground-wave signals.

1.3.2. Night-time.

After sunset, the D layer gradually dissipates and disappears. Consequently, good propagation conditions can be expected if both ends of the path, plus the area in between, are in darkness. The greatest distances can be covered if both ends of the path are at the opposite ends of the darkness zone (both located near the terminator, which is the dividing line between day and night). During night-time, and with low sunspot activity, the critical frequency may descend to values below 3.7 MHz and dead zones (skip zones) will show up regularly. Skip zones are common on 40 meters during night-time.

1.3.3. Dusk and dawn: twilight periods.

The terminator, mentioned before, is the dividing line between one half of the earth in daylight and the other half in darkness. Visual transition from day to night and vice versa happens quite abruptly in the equatorial zones, and very slowly in the polar zones (see Section 1.3.1). The so-called gray line is a gray band between day and night, usually referred to as the twilight zone. Dusk and dawn periods produce very interesting propagation conditions that are not limited to the lower HF frequencies (low bands).

Long before sunrise there is no D-layer activity above or in the western direction from a particular station location. Hence, there is no absorption at all (situation A in Fig 1-7. Later, as the earth rotates, we come to situation B, where the gradual buildup of the D layer commences at the transmitter site. Initially the density of ionization is rather low, and arriving signals will be refracted rather than absorbed. This

phenomenon can lower the effective angle of radiation as seen from the reflecting E layer. This results in a longer single-hop distance or in a greater signal strength for a given number of hops. This is one of the reasons why signals always peak during the dusk and dawn periods over all E-W, NE-SW and NW-SE paths. This does not apply to N-S paths. There is no sunrise- or sunset-propagation peak for N-S paths.

In addition, the ionosphere, responsible for the refraction of the low-band signals, is changing abruptly in height at sunrise/sunset time. This effective ionospheric tilt helps to create the necessary conditions for trapped-wave or chordal-hop propagation (see further in this section).

There is another reason why we seem to be able to work DX much better during these twilight periods. When the sun is rising in the morning, all signals coming from the east (which can often cause a great deal of QRM during the night) are greatly attenuated by the D layer existing in the east. The net result is often a much quieter band from one direction (east in the morning and west in the evening), resulting in much better signal-to-noise ratios on weak signals from the west.

It is also of utmost importance to know how long these special propagation conditions exist; in other words, how long the effects of the radio-twilight periods last. To understand the mechanism, it should be clear that the rate of D-layer buildup depends upon the rate of sunrise, or in other words the height of the sun at local noon. There are two factors that determine this rate: the season (the sun rises faster in summer than in winter) and the latitude of your location (the sun rises very high near the equator, and culminates in low angles near the poles).

The effect of advantageous propagation conditions at sunrise and sunset has been recognized since the early days of low-band DXing. It was Dale Hoppe, K6UA, and Peter Dalton, W6NLZ, who called the zone in which the special propagation condition exists the gray line (Ref. 108). The gray line is a zone centered around the geographical terminator. (See Fig 1-6.) It should be clear from the above explanation that the effective

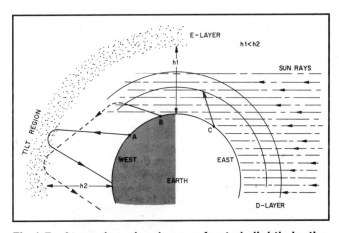

Fig 1-7—At sunrise, signals are refracted slightly by the D layer, which is only marginally ionized, and then refracted back to earth in the E layer. Due to the tilt in the E layer in the region where night changes into day, a further lowering of the effective radiation angle occurs.

width of this zone is certainly not constant over its total circumference, and will actually depend on the speed of sunrise. This means we have a narrow gray line near the equator, and a wide gray line near the poles. The time span during which we will benefit from typical gray-line conditions will accordingly be short near the equator and long in the polar regions. This means that the gray-line phenomenon is much less important to the low-band DXer living in equatorial regions than to his colleague close to the polar circles. This does not mean that there is less enhancement near the equator at sunrise or sunset; it just means that the duration of the enhanced period is shorter.

Definition of gray line:

A gray-line short path exists when the station on the western end of the path is having sunset about the same time that the station on the eastern end of the path is having sunrise. It is not clear whether on the low bands the propagation inside the gray line (along the terminator) has any benefit from it. It is clear, however, that signal launching at the transmit and receive end does benefit greatly from the mechanism.

Some authors (Ref. 108 and 118) have mentioned that gray-line propagation always happens along the terminator. On the low bands there has been occasional proof of such propagation although most of the gray-line situation benefits have been noticed on paths typically perpendicular to the terminator. One of the few really long-distance propagation paths along the gray-line zone is mentioned in Section 3.3.3. (e.g., Europe to JA at sunrise in Europe).

Some authors have shown the gray-line zone as a zone of equal width all along the terminator. This is incorrect as far as the related radio-propagation phenomenon is concerned. R. Linkous, W7OM, recognizes this varying zone width and accordingly emphasizes its importance in his excellent article, "Navigating To 80-meter DX" (Ref. 109).

I have developed an algorithm that calculates the effective width of the gray line on 80 meters as a function of the location as well as the time of year. The total width of the gray line can be calculated as follows:

1) Calculate the sun declination:

$$A = -23.5 \sin \frac{360(D - 80)}{365}$$

where D is the day of the year (1 to 365).

2) Calculate the height of the sun at local noon:

$$H = 90 - (L + A) \frac{360(D - 80)}{365}$$

where L is the latitude. If H is less than zero then add 90 degrees to H. If H = 0 then the width of the gray line (W) = 12. (If no sunrise, the width of the gray line is 12 hours.)

3) Calculate the effective window:

$$W = \frac{1}{4 \tan(0.95 H)}$$

where W is in hours. If W is greater than 12 then W = 12, and

if W is less than 0.1 then W = 0.1. This algorithm is used in the computer module "GRAY LINE," which is part of the *New Low Band Software*.

This algorithm gives a good approximation of the effective width of the gray line as far as low-band propagation is concerned. The correction to the formula makes the gray line no narrower than 6 minutes in the equatorial zones, and no larger than 24 hours in the polar regions during midwinter.

A most striking example of a gray-line QSO involved two 80-meter QSOs I made with Kingman Reef and Palmyra around May 1, 1988. If we analyze sunset and sunrise times, we see that sunset on those islands is roughly 40 minutes after sunrise in my location. This means that there is theoretically no opening, but we can of course force things a little, and take advantage of the gray line. How shall we do that? Split the 40 minutes in half and try a QSO 20 minutes before sunset in Palmyra (or Kingman Reef) and 20 minutes after sunrise here in Belgium? Sounds like a nice 50/50 deal? Certainly not. Those Pacific islands are situated only about 6 degrees north of the equator; Belgium is 51 degrees north! This means that the gray line lasts just seconds out on KH5, and maybe 40 minutes in Belgium. The skeds were made right at Pacific sunrise time. On Kingman the QSO was made 5 minutes after Kingman sunset, on Palmyra 4 minutes after sunset, and in both cases 40 to 45 minutes after sunrise in Belgium (where the gray line is fairly "wide"). This is a striking example of how knowledge of the mechanism of propagation can help you realize a very difficult QSO. Proof of it being a marginal situation is that from Palmyra only one QSO was made with Europe, and only two from Kingman Reef.

On 160 meters, the width of the gray line is much more restricted than on 80. Even in the middle of the winter, I have never made long-haul QSOs more than 15 minutes after sunrise, while on 80 the US East Coast has been worked up to 2 hours after sunrise. A contrasting experience is a QSO with VE1ZZ on 160 meters more than 1 hour before his sunset. But of course, VE1ZZ is not an average station!

During a long period of tests (in November and December) on 160 meters between New Caledonia (FK8CP) and Europe it was noticed that the signals always peaked right around sunrise (from 3 minutes before to 3 minutes after sunrise). This "short" peak is valid only for the very long path to Western Europe. FK8CP reports openings into Asia (UA9, UA0) from much earlier until a little later after sunrise. More nearby DX (2000 km or 1500 miles) can be worked as late as 45 minutes after sunrise on 160 meters, again depending on one's latitude. FK8CP reports working DX in the pacific as late as 50 minutes after his sunrise in the middle of his local summer (which is quite late in view of the latitude of New Caledonia).

On 40 meters, the gray line is of course "wider" than on 80 meters. In winter time, long-haul DX can be worked until many hours after sunrise (or many hours before sunset), again depending on the latitude of the station concerned. Example: Stations in latitudes of 55 degrees or more will see 40 meters open all day long in winter-time. Even at my location (51 degrees north) I have been able to work W6 stations at local noon time, about 3 hours into daylight. At the same time the band sometimes opens up to the east, so we can say that even for my "modest" latitude of 51 degrees, 40 meters is open for DX 24 hours a day on "better" days.

Special propagation mechanisms:

Multi-hop propagation with intermediate ground reflections has long been the only way to explain propagation of radio waves by ionospheric refraction. In the last 15 years a great deal of scientific work has been done, enabling us to calculate exact path losses due to ionospheric absorption (derivative and non-derivative losses), free-space attenuation (path distance related) and earth (ground or water) reflection losses. While the theory of propagation with ground reflections is satisfactory to explain short- and medium-range contacts, the additional losses through ground reflections can no longer be accepted to explain some of the very high signal levels obtained over very long distances, especially when gray-line propagation and genuine long-path situations are involved.

Chordal-hop or whispering-gallery propagation.

Recent work, based on experimental observations (Ref. 100) and theoretical studies (Ref. 131) has firmly established the existence of a specific propagation mode, called whispering-gallery or chordal-hop propagation. This form of ionospheric propagation without intermediate ground reflections appears to offer a good explanation for long-distance propagation.

Right around sunrise or sunset, low-band signals will be refracted in the E layer in a tilted region (Fig 1-8), resulting in a condition that will make the waves enter the ionosphere again without having an intermediate ground reflection. This type of propagation is called chordal-hop propagation. With decreasing chordal-hop length, this propagation turns into the whispering-gallery mode, which means that the waves are guided along the concave bottom of the ionospheric layer acting as a single-walled duct. The flat angles of incidence necessary for chordal-hop propagation are possible through refraction in the building-up D layer, and because of the tilt in the E layer at both ends of the path. Chordal-hop propagation modes over long distances can easily account for up to 12 dB of gain due to the omission of the ground reflection losses. Y.

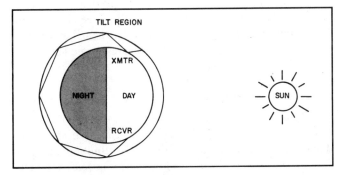

Fig 1-8—Signal ducting. The deformation of the ionospheric layer (the changing altitude and ionization density of the E layer) at sunrise and sunset can produce circumstances where the total internal reflection on the bottom side of the ionosphere sustains very low-loss propagation.

Blanarovich, VE3BMV, described a very similar theory (Ref. 110). Long-delayed echoes, or "round the world echoes" witnessed by several amateurs on frequencies as low as 80 meters can only be explained by propagation mechanisms excluding intermediate ground reflections.

Antipodal focusing.

Every low-band DXer undoubtedly knows that it is relatively easy to work into regions near the antipodes (points directly opposite one's QTH on the globe), although those are the longest distances that one can encounter, and as such one would expect weak signals as a rule. The phenomenon of ray-focusing in near-antipodal regions must be used to explain the high field strengths encountered at those long distances (often in addition to the gray-line phenomenon and chordal hops). Antipodal focusing is based on the fact that all great circles passing through a given QTH intersect at the antipode of that QTH. Therefore, radio waves radiated by an antenna in a range of azimuthal directions and propagating around the earth along great-circle paths are being focused at the antipodal point. Exact focusing can occur only under ideal conditions, i.e., if the refracting properties of the ionosphere are ideal and perfectly homogeneous all over the globe. As these conditions do not exist (patchy clouds, MUF variation, etc.), antipodal focusing will exist only over a limited range of propagation paths (great circle directions) at a given time.

The smaller the section of the shell involved in the focusing (i.e., the narrower the beamwidth), the closer the actual properties will approximate the ideal conditions. This means that in order to gain maximum benefit from antipodal focusing, the optimum azimuth (yielding the lowest average MUF) has to be known.

Fixed, highly directive antennas (fixed on the geographical great-circle direction) may not be ideal, however, as the optimum azimuth is changing all the time. Rotatable or switchable arrays are the ideal answer, but omnidirectional antennas perform very well for paths near the antipodes, at least for transmitting. The focusing gain can be as high as 30 dB at the antipodes, and will range in the order of 15 dB at distances a few thousand kilometers away from the exact antipode.

While on 80 meters the effect seems to spread quite a distance from the theoretical antipode, on 160 the focusing effect appears to be even more pronounced. On 160, the Gs can benefit from the effect into ZL, while on the European continent the effect seems to be all but non-existent, which is very different from 80 meters.

■ 2. LOCATION

In the previous material I have referred a number of times to the geographical location of the station. There is, of course, a close relationship between the time and the location when considering the influence of solar activity. Location is the determining factor in three different aspects of low-band propagation:

1. Latitude of your station vs rate of sunrise/sunset
2. Magnetic disturbances
3. Local atmospheric noise (QRN)

2.1. Latitude of Your Location vs Solar Activity

This aspect has already been dealt with in detail. The latitude of the QTH will influence the MUF, the best season for a particular path, and the width of the gray-line zone.

2.2. Magnetic Disturbances (Aurora)

The aurora are a very important factor in the long-distance propagation mechanism on the low bands, and certainly the most important one for those living at latitudes of 60 degrees or more and within a few thousand miles of the magnetic poles. During a solar storm, clouds of charged particles are thrown off by the sun; these clouds can reach the earth approximately 26 hours after the storm. The particles, when approaching the earth, are trapped by the earth's magnetic field. Hence, they follow the magnetic field lines and travel toward the magnetic north and south poles. As they approach the poles, the particles collide with atoms of the upper atmosphere and create violent ionization. This collision forms a ring of extremely dense ionization, which can be seen as a fluorescent ring around the magnetic poles, called Aurora Borealis near the north pole and Aurora Australis near the south pole. As far as low-band propagation is concerned, this heavily ionized belt, at a height of approximately 65 miles (100 km) as a rule acts much like the D layer in existence during the day; it totally absorbs all low-band signals trying to go through the belt.

On at least one occasion, it has been noted that on 160 meters, propagation conditions have occurred similar to those well known on VHF during an extremely heavy aurora. Around 1600 to 1800 UTC on Feb 8, 1986, at the same time that auroral reflection was very predominant on VHF and 28 MHz, as witnessed by me, KL7 and KH6 stations were heard and worked on 80 meters in Europe on a path straight across the north pole, with the buzzy sound typical for auroral reflection. This seems to indicate that under exceptional conditions (the aurora was extremely intense), aurora can be beneficial to low-band DXing. The aurora mentioned above generated an A index of 238. K-index values were reported between 8 and 9. This was one of the largest geomagnetic storms since 1960. A similar situation existed in Jan 1987 when in Europe we could work KL7 stations during several days on 160 meters.

Enhanced propagation conditions shortly after a major aurora appear quite regularly. I witnessed a striking example on November 12, 1986, when only nine hours after a major disturbance during the morning hours, N7AU produced S9 signals via the long path for more than 30 minutes, just before sunset in Belgium. Normally, long-path openings occur to the US West Coast from Belgium only between the middle of December and the middle of January, and even then the openings are extremely rare. During the November opening, I monitored N7UA calling CQ Europe with signals between S6 and S9 for almost an hour. The propagation was very selective, as only Belgian stations were returning his calls! A few days earlier DJ4AX was heard working the West Coast and giving 57 reports while the W6/W7 stations were completely inaudible in Belgium, only 200 miles to the Northwest! It is more than likely that an ionospheric ducting phenomenon is responsible for such propagation. This means that very specific launching conditions have to be present at both sides of the path. It now appears that duct "exit" conditions are very critical and thus area selective, and more so as the path length is longer. It also seems that aurora disturbances can create and enhance such critical conditions.

As the aurora phenomenon is linked to solar storms and hence to sudden ionospheric disturbances (SIDs), it is clear that the occurrence of aurora will be greatest at the sunspot maximum. There is some degree of aurora, however, about 200 days a year!

The magnetic north pole lies about 11 degrees south of the geographic north pole and 71 degrees west of Greenwich. The magnetic south pole is situated 12 degrees north of the geographic south pole and 111 degrees east of Greenwich. The intensity of the aurora phenomenon determines the diameter of the aurora belt. In cases of heavy aurora, the belt can split into several smaller belts.

Generally we can say that in most cases of auroral activity, the absorption will exist in a zone delimited by the outer aurora belt. For typical aurora densities the radius of the zone will be approximately 2000 miles (3250 km). Fig 1-9 shows the outline of this zone on great-circle maps centered on Washington, DC, Central United States, San Francisco and Europe.

The great-circle distances from Washington, DC to Tokyo and Yemen are equal. For a signal to travel in a straight line to Tokyo, however, it has to go through the auroral zone. In the Yemen case, the straight-line path stays well clear of the aurora belt region. This means that when there is any degree of auroral activity, the Washington, DC to Tokyo path will be greatly affected, while the Yemen path will remain unattenuated by the aurora phenomenon. Looking at a globe on which are drawn some aurora circles centered on the magnetic poles, it becomes clear why stations located near the equator will suffer much less from auroral absorption than stations located near or inside the aurora belt zones.

Radio waves propagate in a semi-scattering fashion due to refraction and reflection in a "cloudy" type of ionized environment. Therefore the Washington-Tokyo case will often be subject to a large degree of path bending, resulting in a valid propagation path bent round the outer aurora belt. This means that for stations located away from the outer aurora belt, these crooked paths can often bring relief (see also Section 3.3.2). For those living very near or in the actual aurora belt zones, there is no compensating mechanism to alleviate the consequences of aurora.

2.3. Local Atmospheric Noise

Most local atmospheric noise (static or QRN) is generated by electrical storms or thunderstorms. We know that during the summer, QRN is the major limiting factor in copying weak signals on the low bands, at least for those regions where thunderstorm activities are serious. To give you an idea of the frightening power involved, a thunderstorm has up to 50 times more potential energy than an atomic bomb! There are an estimated 1800 thunderstorms in progress over the earth's surface at any given time throughout the year. The

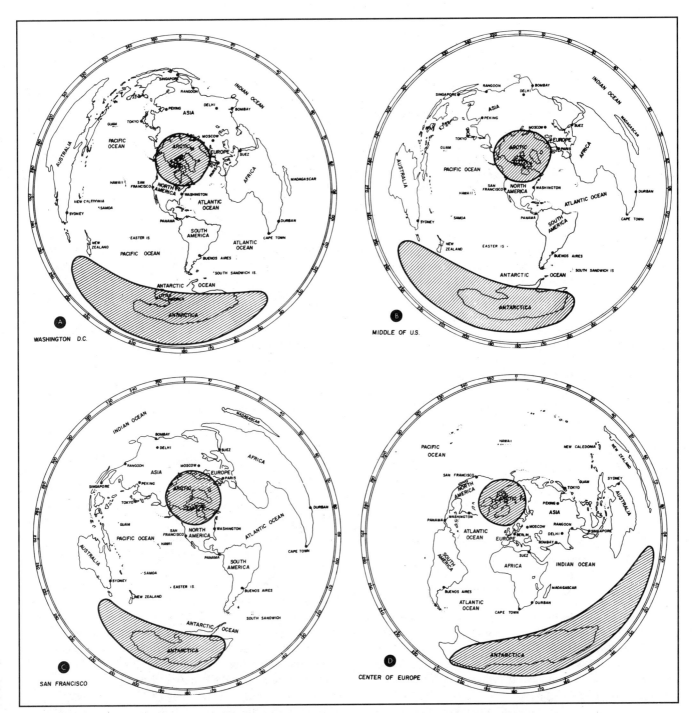

Fig 1-9—Azimuthal projection world maps (great circle maps) centered on different locations in the world. The aurora belt zones are included in each example. A is centered on Washington, DC, B on the middle of the US, C on San Francisco, and D on central Europe.

map in Fig 1-10 shows the high degree of variation in frequency of thunderstorms in the US. On the average, lightning strikes somewhere on the earth 100 times a second, generating a tremendous amount of radio-frequency energy.

In the northern hemisphere, above 35 degrees latitude, QRN is almost nonexistent from November until March. In the middle of the summer, when an electrical storm is near, static crashes can produce signals up to 40 dB over S9, and make even local QSOs impossible (and dangerous). It is obvious that in equatorial zones, where electrical storms are very common

all year long, this phenomenon will be the limiting factor in low-band DXing. This is why, as stated earlier, we cannot generally speak of an ideal season for DXing into the equatorial zones since QRN is a random possibility all year long.

Using highly directive receiving antennas such as Beverage antennas or small loops can be of great help in reducing QRN from electrical storms by producing a null in the direction of the storm. Unless directly overhead, electrical storms in general have a sharp directivity pattern.

Rain, hail or snow are often electrically charged and can

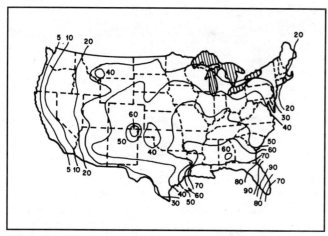

Fig 1-10—This map shows the mean number of thunderstorm days in the US. The figure is related to both mountainous terrain and seasonal weather patterns.

cause a continuous QRN hash when they come into contact with antennas. Some antennas are more susceptible to this precipitation noise than others; vertical antennas seem to be worst in this respect. Closed-loop antennas generally behave better than open-ended antennas (e.g., dipoles), while Beverage receiving antennas are almost totally insensitive to this phenomenon.

■ 3. PROPAGATION PATHS

This section discusses the following items to help increase our understanding of low-band propagation paths:

1. Great-circle short path
2. Great-circle long path
3. Particular non great-circle paths

3.1. Great-circle Short Path

Great circles are all circles obtained by cutting the globe with any plane going through the center of the earth. All great circles are 40,000 km (24,860 miles) long. The equator is a particular great circle, the cutting plane being perpendicular to the earth's axis. Meridians are other great circles, going through both poles.

A great-circle map is an azimuthal projection, centered on one location. For that reason it is often called an azimuthal-equidistant projection. This map has the unique property of showing the great circles as straight lines, as well as showing distances to any point on the map from the center point. On such a projection, the antipodes of the center location will be represented by the outer circle of the map. Great-circle maps are specific to a particular location. They are most commonly used for determining rotary beam headings for DX work.

3.2. Great-circle Long Path

A long-path condition exists when the station at the eastern side of the path is having sunset at approximately the same time as the station at the western end of the path is experiencing sunrise. A second condition is that the propaga-

tion occurs on a path that is 180 degrees opposite to the short-path great-circle direction. This second condition is necessary.

We will see further how a "crooked path" propagation can satisfy the first condition, but clearly is not a long-path propagation (e.g., W. Europe to Japan at 0745Z in mid-winter, but with a propagation path over Northern Siberia and not across South America).

John Kaufman, W1FV (QTH Massachusetts) has noticed that his sunrise long-path openings on 80 meters are best during the sunspot cycle peak. During the low sunspot years the same long path all but disappears. On the other hand, the sunset long paths seem to be predominant during sunspot cycle troughs, John comments.

The increased use of highly directional transmit and receive antennas on the low bands have lead to the discovery of particular long paths that were unknown until now. One striking example is a genuine (great circle) long path between the US West Coast and Europe across the south pole, as reported by D. Schoen, N2KK/6. Whereas the so-called long path between the US West Coast and Europe in mid-winter is a bent path not going across the south pole, the genuine long-path exists around equinox 0400-0700Z). David also mentions that sometimes the band is open on both long as well as short paths. This is probably the same path I experienced when working Alaska across the south pole (Ref par 3.3.2.).

3.2.1. Long path on 160 meters.

Genuine long-path QSOs near the antipodes are quite common, provided there is a full-darkness path. I can hear the G stations working ZL long path on 160 approximately 30 minutes after my sunrise, but only on very rare occasions have I been able to work ZL on long path myself. Near-antipode long-path QSOs have happened between VK6HD (Perth) and the US East Coast in midwinter (e.g., QSO between K1ZM and VK6HD at 2115Z on Jan 27, 1985).

B. Tippet, WØZV, top-notch 160-meter DXer (230 countries worked) admits he has made only two genuine long-path QSOs on top band in almost 10 years of active listening, one with UAØUCO, at his equinox sunrise, and another one in midwinter with JJ1VKL/4S7. Bill's QSO with FT5ZB is almost a long-path QSO, but is really more like a genuine antipode QSO, where he gets the benefit of antipodal focusing. WØZV related other long path 160-meter QSOs to me: PY1RO with JAs in early January at the Japanese sunrise, W1FV with 9M2AX, as well as other East Coast stations with VS6DO and VK6HD, not by accident two of the most outstanding signals from the Far East in the late '80s.

During the 1987-1988 winter I tried for weeks to make a long-path QSO with N7UA on 160 meters, but we never heard signals at either end. During December 1992 I ran a daily test with FK8CP on the long path (his sunset is within minutes of my sunrise), but we never made a QSO. Only one day did I hear his signals very weakly.

3.3. Particular Non Great-circle Paths

Most, but not all paths on 40, 80 and 160 meters are great-circle paths. It is obvious that paths over relatively short distances are more or less straight-line great-circle paths. Let us assume that paths are basically always of the great-circle type, unless there is a good reason for them not to be. Consider some specific cases:

3.3.1. Propagation paths and the heterogeneous ionosphere.

We often think of radio waves as a single ray of energy sent in a specific direction, refracted in the ionosphere and reflected from a perfectly flat reflecting surface on the earth. This has been the standard method of visualizing radio propagation in a simplified way. HF energy is, however, in most practical cases, radiated in a range of azimuths and over a range of elevation angles.

The ionosphere is not a perfect mirror, but should rather be thought of as a cloudy and patchy heterogeneous region. Traveling ionospheric disturbances are wave-like disturbances, or variations in ionization density, usually moving between one and ten km per minute, producing well-known effects such as marked variations in signal strength and a shift in the direction of arrival of received signals.

The non-homogeneous nature of the ionosphere also accounts for the MUF being different at different places on the earth at a given time. Power is radiated by the transmitter in a whole range of directions, and radio waves will propagate in all those directions. D-layer absorption at the launching site and the state of the higher ionized layers all over the world have a large effect on the direction of propagation. Radio waves will be more heavily attenuated by traveling through regions with high MUFs. Where the MUF is below the operating frequency, all power will be lost in space. The lowest degree of attenuation will result from traveling through zones where the MUF is near (and above) the operating frequency.

For relatively short-distance paths (less than 10,000 km or 6000 miles), low-band radio waves will propagate almost in straight lines. This is also true for north-south transequatorial paths (e.g., Europe-Africa, North America-South America). Deviations from great-circle headings will not often be observed. Since the introduction of switchable or rotatable arrays for 80 meters, it has been possible to observe and analyze the phenomena of non great-circle paths in greater detail. On 40 meters the path deviations had been accepted for some time, since rotary Yagis became common antennas for that band.

The most typical example of non-great-circle propagation is caused by the unequal MUF distribution over the world. As stated earlier, there is an indefinite number of great-circle paths to the antipodes. As low-band DX signals travel only over the dark side of the globe, however, the usable number of great-circle paths is limited to 180 degrees (assuming there is no aurora activity screening off part of the aperture). This very seldom means that signals will arrive with equal strength over 180 degrees, however. The principle is that signals will be received with the greatest signal strengths from those directions where the ionization is optimal along the entire length of the path. In general, this means areas with low MUF. Indeed, the attenuation will be lower through the zones with low MUF than through ionosphere regions with higher MUF. Prediction can be done with the help of an MUF map or with the aid of computer programs.

New Zealand is about 19,000 km (11,800 miles) short path from my QTH, or about 21,000 km (13,000 miles) long path. The theoretical great-circle headings are 25 to 75 degrees east of north on short path and 25 to 75 degrees west of south on long path (205 to 255 degrees). When working ZLs on 80 meters on long path during winter (in the northern hemisphere), signals always arrive via North America, which is 90 degrees off from the great-circle direction. Indeed, at that time, it is summer in South America, and the MUF is much higher in the southern hemisphere than in the northern. The path is not a great-circle path, but is inclined in order to leave the southern hemisphere as fast as possible (both the ZLs and the Europeans will beam across North America in the winter). As we continue toward spring, the optimum path between western Europe and New Zealand will move from across North America to across Central America (February-March), and eventually beaming across South America will yield the best signals even later in the year (April onwards). Somewhere around equinox it happens that all three paths produce equally good signals, in which case abnormally strong signal strengths can be recorded (see the discussion of antipodal focusing). It needs no further explanation that these are examples of gray-line propagation. It can also be seen that none of those favored propagation paths ever coincide with the terminator itself. The actual path happens to be more or less perpendicular to the terminator at all times of the year! To summarize, one can say that for long paths and paths to areas near the antipodes, the signal paths will as a rule be bent in such a way that the signals will travel the longest possible distance in the hemisphere where it is winter.

A similar phenomenon is also seen over shorter paths. During the winter, signals from Argentina and Chile regularly arrive in Belgium at beam headings pointed directly at North America, 90 degrees from the expected great-circle direction. This shows again that signals travel along areas of lowest MUF; the signals from South America travel straight north in order to "escape" the summer conditions in the southern hemisphere, and are then propagated toward Europe.

When I worked 3Y1EE on 80 meters on Jan 28, 1987, the signals were totally inaudible from the great-circle direction (190 degrees) but were solid Q5 from 310 degrees (signals coming across North America). If I had not had the Beverages and the possibility to switch directions quickly, I probably would never have worked Peter 1 island on 80 meters! The same happened on Jan 29, but in the following days the propagation mechanism changed totally and signals came in from the great-circle direction. This again proves that one can never be too sure in advance about the direction signals will come from.

3.3.2. Avoiding auroral zones.

A similar path deviation phenomena occurs when signals travel around the auroral belts or zones. In the northern hemisphere signals will travel more southerly than one would expect from great-circle information.

Practical examples: The short path between the West Coast of the US and western Europe has always been a difficult path, because of the interference of the aurora belt with the great-circle path. For the same reason, the short path is almost non-existent between the West Coast and northern Scandinavia (Scandinavia being inside the aurora-belt zone). The writer has experienced several cases where the path was generally believed to be dead, and where nevertheless a good QSO could be made with W6NLZ on 80 meters. Pete was using a 4-element KLM Yagi while I was using my Beverage (for reception) and we were both beaming across South America, which is 90 degrees off the great-circle heading. Similar experiences of southerly bent paths have been confirmed by several West Coast stations.

WØZV reports very similar path skewing during a 160-meter QSO with SM6CPY (April 88) when, during a severe ionospheric disturbance, Bill received SM6CPY at 110 degrees, while the direct bearing is 27 degrees!

An even more striking example was a contact the writer had with KL7U on 80 meters in early 1985. The path between western Europe and Alaska is considered one of the worst, again because of the aurora phenomena. Looking at the globe, there is a great-circle path, only about 7,500 km (5,000 miles) long, but beaming right across the magnetic north pole. The distance is similar to the distance between western Europe and Florida. Straight short-path openings are a rare exception, happening at most a few days every year. There are other more exotic paths that sometimes can bring relief, however. One possible path is a so-called long path, where we would work Alaska at their sunrise and around our sunset. Looking at the globe and the dark side at about 16:00 UTC in the middle of the winter, we can see that the short-path great-circle path (beaming approx. 350 degrees) is following the terminator (gray line). The geographical long path follows the gray line in a southerly direction (170 degrees). In addition we have a whole range of darkness between 350 and 170 degrees.

Another striking example occurred on 160 meters during the first night of the CQ-160-M contest in Jan 1991: With the exception of VE1ZZ, not one North American station was heard until 0400. At that time North American stations started coming through rather faintly, but they were only audible when beaming to South America (240 degrees). No signals from the "usual" 290-320 degree direction! Another example of a crooked path. Between 0400 and 0700 UTC, 80 W/VE stations were worked in 25 states/provinces. All of the signals came through across South America, including K6RK in California! On the North American Beverage receiving antenna only a few of those stations would have been worked.

I have made contacts with KL7U on 80 meters at about 1600 UTC, with excellent signal strengths, hearing him only when listening at 350 degrees. Going only by the time of the contact, this would easily be defined as a long-path QSO; however, it was not, as the signals did not come in from the real long-path direction (approx. 160 degrees) but from the regular short-path direction. It is obvious that this can happen only when there is no auroral absorption at all, as this short path goes right across the magnetic north pole.

An equally extraordinary path was experienced again with KL7U in the morning around my sunrise. At this time you would expect a normal short path (350 degrees). I was called by VE3CDP/W9 informing me that Lon, KL7U was calling

me. As nothing could be heard from him beaming northwest or north, I switched the Beverages, and finally got him Q5 and made a perfect QSO beaming due south. This cannot have been a real long-path QSO, as a large portion of the long-path was in daylight at that time. However, it was obviously a somewhat crooked long-path, where signals came in from the south into my QTH, and traveled very likely in the gray-line zone across South America, the Pacific and up into Alaska.

The opposite sometimes happens as well. When I worked CEØY/SMØAGD on 160 meters (Oct 92), signals were only readable on a Beverage beaming 290 degrees, where the great circle direction to Easter Island is approximately 250 degrees. These kinds of propagation paths are not uncommon. Their existence should be noted, and the mechanism understood in order to be able to work the DX on the other end of the path.

3.3.3. Crooked polar paths in midwinter.

In Northern Europe we can work Japan in midwinter, just after our sunrise (0745 UTC) on 80 meters. The normal or common opening to Japan on 80 is at JA-sunrise, around 2200 UTC. At first you might be tempted to call the 0745 UTC opening a long-path opening. Careful analysis using directive receiving antennas has shown that often the path opens up with signals arriving slightly west of north through the aurora zones, obviously when there is no auroral activity. In a matter of minutes the path can switch to slightly east of north. The opening is rather short at my QTH (typically 15 to max. 30 minutes in midwinter).

On 40 meters the situation is somewhat similar. At the same time (0745 UTC in midwinter), the signals arrive from north or northeast, but when that path fades about 15 to 30 minutes later, it is being replaced by a genuine long path, where the signals now come in across South America. I have never observed this genuine long path across South America on 80, let alone 160 meters.

If we look at the darkness/daylight distribution across the world at that time (0745 UTC in midwinter), we see that we have indeed more than one path possibility: a range of crooked paths bent slightly west to slightly east of the north pole across where those areas are all the way in darkness. These paths are of much shorter distance than the regular long path (approx. 10,000 km vs 30,000 km for the genuine long path) and are better candidates, because of the intrinsically lower attenuation in view of the shorter distance. Note that these paths more or less follow the terminator, and could be considered as typical gray-line propagation paths as defined by Hoppe and others (Ref. 108 and Ref. 118).

Often such openings are very area selective, probably because of the ducting phenomena involved, occurring only when the required specific signal-launching conditions exist. This is only so for very specific locations where D-layer ionization is partial and the F-layer tilt is optimal. In several cases I was able to work several JA stations with signals up to S9, while the same stations were reported to be undetectable in Germany only 300 miles away. In all cases the signals were at the loudest when they were coming in about 10 degrees east of north. In Japan the openings seem to be very selective as well, as can be judged from the call areas worked. Northern Japan

(JA7 and JA8) obviously leads the opening. Central Japan follows 30 minutes later, and southern Japan often comes too late for this kind of opening into my QTH. In midwinter there is a 1.5 hour spread in sunset time between northern and southern Japan. I have not yet observed this particular crooked polar short path on 160 meters.

Similar paths exist on 80 meters in midwinter between California and Central Asia (Mongolia) around 0030 UTC, between eastern Europe (Moscow) and the northern Pacific (Wake Island) around 0615 UTC, and between the East Coast and Midwest of the US and northern Scandinavia around 1230 UTC. All of those polar-region paths are east of the pole and should not be influenced by aurora as much as paths going west of the north pole. The gray-line globe is a tremendous help in finding those paths. R. Rosen (K2RR) calls this path a long path (Ref 675 and 676), which it obviously is not. On 40 meters this "polar" short path is followed by a genuine long path (over South America) minutes after the short path fades.

A geographically similar condition exists in midwinter between Scandinavia and the Midwest/West Coast of the US. In this particular case, however, the alternative crooked path (at the time of the long path) goes right across the magnetic north pole with the well-known consequences of high probability of auroral absorption. Although both cases seem alike from a geographical point of view, they are quite dissimilar from a geomagnetic point of view. In the same publication (Ref 675 and 676), Rosen reports this propagation from SM6EHY's QTH and expects that such a path may also be available on 160 meters. I am not aware, however that Scandinavian stations have worked US stations across that particular path.

In the winter months the Scandinavians have a very common so-called 80-meter long-path propagation path around their sunset, which coincides with sunrise on the US West Coast. This path satisfies all requirements for being a genuine long path, also from an azimuthal launching angle point of view. In Scandinavia the beam headings generally indicate an optimum launching angle of approximately 100 degrees. However, along their way, the signals will be least attenuated in those areas of the ionosphere where the MUF is lowest. This phenomenon will make the signals follow a crooked path, whereby areas of high MUF will be avoided. OZ8BV reports a 90- to 100-degree direction when working the West Coast on 80-meter long path from southern Denmark. Ben is using a 3-element Yagi at 54 m (180 ft) and is well placed to confirm this path (the genuine long path would be 50 to 160 degrees).

D. Riggs, N7AM, who is using a rotary quad for 80 meters, writes: "We have learned that the 80-meter long path between the Pacific Northwest and Scandinavia is following the LUF (lowest usable frequency). I have always believed that the long path to Europe was not across the equator but leaves us at 240 degrees and since the MUF is highest at the equator it cannot continue at 240 degrees but it bends westerly going under the Hawaiian islands, across the Philippines under Japan and across the Asian continent to Scandinavia. The MUF charts prove this fact. The fact that the long path to Europe lies north of the equator is proven by the northern

Europeans working JAs and Southeast Asia before and after the West Coast peak."

■ 4. 160 VS 80 METERS

I'll try to sum up some of the major differences between 80 and 160 meters:

• One-sixty meters has a distinct area in which working DX is more or less like a piece of cake, anything in a circle of approximately 6000 to 7000 km (3750 - 4400 miles) around one's own QTH. For instance, from Europe, working the East Coast of the USA, can be done daily. The "gray" zone is W8 and W9 land. For anything beyond that, conditions must be above normal or the stations must be exceptionally well equipped. It's all or nothing. The same is true in all directions. This is far different from 80 meters where longer distances are possible every day and where the transition between "easy" and "difficult" seems to be much more vague.

• Long path on 160 is a rare exception, except for stations very near the antipode.

• If 80 meters is swinging, there is no proof that 160 will be any good, and vice versa. Same is true when you compare 40 with 80; 40 can be poor, and 80 swinging. So don't extrapolate from the lower or the higher band. There is no guarantee this will work.

• Very typical for 160 is the slow and deep QSB, which I have seldom seen on 80.

• One-sixty has very pronounced peaks at sunrise, especially for the really long-haul stations. For really long-haul distances, the sharp peak is usually within minutes of sunrise. You can almost set your watch by it. During the 1992-1993 winter I had a daily sked with FK8CP on 160, and I could predict with an accuracy of a minute or so when his signals would pop out of the noise. The sunset peak on 160 is much less pronounced. There seems to be a broad "peak" within 1 hour or so after sunset.

• On 160 m the skip is often very selective, even for average distances, just like the long-path skip on 80 meters.

• There is a much more select "public" on 160 than there is on 80. In order to be successful on top band you need quite a bit of room. This is a band where it is very difficult to be successful from a city lot. Most of the 160-meter DXers can fortunately still be categorized as gentlemen. I guess that's why 160 is sometimes referred to as "the gentlemen's band."

■ 5. DXING TOOLS

5.1. The Gray-line Globe

The now famous and exclusive gray-line globe forms an integral part of many a dedicated low-band DXer's shack. Columbus Verlag (D7056, Weinstadt-Beutelsbach, BRD) has been selling the gray-line globe for over 10 years now (Fig 1-11). The globes are not locally distributed in the US. Overseas customers can order globes directly from the manufacturer in single quantities (order number 42 34 59). In 1979 an amateur version was added to the collection. This version has the great-circle lines printed, centered on central Europe (order number 43 34 52-9). The gray-line globe was the first tool available to the dedicated low-band DXer, giving a whole range of accurate information on sunrise/sunset plus the visual three-dimen-

Fig 1-11—The Columbus Verlag gray-line globe. Note the large ring over the equator, which is imprinted with a time-of-day scale.

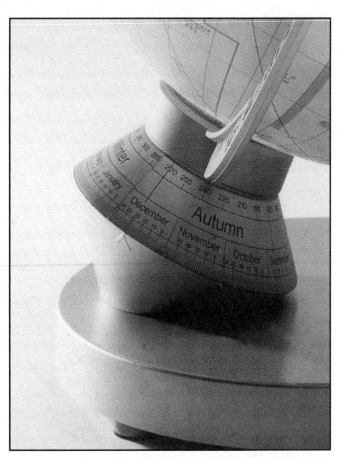

Fig 1-12—The day-by-day calendar on the globe stand can be used to set the inclination of the terminator.

sional information that cannot be replaced by two-dimensional maps.

The amateur version of the globe measures more than 13 inches (33 cm) in diameter, has very detailed printing (all DXCC prefixes, plus the call areas in the larger countries and WAZ zones), and clearly shows the daylight and darkness zones. The inclination of the earth's axis (vs the sun) can be changed and set in increments of 1 day or as little as 0.1 degree! There is a scale on the base of the globe that allows you to set the inclination with the aid of a simple day-by-day calendar (Fig 1-12). In addition to setting the inclination of the terminator, there is also a time-graduated ring along the equator so that you can set the position (rotation) of the globe for any given time, in increments of 15 minutes. Interpolation can easily be done down to a few minutes (15-minute markings being about ½ inch or 12 mm apart on the ring). This allows exact local time and UTC to be accurately read off the scale for any spot on the globe. Inversely, for a given location the sunset and sunrise times (local time or UTC) can be found with an accuracy of a few minutes. The globe mechanism does not take into account the deviations caused by the slightly elliptical orbit of the earth around the sun. Thus, there are slight deviations, but these should fall within the limits of the visual accuracy of the system. If you need sunrise/sunset times with a 1-minute accuracy (and often you do on 160 meters), you need to get the times by direct calculating (e.g.,

computer program or sunrise/sunset tables).

This unique tool is very useful for visualizing the illumination of the earth, and together with the knowledge of aurora phenomena it will undoubtedly help you in understanding particular propagation paths. It is also a superb decorative element for the shack.

5.2. The DX Edge

The DX EDGE (Fig 1-13) is a slide-rule type calculator that gives you roughly the same information as the gray-line globe. It consists of a plastic carrier and a set of 12 slides (one for each month). The carrier is 4 × 11 inches and imprinted with a double (side by side) conform-projection map of the world. Because of its small size, it only shows the 40 zones and a few prefixes for some large countries. The plastic slides are 4 × 6 inches and are imprinted with the terminator (gray line) and the darkness/daylight zones. By sliding the inserts through the carrier you can find the relevant information regarding the darkness/daylight zones and the terminator.

Conversion to local standard time and UTC is not always as straightforward as one thinks. This problem does not occur with the gray-line globe. The fact that one has only 12 slide inserts limits the accuracy of the tool, as interpolation is necessary for more accurate outputs. The DX EDGE is manufactured by DX EDGE, PO Box 834, Madison Square Station, New York, NY 10159. The DX EDGE is also available

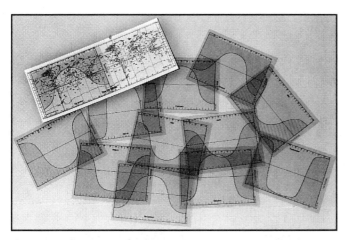

Fig 1-13—The DX-EDGE provides a good visual impression of what happens at any time of the year and the day. In the example of the picture, the January insert is used with the sunrise happening right over Belgium. Note that the sun is setting in New Zealand and in Japan. At that time, the path to Japan is indeed following the terminator, but the (long) path to Japan is almost perpendicular to the terminator, being right across North America (see par. 3.3.)

through distributors (see advertisements in Amateur Radio magazines.) There is also a computer version of the DX EDGE.

The accuracy that can be obtained with the EDGE is in the order of magnitude of 15/30 minutes. Its usefulness is questionable for dedicated 160-meter operators who know that their sunrise/sunset openings may only last a few minutes right around sunset and/or sunrise. Accuracy is certainly an important requirement for 160-meter operations!

5.3. The Geochron Gray-line Map

Geochron Enterprises (899 Arguello St, Unit A, Redwood City, CA 94063), manufactures a wonderful gray-line map, which is available through the Ham Radio Outlet stores. The Geochron, shown in Fig 1-14, has a fixed time scale across

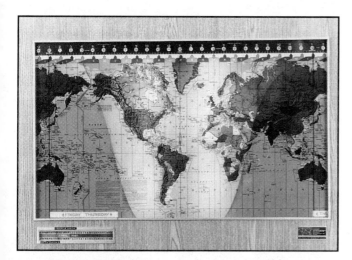

Fig 1-14—The Geochron gray-line map is a magnificent motorized luxury model of the DX-edge, measuring 84 × 57 cm (33 × 22.5 inches).

the top of the map. A continuous-loop map made of polyester (Mylar) is rotated by a motor on two drums, and moves linearly across the Geochron under a glass panel, illuminated by fluorescent bulbs. As the map moves across the Geochron, the darkness/daylight zones are projected onto the map, and the shape is adjusted continuously. The Geochron also carries a calendar, which is moved with the same precision as the map. Manual setting of the date and time can be easily accomplished as well. The Geochron is available in 50- and 60-Hz versions. It is a truly magnificent gray-line map, the only drawback being its high price.

5.4. Calculating Sunrise and Sunset Times

Instead of using the gray-line globe or the DX EDGE, a personal computer can be used to calculate sunrise and sunset times.

Van Heddegem (ON4HW) developed a method based on classical astronomy to calculate sunrise and sunset times. This is the algorithm I use in all my computer programs. The equations are given in Table 1-2 in the form of a BASIC program. The program does not use any arc sin or arc cos functions as they are not available in all BASIC dialects.

5.5. The Sunrise/Sunset Tables

The sunrise/sunset-tables booklet that I had printed several years ago shows sunrise and sunset times for over 500 different locations in the world (including 100 different locations in the US) in tabular form. Increments are given per half month. Fig 1-15 shows an example of a printout for one location.

I have tried all the propagation aids that are described in this book, and many more. The only aid that I use all the time is the sunrise/sunset tables. Why? You can grab the tables any time and look up the required information in seconds. Just keep the little booklet within hand's reach on your operating desk. The data are accurate. Computer programs are great, but you probably will have the PC running with another program when you need the sunrise/sunset information. Also, in the time it takes to load the program, you could already have looked up the required information in the tables. The tables never get outdated, as sunrise/sunset times hardly change over the years. All the graphical systems (globe, slide-rule or computer-screen world maps) are far too inaccurate to be useful for 80 and especially 160 meters.

This handy sunrise/sunset booklet (100 pages) is still available. Send $5 plus $5 for worldwide airmail postage to John Devoldere, ON4UN, Poelstraat 215, B9820, Merelbeke, Belgium.

5.5.1. General rules for using sunrise/sunset times.

For all E-W, W-E, NW-SE and NE-SW paths there are two propagation peaks to be expected (short path):

1. The first peak will occur around sunrise of the station at the eastern end of the path.
2. The second peak occurs around sunset for the station at the western end of the path.

For N-S paths there are no pronounced peaks around

```
                       -ON-
BELGIUM                              (BRUSSELS)

==============================================

50.60 DEG N                       - 4.35 DEG W

    DATE         SUNRISE          SUNSET
    ----         -------          ------
   JAN  1         07.48           15.48
   JAN 15         07.38           16.06
   FEB  1         07.20           16.32
   FEB 15         06.55           16.58
   MAR  1         06.30           17.21
   MAR 15         05.57           17.46
   APR  1         05.22           18.12
   APR 15         04.49           18.36
   MAY  1         04.20           19.00
   MAY 15         03.55           19.23
   JUN  1         03.36           19.44
   JUN 15         03.30           19.56
   JUL  1         03.33           19.59
   JUL 15         03.47           19.50
   AUG  1         04.07           19.30
   AUG 15         04.30           19.04
   SEP  1         04.54           18.32
   SEP 15         05.17           17.59
   OCT  1         05.40           17.25
   OCT 15         06.04           16.53
   NOV  1         06.31           16.21
   NOV 15         06.57           15.58
   DEC  1         07.20           15.42
   DEC 15         07.37           15.38
```

Fig 1-15—A typical printout from the sunset/sunrise tables. Four such printouts are given on each page. There are listings for over 500 locations, including all US states.

either sunset or sunrise. Often the peak seems to occur near midnight.

The use of the tables can best be explained with a few examples.

Example 1.

What are the peak propagation times between Belgium and Japan on February 15? From the tables can be found:

Belgium :
15 Feb: SRW = 0656 SSW = 1659
Japan :
15 Feb: SRE = 2130 SSE = 0824

where

SRE = sunrise, eastern end
SRW = sunrise, western end
SSE = sunset, eastern end
SSW = sunset, western end

The first peak is around sunrise in Japan or SRE = 2130

Table 1-2

BASIC Program to Calculate Sunrise and Sunset Times

The algorithms were provided by W. Van Heddegem, ON4HW.

```
10   CLEAR
20   PI = 3.1415927
30   SW = −0.97460409
40   CW = 0.22393492
50   SE = 0.39777700
60   CE = 0.91748213
70   K1 = −0.014834754
80   PRINT "ENTER WEST LONGITUDE IN DECIMAL
     DEGREES"
90   INPUT LO
100  PRINT "ENTER NORTH LATITUDE IN DECIMAL
     DEGREES"
110  INPUT LA
120  LO = LO * PI / 180
130  LA = LA * PI / 180
140  PRINT "ENTER DAY NUMBER (1 TO 365)"
150  INPUT D
160  M = (2 * PI * D + LO) / 365.24219 − 0.05347
170  L = M − 1.3449463
180  C1 = 1 − 0.03343 * COS (M)
190  C2 = .99944 * SIN (M) / C1
200  C3 = (COS (M) − .03343) / C1
210  C4 = SW * C3 + CW * C2
220  C5 = CW * C3 − SW * C2
230  C6 = SE * C4 : REM SINE OF SUN DECLINATION
240  B1 = K1 − C6 * SIN (LA)
250  B2 = (COS (LA))^2 * (1 − C6^2) − B1^2
260  IF B2 <= 0 THEN R$ = "NO.SR" : S$ = "NO.SS" :
     GOTO 340
270  B3 = ATN (B1 / SQR (B2)) − PI / 2
280  B4 = ATN ((COS(L) * CE * C4 − SIN (L) * C5) / (SIN(L)
     * CE * C4 + COS(L) * C5) )
290  GOSUB 370
300  R$ = STR$ (B6)
310  B3 = −B3
320  GOSUB 370
330  S$ = STR$ (B6)
340  PRINT "SUNRISE : ";R$
350  PRINT "SUNSET: ";S$
360  GOTO 140
370  B5 = B4 + B3 + LO + PI
380  IF B5 < 0 THEN B5 = B5 + 2*PI
390  B5 = INT (B5 * 720 / PI + 0.5) : REM MINUTES PAST
     0000 UTC
400  IF B5 > 1439 THEN B5 = B5 − 1440
410  B6 = 0.4 * INT (B5 / 60 ) + B5 / 100 : REM TIME IN
     HH.MM
420  RETURN
```

UTC. This is after sunset in Belgium (SSW = 1659), so the path is in darkness. Always check this.

The second peak is around sunset in Belgium or SSW = 1659 UTC. This, too, is after sunset in Japan (0824 UTC) so the path is in darkness.

Is there a possibility for a long-path opening? The definition of a long-path opening (see Section 1.3.1) says we must have sunset at the eastern end before sunrise at the western end of the path. In the example this is not true, because SRW = 0656 UTC is not earlier than SSE = 0824 UTC.

Example 2. Is there a long-path opening from Japan to Belgium on January 1?

Belgium:
1 Jan SRW = 0744 UTC, SSW = 1549 UTC

Japan:
1 Jan SRE = 2152 UTC, SSE = 0740 UTC

Here, SRW (0744 UTC) is later than SSE (0740 UTC). This is indeed a valid condition for a long-path opening. It will be of short duration and will be centered around 0746 UTC (see Section 3.2.3).

5.5.2. Remarks

In practice, long-path openings are possible even when the paths are partially in daylight. Near the terminator we are in the so-called gray-line zone and can take advantage of the enhanced propagation in these zones. The width of the gray line has been discussed earlier (Section 1.3.3). A striking example of such an excellent genuine long-path QSO was a contact made between Arie, VK2AVA and me on March 19, 1976 at 0700 UTC on 80 meters. The long-path distance is 22,500 km. Note that the QSO was made almost right at equinox (March 21), and the path is a textbook example of a NE-SW path. On that day we had the following conditions:

Sunrise west (Belgium) = 0555 UTC
Sunset east (Sydney, Australia) = 0812 UTC.

This means that the long path was in daylight for more than two hours. The QSO was made one hour after sunrise in Belgium and more than one hour before sunset in Australia.

Another similar example was a QSO with VKØGC from Macquarie Island (long-path distance 21,500 km). On Jan 21, 1985 a long-path contact was made on 80 meters that lasted from 0800 until 0830 UTC, with excellent signals. This was more than one hour before sunset on Macquarie (0950) and almost one hour after sunrise in Belgium (0731).

Because the locations of these stations (VK2 and VKØ) are fairly close to the antipodes from Belgium, the long paths can safely be considered genuine long paths. Indeed there are no crooked paths that could provide an alternative to the genuine long paths. The gray-line globe is a unique tool to help you visualize a particular path like this.

A third striking example is the Palmyra/Kingman Reef QSO as described earlier in this chapter.

5.6. Personal Computer Programs

The almost universal presence of one or more personal computers in every ham shack, together with an abundance of computer programs, has proved to be a great asset to Amateur Radio. These programs can be divided in several groups:

- training programs (Morse, Amateur Radio exam theory)
- QSO-logging programs with award tracking etc. (an excellent example is DX-Base by W8ZF and AA4LU)
- contesting (e.g., the famous K1EA and K8CC programs)
- modeling programs for antennas and electronic circuits
- antenna physical design programs
- programs for RTTY, AMTOR, packet and other digital modes
- propagation-prediction programs

In a few years these programs have grown from simple tools (computer memory limited!) to often very powerful systems, mostly thanks to the enormous advance made in the PC world, where speed and memory performance has skyrocketed.

Many amateurs also develop their own programs or tools, and share the public-domain software with friends, while other software is made commercially available.

I am convinced that the usefulness of propagation forecasting programs for DXing on the low bands is very limited. If you understand the mechanisms behind the propagation phenomena, as explained in detail in this chapter, you will be able to correctly predict the propagation without the help of any program. In addition, the programs mostly do not go below 2 MHz, and as such are useless for top-band predictions.

5.7. ON4UN Propagation Programs

While writing the original LOW-BAND DXING book, I developed a number of computer programs as aids for the active DXer. The programs have recently been completely rewritten and substantially enhanced, making use of more modern programming languages and techniques (programmed in Quick Basic). The programs are fully color compatible (EGA, VGA), and available only for MS-DOS on a 3½-inch diskette (see order form in the back of this book).

While the majority of programs are technical programs related to antenna design (and are covered in the antenna chapter of this book), a group of programs deals with the propagation aspects of low-band DXing.

The Propagation Software contains the following modules:

1. SUNRISE/SUNSET TIMES.

This program lists the sunrise and sunset times in half-month increments for the user's QTH. The user's QTH can be preprogrammed and is saved to disk. It can be changed at any time, however. On the screen, the sunset and sunrise times of a "target QTH" are listed side-by-side with your own time (see Fig 1-16). The target QTH can be specified either by coordinates or by name. On screen you also see the great circle direction as well as distance. The software works in miles as well as kilometers. The user can also modify the display increments. You can also list the times in single-day increments if you wish.

2. THE DATABASE.

When specified by name, the coordinates are looked up in a database containing over 550 locations worldwide. This database is accessible by the user for updating or adding more locations. The database can contain data for up to 750 locations, and can be sorted in alphabetical order of the country name or the radio prefix. You can also print the data on paper.

3. LISTING SUNRISE/SUNSET TIMES.

The program also allows you to list (scroll on screen) or make a full printout of the sunrise and sunset times (plus directions and distances from your QTH) for a given day of the

```
                    7.56   15.43   JAN   1   12.27   21.39
                    7.50   16.01   JAN  15   12.25   21.52       ═══ W2 ═══
  ═══ ON4UN ═══     7.31   16.29   JAN  31   12.14   22.11      NEW JERSEY
  ==========>>>     7.05   16.56   FEB  15   11.57   22.30       TRENTON
  LAT  =  51.00°    6.38   17.19   FEB  28   11.38   22.45    <<<==========
  LONG =  -3.45°    6.06   17.45   MAR  15   11.15   23.01    LAT  =  40.21°
  ==========>>>     5.30   18.11   MAR  31   10.49   23.18    LONG =  74.76°
                    4.57   18.36   APR  15   10.25   23.33    <<<==========
                    4.27   19.00   APR  30   10.04   23.48
                    4.02   19.23   MAY  15    9.48    0.03
  ALL UTC TIMES     3.44   19.43   MAY  31    9.37    0.17
                    3.38   19.55   JUN  15    9.34    0.25    DIR  =  290 °
                    3.42   19.58   JUN  30    9.38    0.28    DIST =  5898 Km
                    3.56   19.49   JUL  15    9.47    0.23        =  3666 Mi
  ═══ Menu ═══      4.17   19.29   JUL  31   10.01    0.10
  MORE ------> M    4.39   19.02   AUG  15   10.15   23.52
                    5.04   18.29   AUG  31   10.30   23.28
  CHANGE INC-> I    5.27   17.56   SEP  15   10.45   23.04
  PRINT LIST-> P    5.51   17.22   SEP  30   10.59   22.39
  DATABASE  -> D    6.15   16.49   OCT  15   11.15   22.15
  GRAY LINE -> G    6.43   16.17   OCT  31   11.32   21.53
  or EXIT   -> X    7.09   15.53   NOV  15   11.50   21.37
                    7.33   15.37   NOV  30   12.07   21.29
                    7.50   15.33   DEC  15   12.20   21.29
  -SW by ON4UN-     S.R.   S.S.    DATE      S.R.    S.S.      TIME: 17:57
```

Fig 1-16—Screen dump of the sunrise/sunset display of the propagation module, which is part of the NEW LOW BAND SOFTWARE. The times at the left are the user's sunrise/sunset times. On the right are the times for the target QTH. The target QTH can be specified by name (approx. 1000 names in the database) or by coordinates. The standard display increment is ½ month, but this can be changed to any value (e.g., 1 day for more precision).

NR	PREF	COUNTRY	CITY	LATITUDE	LONGITUDE
415	W0	NEBRASKA	NORTH PLATTE	41.13	100.83
416	W0	MISSOURI	COLUMBIA	39.00	92.50
417	W0	SOUTH DAKOTA	SIOUX FALLS	43.54	96.73
418	W1	RHODE ISLAND	PROVIDENCE	41.83	71.41
419	W1	VERMONT	BURLINGTON	44.48	73.21
420	W1	MAINE	AUGUSTA	44.31	69.76
421	W1	MASSACHUSETTS	MASSACHUSETTS	42.35	71.05
422	W1	NEW HAMPSHIRE	MANCHESTER	42.98	71.46
423	W1	MAINE	PORTLAND	43.50	70.25
424	W1	CONNECTICUT	HARTFORD	41.76	72.68
425	W1	MASSACHUSETTS	PITTSFIELD	42.45	73.25
426	W1	CONNECTICUT	BRIDGEPORT	41.18	73.18
427	W2	NEW YORK	NEW YORK CITY	40.41	73.98
428	W2	NEW YORK	BUFFALO	42.88	73.74
429	W2	NEW JERSEY	NEWARK	40.73	74.16
430	W2	NEW JERSEY	TRENTON	40.21	74.76
431	W2	NEW YORK	ALBANY	42.65	73.74
432	W2	NEW YORK	SYRACUSE	43.11	76.20
433	W3	PENNSYLVANIA	PHILADELPHIA	39.95	75.15
434	W3	MARYLAND	BALTIMORE	39.33	76.66
435	W3	NEW JERSEY	ATLANTIC CITY	39.39	74.40
436	W3	PENNSYLVANIA	PITTSBURG	40.39	80.00
437	W3	DELAWARE	WILMINGTON	39.75	75.74

```
     ENTER = CONTINUE LISTING        B = BACK 1 SCREEN        X = EXIT
```

Fig 1-17—Partial printout of the database used with the sunrise/sunset and gray-line program. For densely populated areas, several major cities are included in the database.

PRF	COUNTRY	CITY	DIST.	DIR.	START	END	WIDTH
VE6	CANADA	CALGARY (ALB)	4485	322	15.23	16.00	45
VE6	CANADA	EDMONTON (ALB)	4341	323	15.30	16.00	54
VE7	CANADA	VANCOUVER BC)	4814	326	15.54	16.00	40
VE8	CANADA	YELLOWKNIFE (NWT)	3884	330	15.55	16.00	175
VK0	HEARD ISL		8250	139	15.24	15.32	7
VK9	NORFOLK ISL		10704	33	7.41	7.47	5
VP8	FALKLAND	STANLEY	7940	216	7.35	7.43	7
W6	CALIFORNIA	SACRAMENTO	5385	319	15.16	15.40	24
W6	CALIFORNIA	FRESNO	5456	316	15.14	15.26	22
W7	OREGON	PORTLAND	5024	323	15.40	16.00	32
W7	WASHINGTON	SPOKANE	4777	321	15.24	16.00	36
W7	WASHINGTON	SEATTLE	4893	324	15.45	16.00	36
W7	IDAHO	BOISE	4958	318	15.14	15.37	29
W7	IDAHO	POCATELLO	4889	315	15.14	15.19	28
W7	NEVADA	RENO	5298	318	15.14	15.35	24
W7	MONTANA	BILLINGS	4610	315	15.14	15.17	33
W7	MONTANA	GREAT FALLS	4601	318	15.14	15.36	36
ZK1	SOUTH COOK ISL	RAROTONGA	10170	330	15.58	16.00	5
ZK1	SOUTH COOK ISL	AITUTAKI	10170	330	15.58	16.00	5
ZL1	NEW ZEALAND-ZL1	AUCKLAND	11355	26	7.34	7.40	5
ZL2	NEW ZEALAND-ZL2	WELLINGTON	11633	34	7.47	7.53	5
ZL3	NEW ZEALAND-ZL3	CHRISTCHURCH	11710	48	8.04	8.10	5
ZL4	NEW ZEALAND-ZL4	DUNEDIN	11647	55	8.13	8.19	5
	END OF RUN			PRESS ANY KEY TO CONTINUE			

Fig 1-18—Screen dump of a partial listing from the gray-line program. This particular run is for a Dec 25 gray-line from Belgium. Notice the "marginal" gray-line openings with the US West Coast from Belgium.

year. This is a really nice feature for DXpeditioners! Fig 1-17 shows a partial printout of the database listing some of the US areas with their coordinates.

4. GRAY-LINE PROGRAM.

This section of the program uses a unique algorithm that adapts the effective radio width of the gray-line zone to the location and the time of the year. This width is also different for 80 and 160 meters. In addition, the user can specify a minimum distance under which he is not interested in gray-line information. The printout (on screen or paper) lists the distance to the target QTH, the beginning and ending times of the gray-line window, as well as the effective width of the gray line at the target QTH. Fig 1-18 shows a printout of a gray-line run for Belgium on Dec 25 (notice the marginal long-path gray line with the US West Coast).

The cost of the NEW LOW BAND SOFTWARE is $50. It can be ordered from either of the following sources: John Devoldere, ON4UN, 215 Poelstraat, B9820 Merelbeke, Belgium, or George Oliva, K2UO, 5 Windsor Dr, Eatontown, NJ 07724 USA. See also the order form in the back of this publication.

The antenna software modules are the subject of Chapter 4 in this book.

■ 6. THE 160-M MYSTERY

Understanding and predicting propagation on 40 meters is pretty straightforward. Eighty meters is well understood as well. With the right equipment and knowledge on both ends,

one could probably work 300 countries in a year on 80 meters.

One-sixty is a totally different ball game. The more I have been active on 160, the more I am convinced of how little we know about propagation on that band. True, we know a few of the parameters that influence propagation, but far from all. For a long time I have kept daily records of the K and A indexes, sunspot numbers, etc., together with my observations of conditions on 160, in order to try to find a correlation between the data and the propagation. But I have found very little or none; only negative correlations. We know more or less when it definitely will not work, but not for sure when it will work.

Of course we must realize that on top band we are in a gray area where things are sometimes possible, but often not. There are dozens of parameters that make things happen or not. They all seem to influence a delicate mechanism that makes really long-haul propagation on 160 meters work every now and then. Understanding all of the parameters and being able to quantify them and feed them into a computer that will tell exactly when we can work that evasive DX station halfway around the globe will probably be an illusion forever. There is no interest from the broadcasters in this subject. Broadcasters and utility traffic operators are interested in knowing the frequency that will give them best propagation. They are not interested in studying the subject of "marginal" propagation on the edge of what is possible. Therefore, long-haul DXing on 160 meters will probably always remain a real hunting game, where limited understanding, feeling, expertise, and luck will be determining factors of success, not to forget your hunting weapons—the antennas and the equipment.

OPERATING TECHNIQUES

- **1. THE CHALLENGE**
- **2. THE FREQUENCIES**
  - 2.1. 160 Meters
  - 2.2. 80 Meters
  - 2.3. 40 Meters
- **3. SPLIT FREQUENCY OPERATION**
  - 3.1. 160 Meters
  - 3.2. 80 Meters
  - 3.3. 40 Meters
- **4. THE CLARIFIER**
- **5. ZERO BEAT**
- **6. DXPEDITIONS**
- **7. NETS AND LIST OPERATIONS**
- **8. LISTEN OR TRANSMIT?**
- **9. BEACON STATIONS**
- **10. ARRANGING SKEDS FOR THE LOW BANDS**
- **11. GETTING THE RARE ONES**
  - 11.1. DX News Publications
  - 11.2. DX Information Nets
  - 11.3. Packet Radio and DX Clusters
- **12. ACHIEVEMENT AWARDS**
- **13. THE SURVEY**
- **14. THE SUCCESSFUL LOW-BAND DXER**
- **15. THE DON'TS**

OPERATING 2 TECHNIQUES

L ow-band DXing is far from just a communications sport. It's a highly competitive technical hobby.

■ 1. THE CHALLENGE

Low-band DXers always wander near the edge of what is possible. The most successful low-band DXers are the pioneers that keep moving this edge. Improved knowledge of propagation, together with better equipment and most of all, better antennas, make it possible to dig deeper and deeper into the noise to catch the previously evasive layer of buried signals.

If you are looking for an easy pastime, stay away from low-band DXing. Maybe one of the many lists that are abundant on the higher bands is something for you. K1ZM, who has over 225 countries on 160 meters, wrote on his survey reply: "160 is truly a MAN's as well as a GENTLEMAN's band. You want a challenge? Get on 160."

On 80 and 40 meters you do not need to have a genuine antenna farm to work DXCC, even within one year's time. There are many examples of rather modest stations on a city lot that have done extremely well. N4KG worked over 200 countries on 80 on a city lot before he even knew what a Beverage (antenna!) was. To be so successful from an average QTH requires a better than average knowledge of propagation as well as a substantial dose of perseverance, however.

■ 2. THE FREQUENCIES

Probably the most important operating skill one can acquire is to learn where (and when) to find the DX.

2.1. 160 Meters

The frequency allocations on 160 meters vary widely all over the world, but almost all countries with the exception of Japan have a CW section in the 1.820- to 1.840-kHz window.

An excellent operating aid for the 160-meter DXer is a publication by N7CKD entitled *World Top-Band Frequency Allocations*. It contains all 160-meter frequency allocations available, and is updated regularly. Copies can be obtained from: D. G. Peterson, N7CKD, 4248 "A" St, SE, Space 609, Auburn, WA 98002. Prices are: $3.50 in North America, $5.00 overseas.

One-sixty meters is a shared band in most if not all countries. This means there can be QRM from nonamateur users. In Europe most ship-to-shore and other commercial or military stations are systematically being moved outside the 1820- to 1850-kHz segment. The well-known beacons OSN and DHJ have cleared the 1821-1832 kHz window. Finally, on January 1, 1993, after years of hard work by Peter Bobek,

DJ8WL, top-notch 160-meter DXer from Germany, and many others, the Deutsche Bundespost finally assigned another SSB allocation, outside the CW DX window. The old allocation of 1835 made 1832 to 1835 a total loss for most of the night. Peter told me that over the years he has missed approximately 20 countries because of this ridiculous situation.

In the last year there has been an increased use of 1840 by SSB stations in Europe, also during prime DX hours. It appears that many are not aware that on LSB their sideband spreads 2.5 kHz down, and that they are taking out 40 percent of the primary DX CW window in Europe. I would urge all SSB stations not to transmit on SSB below 1842.5 kHz.

Over the past 5 years, 1820 to 1840 kHz has been the de facto DX window for 160-meter CW, with 1840-1850 kHz serving as phone DX band for all countries including the ex-USSR countries (1.850-1930 kHz). From 1907.5 kHz through 1912.5 kHz is the Japanese 160-meter DX window. From 1830 to 1840 kHz is generally considered the European CW transmit segment, while 1820 to 1830 kHz is considered the DX window in Europe (that's where the DX is, and where the Europeans as well as the US stations stay out of).

2.2. 80 Meters

Although the 80-meter band is not allocated uniformly in all continents and countries, this does not really represent a problem for the DXer. On CW all countries have an allocation starting at 3500 kHz. The DX window for CW is the same all over the world: 3500 to 3510 kHz. A secondary window exists between 3525 and 3530 kHz, which is the lower limit for General and Advanced Class amateurs in the US.

Until a few years ago, the 80-meter SSB DX window was 3790 to 3800 kHz. A number of countries still do not have their main phone subband in that area, e.g., ex-USSR with 3600 to 3650 kHz as their phone subband. Many countries such as Japan and Australia have a small window just below 3800 kHz for DX operating, although their main phone band is in a different section of the 80-meter band. The ex-USSR stations now are also allowed to operate up to 3800 kHz during contests. Recently we have witnessed ex-USSR stations operating around 3.8 MHz outside contests, and it is probable that, with the political restructuring in the ex-USSR, different operating privileges will result.

Since the FCC decided to expand SSB privileges in the US, first to 3775 and later to 3750 kHz for Extra Class amateurs, the DX window has de facto expanded from below 3750 to 3800 kHz during openings to the US, although the top 10 kHz is still the focal area. DXpeditions very often use 3501 to 3510 kHz and 3795 to 3800 kHz as their primary operating frequencies.

Many amateurs are unaware that 80 meters is a shared band in many parts of the world. In the US, 80 meters sounds like a VHF band compared to what it sounds like in Europe. Because of the many commercial stations on the band, the 25-kHz DX window can often hold only five QSOs in between the extremely strong commercial stations in the local evening hours. If you are fortunate enough to live in a region where 80 meters is an exclusive band, please be aware of this, and bear with those who must continuously fight the commercial QRM.

In the middle of the day, the DX segments can be used for local work, although one should be aware that local QSOs could cause great QRM to a DXer (at, say, 500 miles) who is already in the grayline zone, and who could just enjoy peak propagation conditions at his QTH. In Europe situations like this occur almost daily in the winter when northern Scandinavian stations can work the Pacific and the West Coast of the US at 1300 to 1400 UTC, while western Europe is in bright daylight and does not hear the DX at all. Western Europeans can hear the Scandinavians quite well, and consequently the Scandinavians can hear western Europe certainly well enough to get QRMed by other hams there. The DXer must be aware of these situations so as not to interfere with his counterparts in other areas.

US DXers generally complain about the narrow segment that has been officially reserved for DX on 80 meters. Most suggest the US should follow the European band plan (3775-3800 kHz). They complain bitterly about the little cooperation from the rag-chewers, who have 200 kHz for their local contacts.

The increased popularity of 80-meter DXing, together with the few DX channels available in the phone DX window, have created a new problem where certain individuals would sit on a frequency in the DX window for hours (seems like days) on end, without giving anyone else a chance. This problem is nonexistent on CW, where you have an abundance of DX channels in the DX window.

2.3. 40 Meters

Forty meters is pretty straightforward. The CW DX QSOs happen between 7000 and 7010 kHz, with rare exceptions around 7025 kHz.

In the European or non-US phone band, being as narrow as it is, you can find DX anywhere between 7040 and 7100 kHz, with 7045 to 7080 kHz as a focal area.

■ 3. SPLIT-FREQUENCY OPERATION

The split-frequency technique is highly recommended for the rare DX station or DXpedition working the low bands. It is the most effective way of making as many QSOs as possible during the short low-band openings, because the marginal conditions often encountered are conducive to great chaos if stations are calling the DX on his frequency. It also gives a fair chance to the stations that have the best propagation to the DX station. With list operations this is not necessarily so, and stations having peak propagation can bite off their

fingernails while the MC is passing along stations who barely make contact and have to fight to get a 33 report. With split operation the DXer with a good antenna and with good operating practice is bound to have a lead over the modest station, which is only fair. Why else would we build a station which performs better than the average?

There are two good reasons for the DX station to work split frequency:

1. First he must realize that when he stops his CQ, there are likely many stations to be calling him. Though he might have picked out a good strong signal, others may still call him, and his reply to a particular station may be lost in the QRM. This will be evidenced by a slow QSO rate, even though the DX station is hearing the callers well. If he works split, the callers will have more chance to get the DXers reply right from the first time. The reason here is obviously that the callers cannot cope with the QRM they are creating themselves on the DX's frequency. In this case the DX station should simply specify a single frequency (e.g., up 5) where he will be listening.

2. Another reason is that there are such large numbers of stations calling the DX station that the DX cannot discriminate the callers. In this case it is the DX station who will not be able to handle the situation without going split. In this case he will specify a frequency range where he will be listening, in order to spread out the callers, and make the layer less thick.

A few general rules apply for split-frequency operation:

1. If possible, the DX station should operate from a part of the band where the stations from the area he is working into cannot operate, or from a section of the band that is generally considered the DX section.

2. The DX station should indicate his listening frequency at least every minute! It only takes a second to do so, and it goes a long way toward keeping order.

3. If the DX station is working by call area, he should impose enough authority to reject those calling from areas other than those specified. He should not stay with a particular call area too long. At five stations from each area, at a rate of three QSOs a minute (that's fast!) it still takes almost 20 minutes to get through the 10 US call areas!

4. It is a good idea for the DX station to check his own part of the world to make sure the frequency is clear. This can be done periodically, especially if there is a sudden unexplained drop in QSO rate.

Sometimes we are forced to work split in the midst of deliberate QRM. In such a case, announce the split frequency very briefly during the jammer's transmission so that he cannot copy your new listening frequency.

According to the band plan in the country of the DX station, split-frequency operation may be unavoidable. For instance, if a station in the US wants to work a station in the ex-USSR on SSB, the stations must work split, because the ex-USSR amateur cannot transmit on SSB above 3650 kHz (except during contests), and SSB privileges in the US do not extend below 3750 kHz. When you encounter such a situation, always make it a point to indicate your receiving frequency accurately, and make it a single frequency, or, if the pileup is too big, make it a reasonable range (10 kHz is usually sufficient). There is really no need to take more of the frequency spectrum than is absolutely necessary.

3.1. 160 Meters

Rare DX stations should as a rule operate split frequency. The generally accepted transmit window for the DX stations is 1820 to 1830, with 1823 and 1824 as the most popular frequencies.

As stated before, JAs use 1907.5 to 1912.5 as their window, and they usually listen between 1820 and 1835.

If you want to work ex-USSR stations on phone from Europe, you may have to go split, at least if your phone allocation does not extend above 1850. That's where the ex-USSR phone band starts (at least it used to be that way, although lately we have seen USSR stations below 1850 kHz, even running DX nets with the usual "LAST HEARD YOU WERE 33" business.

If you have a frequency allocation around 1910 kHz, stay away from the JA windows around sunrise and sunset time in Japan. Never call JA stations on their frequency. Force them to go split frequency. They will be happy to listen around 1830 and it will greatly improve the QSO rate.

If you are a Japanese station, always work split frequency when the band is open into Europe. If not, you will attract many stations from Eastern Europe on your frequency, and they will cover up your signal with farther away DX stations. If you work split, indicate your QSX frequency at every call. I have witnessed time after time JA stations working European stations (or trying to) without indicating their listening frequency. Send QSX 25 or QSX 32 repeatedly in every CQ or QRZ.

3.2. 80 Meters

On CW the main reason to go split is that the response to the DX station becomes too great (too big a pileup). Another nice reason would be for the DX station to listen "up 25" for the General class stations in the US.

On SSB I can think of many good reasons to go split: in the first place, not to occupy the DX window more than necessary. US stations wanting to work Europe could transmit above 3800 and listen below 3750 in order to keep the DX window as uncongested as possible.

Middle-East stations could transmit on a frequency below 3750 kHz when working North America in order to avoid the QRM for European stations. Stations in the Pacific working Europe should transmit above 3800 kHz and listen below 3800 kHz.

It is not reasonable, however, for a European to transmit inside the US phone band (3780 kHz, for example) and listen on 3805 kHz. If this is done, two windows inside the US subband are occupied for one QSO, and the potential for QRM and confusion is increased. The inverse situation would be equally undesirable.

3.3. 40 Meters

The nature of the frequency allocations in the different regions makes split-frequency operation a very common practice on 40-meter phone.

The US stations in particular should be aware of the fact that they operate in the middle of very strong broadcast stations in Europe, in the 7150-7300 kHz window. These broadcast stations are not on the same frequency 24 hours a day, and what may be a clear frequency one minute can be totally covered by a 60-over-S9 BC station the next minute. These BC stations usually appear on the hour or on the half hour. Especially in contests, make sure your "clear" transmit frequency remains clear!

■ 4. THE CLARIFIER

Zero beat is a term indicating that the two stations in contact are transmitting on exactly the same frequency. It is common practice to zero beat on phone. The RIT (Receiver Incremental Tuning) or RX Clarifier on present-day transceivers has created a problem where stations in QSO drift apart and use RIT to compensate instead of making sure that they stay on the same frequency. Fortunately, modern equipment is practically immune to frequency drift, so this is not as much of a problem as it used to be, especially with some of the home-built equipment.

As an example of where this is a problem, let us assume station A does not have a stable VFO. If station A and station B start a QSO at zero beat (station A and station B on exactly the same frequency), there are three sequences of events that a monitoring station might observe:

1. Neither station uses RIT: One station always follows the other. The QSO may wander all over, but at least there will be no sudden frequency jumps when passing the microphone, and the QSO will be on one drifting frequency.
2. One station uses RIT, the other does not: If we are still listening on the same frequency that the QSO began on, there will be a frequency jump at the start of transmission of one of the stations, but not for the other station. The QSO will still drift.
3. Both stations use RIT: Again, if we are listening on the original frequency, there will be a frequency jump at the start of transmission for both stations, and the two stations may drift away from one another. The QSO will take up more space on the band, and it will be very annoying to listen to. Should RIT be used in such a case? Decide for yourself!

Some of the recent transceivers not only have an RIT control but also an XIT control (TX clarifier). This one makes things even more complicated. Be careful when using it. There are some instances where RIT could be a welcome feature:

1. Some operators like to listen to SSB signals that sound very high-pitched, like Donald Duck. That means that they tune in too high on LSB. To the other operator, their transmission will sound too low-pitched, because they are no longer zero beat. Tuning in a station using RIT will allow one to listen to the voice pitch he prefers, while staying zero beat with the other station(s) on frequency.
2. When trying to beat a pileup, it can be advantageous to sound a little high in frequency. Adjusting the RIT slightly in such a case will yield that result.
3. Let us assume our transceiver is designed for working CW at an 800-Hz beat note, and it is only when listening at this

note that the transmit frequency will be exactly the same as the receiving frequency. One can use RIT to offset the transmit frequency (by, say, 300 Hz) to bring the note down to 500 Hz, and still transmit on the receiving frequency. So you can see that RIT can be a useful feature without creating unnecessary QRM at the same time.

As previously stated, most DX QSOs on 80 meters are on only one frequency. There is no need to waste space on the band by working a station slightly off your frequency. It can, however, sometimes be necessary to work split-frequency, such as when someone causes deliberate QRM, when working rare DX stations or DXpeditions, or when working into areas where a different band plan exists.

By the way, I never use the RIT on my transceiver. As far as I am concerned, the modern transceiver with dual VFOs simply has no need for RIT or XIT.

■ 5. ZERO BEAT

The terminology of zero beating stems from the AM days. On AM one used to really zero-beat. Tuning the transmitter VFO onto the receiving frequency produced a beat note, when the mixing product of the two signals produced an audio note. When the tone became 0 Hz, the transmitter and receiver were on the same frequency. The operator had zero-beated the received signal.

On CW, tuning exactly onto the received signal's frequency, results in producing a beat tone that has the same frequency as the tone you are using for receiving the other station.

Most transceivers were designed so you are transmitting on the same frequency as the station you are working only if the beat note is some specific frequency. With the older variety of transceivers this was a fixed beat note, usually 800 Hz. This beat-note frequency is usually specified in the operating manual. Because many hams do not care for the specified 800-Hz beat note, they just listen to what pleases them (450 Hz is my preference). As a result of this, those operators are always off frequency by 350 Hz or so on CW. This is not a problem if the receiving station uses a 2-kHz filter, but it could be a real problem if he uses a 250- or 500-Hz filter. Also, think of all the wasted space on the band. This is the reason that in the past I advocated the use of a separate receiver and transmitter on CW. Then, at least one could really listen to one's own frequency! The better transceivers now have the provision for operating right on frequency on CW. A good transceiver should at least have an adjustable beat note. The CW monitor note should shift accordingly. Continuously adjustable down to 200 Hz is the best. Some people like to listen at very low pitches (WØZV likes 250 Hz!). The only precaution here is to tune in the station you want to work at exactly the same beat note as your CW monitor note. That's all there is to it. This way, one can get easily within 50 Hz of the other station and still listen to the preferred beat note.

There is a lot of personal preference involved in choosing the beat note itself. It is generally accepted that it is very tiring to listen to a beat note over 700 Hz for extended periods of time. Also, the ability of the normal ear to discriminate signals

very close in frequency is best at lower frequencies. For example, listen to a station with a beat note of 1000 Hz. Assume a second station of very similar signal strength and keying characteristics starts transmitting 50-Hz off frequency (at a 950-Hz or 1050-Hz beat note). Separating these two signals with IF or audio filters would be very difficult. Let us assume we have to rely on the "filters" in our ears to do the discrimination. The relative frequency difference is

$$\left(\frac{1050 - 1000}{1000}\right) \times 100 = 5\%$$

If you were using a 400-Hz beat note, the offender would have been at 450 Hz (or 350 Hz), which is a 13% relative frequency difference. This is much more easily discernible to the ear.

■ 6. DXPEDITIONS

DXpeditions usually operate split frequency, both on CW and SSB. The late Gus Browning, W4BPD, was one of the first to include the low bands in his DXpeditions in the early 1960s. The advantage of split-frequency operation on the low bands is even more outstanding than on the higher bands, because the openings are much shorter and signals can be much weaker than on the higher bands. Working split makes it easier for calling stations to hear the DX. Otherwise, the strong pileup of callers will inevitably cover up the DX station, resulting in a very low QSO rate.

Sometimes we hear DXpeditions spreading the pileups over too wide a portion of the band, which is not generally advantageous for the QSO rate, and most of all very inconsiderate toward the other users of the band. It is also not unheard of for two DXpeditions to be on at the same time, both listening in the same part of the band. The net result of this is maximum confusion and frustration on the part of everyone involved. There will inevitably be many "not in log" QSOs where people ended up in the wrong log.

When the pileup becomes too big, it has become common practice in recent years to call "by numbers." This is a good practice provided they don't stay with the same call area for say more than five QSOs. Otherwise one might lose propagation to certain areas before going around the 10 digits. Even at a 2-QSO-per-minute rate (which is high for the low bands), it takes almost half an hour to go through the 10 US call areas!

An excellent system is to use just one exact frequency on which the DXpedition will listen. This system is very friendly and works extremely well when the pileup is not too big. It at least keeps the callers from the DXer's frequency. With modern equipment having digital readouts to 10 Hz and an abundance of memories, this approach seems very reasonable (Ref. 501). Rudy Klos, DK7PE, outstanding low-band DXpeditioner, uses this system all the time and is very successful with it.

It is also advisable that a DXpedition station uses the same split on all bands, this eliminates the guesswork that sometimes takes place.

On 160 CW, 1823-1826 kHz (with 1825 as a focal point) seems to be the most widely used DXpedition spot, with QSX 1830 to 1835 in areas where these frequencies are available.

On 80 meters, the typical DXpedition frequencies are

3501 to 3510 kHz for CW, listening 5 to 10 kHz up, and sometimes 3525 (the bottom end of the General and Advanced class subband in the US), listening up 5 or 10 kHz.

Do not send merely UP. This inevitably will attract people calling less than 1 kHz from the DXpedition's frequency. Instead, specify QSX UP 5 or UP 5 TO 10. In Europe, 3500 to 3505 kHz has often been covered with a lot of QRM in recent years. There often is marine mobile on USB operating on 3500, spreading to 3.503 and we often have some kind of commercial digital station on 3.505. This picture can of course change anytime. It therefore is advisable to check with a knowledgeable local to determine the best transmit frequency before taking off on your DXpedition.

The most common 80-meter SSB frequencies are 3795 to 3800 kHz. In the past, one of the problems DXpeditions encountered frequently on the low bands was difficulty discerning the part of the world to which propagation was peaking at a given time. Knowledgeable DXpeditioners nowadays are well prepared with propagation knowledge to all parts of the world, as well as the latest propagation forecasts.

Unfortunately we still hear and read about (famous) DXpeditioners who will only appear on the low bands the last day or the last two days of their operation. Some even seem to brag about this! One particular and very rare DXpedition during 1992 remained for 75% of its time on a single band (10 meters), "in order to work as many different stations as possible." Critics may also say that this guarantees a better $ return rate with the QSLs. Pure logic tells you to start tackling the most difficult bands (160 and 80) from the first day, as there may not be openings every day. Waiting for the last day to find out that there is no propagation just proves that one does not understand low-band propagation at all, or that one simply does not care about low-band contacts. WØCD writes in his survey reply: "DXpeditions going to new countries should give more time to 160 to be sure there is decent propagation. Not just a few hours the last night . . ."

When operating the low bands from a DXpedition, it is wise to jump regularly from one (low) band to another, each time making sure the callers know where you are going. This way you are sure you will not miss the "outstanding" short opening. Especially on 160 meters, the band openings may be short. Always go QSX on 160, call slowly, and frequently indicate the listening frequency. Do not transmit complicated instructions; chances are that half of the callers won't understand the instructions, which will lead to confusion.

Twenty-five years ago it was a rarity to have a DXpedition show up on 80 meters. One-sixty was out of the question. That was just the gentlemen's band for daytime rag-chews. Eighty meters was thought by most to be only for local QSOs as well. The majority of the DXpeditioners did not seem to know better. Fortunately, for years now, for most expeditions 80 meters has been just another band. And during the lower parts of the sunspot cycle it is definitely capable of bringing in a lot more DX than 21 and 28 MHz! The 5-Band DXCC, 5-Band WAS and 5-Band WAZ awards have greatly promoted low-band DXing, together with the single-band scores and record listings in the DX contests. Nowadays we have top-band specialists who will travel halfway around the world to put on DXpeditions to the rarest countries with mainly low-band DX contacts in mind. Rudi, DK7PE, Pekka, OH1RY and Chris, ZS6EZ are examples of such outstanding operators and low-band DXpeditioners.

When you show up on a low band, stay there for a while, at least if the band is open. It takes some time before the news gets out on the Cluster! It also takes a few minutes before you get your buddies out of bed and on the band.

■ 7. NETS AND LIST OPERATIONS

List operations, which occur daily on the HF bands, stem from net operations such as the Pacific DX net, the P29JS/VK9NS net, and others. In these nets, a "master of ceremonies" (MC) will check in both the DX and the non-DX stations, usually by area. After completing the check-in procedure, the MC directs the non-DX stations (one at a time, in turn) to call and work the DX station. In most cases the non-DX station has indeed worked the DX station, but there was no competition, no challenge, no know-how involved. Some even call the MC on the telephone to get on his list. What satisfaction can one derive from such a QSO? Yes, it gives the QRP operator a better chance to work the DX station, and the only thing you have to do is copy your report. The MC will QSP your call. And if the DX station is a DXpedition, there is a good chance that he will give everyone a 59 report, so it becomes even simpler. Just like shooting fish in a barrel, in my opinion.

In the late 1970s, list operations run by organized nets suddenly started showing up in great numbers all over the bands, run by "voluntary" MCs. This list system soon spread to 80- and 40-meter phone. Fortunately, lists have never made it on CW. This is yet another reason why real DXers love CW (Ref. 505). Many prominent low-band DXers dislike the list system, but most have learned to live with it.

The list system cannot be used if the DX station refuses to take part in it. Fortunately, we have seen such operations, and they have all proved that DXpeditions can work much better without lists. I have witnessed stations asking Carl, WB4ZNH, operating as 3C1BG, if they could run a list for him. Carl was insulted by the proposition, so he asked the station to announce on his transmitting frequency (he was working split, of course) that he would not work anyone whose call sign was passed along by another station.

If the DX station is involved in a list operation, it generally means he cannot cope with the situation. An ability to cope is part of "the game" for rare DX stations. There should definitely be no excuse for such things to happen to DXpeditions. If you are not a good enough operator to handle the situation yourself, you should not go on a DXpedition. DXpeditioners often complain that the 80-meter DXers don't listen well enough, and sometimes the DXpedition has difficulty getting an operation going on the low bands. This would be an excuse for operating with lists. If the DXpeditions announced their operating schedules (bands, times) more regularly (every 5 or 10 minutes at least), and stuck to the schedule, QSYs to the low bands would work out better.

Some years ago I worked a DXpedition in the Caribbean on 80, when the operator asked me to make a list of approximately 100 (!) European stations for him, which he would then work the next (!) morning. I flatly refused to do so with the comment that it was ridiculous to ask this, as he was S9 plus in Europe for hours every day, and he could probably work two stations per minute if he worked split-frequency. He was offered the frequency so he could find another European station to "work" for him. An HB9 station took a long list for the next hour or more. The confusion the next morning was worse than anything I'd ever heard. Half of those on the list were not there, and more wanted to get on the list. The same operator on that DXpedition must have recalled my refusal to make the list for him, as years later he refused to work me on 160 meters from a later DXpedition. But this time I did not hear him working off lists, so he must have learned something after all.

Don't ask a DX station to make a list for him. It will simply offend him if he is a good operator.

If the DX station unfortunately chooses to work from a list, here are the "11 Commandments" of list operation that the DX station and the MC should stick to:

1. The MC station should have absolute Q5 copy of the DX station.
2. The lists should be taken at the time of operation. Only short lists should be taken. Ideally they should contain no more than 10 stations.
3. The MC should try to be as objective as possible when picking calls in the pileup. He should not ask the pileup "only to give the suffix (last two letters) of their call." This is even illegal in most countries (W3BGN calls it "the last-2-letter syndrome").
4. The MC should make use of a second station far enough away to cover different areas. The second station could also take short lists on a different frequency.
5. The MC should never pick up stations that continually break out of turn, or keep calling when no list is being taken. Tail-ending is a good way to get one's call in, provided it really is tail-ending. It is extremely frustrating to hear so-called tail-enders calling right when the DX station is giving the report and a second later give a Q5 report to the DX station.
6. The MC should never make mention of deliberate jamming on the frequency. If there is deliberate jamming and many comments, shouldn't he suspect that he is doing something wrong after all?
7. The MC should listen for other DX when taking a list (sometimes DX likes to work other DX). The MC should be aware of propagation conditions to the DX station as well as the grayline conditions at the DX station's QTH. When taking the lists, the MC should use selective calling, always giving priority to stations which are near their sunset or sunrise and are about to lose propagation to the DX station. In other words, the MC should be very knowledgeable about low-band DXing.
8. The MC should never relay a report.
9. In order to speed up the operation, a calling station should be given no more than two tries by the MC to get his report across. If the station can't make it with two tries, chances are that he would not even be answered by the DX if he was on his own. If it is clear guesswork is going on, the MC should continue with the next station.

10. It is up to the MC, but I strongly suggest that the MC check the exchange of reports and make sure that the correct reports are confirmed at both ends to ensure that a valid QSO took place. He should make sure that the report is confirmed at both ends. If no exchange can be made, he should advise the DX station that no QSO took place, and if anyone has relayed a report, the MC might advise the DX station to change the report and try another exchange.
11. The list system should only be used as a last resort.

There are also a few rules for the "mere participant" in the list game:

1. The QSO should consist of a fully exchanged and confirmed report. The caller should confirm the report with the DX station so that both the MC and the DX station can make sure a valid QSO was made.
2. The caller should not repeat the DX station's call sign. The exchange length should be kept to a minimum. Unless you want to make a fool of yourself don't say "last heard you were 55." Was that yesterday you heard him last?
3. The caller should not get on the list if he cannot copy the DX station reasonably well. If the caller does not come back when the DX station turns it over to him, and if this situation repeats itself, he is just making a fool of himself.
4. If the caller cannot hear the MC, but hears the DX very well, he can try to ask the DX station to ask the MC to put him on the list. This happened to me when trying to work a station in Africa when the MC was in Germany and skip prevented my getting on the list in the normal way.

In almost all cases, list operation can be avoided by working split frequency.

The fact that I give so much attention to list operations does not in any way mean that I agree with this modus operandi. I think it is always a poor solution. Because we are confronted with a very limited bandwidth on 80-meter SSB (maybe 5 or 6 channels between 3775 and 3800 kHz), and because there always will be a number of poor operators as well as newcomers, it is likely that we will have to live with lists for a while longer. If you really hate lists as much as I have come to, stay away from 80-m SSB, and try CW. Or try 160 meters for a *real* challenge.

To close the subject of list working, let me quote this story by Don Newlands, VE3HGN, originally published in January 1985 *Radiosporting*.

My granddaddy used to fish for food, my dad fished for sport, and I don't fish at all. I buy fish at the fish store, along with most other folks. No fuss, no muss. Evidently we three had something in common: we all wanted fish. Granddad would stand in the icy water, casting and reeling until his limbs went numb; one man in harmony with nature. My memory of him is a bit misty. He didn't talk much, but seemed confident and content.

My dad, on the other hand, had an expensive yacht, filled with gear. He bragged about his catch and had a lot of big ones stuffed and varnished which he would point to with pride.

Now I haven't time for all that crab. I'm prepared to

stand a few minutes in line at a fish market and I can either eat it or mount it, but for anybody to freeze his butt in water? Or lay out big bucks for a boat just to fish from? Today he's hopelessly out of touch.

Now you may ask what this has to do with ham radio? Simple! My grandpappy was an original DXer, wire antennas, 20 watts and a spark that could set a house on fire. My dad was a DXer with stacked antennas, 12 Beverages, phased verticals, transmission lines as thick as a wrist, 2-meter spotting nets, DX Cluster and all. And he kept the family up all night with his yelling and screaming.

From my perspective this all sounds primitive and disorganized. I prefer a simple lil' tribander at 40 ft and a low-band trap dipole with the apex at 35 ft. All I do is give my call (or just the suffix—I know it's not legal, but it's in) to the list-taker, and in a minute it's all over: "last heard (whenever that was) you were 55, rifle shot, bang bang." All I then do is listen to the MC's "Good contact." No fuss, no muss. Oh, my certificates (all framed, of course) are the same as theirs. Now that's what I call progress!

CQ DX, CQ DX is a call of the endangered species. Now it's "put me on the list." Now, how do you get on the list? Ya' phone 'em, that's how! And while you're on the phone, ask 'em if they have any fish . . .

■ 8. LISTEN OR TRANSMIT?

We frequently hear or read about how every respectable and wise DXer spends all his time listening, and only transmits when he's sure to make a contact. He never calls CQ DX, just listens all the time and grabs the DX before someone else does.

I am not sure this works all the time for the low bands, especially 160 and 80 meters (CW). If we all would do that, we would hear very little. It is obvious that if nobody calls CQ, even a perfect band will sound dead. That's why well-equipped stations should indeed call CQ when the band sounds dead. It may not be dead at all, but just a lack of activity, which it often is. So, don't get excited if you hear a big gun calling CQ on a dead band. He might be doing you a favor by acting as a beacon for some faraway DX station.

■ 9. BEACON STATIONS

In some areas of the world, where the low bands are shared between the amateur and other services, we have "commercial" stations that are on the air 24 hours a day, and as such can be used as useful band indicators. On 160 meters we used to have DHJ and OSN (on 1830/1831 kHz) that were excellent beacons for our US friends.

I remember clearly one morning on 80 meters—it must be 20 years ago, when the band was red hot and the West Coast was S9 plus—K6UA kept repeating almost in ecstasy that DHJ "has been S9 on 1832 for several hours."

Fortunately, from a QRM point of view, these stations have now gone from the prime window of 160 meters, but with them, two excellent beacon stations are gone as well.

It would of course be ideal if we had a number of dedicated beacon stations on the low bands. On 160 and 80 meters they would need to have a reasonable amount of power

(500 W on 160 and 200 W on 80) and a good low-angle transmitting antenna. They could all be on exactly the same frequencies, one on 80 and one on 160, provided they apply the time-sharing principle like the beacon stations on 14.100.

■ 10. ARRANGING SKEDS FOR THE LOW BANDS

Once you work your way up the DXCC ladder, you will inevitably come to a point where you will start asking stations on the "higher" bands (if you work the higher bands) for skeds on the low bands. Years ago if you asked someone on 15 or 20 meters for a sked on the low bands, the typical reply would have been either a "sorry, I only work DX . . . " or "yes, I work 40 meters." In the last 20 years, many high-band DXers have extended their horizons, and 80 meters has been added to their vocabulary and low-band definition. The answer has now become, "yes, I am QRV on 40 and 80." But for most, 160 meters is still very much unknown and unexplored territory.

Once in a while, the high-band DXer will say "Well, you're not the first one to ask; maybe I should do something about it . . . can you tell me what antenna I should use . . . " So, don't hesitate to ask, at least it will help some of the others realize that our HF spectrum extends all the way down to 160 meters.

If you are asked to help with antenna suggestions for 160 meters, don't give the candidate newcomer the idea that a wet string will do wonders. I always advocate an inverted L for transmitting, and if the inverted L is too noisy for receive, I tell him to try his 80-meter dipole for receiving. If he has an amplifier that works on 160, tell him to use it. Power is helpful on 160. Don't fool yourself, and don't fool the candidate newcomer.

If you get a positive answer, it will be your turn to indicate the best time. Take into consideration that you are the asking party, and try an opening that is not in the middle of his night. Rather, get yourself up in the middle of the night! Also, don't go by a single sked. Arrange a minimum of three skeds, or maybe a week's skeds, in order to hit the day with the right propagation. Tell the other party that the band may be okay only one day out of 3 or 5. Find out how much power he runs on 160 and what antenna he is using, so that you know what signal to expect.

Don't forget to have your sunrise/sunset information ready at all times. The easiest and most accurate way to do that is to use the SUNRISE/SUNSET booklet (over 100 pages of data) which is available from me. If you use one of the sophisticated computer logging programs (e.g., DXBASE), it is likely that the information is on line for you.

Tell your sked not to call you. Rather, you should call him (don't give his full call; just his suffix!), or just call CQ DX at the sked time exactly on the agreed frequency. Make the others (the listeners) a little nervous if they don't know about the sked, and do everything that's necessary not to give away "your" sked to strangers. If you work QSX, don't give away the listening frequency before you've worked him! If you think your chances are not the best (maybe because your set-up is not as good as your friend's), call your friend who's got a better station and inform him about the sked. He will probably help you, and you still have a good chance of being no. 2 to work the new one. By the way, once you have worked the new one, sign properly, give the full call of the station you've just worked, and clear the frequency (CL). If you have packet radio and are connected into a DX Cluster, announce the station you've just worked, so that others have all the info and may work him as well. Don't be so stupid as to put the sked in the Cluster, unless you're a masochist.

It's also a good idea to arrange an "escape" frequency: 40 meters is in most cases the most suitable band to go to after the sked, to exchange information about the test on 160.

■ 11. GETTING THE RARE ONES

Working the first 100 countries on 80 or 40 meters is fairly easy. Well-equipped stations have done it in one contest weekend. Anyone with a good station should be able to do it easily within a year. A growing number of stations have achieved DXCC on 160 meters. The major DX contests (CQ-WW, ARRL DX, WAE, All-Asia, etc) are excellent opportunities to increase low-band scores. Almost all DXpeditions now include a fair amount of low-band DXing in their operating scheme.

11.1. DX News Publications

The best way to keep yourself informed about what is happening (long term) on the bands is to subscribe to one of the many DX bulletins or news sheets. Some of the major ones are listed below:

Bulletins and News Sheets

The DX Bulletin
c/o Chod Harris, WB2CHO
PO Box 50
Fulton, CA 95439

Long Island DX Bulletin
c/o J. H. McCoy, 72IYX
PO Box 173
Huntington, NY 11743-0173

NCDXF
PO Box 2368
Stanford, CA 94309-2368

QRZ DX
c/o Bob Winn, W5KNE
PO Box 832205
Richardson, TX 75083

The Bullsheet
Texas DX Society
PO Box 540291
Houston, TX 77254-0291

Top Band Newsletter
Don Field, G3XTT
105 Shiplake Bottom

Peppard Common
Henley-on-Thames RG9 5HJ
England

The Top Band Bulletin
Brad McCarter, VE3KQS
PO Box 262
Mactier, Ontario P0C 1HO
Canada

DX News RSGB
Lambda House, Cranborne Rd
Potters Bar
Herts EN6 3JE
England

DX NL
c/o W. Geyrhalter, DL3RK
PO Box 1328
D-8950 Kaufbeuren
FRG

DX Press
Alex Van Eijck, PA3DZN
PO Box 162
NL-5170 AD Kaatsheuvel
The Netherlands

HIDXA
PO Box 90
Norfolk Island 2899
Australia

Japan DX News
PO Box 42
2025 Urawa Saitama
336 Japan

LES NOUVELLES DX, F6AJA
515 Rue du Petit Hem
Bouvignies
59870 Marchiennes
France

Even under the best of circumstances, the news relayed in the bulletins is always a few days old.

11.2. DX Information Nets

Local DX nets on VHF/UHF can be very rewarding if the members of the local DX community make it a habit to announce the hot news on the repeater or local net frequency. This works very well in areas with lots of active DXers, as after having a QSO with a good DX station, an announcement on the DX repeater brings in many callers within just a few minutes. In the last few years, however, the role of DX information nets as well as the function of the DX bulletins and news sheets has largely been taken over by the DX Clusters.

11.3. Packet Radio and DX Clusters

In recent years the DX repeaters and FM DX nets have largely been replaced with DX Clusters on packet radio. Such clusters consist of a large network of packet-radio links, where DX announcements are circulated to all stations that have checked into the cluster. The same stations also provide the real-time DX information that is circulated to all other stations that have checked in with one of the nodes of the network. In Europe in the past few years the DX Cluster network has evolved from a few isolated cells to a major network spreading from Scandinavia, through the UK and France into Belgium, Holland, Germany, Italy, Switzerland, Hungary, Poland, Spain, Portugal, Czech Republic, Slovakia, etc. Most of Western Europe is already linked up.

In the US, several very comprehensive networks are operating day and night. Sometimes over 500 stations are logged in such networks.

The DX Clusters also have a limited message (mailbox) service available, where information of general or specific use (should be DX related as a rule) can be stored and made available to all (such as DX bulletins, announcements of DXpeditions, QSL routes, etc.) or specific areas or individuals.

It is true that packet radio and the DX Clusters have changed DXing in general. I've seen publications where the DX Clusters have been pictured as the greatest evil in Amateur Radio. It is said to undermine the art of listening. It is true that the DX Clusters are changing the face of DXing. The "little" station with the operator who spent all his time listening, and who often was number one catching the DX station showing up, will often lose the advantage, as the better-equipped stations will now be informed much faster of the DX showing up on the bands. Fact is that DX Clusters and packet radio are here to stay, and we will all have to develop skills that will help us keep the advantage over our "competitor" fellow DXers in this ever faster changing world.

I am convinced that packet radio and the DX Cluster are just another superb tool that has resulted from our wonderful hobby.

DX Clusters bring together so many specialists from diverse fields in Amateur Radio: the digital guys take care of the hardware, the software freaks improve on operating systems, while the UHF/SHF guys establish and maintain reliable packet radio links over large areas. And of course there are the DXers who make the best use of the wonderful system and support the DX Cluster by their financial contributions. I cannot recall any other activity in Amateur Radio where people with such different interests work together and enjoy the results of their work as much as is the case with packet radio used for DX Clusters. DX Clusters are just another step forward in our wonderful hobby, where we make use of all the newest techniques and technologies to keep moving the boundaries of the achievable.

There is superb software on the market now that combines most of the functions needed by any DXer in a single package: log keeping, award tracking, DX Cluster operation, linking the DX Cluster info with the data from your own database, and creating alert signals, CW and even digital voice operation, etc. All you have to do is listen and make decisions.

Makes you feel like a CEO. DX-BASE (available from Scientific Solutions, 736 Cedar Creek Way, Woodstock, GA 30188) is such a very advanced program which I use to keep track of all the data. Ever wonder how it is I remember the names of all of you guys when you work me on the low bands?

■ 12. ACHIEVEMENT AWARDS

There are a number of low-band-only DX awards. ARRL (225 Main Street, Newington, CT 06111, USA) issues 160- and 80-meter WAC (Worked All Continents) awards, as well as separate DXCC awards for 160 meters, 80 meters and 40 meters.

CQ magazine issues single-band WAZ awards (for any band). Applications for the WAZ award go to: K1MEM, Jim Dionne, 31 de Marco Road, Sudbury, MA 01776, USA.

In addition, there are 5-band awards which are very challenging: 5-band WAS (Worked All States), 5-band DXCC (worked 100 countries on each of 5 bands), both issued by ARRL, and 5-band WAZ (worked all 40 CQ zones on each of the 5 bands, 10 through 80 meters), issued by CQ (via K1MEM, see above).

The achievement awards issued by the sponsors of the major DX contests that have single-band categories are also highly valued by low-band DX enthusiasts.

The major contests of specific interest to the low-band DXers are:

- The CQ WW phone contest (last weekend of October)
- The CQ WW CW contest (last weekend of November)
- The 160-m CW DX contest: usually last weekend of January.
- The 160-m SSB DX contest: usually the last weekend of February
- The ARRL Phone contest
- The ARRL CW contest
- The 160-m ARRL contest

Continental and world records are being broken regularly, depending on sunspots and improvements in antennas, operating techniques, etc.

Collecting awards is not necessarily an essential part of low-band DXing. Collecting the QSL cards for new countries is essential, however, at least if you want to claim them.

Unfortunately there are too many bootleggers on the bands, and too many unconfirmed exchanges that optimists would like to count as QSOs. These factors have made written confirmation essential unless, of course, the operator never wishes to claim country or zone totals at all. Many other achievements can be the result of a goal one has set out to reach.

The ultimate low-band DXing achievement would be to work all countries on the low bands. This goal is quite achievable on 40, possible on 80, but quite impossible on 160 meters, although we see the 160-meter scores slowly climbing steadily to the 300 mark as well.

Now that we have separate DXCC awards for 40, 80 and 160, it is a pity there is no "honor roll" classification as with the all-band DXCC.

■ 13. THE SURVEY

During 1991 and 1992 a survey was made with over 150

of the leading 160 and 80-meter DXers worldwide. The call signs were mainly chosen from the top-ranking (80- and 160-m) DXCC stations as well as some of the well-known contest stations that regularly take part in major contests and score well on the low bands.

The purpose in collecting the information is to show the achievements of the leading low-band DXers, as well as the equipment and antennas they are using. The achievement figures are listed in Table 1 while equipment and antennas are listed in Table 2. The call signs are listed in alphabetical order. The scores were collected over a period of over one year, from mid-1991 to the end of 1992. It is obvious that by now the scores of many have skyrocketed. The purpose of the listing is not to give an accurate DXCC status report, but to show what some of the leading low-band DXers have achieved and what they are using to do it. A few well-known DXers are missing in the tables. They have chosen not to reply to the questionnaire, which of course is their privilege.

2-1

Table 1

Low-Band DXer's Survey

Major accomplishments realized by some of the best known DXers.

The DXCC scores are all-time scores (including deleted countries). The scores were collected during 1991 and 1992 and do not reflect the present or past comparative performance status for the stations listed.

CALL	DXCC/80 M			DXCC/160			80 M WAZ	160 M WAZ	5-BAND			80 M		160 M	
	WKD	CFD	SINCE	WKD	CFD	SINCE	WAZ	WAZ	DXCC	WAS	WAZ	%CW	%SSB	%CW	%SSB
AA1K*	250+	?	1965	226	226	1968	—	—	Y	Y	N	50	50	90	10
AD6C	212	209	1953	127	119	1975	—	—	WKD	N	199	80	20	95	5
DJ2YA	258	255	1955	118	118	1980	40	28	Y	N	Y	—	—	—	—
DJ4AX	259	245	1957	69	53	1977	38	19	Y	N	N	10	90	40	60
DJ8WL	—	—	—	196	195	1972	—	40	N	N	N	—	—	80	20
DL1YD	280	250	1957	186	180	1957	40	39	Y	N	Y	60	40	90	10
F5VU	274	274	—	40	34	—	—	—	Y	N	Y	0	100	0	100
F6BKE	—	—	1978	173	171	1984	—	—	Y	N	Y	30	70	50	50
G3KMA*	270	265	1969	165	158	1979	40	37	Y	N	Y	40	60	80	20
G3PQA*	—	—	—	202	166	1963	—	38	N	M	M	90	10	80	20
G3RBP	—	—	—	214	212	1962	—	40	N	N	N	—	—	95	5
G3SZA	*	*	1990	216	214	1969	—	40	*	*	*	10	90	50	50
G3XTT	222	218	1978	162	160	1970	40	36	Y	N	Y	75	25	90	10
GD4BEG	205	200	1974	194	194	1974	—	—	Y	N	N	100	0	98	2
GW3YDX*	—	*	1969	234	180	1969	—	—	Y	Y	N	99	1	99	1
HB9AMO	251	249	1980	204	202	1985	40	40	Y	Y	Y	50	50	95	5
HK1AMW*															
IT9ZGY*	240	240	1953	150	146	1985	40	35	Y	N	Y	50	50	90	10
JAQELY	275	272	1969	—	—	—	40	—	Y	Y	Y	20	80	—	—
JA2AAQ	278	278	1969	38	32	1985	40	—	Y	N	Y	—	—	—	—
JA3EMU	267	267	1974	95	95	1986	—	—	Y	Y	Y	50	50	100	0
JA4LXY	230	228	1981	124	123	1984	—	—	Y	N	Y	80	20	100	0
JA6IEF	286	282	1973	138	136	1980	40	34	N	N	N	30	70	100	0
K0HA	*	*	1969	*	*	1978	*	*	*	*	*	75	25	85	15
K1MEM	286	284	1983	202	201	1980	40	35	Y	N	Y	90	10	98	2
K1MM	296	295	1980	207	205	1981	40	34	Y	N	Y	80	20	100	0
K2RIH	170	162	70's	182	180	80's	35	34	Y	N	N	5	95	75	25
K1ZM	—	—	—	227	225	1983	—	36	N	N	N	—	—	90	10
K2CL*	183	179	1973	186	184	1985	—	—	Y	N	Y	95	5	95	5
K2UO*	185	182	1978	117	111	1985	—	—	Y	N	N	95	5	95	5
K3LR	*	*	1978	*	*	1978	*	*	N	N	N	90	10	99	1
K3ZO	—	—	1952	—	—	1953	—	—	Y	N	N	60	40	80	20
K4CIA	274	274	1968	133	132	1971	38	—	Y	Y	N	—	—	—	—
K4DY*	299	297	1970	185	185	1976	40	38	Y	Y	N	65	35	80	20
K4MQG	295	295	1970	—	—	—	40	—	Y	Y	Y	—	—	—	—
K4PI	247	246	1975	177	176	1983	—	—	Y	N	N	85	15	95	5
K4UEE*	185	183	1975	179	179	1976	38	33	Y	Y	N	50	50	90	10
K5TSQ*	209	206	1978	102	102	1985	40	29	Y	N	Y	50	50	80	20
K6NA	272	?	1968	110	?	1968	—	—	Y	N	199	65	35	95	5
K4TEA	—	—	—	169	168	1985	—	32	—	—	—	—	—	90	10
K6UA	301	300	1950	—	—	—	—	—	N	N	N	10	90	100	0
K8CFU*	—	—	—	120	105	1965	—	—	N	N	N	—	—	100	0
K9UWA*	270	260	1971	198	196	1975	40	39	Y	Y	Y	50	50	50	40
KA1PE	—	—	—	199	197	1982	—	36	N	N	N	—	—	75	25
KA5W	234	233	1979	118	118	1983	—	—	Y	N	198	50	50	85	15
KC7EM	205	195	1985	—	—	—	40	—	Y	N	Y	40	60	—	—

CALL	DXCC/80 M WKD	CFD	SINCE	DXCC/160 WKD	CFD	SINCE	80 M WAZ	160 M WAZ	5-BAND DXCC	WAS	WAZ	80 M %CW	%SSB	160 M %CW	%SSB
KH6CC	*	*	1967	173	141	1934	*	36	Y	Y	N	50	40	75	24
KJ9I	—	—	—	165	165	1987	—	—	Y	N	N	—	—	90	10
KV0Q	162	138	1965	142	142	1970	36	28	*	*	*	—	—	65	35
LU8DPM*	190	153	1978	102	102	1983	40	35	Y	N	Y	10	90	30	70
N0XA *	290	285	1980	221	219	1984	40	—	Y	Y	Y	50	50	90	10
N2KK/6	317	315	1969	37	37	—	—	—	Y	Y	Y	33	67	—	—
N4JJ	295	294	1964	214	213	1964	40	34	Y	Y	Y	90	10	95	5
N4KG	301	300	1960	196	191	1983	40	35	Y	Y	Y	70	30	90	10
N4SU	220	182	1978	212	211	1978	40	36	Y	Y	Y	—	—	—	—
N4WW	290	290	1972	225	225	1977	40	—	Y	Y	Y	40	60	80	20
N4ZC	254	249	1968	—	—	—	39	—	Y	Y	N	75	25	—	—
NR1R*	250	243	1976	165	165	1984	—	—	Y	Y	Y	95	5	95	5
NX1G	—	—	—	193	191	1974	—	—	N	N	N	—	—	50	50
OH1XX	308	305	1972	213	208	1977	40	40	Y	Y	Y	40	40	80	20
OH3YI#	309	309	1970	—	—	—	—	40	Y	N	Y	30	70	—	—
OK1DOT	—	—	—	166	154	1982	—	33	N	N	N	—	—	100	0
OK1DWJ*				156	154	1985	—	36	N	N	N	—	—	90	10
OK1JDX*	—	—	—	160	142	1977	—	31	—	—	—			80	20
OK1MP*	243	242	1970	78	77	1982	40	12	Y	N	Y	15	85	70	30
ON4UN	339	339	1962	241	239	1987	40	40	Y	Y	Y	80	20	98	2
OY9JD*	217	210	1987	103	99	1987	39	25	N	N	N	90	10	90	10
OZ1LO*	255	254	1963	174	170	1980	—	—	Y	Y	N	95	5	95	5
PA0HIP	—	—	—	209	207	1973	—	40	N	N	N	—	—	80	20
PA0LOU*	180	155	1955	114	113	1960			Y	N	N	100	0	100	0
PY1BVY*	—	—	—	190	179	1982	40	40	Y	Y	N	100	0	100	0
SM0AJU*	286	281	1969	152	145	1982	40	34	Y	Y	Y	60	40	90	10
SM4CAN	260	254	1970	144	140	1986	40	37	Y	N	Y	50	50	95	5
SM7CRW*	309	303	1962	36	21	1991	40	11	Y	Y	Y	85	15	15	85
SP3GEM*	305	202	1973	—	—	—	—	—	Y	N	N	10	90	—	—
SP5INQ	225	181	1979	150	150	1980	40	40	N	N	N	—	—	—	—
UG6GAW	187	164	1989	198	195	1985	38	39	—	—	—	85	15	90	10
VE1ZZ	297	289	1948	225	223	1950	40	36	N	N	N	60	40	70	30
VE3EJ	230	221	1974	119	109	1978	40	24	Y	Y	Y	50	50	75	25
VE7BS*	—	—		120	106	1946	—	—	N	N	N	—	—	60	40
VE7SV*	261	255	1975	—	—	1992	40	—	Y	Y	Y	70	30	100	0
VK5KL	65	61	1965	60	58	1970	—	—	N	N	N	—	—	—	—
VK6HD	270	270	1969	156	155	1969	40	33	Y	Y	Y	95	5	99	1
W0LYI	228	216	1978	166	164	1985	—	—	Y	Y	N	50	50	75	25
W0CD	—	—	1975	192	191	1970	—	36	Y	Y	N	50	50	95	5
W0CM	185	194	1980	149	148	1980	36	30	Y	N	N	100	0	50	50
W0EJ	114	114	1976	108	107	1981	25	18	Y	Y	N	60	40	75	25
W0ZV	293	292	1980	224	224	1984	—	—	N	N	Y	90	10	75	25
W1FV	*	*	1983	*	*	1983	*	*	N	N	N	95	5	100	0
W1JZ*	—	—		182	182	1973	—	—	—	—	—	—	—	99	1
W1NH	309	307	1965	—	—	—	40	—	N	N	N	99	1	—	—
W2BXA	—	—	—	192	189	1983	—	—	Y	Y	Y	—	—	90	10
W2JB*	—	—	1936	186	184	1982	—	—	Y	N	N	80	20	99	1
W2NQ/7	274	270	1955	157	154	1983	40	36	Y	Y	Y	—	—	—	—
W2OKM	—	—	1980	206	205	1984	—	—	Y	Y	N	25	75	95	5
W2SM *				206	203	1984	—	—	—	—	—	—	—	95	5
W2TQC	197	172	1980	201	201	1980	37	33	Y	N	N	95	5	90	10
W3BGN	—	—	1961	218	190	1974	—	—	N	N	N	75	25	75	25
W3MFW	318	318	1946	—	—	—	—	—	Y	N	N	100	0	—	—
W4OWJ*	261	235	1933	201	199	1979	—	—	Y	Y	N	90	10	90	10
W6AJJ	—	—		144	140	1976	—	33	N	N	N	—	—	95	5
W6GO	224	220	1980	64	60	1980	—	—	Y	N	Y	75	25	50	50
W6RJ	277	250	1959	—	—	1970	39	—	—	—	—	40	60	—	—
W8UVZ*	244	241	1978	182	181	1984	40	33	Y	N	Y	80	20	95	5
W9ZR*	314	314	1971	222	222	1979	40	35	Y	Y	Y	25	75	95	5
WA3EUL*	265	?	1980	208	201	1982	—	—	Y	Y	N	90	10	98	2
WB9Z	258	255	1986	190	189	1986	40	35	Y	N	Y	50	50	50	50
ZL3GQ	252	?	1949	142	139	1956	40	32	Y	Y	Y	80	20	90	10
ZS5LB*	242	238	1976	153	151	1893	40	36	Y	Y	Y	70	30	95	5
4X4NJ*				191	185	1973	—	38	Y	N	—			99	1
4Z4DX*	289	275	1978	212	211	1982	—	—	y	y	y	30	70	85	15
9M2AX	*	*	1974	104	99	1969	—	28	N	N	N	90	10	100	0

The DXCC status is the all-time status. The WAZ status for 160 and 80 meters is shown as well.

It is interesting to see how much the top DXers work on CW and how much on phone. For 160 meters, the top DXer works 84% CW and 16% phone on average, while the 80-meter top DXer spends 61% on CW and 39% on phone.

I did a similar survey about 7 years ago, and another one over 20 years ago. One of the most striking differences is that much bigger and better antennas are being used all the time. The scores have skyrocketed accordingly. The use of Beverage antennas has also become very common among the top low-band DXers. Those not using a Beverage antenna often said "No room for a Beverage." Of the listed top low-band DXers, 65% use Beverages. Low horizontal wires (dipoles, loops) and magnetic loops are also popular receiving antennas. Only those using a Yagi or a multielement array feel no need for special receiving antennas.

As far as equipment is concerned we noted the following results:

Kenwood: 44%   Drake 12%
ICOM: 22%   Ten-Tec: 5%
Yaesu: 12%   Other 5%

2-2

Table 2

Low-Band DXer's Survey

Equipment and antennas used by some of the best known DXers.

CALL	TRANSCEIVER	TRANSMIT ANTENNAS 80-M	160-M	RX ANTENNA
AA1K	TS940, TS180	WIRE YAGI	INV L 4 ELEV RADS	8 BEVERAGES
AD6C	TS940, TS930	1/2 WV SLOPERS	3/8 WV VERT	6 BEVERAGES
DJ2YA	IC751, TS930	INV L, VERT 80'	3/8 WV INV L	NO ROOM FOR BEVER
DJ4AX	R4C/T4XC	2EL YAGI @165',VERT	120 FT WIRE @165'	NO
DJ8WL	R4C/T4XC	-	PHASED INV L'S	BEVERAGES, LOOP
DL1YD	TS930	HALF SLOPER	HALF SLOPER	BEVERAGE
F5VU	TR7, FT102	DIPOLE, 1/4 SLOPER	1/4 SLOPER	NO
F6BKE	TS930	90' VERT, DIP 50'	90' VERT, DIP 50'	BEVERAGES
G3KMA	TS940, TR7	DELTA LOOP	SH FED TWR, INV L	BEVERAGE
G3PQA	T4XC,T4XC, FT102	50-M LONG INV V	21-M INV L (100RAD)	4 BEVERAGES
G3RBP	IC745, RA329B	-	T-VERTICAL	BEVERAGES, LOOP
G3SZA	IC765	PHASED 1/4 WV VERTS	100' TOPLOAD VRT	BEVER-s, LOW DIP
G3XTT	TS940	IN V, DELTA, VERT	INV L, SH FED TWR	NO ROOM FOR BEVER
GD4BEG	T4XC/T4C, MODFD HRO!	VERT, DIPOLE, DELTA	BOBT, PHASED VERTS	LOOPS, LONG WIRES
GW3YDX	TS930, TS850	50' VERT 2500' RADS	105' VERT TWR	BEVERAGE
HB9AMO	TS940	DELTA LOOP	90 FT VERT (TOP L)	COAX LOOP, BEVER
IT9ZGY	IC781, FT1000,TS940	3 PHASED VERT	INV V, SLOPER	MAGN LOOP 3.7 M
JA1ELY	FT1000, IC780	ROT. IN V. 90 FT	NO	NO
JA2AAQ	TS930	3 DIPOLES	INV V	NO
JA3EMU	IC761	SHORT DIPOLE 28 M	1/4 WVE VERT	NO SPACE
JA4LXY	IC760	1/4 WAVE SLOPER	1/4 WAVE SLOPER	4 BEVERAGES
JA6IEF	TS930, IC760,TS820	ROT DIP, INV V	INV V	BEVERAGE, LOOP
K0HA	TS-830, TS440	6 EL PARAS. VERT ARR	6EL PAR VERT AR	LOOP, RANDOM WIRE
K1MEM	R4C/T4XC, PARAGON	2 EL PHASED ARRAY	INV V AT 70'	BEVERAGE
K1MM	TS940, TS830	SLOPERS AT 90°	INT V, SLOPER	LOW DIPOLE
K2RIH	IC761A, FT576X	DIPOLE 100'	DIP 100' VERT 1 0'	6 BEVERAGES
K1ZM	IC765, TS940	PHASED VERT, DIPOLE	1/4 WV VERT, INV V	BEVERAGES, LOOP
K2UO	IC-765	DIPOLE	LOW DIPOLE	NO ROOM
K3LR	IC765	4-SQUARE	1/2 W CV SLOPER	BEVERAGES 600 FT
K3ZO	TS830, R4C	3 EL KLM YAGI 140'	1/2 SLOPERS, INV L	DDRR, BEVERAGE
K4CIA	IC761, 75A4	VERT, DELTA, SLOPER	TOP LOADED VERT	LOOPS, HORIZ ANT
K4DY	IC-750	LOOP, INV V, SLOPER	SH FED TOWER	NONE
K4MQG	FT102	2 EL CREATE YAGI	NONE	NONE
K4PI	TS940	INVERT L	SH FED 100' TWR	LOOPS, BEVERAGES
K4TEA	KWM380	-	1/2 SQ VERT LOOP	BEVERAGES
K4UEE	TS850S	1/4 WV VERT, INV V	INV V @ 80 FT	2 BEVERAGES
K5TSQ	TS-940	1/4 SLOPER, DELTA LP	1/4 SLOPER	SHORT BEVERAGE
K6NA	TS940, R7	2 EL ARRAYS @ 135'	SH FED 140' TWR	BEVERAGES
K6UA	TS930	8JK, QUADS	130' VERT, DIPOLE	BEVERAGES
K8CFU	TENTEC OMNI V	-	VERT +COUNTERPOISE	4 BEVERAGES
K9UWA	IC-765, DRAKE C-LINE	4 EL INV V ARRAY	4 EL INV V ARRAY	3 BEVERAGES
KA1PE	TEN TEC OMNI V	-	137' VERT	BEVERAGES
KA5W	TS940	VERT, DIPOLE 80'	SH FED TWR 70'	4 BEVERAGES
KC7EM	TS940	4-SQUARE VERT	NO	NO
KH6CC	TS830, R4C	125' VERT ELEV RADS	SAME	2 BEVERAGES
KJ9I	IC765A		1/2 WV SLOPERS 160'	BEVERAGES
KV0Q	IC781, R4C, FT980	-	4 EL VERT ARRAY	
LU8DPM	IC-735	VERT, SLOPER, INV V	VERT, SLOPER, INV V	

CALL	TRANSCEIVER	TRANSMIT ANTENNAS 80-M	160-M	RX ANTENNA
NØXA	TS930, TS940	2EL YAGI, PHSD VERT	VERTICALS	BEVERAGES
N2KK/6	FT1000	4SQUARE ELEV RAD		
N4JJ	R4C/T4XC	3 EL VERT ARRAY ETC	SH FED 110' TWR	BEVERAGE
N4KG	TS940	VERT ELEV FD, DIPOL	100' DH FD TWR	8 BEVERAGES
N4SU	TS830, OMNI V	PHASED LOOPS @ 75'	PHASED LOOPS @106'	BEVERAGES
N4WW	TS940	DIP 130', SLOPER	1/4 WV SLOPERS	BEVERAGES
N4ZC	TS830	4 EL LOG PERIODICS		4 BEVERAGES
NX1R	IC765	4 EL PHSD ARRAY	INV V AT 110'	10000' BEVERAGE
NX1G	IC765	DIPOLE	1/4 WV VERT	5 BEVERAGES
OH1XX	FT1000	70' VERT, SLOPERS	INV L, DELTA LOOP	BEVERAGES
OH3YI#	C-LINE, DATONG FL2	VERTIV, ELEV FEED		40 M ANTENNA ON 80
OK1DOT	HOME MADE	-	SLOPER, INV V, LW	BEVERAGE
OK1DWJ	HOME MADE, 750 W	-	INV V	1000 M BEVERAGE
OK1JDX	TS520		27 M TP LOAD VERT	BEVERAGE, LOOPS
OK1MP	FT102	INV V	INV V	NO ROOM
ON4UN	FT1000	4 SQUARE VERT	135' VERT	12 BEVERAGES
ON5NT	TS940	DELTA LOOP	60' SH FED TWR	BEVERAGES
OY9JD	R7A, TR7, PARAGON	VERT,DELT, VERT DIP	2 INV L ANTS	SHIELDED LOOP
OZ1LO	TS950	30-M VERT, IN-V 20-M	30 M VERT	LOW WIRE
PAØHIP	R4C/T4XC, FT980	-	90' VERT, SLOPERS	BEVERAGE, LOOP
PAØLOU	FT-ONE	DELTA LOOP	HALF SLOPERS	NO ROOM
PY1BVY	TS850, TS430	11-M VERT, DIP, LW	SH FED TWR, LW	NO ROOM
SMØAJU	TS940	SLOPER, DIPOLE	SLOPER, DIPOLE	NO ROOM
SM4CAN	IC761, 75S-3	BOBTAIL,DELTA, VERT	SH FED 86 FT TWR	BEVERAGES
SM7CRW	DRAKE C LINE	SLOPERS + VERTICAL	SLOPERS	BEVERAGE
SP3GEM	TS830	VERT 28 M (120 RAD)		BEVERAGES
SP5INQ	IC735	2 EL DELTA, VERTIC	INV L, 2 EL IN V	BEVERAGES
UG6GAW	HOME MADE	2 EL LOOP, GP	DELTA LOOP AT 120'	SMALL LOOP
VE1ZZ	TS830	4 SQUARE,3EL WIRE BM	2 EL INV L ETC	6 BEVERAGES
VE3EJ	TS940	4 SQUARE, DIPOL 75'	DELTA+INV V @ 150'	1000' BEVERAGES
VE7BS	CORSAIR, OMNI-C		HORIZ LOOP, DELTA	BEVERAGE
VE7SV	IC-761	DIPOLES, IN Vs	1/4 WAVE SLOPER	BEVERAGES
VK5KL	FT102	INV V	INV V	COAXIAL LOOP
VK6HD	FT1000, IC740	1/4 WVE VERT	LOADED VERT	HORIZONTAL LOOP
WØLYI	IC751, IC7210A	INV L + INV V	VERT, INV L, INV V	LOOP, BEVERAGES
WØCD	TS930	3 EL VERT ARRAY	3 EL ARR (MINOOKA)	BEVERAGES, LOOPS
WØCM	IC720A	1/4 WV VERT ELEV RAD	SAME	3 600' BEVERAGES
WØEJ	TS950	INV V AT 10O'	1/4 W SLOPER	3 BIDIR BEVERAGES
WØZV	TS930	DIPOLES 95' @ 145'	VERT, DIPOLE 145'	7 BEVERAGES
W1FV	TS940	PHASED VERTS	VERTICAL	2-WIRE BEVER.
W1JZ	IC-751, IC-765	-	114' VERT	4 BEVERAGES
W1NH	HQ170,	4 SQUARE, SLOPERS	NONE	6 1000 FT BEVER.
W2BXA	TS830	-	VERT, LOADED TWR	BEVERAGES, LOOP
W2JB	IC-765	INV V @ 90 FT	2 BEVERAGES	
W2NQ/7	TS820	DELTA, IN V	INV L, DELTA	NO
W2OKM	TS940	SH FED TWR 64'	SAME + DIPOLE	4 BEVERAGES
W2SM	TS830	-	60' SH FD TWR	BEVERAGE
W2TQC	TS830	SLOPING VERT	SH FED 50' TWR	SHORT BEVERAGE
W3BGN	TS940	2 EL VERT, SLOPERS	SLOPERS, IN V, LOOP	BEVERAGES
W3MFW	75S3C	PHASED VERTS	NONE	9 BEVERAGES
W4DR	TS940	4 SQUARE (WIFC)	2 EL VERT 1/4 WV	6 BEVERAGES
W4OWJ	FT1000	SH FD TWR, INV V	1H FED TOWER	6 FT LOOP
W6AJJ	CX-11A, MOD 51J4	HORIZONTAL LOOP	LOADED VERT, LOOP,	BEVERAGES
W6GO	IC765	KLM ROT DIPOLE 150'	SH FED TWR 158'	80 M DIPOLE ON 160
W7AWA	OMNI V, TS850	42' VERT BASE @ 40'	42' VERT BASE @40'	LOW DIPOLE, LOOPS
W8AH	TS940, TS930, IC781	2 PHASED VERTS\	SHUNT FED TOWER	
W8UVZ	TS930	3 EL SLOPER ARRAY	SH FED TOWER AOO'	NO SPACE
W9ZR	FT-1000	4 EL VERT ARRAY	SH FED TOWER	5 BEVERAGES
WA3EUL	DRAKE C-LINE	VERT	SHUNT FED TWR	SHORT 2 WIRE BEVER
WB2P	TS-940	3 EL 1/4 WV SLOPERS	3 EL 1/4 WV SLOPER	3 2-WIRE BEVERAGE
WB9Z	IC781, TS930, FT1000	180' VERT	180' VERT	BEVERAGES
ZL3GQ	IC765	2 DIPOLES AT 100'	DIPOLE	2 450FT BEVERAGES
ZS5LB	TS830, TS430, FT102	VERT	VERT	BEVERAGE
4X4NJ	DRAKE C, SHERWOOD FL	GROUNDPLANE	SHUNT FED TWR	LOW LOOP, BEVER.
4Z4DX	DRAKE C LINE	INV V, DELTA, L.W.	L.W., INV V	BEVERAGE
9M2AX	TS830, IC731	1/4 WV VERT, 160 RDS	SLOPER	MINI LOOP

It is amazing to see that quite a few years after the Drake company has stopped its production of amateur equipment, there are still many Drake lines around, especially 4C lines. Those that have the line swear by it.

■ 14. THE SUCCESSFUL LOW-BAND DXER

If we want to analyze what's required to become a successful low-band DXer, we must first agree on what is success. Success can be very relative. If you have only a ⅛-acre city lot and you want to work the low bands, your goals will have to be different from the guy who's got 10 acres and a well-filled bank account. But you can be successful just as well, in your own way, relative to your own goals.

There are a few essential qualities that make good low-band DXers, I think. They apply even for the modest low-band DXer.

- **Knowledge of antennas**: For the low bands, it just does not work like opening a catalogue and ordering an antenna. You'll have to understand the antennas, the whys and the why nots. You will have to become an antenna experimenter to be successful, even more so if you'll have to do it from a tiny city lot!
- **Knowledge of propagation**: Don't expect to turn on the radio at "any time" of the day on 80 or 160 and work across the globe. You must understand that you are trying to do something that is very difficult, something that requires a lot of expertise in order to become successful. You'll have to be able to predict openings, sometimes with an accuracy of minutes. You will have to understand the mechanisms behind it. The successful low-band DXer will build up his propagation expertise over a long period.
- **Equipment and technologies:** Receivers are getting better at every vintage. Maybe not as fast as we would like, but this evolution helps us unveil the previously buried weak signals from under the mud. The successful low-band DXer uses the best equipment that is available, and uses it in a professional way. He gets involved with the latest technologies in radio communication, such as packet radio and DX Clusters that will provide him with real-time information about the activity on the different low bands.
- **Good QTH**: If we look at non-relative success on the low bands, we see that the success stories are all written from an excellent QTH. They are not all mountaintop QTHs, but each success-story, in its own way, has been written from an "above average" QTH. This does not mean that a successful low-band DXer has to be a rich land owner. I, for one, have just over half an acre, but the location is excellent. The neighbors are nice, and I can use the fields in the wintertime for my Beverage antennas.
- **Perseverance, dedication:** If you are not prepared to get up in the middle of the night 5 days in a row to try to work your umpteenth country on 80 or 160, top success will not be for you. If you think it's too hard to go out at night, in the fields or through the woods, in the dark, and roll out a special one-time Beverage for the new country you have a sked with in a few hours, then you better forget about becoming success-

ful in the game, or rather the art, of low-band DXing.

■ 15. THE DON'TS

If you love to make lifetime enemies, here are some suggestions for you:

- Before starting to call CQ, look where it's very busy (preferably where a very rare DX station is operating), and start up 300 Hz (1800 Hz on phone) below the DX QSO. Ask QRL? (anyone using this frequency?), but don't wait for the answer (or turn the receiver audio gain down), and call CQ for 5 minutes.
- Use the information from the DX Cluster to improve your jamming efficiency. It is a perfect tool for finding the busy frequencies where you can exercise. When you are 300 Hz below the DX station, and you are asked by everyone to QSY, move up 600 Hz so that you are now 300 Hz above the DX station. When again asked to QSY, get excited and ask if they need the entire band. Finally agree to QSY and move back 300 Hz below the DX station. You'll really get a kick out of this. It will drive your supporters crazy. And you'll have lots of them. Watch out for them calling you (names) on the frequency.
- On 80-meter (phone band) work split frequency, but do it from right on a choice frequency in the middle of the DX window (3.798 is excellent; it is close enough to 3.8 so there is just not enough room for another QSO), and indicate your listening frequency on 3803 or 3805, so that you now occupy *two* DX window frequencies. That's what I call real efficiency.
- Own a frequency in the DX window. Owning a frequency in the 80-meter phone DX window is a privilege for few. Never call CQ without an answer. If necessary turn back a few pages in the log and . . . (well, you know)
- To improve your image, make "very difficult" QSOs from time to time. Work stations nobody else can hear. When asked about it tell them "he was very weak, but I could just work him. Gee that was a nice one . . . ." Make sure you invent "possible" QSOs. I once heard someone working ZD8Z on 160—two hours before sunset in ZD8. When asked about it the chap said "yes, he was very weak, but a new country for me . . . " On 160 work phone on 1840, so that your LSB covers the CW band all the way down to 1837. When asked to QSY, tell them that the phone band starts on 1840, and that you are on 1840. Don't give a damn about your lower sideband.
- When you have raised a very exotic DX (and you know of course half of your continent is listening in), sign with him, and call QRZ DX without bothering about the others. Never give away "your" frequency. It's yours.
- Always run the audio gain up as high as you can when transmitting. This will make more elbow room for you. By the way, don't forget to turn it down if someone answers you, so that he may understand you.
- Never announce in the Cluster the rare DX you have just worked. Someone else might work the station as well.

EQUIPMENT

■ 1. THE RECEIVER

1.1. Receiver Specifications
1.2. Sensitivity
   1.2.1. Thermal noise
   1.2.2. Receiver noise
   1.2.3. Atmospheric noise
1.3. Intermodulation Distortion
1.4. Gain Compression or Receiver Blocking
1.5. Dynamic Range
1.6. Cross Modulation
1.7. Reciprocal Mixing (VCO Noise)
   1.7.1. Measuring reciprocal mixing
      1.7.1.1. *Conversion to dBc*
1.8. Selectivity
   1.8.1. SSB bandwidth
   1.8.2. CW bandwidth
   1.8.3. Passband tuning
   1.8.4. Continuously variable IF bandwidth
   1.8.5. Filter shape factor
   1.8.6. Static and dynamic selectivity
   1.8.7. IF filter position
   1.8.8. Built-in audio filters
   1.8.9. Notch filter
      1.8.9.1. *Analog notch filters*
      1.8.9.2. *Auto-notch filters*
   1.8.10. Outboard audio filters
   1.8.11. Digital signal processing (DSP)
1.9 Stability
1.10. Frequency readout
1.11. Switchable sideband on CW
1.12. Outboard front-end filters
1.13. Noise blanker
1.14. Receiver evaluations
1.15. Graphical representation
1.16. In practice
1.17. Areas for improvement
1.18. Intermodulation outside the receiver

■ 2. TRANSMITTERS

2.1. Power
2.2. Linear Amplifiers
2.3. Phone Operation
   2.3.1. Microphones
   2.3.2. Speech processing
2.4. CW Operation
2.5. DSP in the Transmitter
2.6. Monitoring Systems
2.7. Areas of Improvement

3

EQUIPMENT

The performance of our communication equipment has progressed by leaps and bounds over the years. We see the tendency, however, for many commercial manufacturers to just add bells and whistles, instead of further concentrating on the essential characteristics of a state-of-the-art receiver. I hope this chapter will broadcast a clear message to the manufacturers of amateur communications equipment.

Many years ago every amateur station consisted of a separate transmitter and receiver. The Collins KWM-1 was the first transceiver I remember (late fifties). Today almost everybody uses a transceiver. Separate receivers/transmitters seem to be gone forever. For a very long time I was a very fervent advocate for the "separate" setup. I still think very highly about the Drake twins that closed the "separate" era with great honors.

In this chapter we will briefly discuss the specification topics of both the receiver and the transmitter section of a station, as well as any other equipment that may be included in the transmit and receiver chain of a good low-band DXing station.

■ 1. THE RECEIVER

1.1. Receiver Specifications

Until about 15 years ago, receiver performance was most frequently and almost exclusively measured by sensitivity and selectivity. In the fifties and early sixties a triple-conversion superheterodyne receiver was a status symbol. It was not until the mid-sixties that strong-signal handling came up as an important parameter (Ref. 250). Today we consider the following topics to be most important for a communication receiver (not necessarily in order of importance):

1) Sensitivity
2) Intermodulation distortion
3) Gain compression
4) Dynamic range
5) Cross modulation
6) Reciprocal mixing (VCO noise)
7) Selectivity, notch filter
8) Noise blanker
9) Stability
10) Frequency display accuracy

The above parameters will be discussed in detail and their importance will be highlighted, especially in view of low-band DXing. Fig 3-1 shows the voltage and power relationships involved in the discussion and evaluation of receiver parameters.

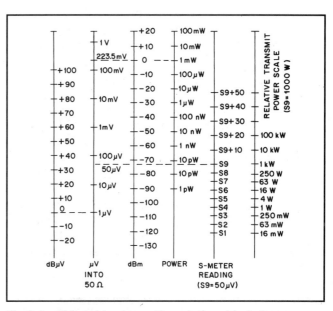

Fig 3-1—This table shows the relationship between receiver input voltages, standard S-meter readings and transmitter output power.

1.2. Sensitivity

Sensitivity is the ability of a receiver to detect weak signals. The most important concept related to sensitivity performance is the concept of signal-to-noise ratio. Good reception of a weak signal implies that the signal is substantially stronger than the noise. It is accepted as a standard that comfortable SSB reception requires a 10-dB signal-to-noise ratio. CW reception may have a much lower S/N ratio, and any CW operator can deal with a 0-dB S/N ratio quite well. Experienced operators can dig CW signals out of the noise at −10 dB S/N ratio. This proves again the inherent advantage of CW over SSB for weak-signal communications.

1.2.1. Thermal noise.

The noise present at the receiver output terminals is generated in different ways. Receiver noise is produced by the movement of electrons in any substance (such as resistors, transistors and FETs) that has a temperature above absolute zero (−273 degrees Celsius or 0 kelvins). Electrons move in a random fashion, colliding with relatively immobile ions that make up the bulk of the material. The final result of this effect is that in most substances there is no net current in any particular direction on a long-term average, but rather a series of random pulses. These pulses produce what is called thermal-agitation noise, or simply thermal noise.

The Boltzmann equation expresses the noise power in a system. The equation is written as:

$$p = kTB$$

where

p = thermal noise power, watts
k = Boltzmann's constant (1.38×10^{-23} joules/kelvin)
T = absolute temperature, kelvins
B = bandwidth, Hz

Notice that the power is directly proportional to temperature, and that at 0 K the thermal noise power is zero.

Expressing equivalent noise voltage, the equation is rewritten as:

$$E = \sqrt{kTBR}$$

where R is the system impedance (usually 50 ohms).

For example, at an ambient temperature of 27 degrees C (300 K), in a 50-ohm system with a receiver bandwidth of 3 kHz, the thermal noise power is

$$p = 1.38 \times 10^{-23} \times 300 \times 3000 = 1.24 \times 10^{-17} \text{ watt}$$

This is equivalent to $10 \log (1.24 \times 10^{-17}) = -169$ dBW or −139 dBm (139 dB below 1 milliwatt), and is equivalent to 32 dB below 1 μV or −32 dBμV (Ref. 223). This is the theoretical maximum sensitivity of the receiver under the given bandwidth and temperature conditions.

1.2.2. Receiver noise.

No receiver is noiseless. The internally generated noise is often evaluated by two measurements, called noise figure and noise factor. Noise factor is by definition the ratio of the total output noise power to the input noise power when the termination is at the standard temperature of 290 K (17 degrees C). Being a ratio, it is independent of bandwidth, temperature and impedance. The noise figure is the logarithmic expression of the noise factor:

$$NF = 10 \log F$$

where F is the noise factor.

1.2.3. Atmospheric noise.

Fig 3-2 shows the maximum usable receiver sensitivity for (a) an urban environment, (b) a quiet rural environment during the day and (c) a quiet rural environment at night. The curved lines correspond to the limits imposed by the atmospheric noise. The figures apply for a receiver with 3-kHz bandwidth. For a 300-Hz bandwidth (CW) all noises (thermal, receiver and atmospheric) drop by a factor of the square root of ten, or 3.2 times. The noise levels shown are typical for a receiving system consisting of an efficient half-wave dipole or quarter-wave vertical. Less efficient antennas will produce less noise and will therefore require a more sensitive receiver

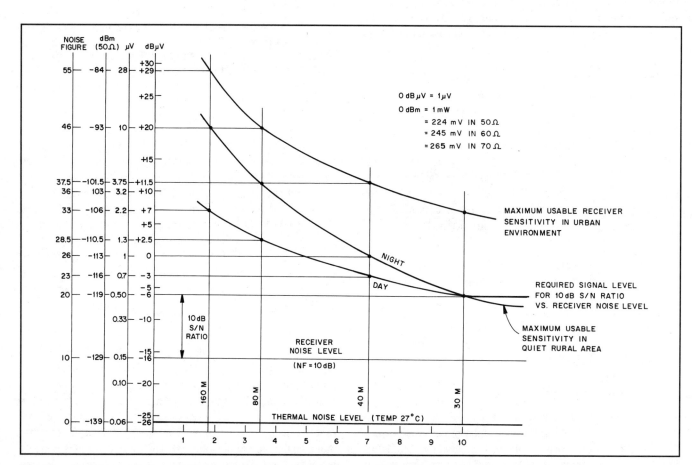

Fig 3-2—Usable receiver sensitivity on the low bands. This example is for a receiver with a noise floor of −129 dBm.

(Ref. 201, 202, 205, 223 and 247).

A typical present-day receiver has the following sensitivity characteristics (specified for a 3-kHz bandwidth):

- Noise figure: 10 dB
- Noise floor: –129 dBm
- Required signal for 10 dB S/N ratio: –119 dBm or 0.25 µV

The minimum required receiver sensitivity for the low bands under typical circumstances is shown in Table 3-1. To have a 10-dB S/N ratio, the signal has to be 10 dB stronger than the listed minimum sensitivity. Atmospheric noise on 160 and 80 meters is so great that most receivers have some "surplus" sensitivity. You may notice that the S-meter will be riding quite high on noise (maybe up to S7 in an urban environment) at all times. This is not necessarily a problem, but with higher input signal levels, the chances are greater that an (imperfect) receiver will generate internal distortion products. Better receivers have an input attenuator, and a good system will be adjustable (in steps) from 0 to at least 30 dB of attenuation.

When using a separate receiving antenna such as the Beverage antenna, the "extra" sensitivity may come in quite handy, as some of those antennas are very inefficient and much less susceptible to noise (atmospheric and man-made) because of their directive characteristics. This means that the noise (and desired signal) input from these antennas is lower, and the extra receiver sensitivity is useful.

I have had many occasions to use an input attenuator. In almost all cases, 10 or 20 dB of additional front-end attenuation did not change the readability and signal-to-noise ratio at all. Even with well-designed Beverage antennas with reasonably loss-free feeders, attenuation can still be useful.

1.3. Intermodulation distortion.

Intermodulation distortion (IMD) is an effect caused by two strong signals that drive the front end of the receiver beyond its linear range so that spurious signals called Intermodulation-distortion products are produced. Third-order IMD is the most common and annoying front-end overload effect. Fig 3-3 shows the IMD spectrum for an

3-1

Table 3-1
Minimum Required Receiver Sensitivity

	Quiet Rural Day	Quiet Rural Night	Urban	Freq (MHz)
Acceptable Noise Figure	33 dB	46 dB	55 dB	1.8
Minimum Sensitivity	2.2 µV	10 µV	28 µV	
Acceptable Noise Figure	28 dB	37.5 dB	46 dB	3.5
Minimum Sensitivity	1.3 µV	3.75 µV	10 µV	
Acceptable Noise Figure	23 dB	26 dB	37.5 dB	7.0
Minimum Sensitivity	0.7 µV	1 µV	11.5 µV	
Noise Figure	10 dB	10 dB	10 dB	Typical
Sensitivity	0.15 µV	0.15 µV	0.15 µV	Receiver

These are typical receiver sensitivities required on the low bands. The values assume a receiving antenna such as a dipole or a vertical. Special low-gain receiving antennas require more sensitivity (up to 10 dB).

example where the parent signals are spaced 1-kHz apart.

Third-order IMD products increase in amplitude three times as fast as the pair of equal parent signals (Ref. 210, 211, 213, 226, 239, 247, 255, 274, 281). Fig 3-4 shows two examples for third-order intercept points. The vertical scale is the relative output of the receiver front end in dB, referenced to an arbitrary zero level. The horizontal axis shows the input level of the two equal-amplitude parent signals, expressed in dBm. Point A sits right on the receiver noise floor. Increasing

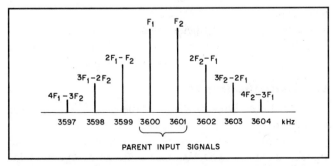

Fig 3-3—Third, fifth and seventh-order intermodulation products generated by parent input signals on 3600 and 3601 kHz.

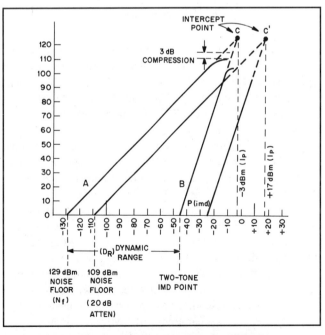

Fig 3-4—Third-order intercept point showing two examples, with and without 20 dB of front-end attenuation. The intercept point increases by the same amount as the attenuation introduced.

the power of the parent signals results in an increase of the fundamental output signal at a one-to-one ratio. Between −129 dBm and −44 dBm, no IMD products are generated that are equal to or stronger than the receiver noise floor. At −44 dBm, the third-order IMD products have risen to exactly the receiver noise floor level.

Point B is called the two-tone IMD point. It is usually expressed in dBm. Further increasing the power of the parent input signals will continue to raise the power of the third-order IMD products three times faster than that of the parent signals. At some point, the fundamental and third-order response lines will flatten because of "gain compression." Extensions of both response lines cross at a point called the third-order intercept point. The level can be read from the input scale in dBm.

Fig 3-5 shows the third-order intercept point for a modern-day receiver versus frequency separation of the two parent signals. Two cases are shown, with and without a preamplifier.

The intercept point (I_p) can be calculated from the IMD point as follows.

$$I_p = \frac{2 \text{ MDS (noise floor)} + 3 \text{ IMD}_{DR}}{2}$$

where

    MDS = minimum discernible signal
    IMD_{DR} = IMD dynamic range

Inversely, the two-tone IMD point can be derived mathematically from the intercept point as follows.

$$P_{IMD} = \frac{2I_p + Nf}{3}$$

where Nf = noise floor.

An example (for a receiver having a −3 dBm intercept point and −129 dBm noise floor is

$$P_{IMD} = \frac{2 \times (-3) + (-129)}{3} = -45 \text{ dBm}$$

What does this figure mean? It means that signals below −45 dBm will not create audible IMD products, while stronger signals will. This means that signals at around S9 + 30 dB will start generating audible IMD products! In Europe this is an everyday situation on the 7-MHz band where 30 to 50 mV signals are common.

When evaluating third-order intercept points, we must always look at receiver noise floor levels at the same time. When we raise the noise floor from −129 dBm to −109 dBm (for example by inserting 20 dB of attenuation into the receiver input line), both response lines and the intercept point will shift 20 dB to the right (see Fig 3-4). This means that the intercept point has been improved by 20 dB! Any (average) receiver with a +5-dBm intercept point can be raised to +25 dBm merely by inserting 20 dB of attenuation into the input. Remember that this can frequently be done with present-day receivers, as they often have a large "surplus" sensitivity.

The frequency separation of the two parent input signals can greatly influence the intermodulation results. The worst case applies when there is no selectivity in the front end to attenuate one of the signals. This happens when both input

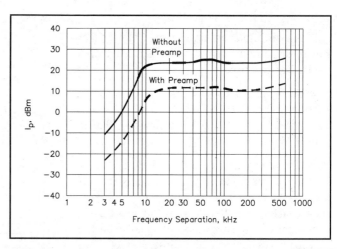

Fig 3-5—Third-order intercept point for a 1992 vintage quality receiver. The graph shows clearly that the first-IF (roofing) filter has a bandwidth of approximately 10 kHz. Decreasing the bandwidth of this filter, together with the use of a lower noise VCO, would dramatically improve the dynamic range at closer frequency spacings.

signals are within the passband of the first-IF filter and the intermodulation products are produced in the second mixer. Most present-day receivers have a rather wide first IF so they can accommodate narrow-band FM and AM signals without requiring filter changes.

Measurements at 2-kHz spacing using a 500-Hz second-IF filter (CW filter) are often used to find the worst-case IMD performance. Measurements at 20- and 100-kHz spacing are also used for assessing receiver intermodulation performance. With this much spacing, the first-IF filter often improves the picture considerably, while in some receivers with high-Q tuned input circuits the front-end tuned input circuits will also add to the selectivity and further improve the IMD performance. The 100-kHz spacing is typically used for measuring receivers where the local oscillator (LO) noise limits measurement accuracy at 20 kHz and closer spacings (see par 1.7).

1.4. Gain Compression or Receiver Blocking

Gain compression occurs when a strong signal drives an amplifier stage (for example, a receiver front end) so hard that it cannot produce any more output. The stage is driven beyond its linear operating region and is saturated. Gain compression can be recognized by a decrease in the background noise level when saturation occurs (Ref. 223, 239, 281). Gain compression can be caused by other amateur stations nearby; such as in a multi-operator contest environment. Outboard front-end filters are the answer to this problem. (See par .1.12.)

1.5. Dynamic Range

The lower limit of the dynamic range of a receiver is the power level of the weakest detectable signal (receiver noise floor). The upper limit is the power level of the signals at which IMD becomes noticeable (intermodulation products are equal to the receiver noise-floor level). Refer to Fig 3-4 for a graphical representation of dynamic range. Dynamic range can be calculated as follows.

$$DR = P_{IMD} - Nf$$

where

> DR = dynamic range, dB
> P_{IMD} = two-tone IMD point, dBm
> Nf = receiver noise floor, dBm

If the intercept point is known instead of the two-tone IMD point we can use the following equation.

$$DR = \frac{2\left(I_p - Nf\right)}{3}$$

where I_p is the intercept point in dBm.

The dynamic range of a receiver is important because it allows us to directly compare the strong-signal handling performance of receivers (Ref. 234, 239, 255).

1.6. Cross Modulation

Cross modulation occurs when modulation from an undesired signal is partially transferred to a desired signal in the passband of the receiver. Cross modulation starts at the 3-dB compression point on the fundamental response curve as shown in Fig 3-4. Cross modulation is independent of the strength of the desired signal and proportional to the square of the undesired signal amplitude, so a front-end attenuator can be very helpful in reducing the effects of cross modulation. Introducing 10 dB of attenuation will reduce cross modulation by 20 dB. This exclusive relationship can also help to distinguish cross modulation from other IMD phenomena (Ref. 223, 247).

1.7. Reciprocal Mixing (VCO Noise)

Reciprocal mixing is a large-signal effect caused by noise sidebands of the local oscillator feeding the input mixer. Oscillators are mostly thought of as single-signal sources, but this is never so in reality. All oscillators have sidebands to a certain extent. One example of the sidebands produced by an oscillator is shown in Fig 3-6.

The detrimental effect of these noise sidebands remained largely unnoticed until recently, when voltage-controlled oscillators (VCOs) were introduced in state-of-the art receivers. J. Grebenkemper, KI6WX covered the effects of phase noise on amateur communications in full detail in his publication in *QST* (Ref. 286 and 289). Fig 3-7 shows the levels of the interfering signals produced versus frequency spacing, the standard method of evaluating the effects of the VCO noise in a receiver.

VCOs are much more prone to creating noise sidebands than LC oscillators. The wide-range phase-locked loops in VCOs are responsible for the poor noise spectrum (Ref. 209). Fig 3-8 shows the relationship in the usual superheterodyne receiver between the input signal, the IF and the local oscillator for both the ideal situation of a noiseless LO and for the case where the LO has realistic noise sidebands.

Reciprocal mixing introduces off-channel signals into the IF at levels proportional to the frequency separation

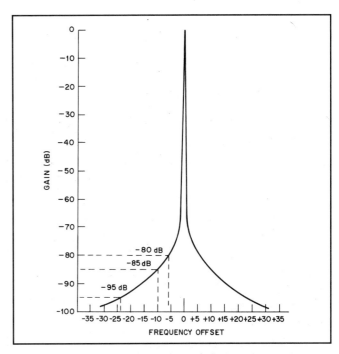

Fig 3-6—Output spectrum of a voltage-controlled oscillator. If the measurement was done at a 3-kHz bandwidth, the oscillator sideband performance referred to a 1-Hz bandwidth is 85 + 34 = 119 dBc (dB referenced to the carrier).

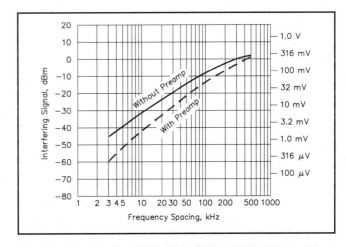

Fig 3-7—The levels of interfering signal (vertical axis) at a given signal spacing (horizontal axis) that causes the AF noise to increase by 3 dB. A 2.7-kHz IF bandwidth is assumed. This is the standard method of evaluating the effects of the VCO noise in a receiver. See text for details.

between the desired signal and the unwanted signal. This effectively reduces the selectivity of the receiver. In other words, if the static response of the IF filters is specified down to –80 dB, the noise in the LO must be down at least the same amount in the same bandwidth in order not to degrade the effective selectivity of the filter.

According to the thermal-noise equation (see Section 4.2.1), the noise power is –174 dBm at room temperature for

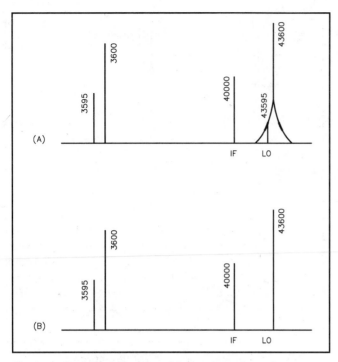

Fig 3-8—An LO with noise sidebands can produce reciprocal mixing products inside the bandwidth of the IF filter. At A, the undesired signal at 3595 kHz mixes with sideband energy from the LO at 43,595 kHz to produce an output signal at the IF of 40,000 kHz. The LO at B has no sideband energy, so the unwanted signal produces a mixing product at 40,005 kHz, outside the IF passband.

a bandwidth of 1 Hz. The noise in an SSB bandwidth of X Hz can be scaled to a 1-Hz bandwidth using the factor (10 log X). This equation yields a factor of 34.8 dB for a 3-kHz bandwidth, 34.3 dB for 2.7 kHz and 33.2 dB for 2.1 kHz. Continuing with the example where the static response of the IF filter is –80 dB and the filter has a 3-kHz bandwidth, the noise of the LO should be no more than 80 + 34 = 114 dBm referenced to a 1-Hz bandwidth. The carrier noise referenced to a 1-Hz bandwidth is usually called dBc.

1.7.1. Measuring reciprocal mixing.

If we specify the offset between two signals and the bandwidth of the IF filter, and then gradually raise the strength of one signal, we will find that at some signal strength the signal-to-noise ratio of the other signal will be degraded by 3 dB. (Ref. 281, 274, 247)

1.7.1.1. *Conversion to dBc.*

If, with a filter of 2.7 kHz, it takes an input level of –60 dBm at a spacing of 10 kHz to reduce the desired signa l 3 dB, and given a receiver has a noise floor of –135 dBm, the level with respect to the noise floor is: 135 – 60 = 75 dB. Referred to a bandwidth of 2.1 kHz, we must add our conversion factor of 33 dB (ignoring the decimal fraction), which gives an oscillator noise sideband performance of 75 + 33 = 108 dBc.

1.8. Selectivity

Selectivity is the ability of a receiver to separate (select) a desired signal from unwanted signals.

1.8.1. SSB bandwidth.

On a quiet band with a reasonably strong desired signal, the best audio and signal-to-noise ratio can be obtained with selectivities on the order of 2.7 kHz at 6 dB. Under adverse conditions, selectivities as narrow as 1 kHz can be used for SSB, but the carrier positioning on the filter slope becomes very critical for optimum readability. The ideal selectivity for SSB reception will of course vary, depending on the interference on adjacent frequencies.

1.8.2. CW bandwidth.

For most DX work a 500 Hz (at –6 dB) IF filter is adequate. If the transceiver is equipped with a continuously variable bandwidth control (or shift + width control), you can also narrow down the bandwidth further, but remember that the shape factor worsens as you reduce the bandwidth. If you are a serious CW operator, it is my advice to use a 250- or 300-Hz filter in addition to the 500 Hz filter for when things get rough.

1.8.3. Passband tuning.

Passband tuning (IF shift) allows the position of the passband on the slope to be altered without requiring that the receiver be retuned. The bandwidth of the passband filter remains constant, however. In some cases interfering signals can be moved outside the passband of the receiver by adjusting the passband tuning. In better receivers, passband tuning has been replaced by a filter system with a continuously variable bandwidth (eg, Kenwood TS-930, -940, -950, FT-1000, FT-990, etc).

1.8.4 Continuously variable IF bandwidth.

A continuously variable IF bandwidth, where the filter can be independently narrowed down from both sides (low pass and high pass) is ideal (Kenwood). The equivalent is the passband (WIDTH) plus SHIFT-tuning as encountered on the latest Yaesu equipment. This feature is nowadays available on all state-of-the-art receivers.

The mechanism in producing a continuously variable bandwidth consists in passing the signal through two separate filters, on two different IFs (e.g., 9 MHz and 455 kHz). The mixing frequency is slightly altered so the two filters do not superimpose 100%, but have their passbands sliding across one another, effectively creating a continuously variable bandwidth. You must understand, however, that a variable bandwidth system as described will never have as good a shape factor as individual well-shaped crystal filters, as the shape factor always worsens when you narrow the bandwidth.

1.8.5. Filter shape factor.

The filter shape factor is expressed as the ratio of the bandwidth at 60 dB to the bandwidth at 6 dB. Good filters should have a shape factor of 1.5 or better. In recent years it has been common to see transceivers equipped with rather wide IF filters (typically 2.7 kHz at 6 dB) having mediocre skirt selectivity. For the average operator this may be an acceptable situation, although the serious DXer and contest operator may want to go a step further.

Several sources (eg, International Radio, Fox Tango and Sherwood Engineering) offer modification kits for modern transceivers, where the wider (2.7-kHz) IF filters can be replaced with sharper 2.1-kHz filters. A combination of two matched 2.1-kHz-wide filters in the 8.8-MHz and 455-kHz IF strips of the Kenwood TS-930 or TS-940 yields a shape factor (6/60 dB) of 1.25, which is quite spectacular. The paired filters for CW give a –6 dB bandwidth of 400 Hz and a –60 dB bandwidth of less than 700 Hz.

The Yaesu FT-1000 is a transceiver which does not need any filter boosting up. The excellent shape factor of the factory-installed filters make them the best quality filters I have encountered so far in amateur receivers.

1.8.6. Static and dynamic selectivity.

Fig 3-9 shows the typical static selectivity curve of a filter system with independent slope tuning (eg, TS-940S). The static selectivity curve is the transfer curve of the filter with no reciprocal mixing. The dynamic selectivity of the receiver front end is shown in Fig 3-10. The dynamic selectivity is the combination of the static selectivity and the effects of recipro-

cal mixing. Note that the static selectivity can be deteriorated by the effect of reciprocal mixing with noise from the local oscillator.

If the amplitudes of the reciprocal mixing products are greater than the stop-band attenuation of the filter, the ultimate stop-band characteristics of the filter will deteriorate. Good frequency-synthesizer designs can yield 95 dB (–129 dBc), while good crystal oscillators can achieve over 110 dB (–144 dBc) at a 10-kHz offset. This means it is pointless to use an excellent filter with a 100-dB stop-band characteristic if the reciprocal mixing figure is only 75 dB.

1.8.7. IF filter position.

The filter providing the bulk of the operational selectivity can theoretically be inserted anywhere in a receiver between the RF input and audio output. When considering parameters other than selectivity, however, it is clear that the filter should be as close as possible to the antenna terminals of the receiver. In par. 1.3 we saw that front-end selectivity can help reduce IMD products.

Most modern receivers use triple or even quadruple conversion. In order to be most effective, the selectivity (filter) should be as far ahead in the receiver as possible. The logical choice is the first IF. Most modern designs use a first IF in the 50- to 100-kHz range, for image selection reasons. This is not

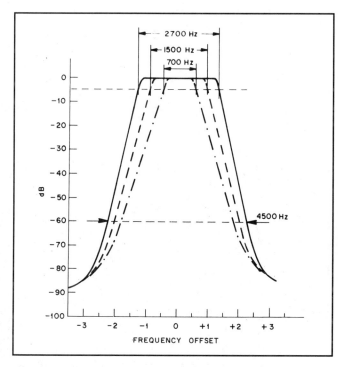

Fig 3-9—Static selectivity curve of a receiver using continuously variable bandwidth. This result is obtained by using selective filters in the first (or second) and second (or third) IF, and by shifting the two superimposed filters slightly through a change in the mixing frequency. Note that the shape factor worsens as the bandwidth is reduced. It is not ideal to use this method to achieve CW bandwidth. The shape factor may deteriorate to 4 or more, while a good stand-alone CW filter can yield a shape factor of less than 2.

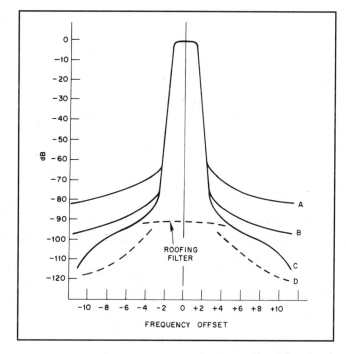

Fig 3-10—The total dynamic front-end filter response is the combination of the main selectivity filter (second IF) and the roofing filter (first IF). Curve A is the selectivity curve with an LO having an 80-dB noise suppression (at 10-kHz spacing). Curve B is for 95-dB suppression, and Curve C is for an LO with 115-dB suppression. Dashed Curve D represents the noise level from the LO that yields Curve C. In Curve C, the selectivity is not influenced by the LO noise (up to ±10 kHz from the center frequency), but is made up by a combination of the main selectivity filter and the first-IF roofing filter.

the most ideal frequency for building crystal filters with the best possible shape factor. In general, we find rather simple 2-pole crystal filters with a nominal selectivity of 15 to 20 kHz (at –6 dB) in the first-IF chain. The reasons for this very wide bandwidth are twofold:

• To retain the original impulse noise shape (short rise time) in order to be able to incorporate a (more or less) useful noise blanker.
• Most of the modern (all bells and whistles transceivers) must operate on FM as well, where a selectivity of less than 15-20 kHz cannot be tolerated.

I am convinced that most successful low-band DXers live in a quiet area. No need for noise-blankers to reduce man-made noise. If we are plagued with this kind of noise, we will cure the problem at the source. Therefore I am convinced that noise blankers are of little use to most low-band DXers. I also am not at all interested in being able to receive FM on my transceiver. This means we really could use better (narrower) first-IF filters. They would greatly improve the dynamic selectivity of our receivers (see par 1.8.6).

The second IF is often in the 9-MHz region, the third IF usually on approx. 455 kHz. Both these frequencies are very well suited for building high-quality crystal filters with excellent shape factors. In some receivers ferrite filters are used on 455 kHz, but they have a much inferior shape factor compared to a good crystal filter.

Modern transceivers often will be equipped with IF filters only in the first and second IFs. Filters in the third IF are obtainable as options. I strongly suggest not to compromise in this area. Install all the available filters in the transceiver. If you don't install the optional filters in the third IF, the shape factor of the variable bandwidth control will also be very mediocre (using the slope of the standard 2.7-kHz filter).

Ideally, the last-IF filters should be placed just ahead of the product detector, in order to reduce the IF wide-band noise generated by the IF amplifier stage beyond the last filter. Many (most) modern receivers show an annoying wide-band noise (hiss) which is especially noticeable on narrow CW when the band is very quiet.

1.8.8. Built-in audio filters.

Audio filters can also be used to improve the signal-to-noise ratio caused by wide-band noise introduced in the receiver IF. If audio filtering is relied on for the signal selectivity proper, however, strong signals in the passband of the wider IF filter can reduce the gain of the receiver (if the AGC is IF-derived, as in almost all receivers), and hence reduce the post-filter dynamic range. This can only be overcome with audio-derived AGC.

Most modern transceivers have a built-in APF (audio peak filter) which adds some selectivity to the audio channels and eliminates the above-mentioned IF hiss. Ideally this APF filter should have an adjustable width control, which is lacking on today's receivers.

1.8.9. Notch filters.

1.8.9.1. *Analog notch filters.*

Another useful feature is a notch filter. As its name

implies, a notch filter is used to reduce the amplitude of signals in a narrow stop band. A good receiver needs a good notch filter to help the low-band operator "notch out" strong adjacent signals. Ideally, the notch filter should be incorporated in the receiver chain ahead of the AGC detector (see par. 1.8.7).

Very sharp notch filters can only be achieved at low frequencies. Triple-conversion or quadruple-conversion receivers often use very low frequencies for the last IF (for example, the TS-930S and -940S use a 100-kHz last IF). At this frequency, a reasonably sharp notch filter with a notch depth of better than 60 dB is practical. Even sharper notch filters can be realized at audio frequencies.

Fig 3-11 shows the notch depths that can be reached with IF and AF notch filters, and shows the effect of using the IF and the AF notch filter simultaneously. The curves are representative for the combination of a TS-930S IF notch and the Datong FL2 or FL3 audio notch filter (see par. 1.8.10).

1.8.9.2. *Auto-notch filters.*

The Datong FL1 and FL3 filters are top-grade audio auto-notch filters. They will scan for a carrier through the audio passband, lock on it and notch it out. The response time is typically 200 mS. This type of auto-notch filter is ideal on SSB, where it eliminates bothersome tuner-uppers. Of course, as the filter is located beyond the AGC detector, it will not

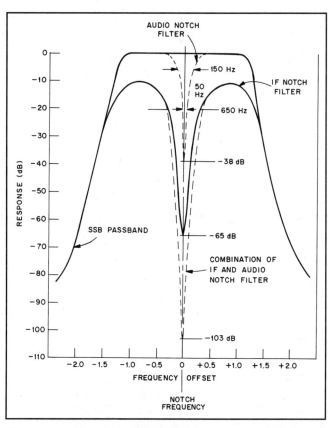

Fig 3-11—Notch-filter frequency response. The 100-kHz IF filter has a very deep notch but relatively wide shoulders. The audio filter provides a very sharp notch with narrow shoulders, but the notch is shallower. The combination of both yields a remarkable notch depth of over 100 dB!

prevent the receiver from being desensitized by a strong carrier.

This could in principle be prevented by incorporating such a filter in the receiver, and by using audio-derived AGC. Another alternative would be to use a quadruple conversion receiver and incorporate such an auto-notch filter in the last IF (around 50-kHz IF).

Analog audio filters are steadily being replaced with circuits employing DSP (digital signal processing) techniques (see par 1.8.11).

1.8.10. Outboard audio filters.

Audio filters can never replace IF filters (see par. 1.8.7). They can be welcome additions, however, especially on CW if your receiver lacks a good built-in filter. Introducing some AF filtering reduces any remaining wide-band IF noise, and can improve the S/N ratio. Removing some of the higher pitched hiss can also be quite advantageous, especially when long operating times are involved, such as in a contest (Ref. 237).

A wide variety of audio filters has been described in Amateur Radio literature, using either LC networks (Ref. 236, 246, 261, 265, 278, 283, 284 and 285) or op-amp systems (Ref. 200 and 264). Tong, G4GMQ, has developed a very effective auto-tune AF notch-filter system, which he incorporated in the Datong FL1 (Ref. 270) and FL3 filters.

The FL3 filter is a very complete and performing audio filter. On SSB, one or both slopes can be adjusted independently, and the auto-notch feature performs extremely well. Within a fraction of a second, the filter will notch out a strong signal that has come into the passband. When used in addition to a good IF notch filter, which has the advantage of acting prior to the AGC detector, signals of S9+ can be completely eliminated.

1.8.11. Digital signal processing (DSP).

Digital signal processing consists in digitizing (ADC) the analog signal (e.g., an audio signal) so that a digital processor can handle the signal and do whatever is needed before converting it back to an analog signal (DAC). (Ref. 290 and 291). In order to be able to handle the digitized signals, we use a CPU with a high clock frequency (20 to 50 MHz). The heart of a DSP device is the software.

DSP can be used in the transmit chain as a very effective passband filter, effectively reducing the bandwidth of the transmitted signal.

Outboard DSP signal processors for use in the receiver audio chain are becoming available in the commercial market. It is obvious that in the years ahead, DSP and its applications in receivers will progress noticeably.

An area where DSP can excel is in notch filtering. DSP units have been made available that can handle multiple carriers in the audio spectrum. The great advantage over the analog auto-notch filter (e.g., the Datong FL3; see par 1.8.8.2.) is that the response time of the DSP unit is much shorter. This means that carriers are notched out before the user even notices a carrier came on.

The disadvantage of an outboard DSP notch filter on audio frequencies is that the interfering carrier (which the user will not hear) can capture the AGC and severely desensitize the receiver. The cure is to have a DSP device operating at the receiver before the place where the AGC detection takes place. This would require CPUs with even higher clock frequencies, using a 50-kHz last IF. We will probably see IF DSP popping up in commercial receivers before too long.

1.9 Stability

State-of-the-art fully synthesized receivers have the stability of the reference source. All present-day receivers have achieved a level of stability which is adequate for all types of amateur traffic.

1.10. Frequency Readout

A frequency readout displaying frequency to the nearest 100 Hz is adequate for amateur SSB and most CW operation, but for fixed-channel digital-mode operation, 10-Hz resolution is mandatory. On CW the display should show the carrier frequency. Most older receivers and transceivers actually display the carrier frequency ± the beat note (usually 400 to 1000 Hz), and this can cause confusion when arranging a schedule on CW.

1.11. Swtichable Sideband on CW

A novel and very interesting feature of the Kenwood TS-850 is that the user can switch CW reception from lower sideband to upper sideband. Although the terminology of lower and upper sideband is not so common on CW, CW signals are indeed received with the beat oscillator frequency either above (as an LSB signal) or below (as a USB signal). In the past, none of the commercial receivers offered the capability of switching sidebands on CW. I must say that in practice this feature can be quite handy in our fight against QRM. I would like to see this feature on all new transceivers.

1.12. Outboard Front-end Filters

Most of our present-day amateur receivers and receiver sections in transceivers are general coverage (100 kHz to 30 MHz). They make wide use of half-octave front-end filters, which do not provide any narrow front-end selectivity. Older amateur-band-only receivers used either tracked-tuned filters or narrow band-pass filters, which provide a much higher degree of front-end protection, especially in highly RF-polluted areas. Instead of providing automatic antenna tuners in modern transceivers, I believe that same space could more advantageously be taken up by some sharply tuned input filters which could be switched into the receiver when needed.

Excellent articles are available that describe selective front-end receiving filters (Ref. 219, 221, 251 and 266). Martin (Ref. 219) and Hayward (Ref. 221) describe tunable preselector filters which are very suitable for low-band applications in highly polluted areas (Ref. 294).

Sherwood Engineering of 1268 S. Ogden St, Denver CO 80210 offers front-end crystal filters, which are the ultimate solution for multi-op contest stations and for protection against megawatt broadcast stations in the 7-MHz band. The bandwidth of the six-pole 50-ohm filters is 50 kHz on 20 meters,

25 kHz on 40 meters, 12.5 kHz on 80 meters and 5 kHz on 160 meters. The shape factor (6/60 dB) is 2.5:1. The customer can specify the design frequency of the filter. Eight-pole filters with a 2:1 shape factor and a bandwidth of 12.5 kHz are also available for 20, 40 and 80 meters.

L. Gordon, K4VX described band-pass filters for HF transceivers for use in multi-op contest stations. (Ref 295).

1.13. Noise Blanker

A common complaint heard about noise blankers is their very limited efficiency when the band is fully loaded, as during contests. W7AWA suggests using a frequency outside the amateur bands to sense the noise. I remember this was done 30 years ago with the first commercially available noise blankers in the Collins 75A4.

1.14. Receiver Evaluations

It is important that every avid low-band DXer understand the parameters which make a receiver good for the low bands. It is not possible for most of us to perform the tests ourselves, however.

The test methods have been very well defined in the amateur literature (Ref. 210, 211, 234 and 255), and Schwarzbeck, DL1BU, and Hart, G3SJX, have been publishing a series of excellent equipment evaluations in *CQ-DL* and *Radio Communication* (Ref. 400-417).

In order to minimize confusion, I have refrained from quoting test measurement data. Exhaustive test reports on the new equipment are published regularly by Schwarzbeck, DL1BU (in *CQ-DL*) and Hart, G3SJX (in *RadCom*). Taking just a few test data out of several pages of test results does not seem fair to me. Anyone with a serious interest in these professional test reports can find all the reports listed in the literature section of this book.

1.15. Graphical Representation

Hart, G3SJX, uses an interesting graphical representation of the main receiver parameters. Two examples are shown in Figs 3-12 and 3-13. The following information can be found on the graphs:

- Receiver noise floor
- Dynamic filter response
- Local-oscillator noise output
- Front-end blocking level in dBm
- Second-mixer blocking in dBm
- Two-tone (spurious-free) dynamic range as a function of parent signal spacing

The performance of a run-of-the-mill present-day receiver is shown in Fig 3-12. The graph in Fig 3-13 shows what a really good receiver would look like. This receiver would show a steep IF filter response (1.5 shape factor), where the ultimate rejection would be over 120 dB, and where the dynamic broadening of the filter passband would not show up before at least −100 dB. To perform this well, the receiver would need an excellent local oscillator with a noise sideband performance of greater than 134 dBc. The better receiver would have narrow first-IF filters to match the mode to be used

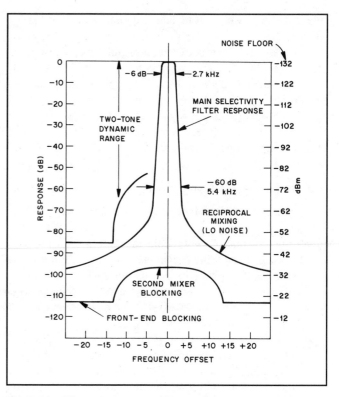

Fig 3-12—The receiver merit graph as introduced by G3SJX. This example is for an average-quality receiver with no outstanding features.

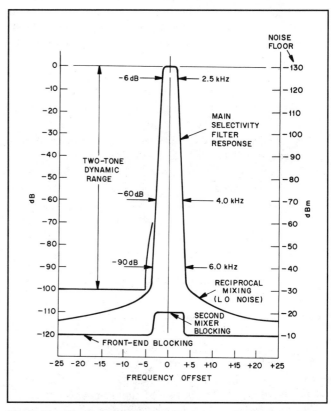

Fig 3-13—Merit graph for a "dream receiver." Note that the first-IF filter (roofing filter) has a bandwidth that is similar to the bandwidth of the main selectivity filter.

(3 kHz for SSB and 500 Hz for CW), in order to have a two-tone spurious-free dynamic range that would be at least 100 dB both on close spacing (5 kHz) and wide spacing (50 kHz). The figures for our ideal receiver would read:

- Spurious-free dynamic range: 100 dB min.
- Noise floor: −130 dBm
- Third-order intercept point: +30 dBm at full sensitivity (with preamp)
- IMD point level: −30 dBm (equivalent to over 10 mV or nearly S9 + 60 dB)
- LO sideband noise performance: Better than 135 dBc at close spacing

1.16. In Practice

After you understand what makes a receiver good or bad for low-band DXing and after you study all the available equipment reviews, remember that what really counts is how the radio operates at your location, in your environment, with your antennas, how it satisfies your expectations, and how it compares to the receiver you have been using. The easiest test is still to try the receiver when the band is really crowded, when signals are at their strongest. When you listen closely where it is relatively calm, you may hear weak crud that sounds like intermodulation or noise mixing products. If you insert 10 dB or 20 dB of attenuation in the antenna input line, and the crud is still there, there is a good chance that the signal is really there. As the attenuation raises the intercept point by the same amount in dB as the attenuation figure, it is likely that raising the intercept point by 10 or 20 dB would have stopped intermodulation.

1.17. Areas for Improvement

The really devoted DXer, and especially the low-band buff, would certainly welcome further improvements to our present-day receivers. This does not mean that we have not been witnessing quite spectacular improvements over the years with all brands of equipment. Not every low-band DXer seems to agree with this statement. M. Greenway (K4PI) writes in his survey reply, "Would like to see a major break-through in receiver performance. Have not seen anything new on rig in many years. Just bells and whistles."

In preparation of this book, a questionnaire was sent to over 150 top low-band DXers from all over the world. Two questions dealt with receiver specifications. The list below shows an overview of what our top low-band DXers consider to be the most important specification items for an ideal low-band receiver. The percentage refers to the number of DXers that found the subject topic was important or needed improvement.

- Better selectivity: 59%
- Better strong-signal behavior (dynamic range, 3rd order intercept): 30%
- Close-in dynamic range (specifically): 3%
- Less VCO noise: 21%
- Better noise blanker: 13%
- More sensitivity: 12%
- Better notch filter: 8%
- Better AGC: 4%

- Better front-end selectivity: 4%
- Less internal noise (IF hiss?): 4%
- CW continuous trackable sidetone: < 3%
- No wide-band audio noise: 3%
- (Better) audio peak filter: 2%
- Better audio: 2%
- Dual reception: 2%
- Auto-notch for multiple carriers: 2%.
- Full QSK: 2%
- Better (more) DSP: 1%
- RF DSP: 1%
- Manual RF gain control: 1%
- Auto multiple notch filter (DSP) in IF: 1%
- Separate RX input: 1%
- Finer tuning rate: 1%

Before summing up some of the improvements I would like to see, I'd like to comment on the above list.

Clearly everyone wants better strong-signal-handling capabilities also with close spacings. This means better first-IF filters, much lower VCO noise, and better skirts on the IF filters. The third-order intercept should be high, together with a high sensitivity. I was amazed to see how many rated sensitivity as an important factor on the low bands. It must be the guys using loops or Beverage receiving antennas.

Here are my own suggestions for improvements.

1) A tunable ham-band-only preselector to improve front-end selectivity. The operator should be able to switch the preselector in and out of the circuit.

2) A switchable selection of varying-bandwidth first-IF filters. Three selectivities should be provided as options:

- wide for AM or noise-blanker operation (15 kHz)
- medium for SSB (2.1 kHz)
- narrow for CW (500 Hz)

3) These filters should have selectivity characteristics approaching those of the present-day main (2nd-IF) selectivity filters.

4) Main selectivity IF filters with a stop-band attenuation of over 100 dB.

5) Improvement of the LO noise performance to 135 dBc or better at 2 kHz spacing.

6) Built-in IF DSP multiple-carrier IF notch filters.

7) At least +30 dBm third-order intercept point at close spacing (5 kHz).

8) Eliminate IF hiss via DSP in last IF crystal filter ahead of product detector (Ref. DJ8WL) APF with variable bandwidth

9) Perfectly clean audio (audio and AGC circuitry)

10) Noise blanker that works with very strong adjacent-frequency signals

11) Inverted sideband switching on CW (Ref. TS-850)

12) Last-IF DSP to enhance SSB S/N ratio

13) Every transceiver to have two VFO knobs (one TX, one RX). Do away with the RIT, XIT, Clarifier confusion.

Instead of spending more money on bells and whistles like more memories, more sophisticated readouts, etc, new development efforts should be channeled toward the needs of better basic performance, as specified above. If the conscious ham tells his supplier about his real demands, he will contribute to achieving this goal.

Development of modern Amateur Radio equipment is largely market driven. If the marketers keep telling the designers they want more bells and whistles, that is what the user will get. If users tell the manufacturers they want better basic performance often enough, maybe the designers will get the right message and we will see more progress toward better receiver performance.

1.18. Intermodulation Outside the Receiver

It was very interesting to see J. Sluymer, VE3EJ, mention to me the possible problem of intermodulation generated outside the receiver.

I have witnessed this problem with aging Beverage antennas. Sometimes it is referred to as bad ground loops, or bad contacts, but the effect of nonlinearity caused by corrosion can create the well-known effects of overload, cross modulation and intermodulation. It isn't because you will not be running "power" into the Beverage antenna that you don't need to have good contacts in the system. If you suddenly hear all kinds of alien signals pop up in the band where they don't belong, it's time to go and check all the contacts of the receiving antenna system. Also check proper grounding of the coaxial feed line.

■ 2. TRANSMITTERS

2.1. Power

It should be the objective of every sensible ham to build a well-balanced station. Success in DXing can only be achieved if the performance of the transmitter setup is well balanced with the performance of the receiving setup. It is true that you can only work what you can hear, but it is also true that you can only work the stations that can hear you. It is indeed frustrating when one can hear the DX very well but cannot make a QSO, and it must be frustrating for the station on the other end to hear a loud DX station calling without being able to raise it. We all know stations like that. Some characters just like to be loud. When they cannot hear the DX some even go as far as to make fictitious QSOs and "read the Callbook." Fortunately those are the rare exceptions.

A well-balanced station is the result of the combination of a good receiver, the necessary and reasonable amount of power and, most of all, the right transmitting and receiving antennas. It is of course handy to be able to run a lot of power for those occasions when it is necessary. In many countries in the world, amateur licenses stipulate that the minimum amount of power necessary to maintain a good contact should be used, while there is of course a limitation of the maximum power.

There is only one mode of communication where we have real-time feedback of the quality of the communication link, and that is AMTOR as well as other similar error-correcting digital transmission systems. In CW as well as SSB, we can only go by feeling and by the reports received, and therefore we are most of the time tempted to run "power."

There are a number of dedicated operators who have worked over 250 countries on 80 meters without running an amplifier. It can be safely stated that most of the active 80-meter DXers run some form of power amplifier, and that most of them run between 800 and about 1500 W PEP output on SSB and about 700 W output on CW.

In most countries the power limitations are no different on 160 than on other bands (e.g., 1500 W). Some European countries used to impose very low power (10 W) on top-band for fear of interference, as the 160-meter frequencies were shared with maritime and other services. This has changed, and the ship-to-shore and military stations have left the DX portion of 160 meters. In view of the disappearing European borders we anticipate a more common strategy from the PTTs as far as power as well as band planning is concerned.

Many good operators have worked well over 100 countries on 80 and 160 meters running a barefoot rig. This is especially true on CW. But when the kilowatt station with a good antenna is squeezing a 33 or 34 report out of a VKØ station, the low-power station will stand no chance to be heard.

Fortunately most low-band buffs get involved gradually in the DX game. Together with building a better receiving system (e.g., with Beverage antennas), the need for a little more power will become apparent. One word of warning, however: efficient low-band DX antennas by definition have a low angle of radiation. The field intensities in the neighborhood of the transmitting antenna can be quite high, and as such the risks for broadcast interference (BCI) are much higher than with a high-angle radiator.

2.2. Linear Amplifiers

Today the newest technologies are utilized in receivers, transmitters and transceivers to a degree that makes competitive home construction of those pieces of equipment out of reach for but a few. Most of our high-power amplifiers still use vacuum tubes, however, and circuit integration as we know it for low-power devices has not yet come to the world of high-power amplifiers. At any major flea market it is possible to buy all the parts for a linear amplifier.

Amateur Radio has come a long way in the past 30 years, from an era where the vast majority of amateur operators used all home-made equipment, to today where all but a few use state-of-the-art, high-tech (and fortunately also high-performance) equipment. Those among us who were in Amateur Radio 30 years or more ago will remember the immense degree of satisfaction we got from building our own equipment. There are at least two areas in Amateur Radio where the DXer can still get this kind of satisfaction: building his own amplifier and building his own antennas.

Those who say that home-made amplifiers are all running illegal power and that running excessive power is the only driving force behind home-brewing an amplifier have probably never built one themselves. The home builder will usually build more reserve into his design. He will have the option himself to spend a few more dollars on metal work and maybe on a larger power supply transformer in order to have a better product that runs cool all the time and never lets him down. Maybe he will use two tubes instead of one, and run those very conservatively so that the eventual cost-effectiveness of his own design will be better than for the commercial black box.

Excellent amplifier designs have been published in the

Fig 3-14—This home-built amplifier makes use of surplus parts obtained at a hamfest.

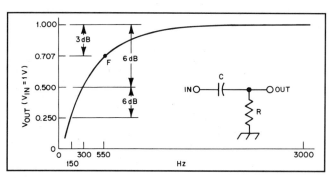

Fig 3-15—Attenuation characteristic of a single-pole high-pass RC network. The roll-off for such a filter is 6 dB per octave, which means the output is halved each time the frequency is halved. Identical sections can be cascaded (2 sections would produce 12 dB per octave).

Amateur Radio literature over the years. Very often the home builder will be driven by the availability of parts, especially final-amplifier tubes. Zero-bias triodes have become very popular over the past 25 years for linear service. The popular 811 was followed by the 872, while the 3-500Z has been holding strong for almost 20 years. The latest ceramic 3CX800, 3CX1200 and 8877 seem to be logical choices if one is prepared to buy new tubes (Ref. 337 and 342). Triodes can take quite a bit of beating. The only thing really to watch is grid dissipation. Excessive grid current and early tube failure can result if the amplifier is too lightly loaded.

Tetrodes such as the 4CX1000 and 4CX1500B can still be found at reasonable prices on the second-hand market and are excellent transmitting tubes. They need far less drive than the triodes, but require careful amplifier design and knowledgeable operation because of the very sensitive screen grid.

P. A. Johnson, W7KBE, described how to tackle the problems of part collecting and of doing the metalwork in conjunction with homebrewing of equipment (Ref. 339).

Fig 3-14 shows an example of a home-built amplifier making use of surplus parts. An important part in the amplifier is the RF switching relay. A good state-of-the-art amplifier should be able to operate in QSK (full break-in) in CW (Ref. 335). This can be achieved with vacuum relays or by PIN-diode antenna switching.

S. M. North, KG2M, described a conversion for the popular SB-200 linear amplifier to add 160-meter coverage (Ref. 341). The addition of 160 meters to the Heath SB-220 was well covered by R. L. Measures, AG6K (Ref. 340). Another excellent modification was described by R. L. Measures, AG6K, who added QSK to the popular Kenwood TL-922 amplifier (Ref. 338).

2.3. Phone Operation

If you choose to play the DX game on phone (SSB), there are a few points to pay great attention to.

2.3.1. Microphones.

Never choose a microphone because it looks pretty. Most

of the microphones that match (aesthetically) the popular transceivers have very poor audio. Most dynamic microphones have too many lows and too few highs. In some cases the response can be improved by "equalizing" the microphone output. Even if you have one of the specially designed communication microphones (e.g., Shure 444), it still may be necessary to apply some tailoring to match the microphone to your voice and the transmitter you are using. The most simple form of microphone equalization is a simple RC high-pass T-filter in the microphone lead. I have successfully matched my voice to a Shure 444 microphone and a variety of transceivers by incorporating an RC filter consisting of a 1000-pF capacitor with a 50-kΩ resistor. The 3-dB cut-off frequency is given by

$$f = \text{approximately } 3.2 \text{ kHz} = \frac{10^6}{2\pi RC}$$

where

    f = 3-dB cutoff frequency
    R = parallel arm resistor, kΩ
    C = series arm capacitor, nF

The optimum value of the capacitor can be determined by cut-and-try methods, while R should be roughly equal to the output impedance of the microphone. The curve of a single-section RC filter is given in Fig 3-15. Heil, K9EID, recognizes the problem of poor audio on our bands, and has tackled the problem by designing a multistage op-amp equalizer which really can do wonders for bad microphones and awful voices (Ref. 301 and 323).

Both lows and highs can be independently adjusted (enhanced or attenuated). The center adjusting frequencies for lows and highs are 500 and 2200 Hz, respectively.

In some cases the audio spectrum of a bad microphone can be drastically improved by changing the characteristics of the microphone resonant chamber. If the microphone has too many lows (which is usually the case), improvement can sometimes be obtained by filling the resonant chamber with absorbent foam material, or by closing any holes in the chamber (to dampen the membrane movement on the lower frequencies).

The most practical solution is to use a microphone designed for communications service. A typical communica-

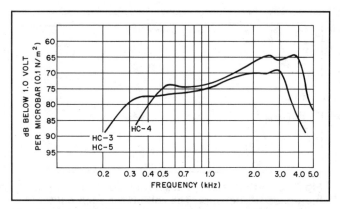

Fig 3-16—Typical response of Heil communication microphones with a 2000-ohm resistive load. Note the sharp cutoff below 300 and 500 Hz.

tions microphone should have a flat peak response between 2000 and 3000 to 4000 Hz, a smooth roll-off of about 7 to 10 dB from 2000 to 500 Hz and have a much steeper roll-off below 500 Hz. Fig 3-16 shows the typical response curve for the Heil communications microphone elements. We should caution against overkill here too, however! We know that the higher voice frequencies carry the intelligence, while the lower frequencies carry the voice power. Therefore a good balance between the lows and highs is essential for maximum intelligibility combined with maximum power.

At this point it should also be mentioned that correct positioning of the carrier crystal on the slope of the filter in the sideband-generating section of the transmitter is at least as important as the choice of a correct microphone. Therefore you should test your equalized microphone system into a good-quality tape recorder before doing the on-the-air tests. Incorrectly positioned carrier crystals will also produce bad-sounding receive audio in a transceiver, as the filter is used in both the transmit and receive chain.

One way of checking to see if the USB and LSB carrier crystals have been set to a similar point on the filter slopes is to switch the rig to a dead band, turn up the audio, and switch from USB to LSB. The pitch of the noise will be a clear indication of the carrier position on the filter slope. The pitch should always be identical on both sidebands.

As important as the choice of the microphone is the use of the microphone. Communications microphones are made to be held close to the mouth when spoken into. Always keep the microphone at maximum two inches from your lips. A very easy way to control this is to use a headset/microphone combination. The BM-10 boom set from Heil contains an HC-5 cell in a very lightweight combination that makes DXing under the most difficult circumstances a real pleasure, even over very long periods. If you do not speak closely into the microphone, you will have to increase the microphone gain, which will bring the acoustic characteristics of the shack into the picture, and they are not always ideal. We often have high background noise levels because of the fans of our amplifiers. It is this background level, and the degree to which we practice close-talking into our microphone, that will determine the maximum level of clipping we can use in a system.

2.3.2. Speech processing.

Speech processing should be applied to improve the intelligibility of the signal at the receiving station, not just to increase the ratio of average power to peak envelope power. This means that increased average power together with the introduction of lots of distortion may achieve little or nothing. Although audio clippers can achieve a high degree of average power ratio increase, the generation of in-band distortion products will raise the in-band equivalent noise power generated by harmonic and intermodulation distortion and in turn decrease the intelligibility (signal-to-noise ratio) at the receiving end.

RF clipping generates the same increase in the ratio of transmitted average power to PEP, but does not generate in-band distortion products. This basic difference eventually leads to a typical 8-dB improvement of intelligibility over AF clipping (Ref. 322). All commercial manufacturers of ham equipment realized this long ago, and virtually all the current transceivers are equipped with RF clippers.

Adjusting the speech-processor level seems to be a difficult task with some modern transceivers if you judge from what we sometimes hear on the air. Each RF clipper should have at least two controls. The first one controls the input to the clipper. Its setting will determine the amount of clipping. This control is usually called processor or PROCESSOR IN. The second gain control (sometimes called PROCESSOR OUT or DRIVE) sets the output level of the processed signal; in other words it acts as an RF-drive level control. These controls will have different names depending on the brand of transceiver. There may be a third control on some transceivers, the actual microphone gain. This gain control will be used for setting the mike level when operating without the speech processor. All modern transceivers have a compression-level indicator which is very handy in adjusting the clipping level.

We already said that the acoustics in the shack will be one of the factors determining the maximum allowable amount of speech clipping. By definition, a speech-clipped audio signal has a low dynamic range. In order not to be objectionable, the dynamic range should be kept on the order of 25 dB. This means that during speech pauses the transmitter output should be at least 25 dB down from the peak output power during speech. Let us assume we run 1400 W PEP output. A signal 25 dB down from 1400 W is just under 5 W PEP. Under no circumstances should our peak-reading wattmeter indicate more than 5 W peak (about 3 W average), or we will have objectionable background noise (Ref. 305). The clipping level should be increased by increasing the PROCESSOR IN control, until we come to the point where the shack ambient noise produces 5 W PEP maximum or where the transceiver compression level indicator indicates maximum 20 dB or whatever the manual recommends as a maximum clipping level.

The PROCESSOR OUT (DRIVE) control should only be used to obtain the correct amount of drive from the transceiver into the final or the correct amount of ALC. Never use the microphone gain or the PROCESSOR IN adjustment to adjust the drive to the final.

There is a way to completely eliminate the annoying background noise and still run a fair amount of RF clipping.

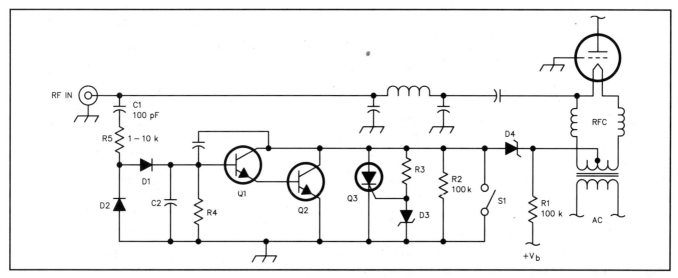

Fig 3-17—Typical electronic bias switch (EBS) for a grounded-grid amplifier.

Commercial amplifiers such as the Alpha 77DX use an electronic bias switch (EBS). By using an electronic bias switch in the linear amplifier, one can adjust the sensitivity of the switch in such a way that it does not switch on with the background noise but is turned on only when a given threshold level is exceeded. This way, we can achieve a very impressive dynamic range. The electronic bias switch is a semiconductor switch that switches the final tube(s) from the normal transmitting condition to cutoff at the rate of the modulating signal (Ref. 316 and 320). It acts as a Schmitt trigger, which means that above a certain RF drive level the switch is on and will be off for all levels below this threshold.

A well-engineered EBS circuit has a means to adjust the threshold level. In our previous example we would like to set this threshold at approximately 0.5 W PEP driver output, assuming a 10-dB-gain amplifier. The electronic bias switch has the great advantage of reducing the average power dissipation of the final tube(s). This is also the case in CW where the final tube(s) will be cut off during every key-up period.

Fig 3-17 shows a basic EBS schematic for a grounded grid amplifier. This circuit uses a voltage-doubling RF rectifier in order to achieve enough sensitivity, together with the two NPN transistors that are connected as a Darlington pair (very high gain). Typically the input transistor can be a 2N3439 or 2N3440 and the second one a 2N3902. These are all 400-volt devices. The thyristor/Zener circuit across the output transistor is the familiar crowbar protection circuit which serves to short the EBS circuit if a given voltage is reached. With R1 equal to R2, the voltage across the output transistor is normally $V_b/2$. D3 is chosen (operating voltage higher than $V_b/2$) so that it will only conduct if the collector voltage of Q2 exceeds the D3 Zener voltage. When D3 conducts, it will apply a positive voltage to the gate of Q3 and make it conduct. This is to prevent high voltage appearing on the line if for any reason R2 should open up. The sensitivity of the circuit can be adjusted by changing the value of R5. C3 is the integrating capacitor that with R6 determines the switching speed of the EBS. An MOV or Tranzorb semiconductor spike-protection

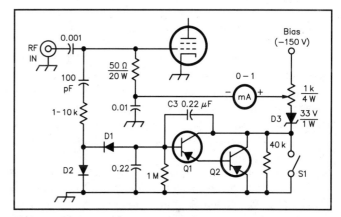

Fig 3-18—Typical EBS switch for a grounded-cathode amplifier. This particular schematic shows a passive-grid amplifier.

device can be connected across the output of the switch (between the collector and the emitter of the output transistor) for added device protection.

The EBS circuit for a grounded-cathode amplifier uses two PNP transistors as a Darlington pair or an integrated pair in one package (Fig 3-18). There is no need for the crowbar protection circuit. The bias voltage should be at least equal to the full cut-off voltage for the tube in question. D3 prevents the bias voltage from going too low (excessive plate idling current). The bias-set potentiometer is a 4-W wire-wound type. Values are typical only and may need changing for particular tubes. This circuit has been successfully used with a 4CX1000 amplifier for many years.

Fig 3-19 shows an ideal CW keying waveform at A, and at B the same output waveform from an amplifier using EBS. Notice the very steep rise and fall from zero to a voltage level B. If the voltage ratio A/B = 5 and the full power (level A) output is 1000 W, the output for level B is $1000/5^2 = 40$ W.

If the drive level for 1000 W out is 100 W, the drive level for 40 W is 4 W (if the amplifier response is linear). This is an

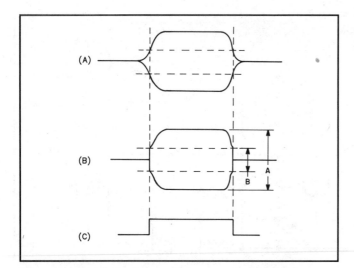

Fig 3-19—CW waveform with EBS (at A) and without EBS (at B). The trace at C shows the switching action of the EBS transistor.

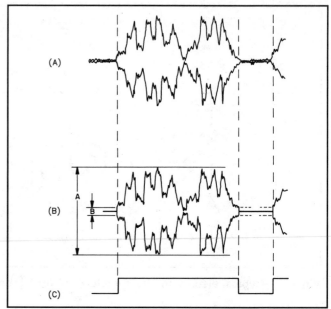

Fig 3-20—SSB output pattern from an amplifier with and without EBS. Note that the background noise noticeable on the trace at A is completely eliminated with the EBS in action, trace B. C shows the EBS transistor switching waveform.

acceptable sensitivity for the EBS circuit for CW operation (dynamic range is 10 log (1000/40) = 14 dB).

For SSB, such a sensitivity adjustment would be incorrect. The EBS circuit would have to be adjusted so the transistor switches at a lower drive level. Fig 3-20 shows a typical SSB waveform with and without EBS, in both cases with approximately 15 to 20 dB of speech processing.

The voltage ratio A/B must be approximately 18:1 in order to achieve a 25-dB dynamic range (25 dB = 20 log 18). This means that if full output power is achieved with 100 W (PEP) of drive, the EBS circuit should trip with about 0.3 W (PEP) of drive. This represents a drive voltage of approximately 4 V (peak) across a 50-ohm line. Fig 3-20C shows the envelope pattern for a properly adjusted EBS circuit and speech processor. Too much sensitivity of the EBS circuit or too much processing would show up in a rippled line on speech pauses, such as in Fig 3-20A. When the adjustment is marginal, the EBS would switch on and off randomly on background noise, which would show up as an intermittent rippled line on the scope and as a crackling, distorted noise on the air.

Always adjust the speech processor first with the amplifier on but with the EBS circuits bypassed (S1 shorted). When the correct settings of the transceiver are found to achieve at least 25 dB dynamic range, then the EBS can be switched on and the sensitivity adjusted as described above. When the EBS is properly adjusted for 15 to 20 dB of speech clipping, it is likely that with the processor switched off, the EBS circuit will switch continuously between speech syllables, which may cause a crackling sound on the transmitted audio. In that case one can switch the EBS off altogether or increase the detector time constant by changing the value of C2 in Fig 3-18 from 220 nF to 2.2 µF. A toggle switch on the amplifier front panel can allow selection of either time constant. The processor is not normally switched out altogether but rather the level is reduced to between 5 and 10 dB, in which case the EBS circuit still functions correctly and no switching effect can be heard with the shorter time constant.

2.4. CW Operation

The most important feature for a CW transmitter is the ability to work full break-in (QSK). This means that you can hear received audio between transmitted dots and dashes. Anyone who is serious about CW must have a transceiver with full QSK capabilities, or operate a separate transmitter and receiver. Before choosing a transceiver, it is interesting to get a copy of a professional review (Ref. 400-416) of the radio, so that the keying of the transceiver using high-speed QSK can be analyzed. Another equally important characteristic is the speed of the keyed antenna relay line (used to switch the antenna relay in an amplifier). The fastest system uses a solid-state keying line, but this requires that the user pay attention to correct polarity, voltage and current. For example, the early models of the Kenwood TS-930S used solid-state line keying, and the built-in timing of the unit made it possible to control an amplifier using vacuum-relay switching in full-QSK mode, without any signs of hot switching (switching the antenna relay with transmitted RF applied to it). With the TS-940S, which uses a relay output in the linear-keying line, severe hot switching occurred.

Fig 3-21 shows monitor scope displays of hot-switching amplifiers. Note the abrupt change in the waveforms for traces B and C, resulting in key clicks on the transmitted signal. Where the relay should have closed before T1, closure actually occurred at T3, and by being almost closed started arcing at T2. At T4 the relay opens, and keeps drawing arcs until T5; it should have opened after T6.

Replacing the built-in relay with a solid-state relay can solve the problem. With some equipment it will be necessary to key the amplifier first (in time sequence) and then the

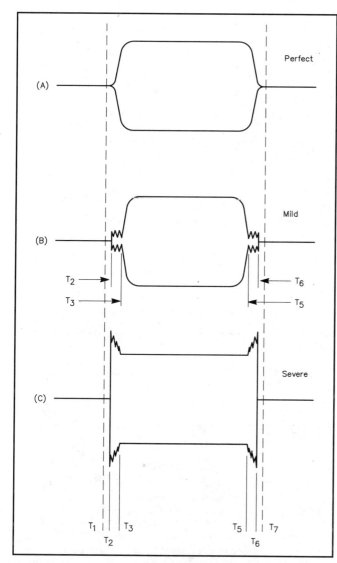

Fig 3-21—Trace A shows a perfectly shaped CW pattern. Traces B and C show both make and break hot-switching. See text for details.

exciter. A PIN diode switching system is faster than any type of mechanical relay and can bring relief. PIN diode antenna-switching systems are usually driven by a timing unit creating the correct timing relationship to switch the diodes (Ref. 318 and 326).

Keying waveform shapes can be very different from one transmitter to another. The shape should not be too soft, and neither be too hard; hard keying can cause terrible key clicks. Fig 3-22 shows photos of different keying waveforms, as well as the delays between key closure and output, for a few popular transceivers. Notice the large difference from one transceiver to another. Some radios exhibit very short dots, especially in full QSK. The shaping itself seems adequate with most radios.

2.5. DSP in the Transmitter

The newest generations of HF transceivers make extensive use of DSP technology. In the future we will certainly see more and more DSP-based gadgets in our transceivers. A few of the possible applications in the transmit chain are:

• DSP speech processing
• DSP audio tailoring (nice velvet-like audio for a rag chew, and piercing sharp quality for the contest)
• CW make and break timing (hard or soft keying)
• DSP VOX control (delayed audio switching)
• Background noise elimination (kill the noisy blower)

2.6. Monitoring Systems

It is essential that the station operator have some means of monitoring the quality of his transmission. All modern transceivers have a built-in audio monitor system which allows the operator to check the transmitted signal. It should not be a mere audio output, but should be a detected SSB signal which makes it possible to evaluate the adjustment of the speech processor. This feature allows the operator to check the audio quality and is very useful for checking for RF pickup into the audio circuits.

A monitor scope should be mandatory in any amateur station. With a monitor scope you can:

• Monitor your output waveform (envelope)
• Check and monitor linearity of your amplifier (trapezoid pattern)
• Monitor the keying shape on CW
• Observe any trace of hot-switching on QSK (CW or AMTOR)
• Check the tone of the CW signal (ripple on the power supply)
• Correctly adjust the speech processor
• Correctly adjust the drive level of the exciter in order to optimize the make and the break waveform on CW
• Adjust the sensitivity and time constant of the EBS circuit for both CW and SSB

I have been using a monitor scope for 30 years now, and without this simple tool I would feel distinctly uncomfortable when on the air. The specific monitor scopes (e.g., Yaesu, Kenwood) are rather expensive and have one distinct disadvantage: You must route the output RF from the amplifier "through" the scope to tap off some RF which is fed directly to the plates of the CRT.

After having burned out three CRT tubes in my monitor scopes, I decided to use a good second-hand professional scope (I bought a Tektronix 2213, which is a 50-MHz dual-trace scope) for the price of a brand new monitor scope. This approach gives you the advantage that you need to sample only a very small amount of RF to feed to the input of the scope. A small resistive power divider can be mounted at the output of the amplifier, from where the millivolts of sampled RF can be routed to the scope with a small coaxial cable.

2.7. Areas of Improvement

Some hams think that the new generation of transceivers should have more output than what seems to be the standard today (100 W). Well, if you really need 200 W, the FT-1000 will give you that together with an excellent receiver.

I think that the equipment designers should aim their efforts toward reducing the distortion products of the new generation of transmitters. In addition, the transmitters should

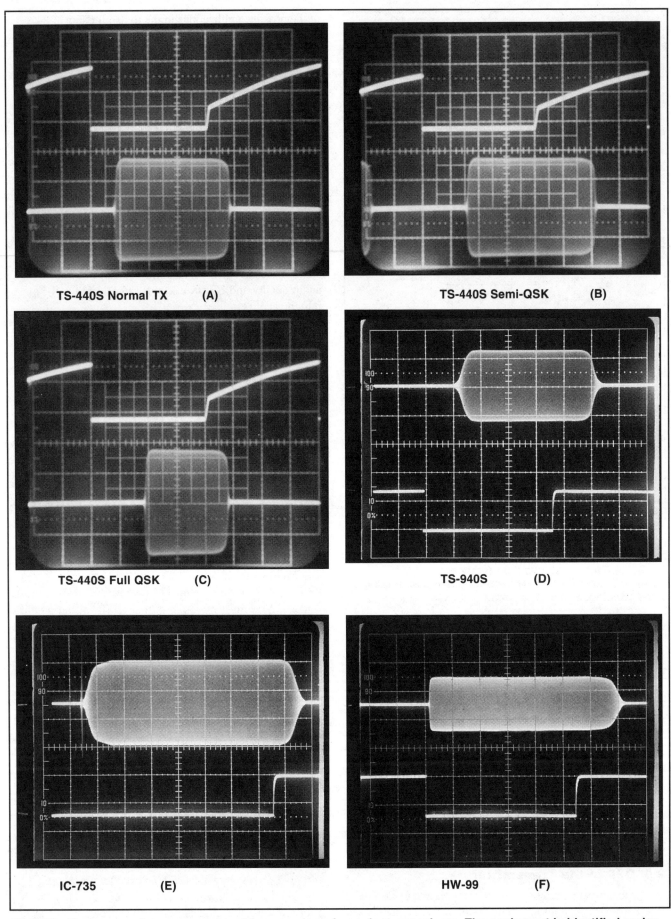

TS-440S Normal TX (A)

TS-440S Semi-QSK (B)

TS-440S Full QSK (C)

TS-940S (D)

IC-735 (E)

HW-99 (F)

Fig 3-22—Keying waveforms as produced from a range of popular transceivers. The equipment is identified under each photo.

be designed in such a way that it is virtually impossible to transmit a poor-quality signal.

DSP (digital signal processing) can be an aid in reducing the distortion products, and will probably become standard once the technology of very fast microprocessors (used in DSP) has matured further and made the technology less expensive. DSP could also be used to obtain the ideal audio response, which may be different under different circumstances (the ideal audio for contesting is different from the ideal rag-chew audio!).

The bandwidth of the transmitted signal can also be significantly reduced on some transceivers without any detrimental effect. Where 20 years ago a bandwidth of 2.1 kHz (at –6 dB) was sufficient for good quality (e.g., Collins mechanical filters), today most transceivers have a 2.7-kHz bandwidth. The audio quality may be more pleasing, but this can hardly be an acceptable reason for increasing the signal bandwidth on our crowded ham bands. A few sources (e.g., International Radio Inc, in Port St Lucie, FL) are supplying kits for popular transceivers (e.g., the Kenwood TS-940S) consisting of 2.1-kHz wide second-IF (8.8 MHz) and third-IF (455-kHz) filters which not only dramatically improve the receiver performance but also reduce the bandwidth of the transmitted signal. Using those narrow-band filters requires more critical adjustment of the carrier position on the filter slope as a function of the operator's voice and the microphone characteristics.

THE NEW LOW BAND SOFTWARE

- ■ 1. PROPAGATION SOFTWARE
- ■ 2. MUTUAL IMPEDANCE AND DRIVING IMPEDANCE
- ■ 3. COAX TRANSFORMER/SMITH CHART
- ■ 4. IMPEDANCE, CURRENT AND VOLTAGE ALONG FEED LINES
    - 4.1. Z, I and E Listing
    - 4.2. Simultaneous Voltage Listing along Feed Lines
- ■ 5. TWO- AND FOUR-ELEMENT VERTICAL ARRAYS
- ■ 6. THE L NETWORK
- ■ 7. SERIES/SHUNT INPUT L-NETWORK ITERATION
- ■ 8. SHUNT/SERIES IMPEDANCE NETWORK
- ■ 9. LINE STRETCHER (PI AND T)
- ■ 10. STUB MATCHING
- ■ 11. PARALLEL IMPEDANCES (T JUNCTION)
- ■ 12. SWR VALUE AND SWR ITERATION
    - 12.1. SWR Value
    - 12.2. SWR Iteration
- ■ 13. RADIATION ANGLE OF HORIZONTAL ANTENNAS
- ■ 14. COIL CALCULATION
- ■ 15. GAMMA/OMEGA AND HAIRPIN MATCHING
- ■ 16. ELEMENT TAPER

Yagi Design Software

- ■ 1. The Analyze Module
- ■ 2. Generic Dimensions
- ■ 3. Element Strength
- ■ 4. Element Taper
- ■ 5. Mechanical Yagi Balance
    - 5.1. Boom Strength
    - 5.2. Weight Balance
    - 5.3. Yagi Wind Load
    - 5.4. Torque Balancing
- ■ 6. Yagi Wind Area
- ■ 7. Matching
- ■ 8. Optimize Gamma/Omega
- ■ 9. Feed Line Analysis
- ■ 10. Rotating Mast Calculation
- ■ 11. Utilities
    - 11.1 Make Input Files for YO, MN or AO
    - 11.2 Your Own Database

Literature Database Software

THE NEW **4** LOW BAND SOFTWARE

The nice thing about personal computers is that everyone can now handle the difficult mathematics that are part of calculating antennas and feed lines. All you need to do is understand the question . . . and the answers. The program will do the hard mathematics for you and give you answers that you *can* understand. The theory of antennas and feed lines is not an easy subject. When it comes down to calculating antennas and feed lines, we are immediately confronted with complex mathematics—mathematics with real and imaginary parts, numbers that have a magnitude and an angle.

We have all been brought up to know how much is 5 times 4. But nobody can tell off the top of his head how much $5 - j3$ times $12 + j12$ is. At least I cannot. When I started studying antennas and wanted not only to "understand" the theory, but also to be able to calculate things, I was immediately confronted with the problem of complex mathematics. That's where the computer came to my aid. While studying the subject I wrote a number of small computer programs that were meant as calculating aids. They have since evolved to quite comprehensive engineering tools that should be part of the software library of every serious antenna builder. The NEW LOW BAND SOFTWARE also includes a number of low-band dedicated propagation programs.

The NEW LOW BAND SOFTWARE is based on the original "Low Band DXing Software" which I wrote in the mid 1980s, while preparing the original *Low Band DXing* book. The new software is a very much enhanced version of the original software, and it also contains numerous new programs. In addition it was written to be much more user friendly. The full-color software is now available only in MS-DOS on a single high-density 3½ inch diskette.

NEW LOW BAND SOFTWARE

Each of the modules starts with a complete introduction (on screen), telling what the software is meant to do, and how to use it. All propagation-related programs are integrated into a single module. Also new are the many help screens in each of the modules. They explain what the program does, how the questions should be answered, and how the final results should be interpreted.

■ 1. PROPAGATION SOFTWARE

The propagation software module is covered in detail in the chapter on propagation. It contains a low-band dedicated sunrise/sunset program and a gray-line program, based on a comprehensive database containing coordinates for over 550

locations, and which can be user changed or updated. The database can contain up to 750 locations.

■ 2. MUTUAL IMPEDANCE AND DRIVING IMPEDANCE

From a number of impedance measurements you can calculate the mutual impedance and eventually, knowing the antenna currents (magnitude and phase), you can calculate the driving impedance of each element of an array with up to 4 elements.

■ 3. COAX TRANSFORMER/SMITH CHART

The original software covered only ideal (lossless) cables. Now there are two versions of the program: for lossless cables and for "real" cables (cables with losses). The real cable program will tell you everything about a feed line. You can analyze the feed line as seen from the generator (transmitter) or from the load (antenna). Impedance, voltage and currents are shown in both rectangular coordinates (as real and imaginary part) or in polar coordinates (as magnitude and phase angle). You will see the Z, I and E values at the end of the line, the SWR (at the load and at the generator), as well as the loss—divided into cable loss and SWR loss.

A number of "classic" coaxial feed lines with their transmission parameters (impedance, loss) are part of the program, but you can specify your own cable as well. Try a 200-ft RG-58 feed line on 28 MHz with a 2:1 SWR and compare it to a ¾-inch Hardline with the same length and SWR, and find out for yourself that a "big" coax is not necessarily there for power reasons. It makes no sense throwing away 2 or 3 dB of signal if you have to spend a lot of effort in building a top performance antenna. This program lets you juggle with facts and figures without any hassle. If you are going to design your own array, you will probably use this software module more than any other.

■ 4. IMPEDANCE, CURRENT AND VOLTAGE ALONG FEED LINES

Again, there are two versions of each module: loss free, and "real" cable.

4.1. Z, I and E Listing

A coaxial cable, when not operated as a "flat" line (SWR greater than 1:1) acts as a transformer: The impedance, current and voltage are different in each point of the cable.

You enter the feed-line data (impedance, attenuation

data), the load data (impedance and current or voltage), and the program will display Z, I and E at any point of the cable.

4.2. Simultaneous Voltage Listing along Feed Lines

This module was written especially as a help for designing a KB8I feed system for arrays. The program lists the voltage along feed lines. This allows the user to find points on the feed lines of individual array elements where the voltages are identical. These are the points where the feed lines can be connected in parallel (see chapter on arrays). This program is also helpful to see how high the voltage really rises on your feed line with a 4.5:1 SWR, for example.

■ 5. TWO- AND FOUR-ELEMENT VERTICAL ARRAYS

These two completely new modules take you step by step through the theory and the practical realization of a 2-element (cardioid) or 4-element (4-square) array, using the W7EL feed system. This tutorial and engineering program uses graphic displays to show the layout of the antenna with all the relevant electrical data. This unique module is extremely valuable if you want to understand arrays and if you are tempted to build your own array with a working feed system. These modules require a VGA display.

■ 6. THE L NETWORK

The L network is the most widely used matching network for matching feed lines and antennas. The module gives you all the L-network solutions for a given matching problem. The software also displays voltage and current at the input and output of the network, which can be valuable in assessing the component ratings of the network.

■ 7. SERIES/SHUNT INPUT L-NETWORK ITERATION

This module was written especially for use in the K2BT array matching system, where L networks are used to provide a given voltage magnitude at the input of the network, given an output impedance and output voltage. See Chapter 11 on phased arrays for details.

■ 8. SHUNT/SERIES IMPEDANCE NETWORK

This is a simplified form of the L network, where a perfect match can be obtained with only a series or a shunt reactive element. It is also used in the modified Lewallen phase-adjusting network with arrays that are not quadrature fed (see Chapter 11 on vertical arrays).

■ 9. LINE STRETCHER (PI AND T)

Line stretchers are constant-impedance transformers that provide a required voltage phase shift. These networks are used in specific array feed systems (modified Lewallen method) to provide the required phase delay. See Chapter 11 on vertical arrays for details.

■ 10. STUB MATCHING

Stub matching is a very attractive method of feed-line matching. This module describes the method of matching a feed line to a load using a single stub placed along the transmission line. The program is very handy for making a stub matching system with an open-wire line feeding a high-impedance load (2000 to 5000 ohms).

■ 11. PARALLEL IMPEDANCES (T JUNCTION)

This very simple module calculates the resulting impedance from connecting in parallel a number of impedances (do you really want to calculate on your calculator what $21 - j34$ and $78 + j34$ ohms are in parallel?).

■ 12. SWR VALUE AND SWR ITERATION

12.1 SWR Value

This module calculates the SWR (eg, the SWR with a load of $34 - j12$ ohms on a 75-ohm line). The mathematics are not complicated, but it's so much faster with the program (and error free!).

12.2. SWR Iteration

This module was especially developed for use when designing a W1FC feed system for an array (the hybrid coupler). See Chapter 11 on arrays for details.

■ 13. RADIATION ANGLE OF HORIZONTAL ANTENNAS

This module calculates and displays the vertical radiation pattern of single or stacked antennas (fed in phase).

■ 14. COIL CALCULATION

With this module you can calculate single-layer coils and toroidal coils. It works in both directions (coil data from required inductance, or inductance from coil data).

■ 15. GAMMA/OMEGA AND HAIRPIN MATCHING

This module is a simplified version of one of the modules of the YAGI DESIGN software (see information later in this chapter). Given the impedance of a Yagi and the diameter of the driven element (in the center), you can design and prune a gamma or omega match and see the results as if you were standing on a tower doing all the pruning and tweaking.

■ 16. ELEMENT TAPER

Antennas made of elements with tapering diameters show a different electrical length than if the element diameters had a constant diameter. This module calculates the electrical length of an element (quarter-wave vertical or half-wave dipole) made of sections with a tapering diameter. A modified W2PV tapering algorithm is used.

The NEW LOW BAND SOFTWARE is available in MS-DOS format on a single 3½-inch disk from:

J. Devoldere, ON4UN, Poelstraat 215, B9820 Merelbeke, Belgium, or from G. Oliva, K2UO, 5 Windsor Dr, Eatontown, NJ 07724.

Price: $50 + $5 for shipping and handling worldwide. Prepayment only, US bank check or international money order. An order form can be detached from the back of this book. If you have the original version of the LOW BAND SOFTWARE, you are eligible for a $10 price reduction, provided you send a copy of the registration form that came with the software, with your order.

YAGI DESIGN SOFTWARE

Together with Roger Vermet, ON6WU, I have written a number of software programs dealing with both the electrical and the mechanical design of monoband Yagis. These programs were used for the Yagi designs presented in Chapter 13 on Yagis and quads.

The 3-element 40-meter Yagi that I have been using since 1989, as well as all my other HF band Yagis, have been designed with the YAGI DESIGN software. The 40-meter Yagi was instrumental in setting two all-time European records in the 1992 ARRL CW and Phone contest on 40 meters. KS9K, one of the top US midwest contest stations, has been using designs from this software program to rebuild the entire antenna farm.

YAGI DESIGN is a multifunctional software package that will take the user through *all* the aspects of Yagi designing (mechanical as well as electrical). It is *not* a modeling program, but is based on a comprehensive database containing all the dimensional and performance data for 100 different HF Yagis (2 to 6 elements). The database contains approximately 20 reference designs by W6SAI, W2PV, N2FB etc, while the majority are newly designed Yagis with a range of properties that are well described in a manual which is available with the software. The literature standards are included so that the user has a known base of reference to compare the new designs. Most of the new designs were verified by either modeling them on a scale frequency (72 MHz) or by making full-size HF-band models.

The YAGI DESIGN database has a Yagi for *every* application: from low to high-Q, contest, CW only, SSB only, narrow band, wide band, gain optimized, F/B optimized, etc. One of the software modules also allows you to create text (ASCII) input files for the MN, AO and YO modeling programs. This allows you to further change and manipulate any of the designs from the system database.

The mechanical design modules are based on the latest issue of the EIA/TIA-222-E standard, which is a much upgraded version of the older, well known EIA RS-222-C specification. The "cross flow principle" is used to determine the effect of wind on a Yagi. Most amateur literature, as well as amateur mechanical design software, uses the principle of "variable area," which has no scientific grounds (see Chapter 13 on Yagis and quads).

The YAGI DESIGN software consists of several modules, which are briefly described. Each time you leave a module, you can save the results in a work file that you can recall from any other module. You can also view the contents of the work file at any time, using the VIEW DATA FILES module.

■ 1. The Analyze Module

Unless you are very familiar with the content of the database, it would take you a long time to browse through all the performance and dimensional data to make your choice. The main-menu option PRINT DATABASE prints out the content of the entire database, either in a tabular format (only the key characteristics) or it can generate a full-blown data sheet for all the Yagis (with two designs per printed page, that represents a little booklet of 50 pages).

In the ANALYZE module you can specify some key characteristics such as boom length (expressed in either wavelengths, feet or meters), minimum gain, minimum F/B, maximum Q factor, etc. The software will automatically select the designs that meet your criteria.

■ 2. Generic Dimensions

Select the SELECT DESIGN module. After having chosen a proper design from the system database, the screen will display all the data relevant to this design—gain, F/B, impedance, etc, on the design frequency and 6 other frequencies spread up to +1.5 and –1.5% of the design frequency.

You must now enter the design frequency (eg, 14.2 MHz). The screen now displays all the generic dimensions of the Yagi for the chosen design frequency. "Generic" means that the element lengths given in inches as well as centimeters are valid for an element diameter-to-wavelength ratio of 0.0010527. These are not the dimensions we use for constructing the Yagi, as the element will be made of tapered sections. The screen display also shows the amount of reactance that the driven element has on the design frequency. The element positions as listed are those that will be used in the final physical design.

■ 3. Element Strength

Before we calculate the actual lengths of Yagi elements with tapering sections, we must first see which taper we will use. What are the required diameters and taper schedule that will provide the required strength at minimal cost, weight and element sag?

The ELEMENT STRENGTH module helps you build elements of the required strength at a minimum weight. Up to 9 sections of varying diameters can be specified (that's enough sections even for an 80-meter Yagi). Given the lengths (and overlap) of the different sections and the wall thicknesses as entered from the keyboard, the program calculates the bending moments at the critical point of every section. The module lets you specify wind speeds and ice loading as well as a vibration-suppression internal rope and several types of aluminum material.

■ 4. Element Taper

It's time now to calculate the exact length of the tapered elements. We follow the taper schedule we obtained with the ELEMENT STRENGTH module. An improved version of the well-known W2PV algorithm is used to calculate the exact length. A wide range of boom-to-element clamps (flat, square, L, rectangular, etc) can be specified. These clamps influence the eventual length of the tapered elements.

■ 5. Mechanical Yagi Balance

This mechanical design module performs the following tasks.

5.1 Boom strength

This routine calculates the required boom diameter and wall thickness. An external sleeve (or internal coupler) can be defined to strengthen the central part of the boom. If the boom is split in the center, the sleeve or the coupler will have to take the entire bending moment.

Material stresses at the boom-to-mast plate are displayed. Any of the dimensional inputs can be changed from the keyboard, resulting in an instantaneous new display of the changed stress values.

5.2 Weight balance

Many of the newer computer optimized Yagis have non constant element spacing, and hence the weight is not distributed evenly along the two boom halves. The WEIGHT BALANCE section shifts the mast plate (attachment point) on the boom until a perfect weight balance is achieved. It is nice to have a weight-balanced Yagi when laboring to mount it on the mast!

5.3 Yagi wind load

The program calculates the angle at which the wind area and wind load are largest. In most literature the wind area and wind load are specified for a wind angle of 45 degrees (a wind blowing at zero degree angle is a wind blowing along the boom; at 90 degrees it blows right onto the boom). This is incorrect, because the largest wind load *always* occurs either with the boom broadside to the wind *or* with the elements broadside to the wind. With large low-band antennas, it is likely that the elements broadside to the wind (wind angle equal to zero degrees) produces the largest wind thrust. With higher frequency long-boom Yagis having many elements (eg, a 5- or 6-element 10- or 15-meter Yagi), the boom is likely to produce more thrust than the elements.

The wind load is calculated in increments of 5 degrees, given a user-specified wind speed.

5.4. Torque balancing

Torque balance ensures that the wind does not induce any undue torque on the mast. This can only be achieved by a symmetrical boom moment. When the boom-to-mast plate is not at the center of the boom, a "boom dummy" will have to be installed to compensate for the different wind area between the two boom halves. The program calculates the area and the position of the boom dummy, if required.

■ 6. Yagi Wind Area

Specifying the wind area of a Yagi is often a subject of great confusion. Wind thrust is generated by the wind hitting a surface, exposed to that wind. The force is the product of the dynamic wind pressure multiplied by the exposed area, and with a so-called drag coefficient, which is related to the *shape* of the exposed body. The "resistance" to wind of a flat body is obviously different from the resistance of a round-shaped body. This means that if we specify or calculate the wind area of a Yagi, we must always specify if this is the equivalent wind area for a flat plate (which should be the standard) or if the area is simply the sum of the projected

areas of all the elements (or the boom). In the former case we must use a drag coefficient of 2.0 according to the latest EIA/TIA-222-E standard, while for (long and slender) tubes a coefficient of 1.2 is applicable. This means that for a Yagi which consists only of tubular elements, the flat-plate wind area will be 66.6% lower (2.0/1.2) than the round-element wind area.

The WIND AREA module calculates both the flat-plate wind area and the round-element wind area of a Yagi.

■ 7. Matching

The software provides three widely used matching systems: gamma, omega and hairpin. When choosing the gamma or omega system, you will be asked to enter the antenna power, as the program will calculate the voltage across and current through the capacitor(s) used in the system. If no match can be found with the given element length and diameter as well as gamma (omega) rod diameter and spacing (eg, very low radiation resistance and not enough negative reactance), then the program leaves you the choice of either changing the physical dimensions of the components (diameter of rod and rod-to-element spacing in order to change the system step-up ratio) or to shorten the element length to introduce some negative feed-point reactance (see above). In all cases a match will be found.

With a hairpin match the procedure is even simpler. The program will tell you exactly how much you will have to shorten the driven element (from the length shown in the table under "generic dimensions") and how long the hairpin should be.

The program also lists the matching data over a total frequency range of 3% (from −1.5 to +1.5% versus the design frequency, in 0.5% steps). These data include antenna impedance before matching, antenna impedance after matching, and SWR value. These data are very important for assessing the bandwidth characteristics of the antenna.

■ 8. Optimize Gamma/Omega

Maybe you would like to see if other dimensions (lengths, spacings, diameters) of your gamma (omega) system would result in more favorable matching-system components? Maybe you would like to "balance" the SWR curve? Most (not all) Yagis show an intrinsic asymmetric SWR curve, which means that the SWR rises faster above the design frequency than below. If you want to have the same SWR values on both band ends, it is obvious that the SWR will not be 1: at the center frequency. The OPTIMIZE GAMMA/OMEGA module allows you to change any of the matching-system variables while immediately observing the results of the output impedance and the SWR value. You can also change from gamma to omega and vice versa. Changing the variables from the keyboard simulates tuning the Yagi in practice. The module is also very well suited for "balancing" the SWR over a given frequency range.

■ 9. Feed Line Analysis

When designing a Yagi, you *must* have a look at the feed line as well. It makes no sense to build an optimized long Yagi, where every inch of metal in the air contributes to gain (and F/B) and then to throw *half of the boom length* away by using a mediocre, lossy feed line.

The FEED LINE ANALYSIS module assesses the performance of the feed line when connected to the Yagi under design. The characteristics of the most current 50-ohm coaxial cables are part of the software (from RG-58 to ⅞-inch Hardline), but you may specify your own (exotic) cable as well.

■ 10. Rotating Mast Calculation

A weak point in many Yagi installations is the rotating mast. The MAST module calculates the stresses in the rotating mast for a mast holding up to ten stacked antennas.

■ 11. Utilities

11.1. Make input files for YO, MN or AO

The popular Yagi modeling programs YO (Yagi Optimizer), MN (MININEC) and AO (Antenna Optimizer) by Beezley (K6STI) require data inputs in the form of a text file (ASCII file). The YAGI DESIGN software package contains a program which automatically creates a text input file of the correct format for YO, MN or AO.

In the case of MN you can also specify a stack of two antennas that are identical (and fed in phase), or different (eg, a 15-meter and a 10-meter Yagi). In this way you can model any of the 100 designs of the database in either YO or MN without having to type those horrible text-input files where you're bound to make errors.

11.2. Your own database

If you'd like to add your own designs, the software package has provided an empty database that can contain up to 100 records (Yagis). The OWNDATA module is used to enter all the dimensional and performance data in the database.

The YAGI DESIGN software is available in MS-DOS format on a single 3½-inch disk from:

J. Devoldere, ON4UN, Poelstraat 215, B9820 Merelbeke, Belgium, or from G. Oliva, K2UO, 5 Windsor Dr, Eatontown, NJ 07724, USA.

Price: $65 + $5 for shipping and handling worldwide. Prepayment only, US bank check or international money order. An order form can be detached from the back of this book.

LITERATURE DATABASE SOFTWARE

This is a dedicated database program, designed to handle literature review. The code is written in HAP91, which is a unique database creation program developed by H. Schampheleer, ON6HS. The database is outstanding in speed and possibilities. Only a very minor part of the possibilities are used in this simple application.

If you like to keep track of the articles and books covering your favorite subject, this program comes in very handy. The manuscript printout for Chapter 14, Literature Review, was generated with this literature database program. Because of the great flexibility and performance of the program, I decided to make it available to the readers.

As supplied, the literature database program can handle two files:
- The generic database which contains all the data concerning the articles and books as listed in the Literature Review chapter of this book.
- A customer database which contains no records, and which can be used by the customer to create his or her own database.

There is no limitation as to the number of records the files can contain. As supplied, the generic file contains 760 records.

Each record has the following fields:
1) Title of article.
2) Name of author.
3) Name of publication.
4) Date of publication.
5) Page.
6) Subject: There are 16 different subject groups (see the chapter on Literature Review).
7) Reference number (this is the literature reference number used in the text of this book).
8) A field, 114 characters long, can be loaded with keywords, which can be used in addition to the "meaningful" words of the Title and Author field to select records.
9) Comments: A special field (comment field) can contain a text of up to 256 characters. It is provided for the user to write his or her comments on the subject article or book.

From the menu the user can:
1) Add records, keywords and comments.
2) Change records, keywords and comments.
3) Select a record by record number.
4) Select records by keywords (any word in the Title or Author fields plus any word from the "free keyword" field).
5) Make printouts in tabular form, selected and sorted in different ways:
- Selected by subject (sorted by reference number).
- Selected by subject (sorted by title).
- Selected by author name (sorted by title).
- Selected by publication (sorted by title).
- Selected by keyword (sorted by title).
- All records sorted by author name (secondary sorting by title).
- All entries sorted by subject (secondary selection by reference number).
- All entries sorted by title (secondary sorting by magazine).

The LITERATURE DATABASE SOFTWARE is available in MS-DOS format on a single 3½-inch disk from:

J. Devoldere, ON4UN, Poelstraat 215, B9820 Merelbeke, Belgium, or from G. Oliva, K2UO, 5 Windsor Dr, Eatontown, NJ 07724.

Price: $20 + $5 for shipping and handling worldwide. Prepayment only, US bank check or international money order. An order sheet can be detached from the back of this book.

ANTENNAS: INTRODUCTION AND DEFINITIONS

■ 1. THE PURPOSE OF AN ANTENNA

1.1. Transmitting Antennas

1.1.1. Wanted direction.

1.1.1.1 *Horizontal directivity.*

1.1.1.2. *Vertical directivity.*

- *40 meters*
- *80 meters*
- *160 meters*

1.1.2. Efficiency.

1.2. Receiving Antennas

■ 2. DEFINITIONS

2.1. The Isotropic Antenna

2.2. Antennas in Free Space

2.3. Antennas over Ground

2.4. Antenna Gain

2.5. Front-to-back Ratio

- *Geometric front-to-back*
- *Average front-to-back (integrated front-to-back)*
- *Worst lobe front-to-back*
- *Front-to-back and gain*

2.6. Radiation Resistance

2.7 Antenna Efficiency

2.8. Standing-wave Ratio

2.9. Bandwidth

2.10. Q-factor

2.10.1. The tuned circuit equivalent.

2.10.2. The transmission-line equivalent.

- *Surge Impedance.*

■ 3. ANTENNA MODELING

1. MININEC-based programs.

- *How it works.*
- *The limitations of MININEC.*

2. The NEC modeling program.

ANTENNAS: INTRODUCTION

AND DEFINITIONS

Before we get involved in the debate on what's the best antenna for the low bands (that must be the key question for most), we must agree on some terms and definitions.

We must also define what we want the antenna to do for us, and how we will measure its performance.

Antennas for the low bands are one of the areas in Amateur Radio where home building will yield results that can substantially outperform what can be obtained from commercially available antennas.

All my antennas are homemade. Visitors often ask me "Where do you buy the parts?", or "Do you have a machine-shop to do all the mechanical work?" Very often I don't "buy" the parts. And no, I don't have a machine shop, just the run-of-the-mill hand tools. But my friends who are antenna builders and I keep our eyes open all the time for goodies that might be useful sometime for our next antenna project. There is a very active swap activity between us. Among friends we have access to certain facilities that make antenna building easier. It's almost like we are a team where each one of us has his own specialization.

Don't look at low-band antenna designing and building as a kit project. It requires know-how, imagination, inventiveness and often a good deal of organizational talent. But unlike the area of receivers and transmitters, where as home-builders most of us do not have access to the custom-designed integrated circuits and other very specialized parts, antennas and antenna systems are built using materials that can be found locally by most of us.

Antennas are one field in Amateur Radio where the old pioneering spirit of the spark age of Amateur Radio is still alive. The most outstanding low-band antenna systems are the ones that came about through hard work and brilliant engineering done by small groups of highly engaged individuals.

A number of successful major low-band antennas are described in this book. These are not meant to be "kit-like" building projects with step-by-step instructions, but are there to stimulate thinking and put the newcomer to antenna building on the right track.

The ARRL Antenna Book (Ref. 600) contains a wealth of excellent and accurate information on antennas. The antenna chapters of this book emphasize typical aspects of low-band antennas, and explain how and why some of the popular antennas work and what we can do to get the best results given our particular constraints.

■ 1. THE PURPOSE OF AN ANTENNA

1.1. Transmitting Antennas

A transmitting antenna must radiate all the RF energy supplied to it in the desired direction with the required elevation angle (directivity).

1.1.1. Wanted direction.

1.1.1.1 *Horizontal directivity.*

The chapter on propagation shows that most of the propagation paths are rectilinear paths (great circle, short path, and so on) for short and medium distances (up to 10,000 km or 6000 miles). We also know that for areas near the antipodes the propagation path can vary almost over a 180 degree angle with season (see Chapter 1 on propagation). All this must be taken into account when designing an antenna system. Rotary systems will provide a great deal of flexibility as far as horizontal directivity is concerned. Here it must be emphasized that the term *horizontal directivity* is really meaningless without further definition. Zero wave angle directivity (perfectly parallel to the horizon) is of very little use, as practical antennas produce no signal at zero wave angle over real ground. Horizontal directivity should always be specified at a given elevation angle. An antenna can have quite different azimuthal directional properties at different elevation angles.

1.1.1.2. *Vertical directivity.*

Very little has been published in amateur literature on optimum wave angles for given paths on the lower bands. Results of tests between England and North America have been extrapolated and are given in Table 5-1. This gives us no information about 160 meters.

Most of the professional literature deals with research near the MUF. For commercial links it is most advantageous to operate near the MUF. In our hobby, when working DX on

5-1

Table 5-1

Angle of Arrival of Signals Between England and North America

Freq (MHz)	Probability <99%	Probability >99%	Probability >50%
7.0	<37°	>11°	>22°
3.5	<53°	>13°	>33°

the low bands, we are certainly not operating near the MUF under most circumstances. We operate far below the MUF and FOT, and in many cases near the LUF (lowest usable frequency).

Contrary to popular belief, it is not true that the lower the angle, the better. A ⅝-wavelength vertical that can produce a very low angle of radiation (as low as 10 degrees over a very good ground) is not a good antenna for 80 meters. It produces too low an angle of radiation for most DX paths. There is a range of optimum radiation angles for different directions and different paths, and they are not the same for the three lower bands.

From experience, the author has learned that the following factors influence the optimum wave angle:

- Time of day.
- MUF at the path ends.
- Time of year.
- Propagation near, through, or into auroral zones.
- Propagation into equatorial zones.

40 meters

As we will see in more detail in this chapter, horizontally polarized antennas (dipoles, inverted-V dipoles, Yagis, etc.) at heights that produce good low-angle radiation will be within reach of all but the most causal DXers. A height of ½ wavelength (21 m or 70 ft) produces a single vertical radiation lobe with an angle of approximately 28 degrees, and an antenna at that height will certainly play well under most circumstances. The most "serious" DXers will have their beams at 30 to 40 m (100 to 130 ft), in order to get a little lower radiation angle and get the extra edge on the very long paths where the extra few degrees of low-angle radiation will pay off. On the shorter paths (e.g., European East Coast), antennas that are high are likely to be inferior to their counterparts at ½ wavelength, however.

80 meters

Of the three low bands, 80 meters is the band where the influence of the above-mentioned factors seems to be most pronounced. Maybe it's because I have had most first-hand experience over the past 30 years with different antennas producing different radiation angles.

- East-west propagation during the night for distances shorter than 6000 km or 3700 miles: 35 to 45 degrees.
- Same paths at dusk and dawn: 20 to 40 degrees.
- Long distances at dusk or dawn (6000 to 20,000 km or 3700 to 12,400 miles): 15 to 25 degrees.
- Paths into or near the (active) aurora zone: 15 to 25 degrees (also for distances as short as 1600 km or 1000 miles).
- Paths into the equatorial zone: 35 to 60 degrees.

It should be clear that in no case is an angle higher than 50 degrees required for an effective DX antenna.

160 meters

On 160 meters, most of us have the choice between an antenna that shoots straight up (a horizontal dipole or inverted-V dipole even at 30 m or 100 ft height will produce a 90-degree radiation angle, so will be of little value in producing a good DX signal), and a vertical (it may be shortened) that produces a good low radiation angle (20 to 40 degrees depending on the ground quality). This means we have little chance to experience the differences in signal strength between different radiation angles. But let it be clear: The lower angles (20 to 40 degrees) are what we want for DXing on 160 meters. *All* good DX signals on top-band are produced by vertical antennas.

1.1.2. Efficiency.

The efficiency of a transmitting antenna is simply the ratio of power radiated from an antenna to the power applied to it. Any energy that is not radiated will be converted into heat in the lossy parts of the antenna.

1.2. Receiving Antennas

For a receiving antenna, the requirements are different. Here we expect the antenna to receive only signals from a given direction and at a given wave angle (directivity), and we expect the antenna to produce signals which are substantially stronger than the internally generated noise of the receiver, taking into account losses in matching networks and feeders. This means that the efficiency of a receiving antenna is not the main requirement. An important asset of a good receiving antenna system is the ability to change directions very rapidly. In practice, this can only be obtained by switching between a number of unidirectional antennas or by using an array of phased verticals, where the directions can be changed by switching the feed current (magnitude and angle) in the array elements.

In most amateur applications, the transmitting antenna is used as the receiving antenna, and the transmitting requirements of the antenna outweigh the typical receiving requirements. On the low bands, however, generous use is made of special receiving antennas, as we will see in Chapter 7 on Special Receiving Antennas.

■ 2. DEFINITIONS

2.1. The Isotropic Antenna

An isotropic antenna is a theoretical antenna of infinitely small dimensions that radiates an equal signal in all directions. This concept can be illustrated by a tiny light bulb placed in the center of a large sphere (see Fig 5-1). The lamp illuminates the interior of the sphere equally at all points. The isotropic antenna is often used as a reference antenna for gain comparison, expressed in decibels over isotropic (dBi). The radiation pattern of an isotropic antenna is a sphere, by definition.

2.2. Antennas in Free Space

Free space is a condition where no ground or any other conductor interacts with the radiation from the antenna. In practice, such conditions are approached only in VHF and UHF, where very high antennas (in wavelengths) are common. Every real-life antenna has some degree of directivity and, if placed in the center of a large sphere, illuminates certain portions better than others. In antenna terms: The antenna radiates energy better in certain directions. A dipole has

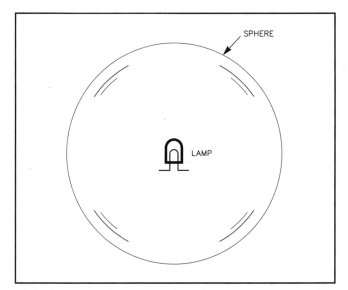

Fig 5-1—In this drawing the isotropic antenna is simulated by a small lamp in the center of a large sphere. The lamp illuminates the sphere equally well at all points.

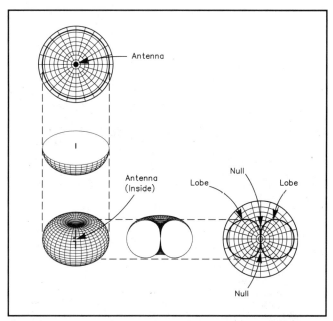

Fig 5-2—The three dimensional radiation pattern (the radiation body) is most frequently reduced to a set of two 2-dimensional radiation patterns. In this example we have obtained two patterns by cutting the radiation body by two planes. One is the plane through the wire; the other one is perpendicular to it. Over ground these patterns are often called horizontal and vertical radiation patterns.

maximum radiation at right angle to the wire, and minimum off the ends. Such a dipole, in free space, has a gain of 2.15 dB over isotropic.

The radiation body of an antenna is the collection of all points with equal field strength. Radiation patterns are collections of all points in a given plane, having equal field strength. Fig 5-2 shows the radiation pattern of a dipole in free space, seen three dimensionally and in two planes, the plane through the wire and the plane perpendicular to the wire.

2.3. Antennas over Ground

In real life, antennas will be near the ground. We can best visualize this situation by cutting the sphere in half with a metal plate going through the center of the sphere. This plate represents the ground, a perfect electrical mirror. Fig 5-3 shows what happens with an antenna near the ground: Direct and reflected waves will combine and illuminate the sphere unequally in different points at different angles. For certain angles the direct and reflected waves will be in phase and will reinforce one another. The field is doubled, which means a gain of 3 dB. In addition, we have only a half sphere to "illuminate" with the same power, and that provides another 3 dB of gain. This means that a dipole over perfect ground will have 6 dB of gain over a dipole in free space.

Over ground the radiation patterns are often identified as vertical (cutting plane perpendicular to the ground) or horizontal (cutting plane parallel to the ground). The latter is of very little use, as practical antennas over real ground produce no signal at zero wave angle. The so-called horizontal directivity should in all practical cases be specified as directivity in a plane making a given angle with the horizon (usually the main wave angle).

Low-band antennas always involve real ground. With real ground, the above-mentioned gain of 6 dB will be low-

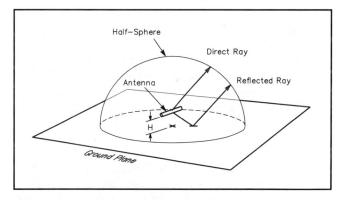

Fig 5-3—The effect of ground is simulated in a sphere by putting a plate (the reflecting ground plane) through the center of the sphere. As the power in the antenna is now radiated in half the sphere volume, the total radiated field in the half sphere is doubled. This means that the ground reflection can add up to 6 dB of signal increase as compared to free space. A smaller total gain is caused in practice, as part of the RF energy is absorbed in the (poorly reflecting) ground.

ered, as part of the RF will be dissipated in the lossy ground. For evaluation purposes, we often use perfect ground, a ground consisting of an infinitely large, perfect reflector. Real grounds have varying properties, in both conductivity and dielectric constant. In this chapter, frequent reference will be made to different qualities of real grounds, as shown in Table 5-2.

Table 5-2

Conductivities and Dielectric Constants for Common Types of Earth.

Surface Type	Dielectric Constant	Conductivity (mS / m)	Quality
Fresh water	80	1.0	
Salt water	81	5000.0	Sea water
Pastoral, low hills, rich soil (typ Dallas, TX to Lincoln, NE areas)	20	30.3	Very good
Pastoral, low hills, rich soil (typ OH, IL)	14	10.0	Good
Flat country, marshy, densely wooded (typ LA nr MS river)	12	7.5	
Pastoral, medium hills and reforestation (typ MD, PA and NY, exclusive of mtns and coastline)	13	6.0	
Pastoral, medium hills and forestation, heavy clay soil (type central VA)	13	5.0	Average
Rocky soil, steep hills (typ mountainous areas)	12-14	2.0	Poor
Sandy, dry flat, coastal	10	2.0	
Cities, industrial areas	5	1.0	Very poor
Cities, heavy industrial	3	0.1	Extremely poor

These definitions are used throughout this book.

2.4. Antenna Gain

The gain of an antenna is a measure of its ability to concentrate radiated energy in a given direction. Antenna gain is expressed in decibels, abbreviated dB. It tells us how much the antenna in question is better than a reference, under certain circumstances. And that's where we enter the antenna gain jungle. Commonly, both the isotropic as well as the "real" dipole are used as reference antennas. In the former case the gain is expressed as dBi, in the latter as dBd. But that's only part of the story. We can do this comparison in free space, or over perfect or over real ground. The only situation that makes generic comparison possible is to compare in free space. The dBi in free space is what can always be compared; there is no inflation of gain figures by reflection. Very often manufacturers of commercial antennas will calculate gains including ground reflections, and often not mention that at all. In this publication we will always quote gain figures in dBi. (Ref. 688).

You might argue why not use a real antenna, such as a dipole, as a reference, since the isotropic antenna is a theoretical antenna that does not exist, while a half-wave dipole does. Comparing gains is really comparing the field strength of the antenna under investigation with that of our reference antenna. With the isotropic antenna the situation is clear: It radiates equally well in all directions, and the three-dimensional radiation pattern is a sphere. What about the dipole as a reference? The gain of a half-wave dipole in free space over an isotropic is 2.15 dB(i). But that does not mean that a "real" dipole has a gain of 2.15 dBi. It only means that the gain of a dipole in free space (that's an unreal condition as well, because nothing is really in free space) is 2.15 dB over an isotropic radiator. If we put the dipole over a perfect ground, it suddenly shows a gain of 8.15 dBi! You pick up 6 dB by radiating the power in half a hemisphere instead of a whole hemisphere as in the theoretical case of free space. With less than perfect ground, part of the power will be absorbed in the ground and the ground reflection gain will be less than 6 dB. It is clear that the only generic way of comparing antenna gains is in dBi, the isotropic antenna being the only generic reference antenna that is not influenced by height or ground conditions.

2.5. Front-to-back Ratio

Being a ratio (just like gain), we would expect front-to-back to be expressed in decibels, which it is. The front-to-back ratio (F/B) is a measure expressing an antenna's ability to radiate a minimum of energy in the back direction of the antenna.

Free-space front-to-back ratio is always measured at a zero-degree wave angle. Over ground the F/B depends on the vertical radiation angle being considered. In most cases a horizontal radiation pattern over real ground is not really the pattern in the horizontal plane, but in a plane which corresponds with the main wave angle. If we look at the back lobe at that angle, it may be okay, but at the same time there may be a significant back lobe at a much different angle.

Geometric front-to-back

In the past, front-to-backs were usually defined in the sense of a geometric front-to-back: the radiation 180 degrees off the front (lobe) of the antenna. At the same time we compare the "forward" power at the main (forward) radiation angle, with the power radiated at the same wave angle in the backward direction.

Front-to-back is a property we are making use of in the real world to discriminate against unwanted signals coming from "other" directions. It is very unlikely that unwanted signals will be generated exactly 180 degrees off the beam direction or at a radiation angle which is the same as the main forward lobe radiation angle. Therefore, the geometric F/B can be ruled out immediately as a meaningful way of defining the antenna's ability to discriminate against unwanted signals.

Average front-to-back (integrated front-to-back)

The average front-to-back can be defined as the average value of the front-to-back as measured (or computed) over a given back angle (both in the horizontal as well as the vertical plane).

Worst lobe front-to-back

Probably the most meaningful way of defining front-to-back is as the ratio of the forward power to the power in the "worst" lobe in the entire back of the antenna.

Front-to-back and gain

Is there a link between gain and the front-to-back ratio of an antenna? Let's visualize a three-dimensional radiation pattern of a (simple) Yagi. The front lobe resembles a long stretched pear, the back lobe (let's assume for the time we have a single back lobe) a (much) smaller pear. The antenna sits where the stems of the two pears touch. The volume of the two pears (the total volume of the three-dimensional radiation pattern) is determined only by the power fed to the antenna. If you increase the power, the volume of the large as well as the small pear will increase in the same proportion. Let's take for definition of front-to-back the ratio of the power radiated in the back versus the power radiated in the front. This means that the F/B ratio is proportional to the ratio of the volume of the two pears.

By changing the design of the Yagi (by changing element lengths or element positions), we will change the size and the shape of the two pears, but as long as we feed the same power to it, the sum of the volumes of the two pears will forever remain unchanged. It's as if the two pear-shaped bodies are connected with a tube, and are filled with a liquid. By changing the design of the antenna, we merely push liquid from one pear into the other. If the antenna were isotropic, the radiation body would be a sphere having the volume of the sum of the two pears.

Assume we have 100 watts of power with 10% of this power applied to the antenna in the back-lobe. The F/B ratio will be $10 \times \log (10 / 1) = 10$ dB. Ninety percent of the applied power is available to produce the forward lobe.

Let's take a second case, where only 0.1% of the applied power is in the back lobe. The F/B ratio will be $10 \times \log (100 / 0.1) = 30$ dB. Now we have 99.9% of the power available in the front lobe.

The antenna gain realized by having 99.9 watts instead of 90 watts in the forward lobe is 10 log (99.9 / 90) = 0.45 dB. Pruning an antenna with a modest F/B pattern (10 dB) to a supreme 30 dB value, "can" give us 0.45 dB more forward gain, provided that the extra liquid is used to lengthen the cone of the big pear.

The mechanism of obtaining gain and F/B is much more complicated than that described above. I am only trying to explain that optimizing an antenna for F/B does not necessarily mean that it will be optimized for gain. What is always true is that a high-gain antenna will have a narrow forward lobe. You cannot concentrate energy in one direction without taking it away from other directions! We will see later that maximum-gain Yagis show a narrow forward lobe, but often a poor front-to-back. This is the case with very high-Q gain-optimized 3-element Yagis.

Conclusion: There is no simple relationship between front-to-back ratio and gain of an antenna.

2.6. Radiation Resistance

Radiation resistance (referred to a certain point in an antenna system) is the resistance which, inserted at that point, would dissipate the same energy as is actually radiated from the antenna. This definition does not state where the antenna is being fed, however. There are two common ways of specifying radiation resistance:

• The antenna being fed at the current maximum $R_{rad\,(I)}$.

• The antenna being fed at the base between the antenna lower end and ground $R_{rad\,(B)}$.

$R_{rad(I)} = R_{rad\,(B)}$ for verticals of $\frac{1}{2}$ wavelength or shorter. $R_{rad(B)}$ is the radiation resistance used in all efficiency calculations for vertical antennas. Fig 9-10 shows the radiation resistance according to both definitions for four types of vertical antennas:

• a short vertical (<90 degrees)
• a quarter-wave vertical
• a $\frac{3}{8}$-wave vertical (135 degrees)
• a $\frac{1}{2}$-wave vertical

2.7 Antenna Efficiency

The efficiency of an antenna is expressed as follows:

$$Eff = R_{rad} / (R_{rad(B)} + R_{loss})$$

where $R_{rad(B)}$ is the radiation resistance of the antenna as defined in Section 2.5, and R_{loss} is the total equivalent loss resistance of all elements of the antenna (resistance losses, dielectric losses, ground losses, etc.).

2.8. Standing-wave Ratio

Standing-wave ratio (SWR) is a measure of how well the feed-point impedance of the antenna is matched to the characteristic impedance of the feed line. If a 50-ohm feed line is terminated in a 50-ohm load, then the impedance at any point of the cable, thus also the impedance at the end of a cable (of any length), is 50 ohms.

If the same feed line is terminated in an impedance different from 50 ohms, the impedance will vary along the line. The SWR is a measure of the match between the line and the load. Changing the length of a feed line does *not* change anything regarding the SWR on the line (apart from minute changes due to the feed-line loss). The only thing that changes is the impedance at the input end of the line.

If changing the line length (slightly) changes the SWR reading on your SWR meter, then your SWR meter is not measuring correctly (many SWR meters fall into this category). It is a good test for an SWR meter to insert short cable lengths between the end of the antenna feed line and the SWR meter (a few feet at a time). If the SWR reading changes, throw away the meter, or just use it as a relative output and SWR indicator, but don't use it expecting to obtain correct SWR values.

Only when we have currents on the outside of the coaxial cable shield can a change in position on the line change the SWR reading (see Chapter 6). That's why we need a balun when feeding balanced feed points with a coaxial cable.

Changing the feed-line length never changes the performance of the antenna. SWR has no relation whatsoever to the radiation characteristics of an antenna.

A perfect match results in a 1:1 SWR. What are the reasons we like a 1:1 SWR or the lowest possible SWR value?

• *Showing a convenient impedance*: It is clear that we would like to live in a world where, unless we want to use the line as an impedance transformer, we would like all feed lines to show a 1:1 SWR. This would be perfect as far as presenting the ideal load impedance (50 ohms) for transistor-final transceivers.

• *Minimizing losses*: All feed lines have inherent losses. This loss is minimal when the feed line is operated as a flat line (SWR = 1: 1) and increases with the SWR value. On the low bands this will seldom be a criterion for working with a very low SWR, because the nominal losses on the low frequencies are quite negligible, unless very long lengths are used.

The SWR value describes the relationship between the antenna (the load) and the feed line. It does not describe an intrinsic (radiation) property of the antenna.

SWR is, for many hams, the only property they can measure. Measuring gain and F/B with any degree of accuracy is beyond the capability of most. That is why most hams pay attention only to SWR properties.

The amount of SWR that can be tolerated on a line depends on:

• additional attenuation caused by SWR; in other words the quality of the feed line. A good quality feed line can tolerate more SWR from an additional loss point of view than a mediocre quality line.

• how much SWR the transceiver or linear amplifier can live with.

• how much power we will run into a line of given physical dimensions (for a given power, a larger coax will withstand a higher SWR without damage than a smaller one).

It must be said that a poor quality line (a "small" cable with high intrinsic losses), when terminated with a load different from its characteristic impedance, will show at the input end a lower SWR value than if a good (low loss, big) cable is used. Remember that a very long poor (having high losses) coaxial cable, whether terminated, open or shorted at the end, will exhibit a 1:1 SWR at the input (a perfect dummy load).

From a practical point of view an SWR limit of 2:1 is usually employed. It is clear that, from a loss point of view, higher values can easily be tolerated on low frequencies. Coaxial feed lines used in the feed systems of multi-element arrays sometimes work with an SWR of 10:1!

An antenna tuner can always be used if near the band edges the SWR value is such that the transceiver or the amplifier would rather see a lower value (usually above 2:1). Remember that the antenna tuner will not change the SWR on the line; it will merely transform the impedance existing at the line input and present the transceiver (linear) with a "reasonable and more convenient" SWR value. While this approach is valid on the low bands, I strongly suggest not using it on the higher frequencies, as the additional line losses caused by the SWR can become quite significant.

2.9. Bandwidth

The bandwidth of an antenna is the difference between the highest and the lowest frequency on which a given property exceeds or meets a given performance mark. This can be gain, front-to-back ratio or SWR. In this book, "bandwidth" refers to SWR bandwidth unless otherwise specified. In most cases the SWR bandwidth is determined by the 2:1 SWR points on the SWR curve. In this text the SWR limits will be specified

when dealing with antenna bandwidths. Many amateurs only think of SWR bandwidth when the term bandwidth is being used. In actual practice, the bandwidth as referred to other properties is at least as important if not more important. Consider a dummy load which has a very "good" SWR bandwidth, but a very poor gain (does not radiate at all!).

Bandwidth is an important performance criterion on the low bands. The relative bandwidth of the low bands is large compared to the higher HF bands. Special attention must be given to all bandwidth aspects, not only SWR bandwidth.

2.10. Q-factor
2.10.1. The tuned circuit equivalent.

An antenna can be compared to a tuned LCR circuit. The Q factor of antenna is a measure of the SWR bandwidth of an antenna. The Q factor is directly proportional to the difference in reactance on two frequencies around the frequency of analysis, and inversely proportional with the radiation resistance and relative frequency change.

$$Q = \frac{|X1 - X2|}{2 \times R \times \Delta F}$$

where

X1 = reactance at the lower frequency
X2 = reactance at the higher frequency
R = average value of resistive part of feed-point impedance at frequencies of analysis ($R_{rad} + R_{losses}$)
F = relative frequency change between the higher and the lower frequency of analysis

Example:

F_{low} = 3.5 MHz
F_{high} = 3.6 MHz
$\Delta F = (3.6 - 3.5) / 3.55 = 0.028$
R_{feed}(aver) = 50 ohms

X1 = –20 ohms
X2 = +20 ohms

$$Q = \frac{|20 - (-20)|}{2 \times 50 \times 0.028} = 14.3$$

It is clear that a low Q can be obtained through:

• a high value of radiation resistance
• high loss resistance
• a flat reactance curve

An antenna with a low Q will have a large SWR bandwidth, and an antenna with a high Q will have a narrow SWR bandwidth. Antenna Q factors are used mainly to compare the (SWR) bandwidth characteristics of antennas.

2.10.2. The transmission-line equivalent.

A single-conductor antenna (vertical or dipole) with sinusoidal current distribution can be considered as a single-wire transmission line on which a number of calculations can be done, just as on a transmission line.

Surge Impedance.

The characteristic impedance of the antenna seen as a

transmission line is called the *surge impedance* of the antenna.

The surge impedance of a vertical is given by:

$$Z_{surge} = 60 \times \ln\left[\frac{4h}{d} - 1\right]$$

where

h = antenna height (length of equivalent transmission line)

d = antenna diameter (same units)

The surge impedance of a dipole is:

$$Z_{surge} = 276 \times \log\left[\frac{S}{d \times \sqrt{1 + \frac{S}{4h}}}\right]$$

where

S = length of antenna

d = diameter of antenna

h = height of antenna above ground

Q-factor

The Q-factor of the transmission-line equivalent of the antenna is given by:

$$Q = \frac{Z_{surge}}{R_{rad} + R_{loss}}$$

Example 1:

A 20-m (66 ft) vertical with OD = 5 cm (1.6 inches), and $R_{rad} + R_{loss}$ = 45 ohms.

$$Z_{surge} = 60 \times \ln\left[\frac{4 \times 2000}{5} - 1\right] = 443 \text{ ohms}$$

Q = 443/45 = 9.8

Example 2:

A 40-m (131 ft) long dipole, at 20 m (66 ft) height is made of 2 mm OD wire (AWG 12). The feed-point impedance is 75 ohms.

$$Z_{surge} = 276 \times \log\left[\frac{4000}{0.2 \times \sqrt{1 + \frac{4000}{4 \times 2000}}}\right] = 1163 \text{ ohms}$$

Q = 1163 / 75 = 16

■ 6. ANTENNA MODELING

Until recently, predicting antenna performance was more a black art than a scientific or engineering activity, especially in Amateur Radio circles. That was also the era when some of the old myths were born and that the rat-race for decibels was started.

One of the first Yagi modeling programs that was reported in the literature was written in 1965 by J. L. Morris for his PhD dissertation at Harvard University. Others (Mailloux, Thiele, Cheng and Cheng) have elaborated on these programs to perform further analysis and optimization.

Such a program was used by Hillenbrand (N2FB) to optimize Yagis. This program was later adapted for use on the IBM PC by Michaelis (N8ATR).

1. MININEC-based programs.

Today, every more or less serious amateur who has any interest in antenna building has a PC and a copy of MININEC (or derivative programs such as MN and ELNEC), the ever so popular antenna modeling program. MININEC (Mini Numerical Electromagnetic Code) was developed at the NOSC (Naval Ocean Systems Center) in San Diego by J. C. Logan and J. W. Rockway. The newest version of the software (MININEC3 at this writing) is public-domain software and can be obtained with the documentation from the NTIS, US Department of Commerce, 5285 Port Royal Rd, Springfield VA 22161, order no. ADA 1811681.

The technical reference, describing the program (The New MININEC, version 3: A Mini Numerical Electromagnetic Code, NOSC TD 938), is available from the NTIS as well. Order document no. ADA 181682. A fee is charged for the program and its documentation.

The original MININEC is not a user-friendly program. Several hams have written the necessary pre- and post-processing codes to make MININEC a user-friendly and powerful modeling tool.

The most popular version is the version known as ELNEC (developed by R. Lewallen, W7EL, and available directly from W7EL, PO Box 6658, Beaverton, OR 97007). Another version is known as MN (by B. Beezley, K6STI, 3532 Linda Vista Dr, San Marcos, CA 92069). Both are regularly advertised in the major Amateur Radio magazines.

How it works.

In MININEC the user splits up all the conductors (called wires) of an antenna into more or less short segments. During modeling, the HF current in each segment is kept constant (one current segment equals a pulse). The program calculates the self impedance and the mutual impedances for each of the pulses, as well as the field created by the contribution from each pulse with its self impedance and range of mutual impedances. I explain what mutual impedance is in Chapter 11 on arrays. The user can specify where he wants to excite the antenna (the source) and, if he wants, can put loads (eg, loading coils, capacitor, tuned circuits, resistors, etc) anywhere in the antenna. Modeling can be done in free space, over perfect ground or over real ground.

Specific modeling issues, such as the required segment length, the segment length tapering technique, etc, are covered in specific antenna chapters (Verticals, Dipoles, Yagis and Quads) where relevant.

The limitations of MININEC.

The major limitation concerns calculations over real ground. The real-ground modeling capability is limited to modeling far-field patterns. In the near field (right near the antenna), a perfectly conducting ground is assumed.

Some of the consequences are:

• You cannot use MININEC to calculate the influence of

radials on the feed-point impedance of a ground-mounted vertical. A quarter-wave vertical will yield a 36-ohm impedance over any type of ground. In reality the ground and the radials in the near field are important in collecting the return currents. This will influence the feed-point impedance and the efficiency of the antenna due to "lost return currents" in a poor ground. Radials can be specified with MININEC, but they will influence only the low-angle reflection-attenuation in the far field (in the Fresnel Zone). See Chapters 8 and 9 on dipole antennas and vertical antennas for details.

• The reported gain as well as the impedance of horizontally polarized antennas at low heights are incorrect. By low I mean less than 0.25 wavelength above ground for dipoles. For larger antennas the minimum height may be higher. At lower heights the reported gain will be too high and the feed-point impedance too low. The shape of the radiation patterns will remain correct, however.

This means that we have a certain handicap when using MININEC on the low bands, as very often we will be modeling antennas under the conditions specified above. As long as we know the limitations, and how to interpret the results, all is okay.

For modeling antennas such as Yagis on the higher frequency bands, this is unlikely to be a problem. There are other modeling problems with quads. These are covered in Chapter 13 on Yagis and Quads.

These and other limitations are very well covered in good detail by R. Lewallen in "MININEC: the other edge of the sword" (Ref. 678).

2. The NEC modeling program.

NEC is the full-fledged brother of MININEC, which means that NEC also employs the method of moments to model antennas. The original versions ran on main-frame computers only, and were accessible to professionals only. The latest version of NEC has always been classified material, as it still is today. Recently, however, older versions have become available that run on AT-type computers.

NEC2 will also model real ground in the near field. It will do away with the limitation I explained for MININEC. It can model radials above and on the ground. NEC3 will in addition model buried radials.

The NEC programs are programs intended for the professionals. Modeling runs can be very time consuming unless you run a 486 machine at 50 MHz or better.

I have frequently used NEC to model antennas where the limitation of MININEC would have made the results unreliable. When dealing with the different antennas, I will come back on specific modeling issues for that specific antenna.

THE FEED LINE AND THE ANTENNA

■ **1. PURPOSE OF THE FEED LINE**

■ **2. FEED LINES WITH SWR**

  • *Conjugate match*

  2.1. The Coaxial Cable Case

  2.2. The Open-Wire Case

  2.3. The Loss Mechanism

  2.4. The Universal Transmission Line Program

  2.5. Conclusions

■ **3. THE ANTENNA AS A LOAD.**

■ **4. THE MATCHING NETWORK AT THE ANTENNA**

  4.1. Quarter-wave Matching Sections

  4.2. The L Network

   4.2.1. Component ratings

    • *Capacitors*

    • *Coils*

    • *The smoke test*

  4.3. Stub Matching

   4.3.1. Replacing the stub with a discrete component

   4.3.2. Matching with series-connected discrete
    components

  4.4. High-impedance Matching System

  4.5. Wideband Transformers

   4.5.1. Low-impedance wideband transformers

   4.5.2. High-impedance wideband transformers

■ **5. 75-OHM CABLES IN 50-OHM SYSTEMS**

■ **6. THE NEED FOR LOW SWR**

■ **7. THE BALUN**

■ **8. BROADBAND MATCHING**

THE FEED LINE 6 AND THE ANTENNA

*T*he feed line is the inevitable link between the antenna and the transmitter/receiver.

It may look strange that I cover feed lines and antenna matching before discussing any type of antenna. The reason is that I want to make clear that antenna matching has no influence on the characteristics or the performance of the antenna itself. Antenna matching is something generic, which means that any matching system can in theory be used with any antenna. Antenna matching must therefore be treated as a separate subject.

The following topics are covered:

- *coaxial lines, open-wire lines*
- *loss mechanism*
- *real needs for low SWR*
- *quarter-wave transformers*
- *L networks*
- *stub matching*
- *wide-band transformers*
- *75-ohm feed lines in 50-ohm systems*
- *baluns*

Before we discuss antennas from a more or less theoretical point of view and describe practical antenna installations, let us analyze what matching the antenna to the feed line really means and how we can do it.

■ 1. PURPOSE OF THE FEED LINE

The feed line "transports" RF energy from a source to a load (e.g., from a transmitter to an antenna).

A feed line, when terminated in a resistor having the same value as its own characteristic impedance, will operate under ideal circumstances: The line will be "flat"; there will be no standing waves on the line. The value of the impedance will be the same in each point of the line. If the feed line were lossless, the magnitude of the voltage and the current would also be the same along the line. The only thing that would change is the phase angle of these values, and the phase angle would be directly proportional to the line length. All practical feed lines have losses, however, and the values of current and voltage decrease along the line in an exponential way.

In our real world the feed line will rarely if ever be terminated in a load ensuring a 1:1 SWR. Since the line is most frequently terminated in a load with a complex impedance, in addition to acting as a transport vehicle for RF energy, the feed line will also act as a transformer, whereby the impedance (also the voltage and current) will be different at each point

along the line. A feed line working under these circumstances is not "flat," but has standing waves.

Besides transporting energy from the source to the load, feed lines can also be used to supply feed current to the elements of an antenna array, whereby the characteristics of the feed lines (with SWR) will be used to supply current at each element with the required relative magnitude and phase angle. This application is covered in detail in Chapter 11, Vertical Arrays.

■ 2. FEED LINES WITH SWR

The typical characteristics of a line with SWR are:

- the impedance in every point of the line is different; the line acts as an impedance transformer. (While the impedances in a lossless line repeat themselves every half wavelength, the impedances in a real-earth lossy line do not repeat.)
- the voltage and the current in every point of the feed line are different.
- the losses of the line are higher than for a flat line

Most transmitters, linears and transceivers are designed to work into a nominal impedance of 50 ohms. Although they will provide a conjugate match to a range of impedances which are not too far from the 50-ohm value (e.g., within the 2:1 SWR circle on the Smith Chart), it is generally a proof of good engineering and workmanship that an antenna, on its design frequency, shows a 1:1 SWR on the feed line. This means that the feed-point impedance of the antenna must be "matched" to the characteristic impedance of the line at the design frequency. The SWR bandwidth of the antenna will be determined in the first place by the Q factor of the antenna, but the bandwidth will be largest if the antenna has been matched to the feed line (1:1 SWR) at some (the design) frequency within that passband, *unless* special broadband matching techniques are employed. This means we want a low SWR for convenience reasons: We don't want to be forced to use an antenna tuner between the transmitter and the feed line in order to obtain a conjugate match.

Conjugate match

A conjugate match is a situation where all power is effectively coupled from the transmitter into the line, and where the wave, reflected from the load (antenna) back to the transmitter due to SWR is reflected back toward the load again. A conjugate match is automatically achieved when we match the transmitter for maximum power transfer into the line. In transmitters or amplifiers using vacuum tubes, this is done by properly adjusting the common pi or pi-L network. Modern transceivers with fixed-impedance solid-state amplifiers do not have this flexibility, and an external antenna tuner will be required in most cases if the SWR is higher than 1.5:1 or 2:1. Many of the present-day transceivers have built-in antenna tuners that automatically take care of this situation.

But this is not the main reason for low SWR. The above reason is a *"reason of convenience."* The real reason is one of *losses or attenuation.* A feed line is usually made of two conductors with an insulating material in between. Open-wire feeders and coaxial feed lines are the two most commonly used types of feed lines.

2.1. The Coaxial Cable Case

Coaxial feed lines are by far the most popular type of feed lines in amateur use, for one specific reason: Due to their coaxial (unbalanced) structure, all magnetic fields caused by RF current in the feed line are kept *inside* the coaxial structure. This means that a coaxial feed line is totally "inert" from the outside, when terminated in an unbalanced load (whether it has SWR or not). An unbalanced load is a load where one of the terminals is grounded. This means you can bury the coax, affix it on the wall, under the carpet, tape it to a steel post or to the tower without in any way upsetting the electrical properties of the feed line. Sharp bending of coax should be avoided, however, to prevent impedance irregularities and permanent displacement of the center conductor caused by cable dielectric heating and induced stresses. A minimum bending radius of five times the cable outside diameter is a good rule of thumb for coaxial cables with a braided shield.

Like anything exposed to the elements, coaxial cables deteriorate with age. Under the influence of heat and ultraviolet light, some of the components of the outer sheath of the coaxial cable can decompose and migrate through the copper braid into the dielectric material, causing rapid degradation of the cable. Ordinary PVC jackets used on older coaxial cables (RG-8, RG-11) showed migration of the plasticizer into the polyethylene dielectric. Newer types of cable (RG-8A, RG-11A, RG-213 and so on) use non contaminating sheaths that greatly extend the life of the cable.

Also, coaxial cables love to drink water! Make sure the end connections and the connectors are well sealed. Because of the structure of the braided shield, the interstices between the inner conductor insulation and the outer sheath will literally suck up liters (quarts) of water, even if only a pin hole is present. Once water has penetrated the cable, it is ruined. Here is one of the big advantages of the larger coaxial cables using expanded polyethylene and a corrugated solid copper outer conductor: As the PE sticks (bonds) to the copper, water penetration is impossible even if the outer jacket is damaged.

It is always a good idea to check the attenuation of feed lines at regular intervals. This can easily be done by opening the feed line at the far end. Then feed some power into the line through an accurate SWR meter (such as a Bird wattmeter), and measure the SWR at the input end of the line. A lossless line will show infinite SWR (Ref. 1321). From the measured value the attenuation of the line can be deduced using the graph in Fig 6-1. It will often be difficult to do this test at low

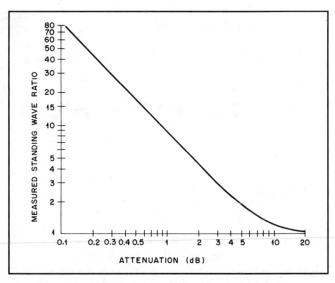

Fig 6-1–Cable loss as a function of SWR measured at the input end of an open- or short-circuited feed line. For best accuracy, the SWR should be in the 1:1 to 4:1 range.

frequencies because the attenuation on the low bands is such that accurate measurements are difficult. For best measurement accuracy the loss of the cable to be measured should be in the order of 2 to 4 dB (SWR between 2:1 and 4:1). The test frequency can be chosen accordingly. Use a professional type SWR meter such as a Bird wattmeter. Many of the cheaper SWR meters are very inadequate.

2.2. The Open-wire Case

Even when properly terminated in a balanced load, an open-wire feeder will exhibit a strong RF field in the immediate vicinity of the feed-line (try a neon bulb close to an open-wire feeder with RF on it!). This means you cannot "fool around" with open-wire feeders as you can with coax. During installation the necessary precautions should be taken to preserve the balance of the line: The line is to be kept away from conductive materials, etc. In one word, generally it's a nuisance to work with open-wire feeders.

But apart from this mechanical problem, open-wire feeders outperform coaxial feed lines in all respects on HF (VHF/UHF can be another matter).

2.3. The Loss Mechanism

The intrinsic losses of a feed line are caused by two mechanisms:

- conductor losses (losses in the copper conductors)
- dielectric losses (losses in the dielectric material)

An excellent insulator is (dry) air. From that point of view the open-wire line is unbeatable. Coaxial feed lines generally use polyethylene as a dielectric, or polyethylene mixed with air (cellular PE or foam PE). Cables with foam or cellular PE have lower losses than cables with solid PE. They have the disadvantage of potentially having less mechanical (impact and pressure) resistance. Cell-flex cables using a solid copper

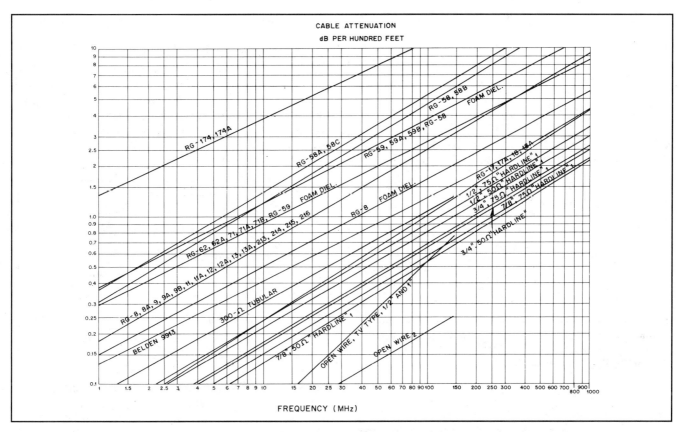

CABLE ATTENUATION
dB PER HUNDRED FEET

Fig 6-2–Nominal attenuation characteristics in dB per 100 ft (30.48 m) for various commonly used transmission lines.

or aluminum outer conductor are the top-of-the line coaxial feed lines used in amateur applications. Sometimes Teflon is used as dielectric material. This material is mechanically very stable and electrically very superior, but very expensive. Teflon-insulated coaxial cables are often used in baluns. (See par. 7.)

Coaxial cables generally come in two impedances: 50 and 75 ohm. For a given cable (outer) diameter, 75-ohm cable will show the lowest losses. That's why 75 ohm is always used in systems where losses are of primary importance, such as CATV. If power handling is the major concern, a much lower impedance is the optimum (35 ohms). The standard of 50 ohms has been created as a good compromise between power handling and attenuation.

Fig 6-2 shows the typical flat-line attenuation characteristics for many commonly used transmission lines. Note how the open-wire line outperforms even the biggest coaxial brother by a large margin. But these attenuation figures are only the "nominal" attenuation figures for lines operating with a 1:1 SWR.

When there are standing waves on a feed line, the voltage and the current will be different in every point on the line. Current and voltage will change periodically along the line and can reach very high values at certain points (antinodes). The feed line uses dielectric (insulating) and conductor (mostly copper) materials with certain physical properties and limitations. The very high currents in the antinodes along the line will be responsible for extra conductivity-related losses. The

voltages associated with the voltage antinodes will be responsible for increased dielectric losses. This is the mechanism that makes a line with a high SWR have more losses than the same line when matched. Fig 6-3 shows the additional losses caused by SWR. By the way, the losses of the line are the reason why the SWR we measure at the input end of the feed line (in the shack) is always lower than the SWR at the load.

The extreme example is that of a very long cable, having a loss of at least 20 dB, where you can either short or open the end and in both cases measure a 1:1 SWR at the input. Such a cable is a perfect dummy load!

We understand by now that for a transmission line to operate successfully under high SWR, we need a low-loss feed line with good dielectric properties and high current-handling capabilities. The feeder which has such properties is the open-wire feeder. Air makes an excellent dielectric, and the conductivity can be made as good as required by using heavy gauge conductors. Good-quality open-wire feeders have always proved to be excellent as feed-line transformers. Elwell, N4UH, has described the use and construction of homemade, low-loss open-wire transmission lines for long-distance transmission (Ref. 1320). In many cases, the open-wire feeders are used under high SWR conditions (where the feeders do not introduce many additional losses) and are terminated in an antenna tuner. Fig 6-2 shows the additional losses due to standing waves on a transmission line. On the low bands, the extra losses caused by SWR are usually negligible (Ref. 1319, 322), especially for good-quality coaxial cables.

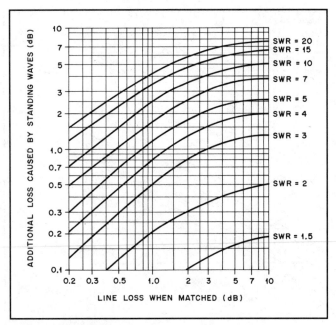

Fig 6-3–This graph shows how much additional loss occurs for a given SWR on a line with a known (nominal) flat-line attenuation.

2.4. The Universal Transmission Line Program

The UNIVERSAL TRANSMISSION LINE computer program, which is part of the NEW LOW-BAND SOFT-WARE, is an ideal tool for evaluating the behavior of feed-lines under any circumstance.

Let us analyze the case of a 50-m (164 ft) long RG-213 coax, feeding an impedance of 36.6 ohms (without matching network). The frequency is 3.5 MHz.

Fig 6-4 shows the screen print obtained from the UNI-VERSAL SMITH CHART module which is part of the NEW LOW BAND SOFTWARE. All the operating parameters are listed on the screen: impedance, voltage and current at both ends of the line, as well as the attenuation data split in nominal coax losses (0.61 dB) and losses due to SWR (0.03 dB). We also see the real powers involved. In our case we need to "pump" 1734 W into the 100-m long RG-213 cable to obtain 1500 W at the load, which represents a total efficiency of 86%. Note also the difference in SWR at the load (1.4:1) and at the feed line end (1.3:1). For higher frequencies, longer cables or higher SWR values, this software module is a real eye-opener.

G. E. Myers, K9CZB, has described a computer program for the Commodore C64 that calculates the essential line parameters (Ref 1349).

2.5. Conclusions

Coaxial lines are generally used when the SWR is less than 3:1. Higher SWR values can result in excessive losses when long runs are involved, and also in reduced power-handling capability. Many of the popular low-band antennas have feed-point impedances which are reasonably low, and can result in an acceptable match to either a 50- or a 75-ohm coaxial cable.

In some cases we will intentionally use feed lines with high SWR as part of a matching system (e.g., stub matching) or as a part of a feed-system for a multi-element phased array.

Let us conclude that it is good engineering practice to use a feed line with the lowest possible attenuation (in a concept

```
  7921              UNIVERSAL  SMITH   CHART  PROGRAM              on4un
   CALCULATING THE IMPEDANCE AT THE END OF COAX, KNOWING THE LOAD (ANTENNA) DATA.

   Z-CABLE: 50.0 ohm         VELOCITY FACTOR: 0.66              FREQ:  3.500 MHz
   WAVELENGTH = 85.66 METERS.                  WAVELENGTH IN CABLE = 56.53 METERS
   CABLE LENGTH =   50.00 m.   or     164.0 feet   or      318.4 deg  or    5.56 Rads
   TOTAL FLAT CABLE ATTENUATION =  0.49 dB      or       0.057 NEPERS

                     RECTANGULAR COORDINATES        POLAR COORDINATES
                     REAL PART      IMAG PART     MAGNITUDE       ANGLE
   IMPEDANCE (ohm) =    36.60          0.00          36.60        0.00      A
   CURRENT (Amp)   =     6.40          0.00           6.40        0.00      N
   VOLTAGE (Volt)  =   234.31          0.00         234.31        0.00      T

   IMPEDANCE (ohm) =    46.63        -13.04          48.42      -15.63      E
   CURRENT (Amp)   =     4.99         -3.36           6.02      -33.91      N
   VOLTAGE (Volt)  =   189.07       -221.67         291.35      -49.54      D

   POWER INTO COAX   =  1688.37 W.
   POWER INTO LOAD   =  1500.07 W.                   EFFICIENCY =   88.85 %
   TOTAL SYSTEM LOSS =   188.29 W.  (- 0.51 dB)      INPUT SWR =    1.3/1
   FLAT COAX LOSS    =   180.88 W.  (- 0.49 dB)      SWR AT LOAD =   1.4/1
   SWR COAX LOSS     =     7.42 W.  (- 0.02 dB)

   H:HELP   X:EXIT   R=RUN   Z=Z-ant   I=I-ant   F=Feedl   V=V.fact   A=Att/Fq   L=Lgth
```

Fig 6-4–Example of screen display of the UNIVERSAL SMITH CHART, a module of the NEW LOW BAND SOFTWARE that covers all technical aspects of a transmission line. See text for details.

of money versus performance) and that we want it to operate at a unity SWR at the design frequency of our antenna system.

■ 3. THE ANTENNA AS A LOAD

It has been proved that very small antennas are able to radiate the supplied power as efficiently as much larger ones (see Chapter 9 on vertical antennas). Small antennas have two disadvantages, however. On one hand, since their radiation resistance is very low, the antenna efficiency will be lower than it would be if the radiation resistance were much higher. If the short antennas are to be loaded along the elements, the losses of the loading devices will have to be taken into account when calculating the antenna efficiency. On the other hand, if the short antenna (dipole or monopole) is not loaded, the feed-point impedance will have a large amount of capacitive reactance in addition to the resistive component.

One solution is to install a transformer at the antenna feed point to match the complex antenna impedance to the feed-line impedance. In this case, the feed line will no longer act as a transformer. Conversion will be done in the transformer at a given efficiency, and transforming extreme impedance ratios inevitably results in poor transformation efficiencies. Transforming the impedance of a very short vertical with an impedance of $0.5 - j3000$ ohms to $50 + j0$ ohms is a very difficult task, and it cannot be done without a great deal of loss. In military applications where very short antennas are often required, one technique used to reduce circuit losses is the cooling of network components to near absolute zero (to achieve super conductivity of the metals involved).

One can also supply power to this feed point without inserting a transformer. In this case the feed line itself will act as a transformer. In the case of the above example, an extremely high SWR would be present on the feed line. The transmission-line transformer is not a lossless component, and the losses will be determined by the quality of the materials used to make the feed line. In the pre-war days, when coaxial cables were still unknown, everybody used 600-ohm open-wire lines, and nobody knew what SWR was.

If we are not particularly interested in the transformation aspect of such a feed line, the line can be terminated in a low-loss antenna tuner. What is a quality antenna tuner? The same qualifications for feed lines apply here: one that can transform the impedances involved, at the required power levels, with minimal losses.

Many of the modern antenna tuners, which are essentially unbalanced to unbalanced tuners, use a toroidal transformer/balun to achieve a high-impedance balanced output. This principle is cost effective, but has its limitations where extreme transformations are required. The "old" tuners, e.g. the Johnson Matchboxes, are ideally suited to match a very wide range of impedances. Unfortunately these matchboxes are no longer available commercially, and are not designed to cover 160 meters.

■ 4. THE MATCHING NETWORK AT THE ANTENNA

Let's analyze a few of the most commonly used matching systems.

4.1. Quarter-wave Matching Sections

For a given design frequency you can transform impedance A to impedance B by inserting a quarter-wave long coaxial cable between A and B having a characteristic impedance equal to the square root of the product $A \times B$.

$$Z_{1/4\lambda} = \sqrt{A \times B} \qquad \text{(Eq 6-1)}$$

Example:

Assume we have a short vertical antenna that we wish to feed with 75-ohm coax. We have determined that the radiation resistance of the vertical is 23 ohms, and the resistance from earth losses is 10 ohms (the feed-point resistance is 33 ohms). We can use a ¼-wave section of line to provide a match, as shown in Fig 6-5. The impedance of this line is determined as $\sqrt{33 \times 75} = 50$ ohms.

Coaxial cables can also be paralleled to obtain half the nominal impedance: A coaxial feed line of 35 ohms can be made by using two parallel 70-ohm cables.

One way to adjust ¼- or ½-wavelength cables exactly for a given frequency is shown in Fig 6-6. Connect the transmitter through a good SWR meter (the author uses a Bird model 43) to a 50-ohm dummy load. Insert a coaxial T connector at the output of the SWR bridge. Connect the length of coax to be adjusted at this point and use the reading of the SWR bridge to indicate where the length is resonant. Quarter-wave lines should be short-circuited at the far end, and half-wave lines left open. On the resonant frequency, a cable of the proper length represents an infinite impedance (assuming lossless cable) to the T junction. At the resonant frequency, the SWR will not change when the quarter-wave shorted line (or half-wave open line) is connected in parallel with the dummy load. At slightly different frequencies, the line will present small values of inductance or capacitance across the dummy load, and these will influence the SWR reading accordingly. I have found this method very accurate, and the lengths can

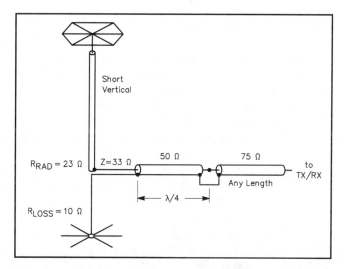

Fig 6-5–Example of a quarter-wave transformer, used to match a short vertical antenna (R_{rad} = 23 ohms, R_{ground} = 10 ohms, Z_{feed} = 33 ohms) to a 75-ohm feed line. In this case a perfect match can be obtained with a 50-ohm quarter-wave section.

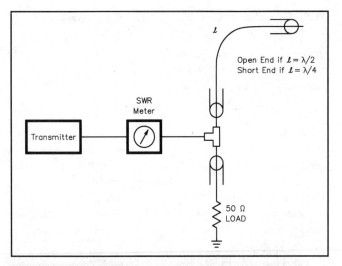

Fig 6-6–Very precise trimming of ¼ λ and ½ λ lines can be done by connecting the line under test in parallel with a 50-ohm dummy load and watching the SWR meter while the feed line length or the transmit frequency is changed. See text for details.

be trimmed precisely, to within a few kHz.

Odd lengths, other than ¼- or ½ wavelength, can also be trimmed this way. First calculate the required length difference between a quarter (or half) wavelength on the desired frequency and the actual length of the line on the desired frequency. For example, if you need a 73-degree length of feed line on 3.8 MHz, that cable would be 90 degrees long on (3.8 × 90 / 73) = 4.685 MHz. The cable can now be cut to a quarter wavelength on 4.685 MHz using the method described above.

The dip oscillator method isn't the most accurate way to cut a 90-degree length of feed line, and it often accounts for length variations of 2 or 3 degrees. One can also use a noise bridge and use the line under test to effectively short-circuit the output of the noise bridge to the receiver.

4.2. The L Network

The L network is probably the most commonly used network for matching antennas to coaxial transmission line. In special cases the L network is reduced to a single-element network, being a series or a parallel impedance network (just an L or C in series or in parallel with the load).

The L network is treated in great detail by W. N. Caron in his excellent book *Antenna Impedance Matching* (ARRL publication). W. Caron exclusively used the graphical Smith Chart technique to design antenna matching networks. The book also contains an excellent general treatment of the Smith Chart and other basics of feed lines, SWR and matching techniques.

Graphic solutions of impedance-matching networks have been treated by I. L. McNally, W1NCK (Ref 1446). R. E. Leo, W7LR (Ref 1404) and B. Baird, W7CSD (Ref 1402).

Designing an L network is something you want to do using a computer program. I have written a computer program (L-NETWORK DESIGN) that will just do that for you. The program is part of the NEW LOW BAND SOFTWARE.

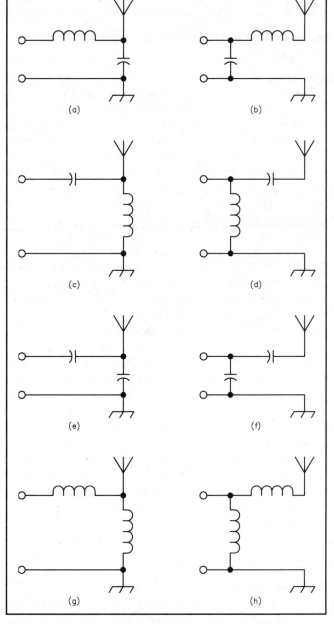

Fig 6-7–Eight possible L-network configurations. (After W. N. Caron, *Antenna Impedance Matching*.)

Similar computer programs have been described in amateur literature (Ref 1441).

So-called shunt-input L networks are used when the resistive part of the output impedance is lower than the required input impedance of the network. The series-input L network is used when the opposite condition exists. In some cases, a series-input L network can also be used when the output resistance is smaller than the input resistance (in this case we have four solutions). All possible alternatives (at least two, but four at the most) will be given by the program.

Fig 6-7 shows the eight possible L-network configurations. Fig 6-8 shows the four different regions of the Smith Chart and which of the solutions are available in each of the areas. Fig 6-9 shows the way to design each of the solutions.

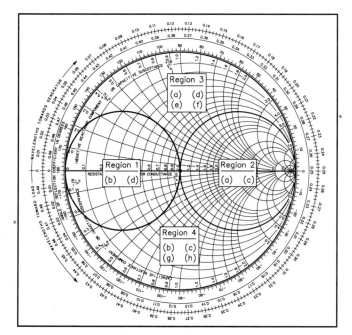

Fig 6-8–The Smith Chart subdivided in four regions, in each of which two or four L-network solutions are possible. The graphic solution methods are illustrated in Fig 6-9. (After W. N. Caron, *Antenna Impedance Matching*.)

For more details on the Smith Chart and how to use it for the graphic design of L networks, *Antenna Impedance Matching* by W. N. Caron is a must (ARRL publication). If you have an IBM or compatible PC, an even easier way to design L networks with an on-screen Smith Chart is with the program ARRL MICROSMITH by W. Hayward, W7ZOI (also an ARRL publication). A detailed knowledge of the Smith Chart is not required to use MICROSMITH.

The choice of the exact type of L network to be used (low pass, high pass) will be up to the user, but in many cases, component values will determine which choice is more practical. In other instances, performance may be the most important consideration: Low-pass networks will give some additional harmonic suppression of the radiated signal, while a high-pass filter may help to reduce the strength of strong medium-wave broadcast signals from local stations.

Some solutions provide a direct dc ground path for the antenna through the coil. If dc grounding is required, such as in areas with frequent thunderstorms, this can be achieved by placing an appropriate RF choke at the base of the antenna (between the driven element and ground).

The L-NETWORK software module from the NEW LOW BAND SOFTWARE also calculates the input and output voltages and currents of the network. These can be used to

Fig 6-9–Design procedures on the Smith Chart for solutions *a* through *h* as explained in Fig 6-8. (After W. N. Caron, *Antenna Impedance Matching*.) If you have a PC, you can use the program ARRL MICROSMITH to quickly and easily calculate the matching values graphically on screen.

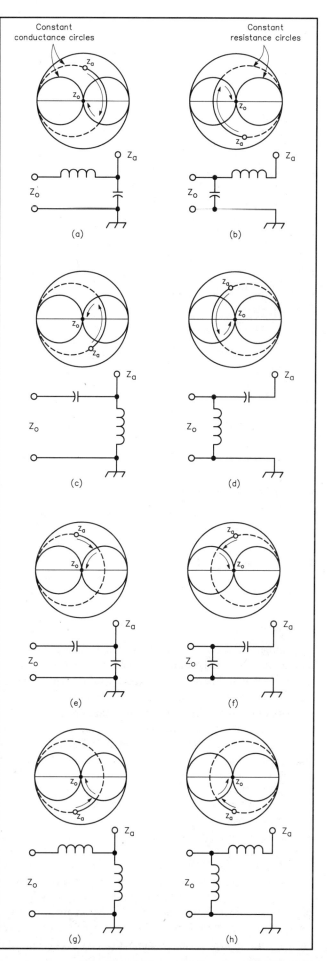

```
Z-Input =   50.0 ohm        OUTPUT SWR =  1.37        FREQUENCY =   3.6 MHz

                    RECTANGULAR COORDINATES          POLAR COORDINATES
                    REAL PART      IMAG PART      MAGNITUDE        ANGLE
IMPEDANCE (ohm)  =    36.60          0.00          36.60          0.00
CURRENT  (Amp)   =     6.40          0.00           0.00          0.00
VOLTAGE  (Volt)  =   234.31          0.00         234.31          0.00
```

```
─────────────────────────── Solution # 1 ───────────────────────────
IMPEDANCE SERIES ARM    =  -22.1 ohm      ==>> CAPACITANCE =    1996 pF
IMPEDANCE PARALLEL ARM  =   82.6 ohm      ==>> INDUCTANCE  =    3.65 µH
CURRENT  (Amp)    =    4.69      -2.84          5.48         -31.18
VOLTAGE  (Volt)   =  234.31    -141.78        273.87        -31.18
```

```
─────────────────────────── Solution # 2 ───────────────────────────
IMPEDANCE SERIES ARM    =   22.1 ohm      ==>> INDUCTANCE  =    0.98 µH
IMPEDANCE PARALLEL ARM  =  -82.6 ohm      ==>> CAPACITANCE =     535 pF
CURRENT  (Amp)    =    4.69       2.84          5.48          31.18
VOLTAGE  (Volt)   =  234.31     141.78        273.87         31.18
```

```
     THE NETWORK HAS THE SHUNT ELEMENT ACROSS THE RESISTIVE INPUT
X:EXIT    N:NEW RUN    R:Z-out    Z:Z-load    E:load volt    I:load curr    F:Freq
```

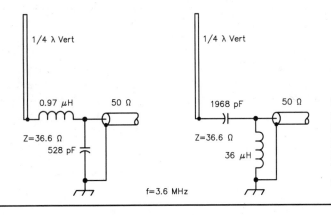

Fig 6-10–Design of an L-network to match a resonant quarter-wave vertical with a feed-point impedance of 36.6 ohms to a 50-ohm line. Note that in practice we must add the ground resistance to the radiation resistance to obtain the feed-point impedance. Therefore, in most cases the impedance of a quarter-wave vertical will be fairly close to 50 ohms.

determine the required component ratings. Capacitor current ratings are especially important when the capacitor is the series element in a network. The voltage rating is most important when the capacitor is the shunt element in the network. Consideration regarding component ratings and the construction of toroidal coils are covered in Par. 4.3.

The L-NETWORK software module inputs to be provided by the user are:

• design frequency
• cable impedance
• load resistance
• load reactance

Fig 6-10 shows the screen display of a case where we calculate an L network to match 36.6 – j0 ohms to a 50-ohm transmission line. From the prompt line we can easily change any of the inputs. If the outcome of the transformation is a network with one component having a very high reactance (low C value or high L value), then we can try to eliminate this

component all together. The SERIES NETWORK or SHUNT NETWORK programs will tell you exactly what value to use, and if the match is not perfect you may want to assess the SWR by switching to the SWR CALCULATION module of the NEW LOW BAND SOFTWARE to do just that.

4.2.1. Component ratings

What kind of capacitors and inductors do we need for building the L networks?

Capacitors

The transmitter power as well as the position of the component in the L network will determine the voltage and current ratings that are required for the capacitor.
• If the capacitor is connected in parallel with the 50-ohm transmission line (assuming we have a 1:1 SWR), then the voltage across the capacitor is given by $E = \sqrt{P \times R}$. Assume 1500 W and a 50-ohm feed line.

$$E = \sqrt{1500 \times 50} = 274 \text{ V RMS}$$

The peak voltage is $274 \times \sqrt{2} = 387$ V.

• If the capacitor is connected between the antenna base and ground, we can follow a similar reasoning. But this time we need to know the absolute value of the antenna impedance. Assume the feed point impedance is $90 + j110$ ohms ($R_r = 90$). The magnitude of the antenna impedance is

$$Z_{ant} = \sqrt{90^2 + 110^2} = 142.1 \text{ ohms}$$

The voltage across the antenna feed point is given by

$$E = I \times Z_{ant} = \sqrt{\frac{P}{R_r}} \times Z_{ant} = \sqrt{\frac{1500}{90}} \times 142.1 = 580 \text{ V RMS} = 820 \text{ V peak}$$

• If the capacitor is the series element in the network, and if the parallel element is connected between the feed line and ground (transmitter side of the network), then the current through the capacitor equals the antenna feed current. Assume a feed-point impedance of $120 + j190$ ohms. The magnitude of the antenna feed-point impedance is

$$Z = \sqrt{120^2 + 190^2} = 225 \text{ ohms}$$

Again assume 1500 W. The magnitude of the feed current is

$$I = \sqrt{\frac{P}{Z}} = \sqrt{\frac{1500}{225}} = 2.58 \text{ A}$$

Assume the capacitor has a value of 200 pF and the operating frequency is 3.65 MHz. The impedance of the capacitor is

$$X_c = \frac{10^6}{2\pi f C} = \frac{10^6}{2\pi \times 3.65 \times 200} = 218 \text{ ohms}$$

where f is in MHz and C is in pF. The voltage across the capacitor is

$$E = I \times Z = 2.58 \times 218 = 562 \text{ V RMS or } 795 \text{ V peak}$$

• If the capacitor is the series element in the L network and if the parallel element is connected between the feed point of the antenna and ground, then the current through the capacitor is the current going in the 50-ohm feed line. Assuming we have a 1:1 SWR in a 50-ohm feed line and a power level of 1500 W, the current is given by

$$I = \sqrt{\frac{P}{Z}} = \sqrt{\frac{1500}{50}} = 5.48 \text{ A}$$

Assume the same 200-pF capacitor as above, whose impedance at 3.65 MHz was calculated to be 218 ohms. The voltage across the capacitor now is

$$E = I \times Z = 5.48 \times 218 = 1194 \text{ V RMS or } 1689 \text{ V peak}$$

In practice we should always use at least a 100% safety factor on these components. For the capacitors across low-impedance points, transmitting type mica capacitors can be used, as well as BC-type variables such as normally used as the loading capacitor in the pi network of a linear amplifier.

For the series capacitors, only transmitting type ceramic capacitors (e.g., doorknob capacitors) can be used. For fine tuning, high-voltage variables or preferably vacuum variables can be used. I normally use parallel-connected transmitting-type ceramics across a low-value vacuum variable (these can usually be obtained at real bargain prices at flea markets).

Coils

Up to inductor values of approximately 5 µH, air-wound coils are usually the best choice. A roller inductor comes in very handy when trying out a new network. Once the computed values have been verified by experimentation, the variable inductor can be replaced with a fixed inductor. Large-diameter, heavy-gauge Air Dux coils are well suited for the application.

Above approximately 5 µH, powdered-iron toroidal cores can be used. Ferrite cores are not suitable for this application, as these cores are much less stable and are easily saturated. The larger size powdered-iron toroidal cores, which can be used for such applications, are listed in Table 6-1.

The required number of turns for a certain coil can be determined as follows:

$$N = 100 \times \sqrt{\frac{L}{A_L}} \qquad \text{(Eq 6-2)}$$

where L is the required inductance in microhenries. The A_L value is taken from Table 6-1. The transmitter power determines the required core size. It is a good idea to choose a core somewhat on the large side for a margin of safety. One may also stack two identical cores to increase power-handling capability, as well as the A_L factor. The power limitations of powdered-iron cores are usually determined by the temperature increase of the core. Use large-gauge enameled copper wire for the minimum resistive loss, and wrap the core with glass-cloth electrical tape before winding the inductor. This will prevent arcing at high power levels.

Consider this example: A 14.4-µH coil requires 20 turns on a T400A2 core. AWG 4 or AWG 6 wire can be used with equally-spaced turns around the core. This core will easily handle well over 1500 watts.

The smoke test

Two things can go wrong with the matching network:

• Capacitors will flash over (short circuit, explode, vaporize, catch fire, burn up, etc.) if their voltage rating is too low.
• Capacitors or coils will heat up (and eventually be destroyed after a certain time), if the current through the components is too high or the component current capabilities too low.

In the second case the excessive current will heat up either the conductor (coil) or the dielectric (capacitor).

6-1

Table 6-1

Toroid Cores Suitable for Matching Networks

Supplier	Code	Permeability	OD (in)	ID (in)	Height (in)	A_L
Amidon	T-400-A2	10	4.00	2.25	1.30	360
Amidon	T-400-2	10	4.00	2.25	0.65	185
Amidon	T-300-2	10	3.05	1.92	0.50	115
Amidon	T-225-A2	10	2.25	1.41	1.00	215

7921 STUB MATCHING PROGRAM on4un

Freq: 3.6 Mhz Z-line: 50.0 ohm SWR: 1.1

	RECTANGULAR COORDINATES		POLAR COORDINATES		
	REAL PART	IMAG PART	MAGNITUDE	ANGLE	
IMPEDANCE (ohm) =	36.60	0.00	36.60	0.00	A
CURRENT (Amp) =	6.40	0.00	6.40	0.00	N
VOLTAGE (Volt) =	234.35	0.00	234.35	0.00	T

Posit.	IMPEDANCE		VOLTAGE		-------------STUB------------				IMP
Stub	Resis	React	Magnit	Angl	Imped	Value	Length	Type	ohm
35	43.2	12.9	265.7	43.7	-157.9	280 pF	17.6	OPEN	45.8
36	43.6	13.1	267.1	44.8	-157.7	280 pF	17.6	OPEN	46.5
37	44.0	13.4	268.6	45.8	-157.8	280 pF	17.6	OPEN	47.2
38	44.4	13.7	270.1	46.9	-158.0	280 pF	17.6	OPEN	48.0
39	44.8	13.9	271.6	47.9	-158.5	279 pF	17.5	OPEN	48.7
40	45.3	14.1	273.1	48.9	-159.2	278 pF	17.4	OPEN	49.4
41	45.7	14.4	274.6	49.9	-160.0	276 pF	17.4	OPEN	50.1
42	46.2	14.6	276.1	50.9	-161.1	274 pF	17.2	OPEN	50.9
43	46.7	14.8	277.6	51.9	-162.3	272 pF	17.1	OPEN	51.6
44	47.2	14.9	279.1	52.8	-163.8	270 pF	17.0	OPEN	52.3
45	47.7	15.1	280.5	53.8	-165.4	267 pF	16.8	OPEN	53.0
46	48.2	15.3	282.0	54.7	-167.3	264 pF	16.6	OPEN	53.7

H:HELP X:EXIT R:RUN Z:Z-cable F:Freq I:Imp.load C:Curr.load V:Volt.load

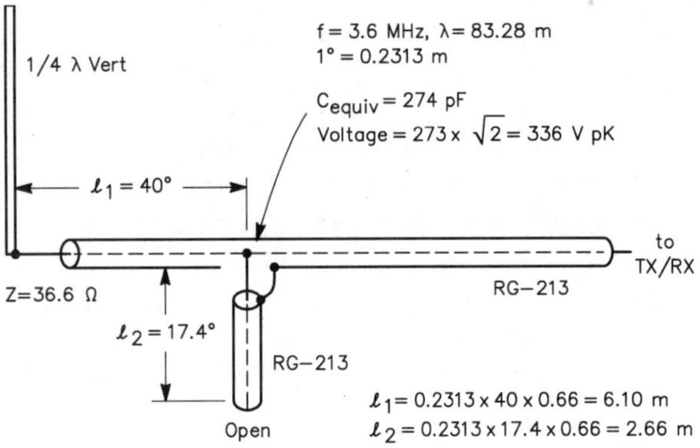

1/4 λ Vert
f = 3.6 MHz, λ = 83.28 m
1° = 0.2313 m
Cequiv = 274 pF
Voltage = 273 x √2 = 336 V pK
ℓ1 = 40°
to TX/RX
Z=36.6 Ω
RG-213
ℓ2 = 17.4°
RG-213
Open
ℓ1 = 0.2313 x 40 x 0.66 = 6.10 m
ℓ2 = 0.2313 x 17.4 x 0.66 = 2.66 m

Fig 6-11—A 36.6-ohm resistive load is matched to a 50-ohm feed line using stub matching.

One way to find out if there are any losses in the capacitor, resulting from large RF currents, is to measure or feel the temperature of the components in question (not with power applied!) after having stressed them with a solid carrier for a few minutes. This is a valid test for both coils and capacitors in a network. If excessive heating is apparent, consider using heavier duty components. This procedure also applies to toroidal cores.

4.3. Stub Matching

Stub matching can be used to match resistive or complex impedances to a given line impedance. The STUB MATCHING software module, a part of the NEW LOW BAND SOFTWARE, allows you to calculate the position of the stub on the line and the length of the stub, and whether the stub must be open or shorted at the end. This method of matching a (complex) impedance to a line can replace an L network. This approach saves the two L-network components, but necessitates extra cable to make the stub. Also, the stub may be located at a point along the feed line which is difficult to reach. Fig 6-11 shows the screen of the computer program where we are matching an impedance of 36.6 ohms to a 50-ohm feed line. Note that between the load and the stub the line is not flat, but once beyond the stub the line is now matched. The computer program gives line position and line length in electrical degrees. To convert this to cable length you must take into account the velocity factor of the feed line being used!

4.3.1. Replacing the stub with a discrete component.

Stub matching is often unattractive on the lower bands because of the lengths of cable required to make the stub. The module STUB MATCHING also displays the equivalent component value of the stub (in either μH or pF). Nothing prevents one from replacing the stub with an equivalent capacitor or inductor, which is then connected in parallel with the feed line at the point where the stub would have been placed. The same program shows the voltage where the stub or discrete element is placed. In order to know the voltage requirement for a parallel capacitor, one must know the voltage at the load.

Freq: 3.6 Mhz   Z-line: 75.0 ohm   SWR: 1.1

	RECTANGULAR COORDINATES		POLAR COORDINATES		
	REAL PART	IMAG PART	MAGNITUDE	ANGLE	
IMPEDANCE (ohm) =	50.00	0.00	50.00	0.00	A
CURRENT (Amp) =	5.47	0.00	5.47	0.00	N
VOLTAGE (Volt) =	273.50	0.00	273.50	0.00	T

Posit.	IMPEDANCE		VOLTAGE		-----------STUB-----------				IMP
Stub	Resis	React	Magnit	Angl	Imped	Value	Length	Type	ohm
34	60.5	23.4	322.6	45.3	-180.0	246 pF	22.6	OPEN	67.8
35	61.2	24.0	324.9	46.4	-180.2	245 pF	22.6	OPEN	69.2
36	61.9	24.5	327.3	47.5	-180.7	245 pF	22.5	OPEN	70.6
37	62.6	25.1	329.6	48.5	-181.4	244 pF	22.5	OPEN	71.9
38	63.3	25.6	332.0	49.5	-182.3	243 pF	22.4	OPEN	73.3
39	64.1	26.1	334.4	50.5	-183.4	241 pF	22.2	OPEN	74.7
40	64.9	26.6	336.8	51.5	-184.8	239 pF	22.1	OPEN	76.0
41	65.7	27.1	339.2	52.5	-186.4	237 pF	21.9	OPEN	77.4
42	66.6	27.6	341.6	53.5	-188.2	235 pF	21.7	OPEN	78.7
43	67.4	28.0	343.9	54.4	-190.2	232 pF	21.5	OPEN	80.0
44	68.3	28.4	346.3	55.4	-192.5	230 pF	21.3	OPEN	81.3
45	69.2	28.8	348.6	56.3	-195.0	227 pF	21.0	OPEN	82.5

H:HELP   X:EXIT   R:RUN   Z:Z-cable   F:Freq   I:Imp.load   C:Curr.load   V:Volt.load

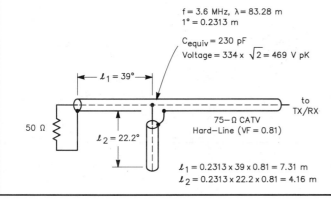

f = 3.6 MHz, λ = 83.28 m
1° = 0.2313 m

C_{equiv} = 230 pF
Voltage = 334 x $\sqrt{2}$ = 469 V pK

ℓ_1 = 39°

50 Ω

ℓ_2 = 22.2°

to TX/RX

75 – Ω CATV
Hard–Line (VF = 0.81)

ℓ_1 = 0.2313 x 39 x 0.81 = 7.31 m
ℓ_2 = 0.2313 x 22.2 x 0.81 = 4.16 m

Fig 6-12–Example of how a simple stub can match a 50-ohm load to a 75-ohm transmission line. Note that between the load and the stub the SWR on the line is 1.5:1. Beyond the stub the SWR is 1:1.

Consider the following example: The load is 50 ohms (resistive), the line impedance is 75 ohms, and the power at the antenna is 1500 W. Therefore, the RMS voltage at the antenna is

$$V = \sqrt{P \times R} = \sqrt{1500 \times 50} = 274 \text{ V}$$

Running the STUB MATCHING software module, we find that a 75-ohm impedance point is located at a distance of 39 degrees from the load. See Fig 6-12 for details of this example. The required 75-ohm stub length, open-circuited at the far end, to achieve this resistive impedance is 22.2 degrees (equivalent to 230 pF for a design frequency of 3.6 MHz). The voltage at that point on the line is 334 V RMS (472 V peak).

Note that the length of a stub will never be longer than ¼ wavelength (either open-circuited or short-circuited).

4.3.2. Matching with series-connected discrete components.

In stub matching with a 50-ohm system, we look on a line with SWR for a point where the impedance on the line,

together with the impedance of the stub (in parallel) will produce a 50-ohm impedance.

A variant consists in looking on the line for a point where the insertion of a *series* impedance will yield 50 ohms. At that point the impedance will look like $(50 + jX)$ ohms or $(50 - jY)$ ohms. All we need to do is to put a capacitor or inductor in series with the cable at that point. The capacitor will have a reactance of X ohms, or the inductor of Y ohms.

Example: Match a 50-ohm load to a 75-ohm line (same example as above).

The software module IMPEDANCE ITERATION from the NEW LOW BAND SOFTWARE lists the impedance along the line in 1-degree increments, starting at 1 degree from the load. Somewhere along the line we will find an impedance where the real part is 75 ohms (see details in Fig 6-13). Note the distance from the load. In our example this is 51 degrees from the 50-ohm load. The impedance at that point is 75.2 + $j30.7$ ohms.

If we want to assess the current through the series element

Freq: 3.6 Mhz   Z-line: 75.0 ohm   SWR: 1.1

		RECTANGULAR COORDINATES		POLAR COORDINATES		
		REAL PART	IMAG PART	MAGNITUDE	ANGLE	
IMPEDANCE (ohm)	=	50.00	0.00	50.00	0.00	A
CURRENT (Amp)	=	5.47	0.00	5.47	0.00	N
VOLTAGE (Volt)	=	273.50	0.00	273.50	0.00	T

Posit.	IMPEDANCE		VOLTAGE		------------STUB------------				IMP
Stub	Resis	React	Magnit	Angl	Imped	Value	Length	Type	ohm
45	69.2	28.8	348.6	56.3	-195.0	227 pF	21.0	OPEN	82.5
46	70.2	29.2	351.0	57.2	-197.7	224 pF	20.8	OPEN	83.7
47	71.1	29.6	353.3	58.1	-200.7	220 pF	20.5	OPEN	84.9
48	72.1	29.9	355.6	59.0	-204.0	217 pF	20.2	OPEN	86.0
49	73.1	30.2	357.9	59.9	-207.5	213 pF	19.9	OPEN	87.2
50	74.2	30.4	360.1	60.8	-211.2	209 pF	19.5	OPEN	88.2
51	75.2	30.7	362.3	61.6	-215.3	205 pF	19.2	OPEN	89.3
52	76.3	30.9	364.5	62.5	-219.7	201 pF	18.9	OPEN	90.3
53	77.4	31.0	366.7	63.3	-224.4	197 pF	18.5	OPEN	91.3
54	78.6	31.1	368.8	64.2	-229.4	193 pF	18.1	OPEN	92.2
55	79.7	31.2	370.9	65.0	-234.8	188 pF	17.7	OPEN	93.2
56	80.9	31.2	372.9	65.8	-240.6	184 pF	17.3	OPEN	94.1

H:HELP   X:EXIT   R:RUN   Z:Z-cable   F:Freq   I:Imp.load   C:Curr.load   V:Volt.load

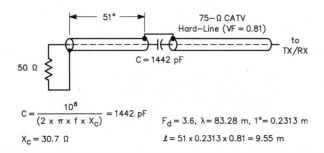

Fig 6-13—Example of how a series element can match a 50-ohm load to a 75-ohm transmission line. See text for details.

(which is especially important if the series element is a capacitor), we must enter actual values for either current or voltage at the load when running the program. Assuming an antenna power of 1500 W, the current at the antenna is

$$I = \sqrt{\frac{P}{R}} = \sqrt{\frac{1500}{50}} = 5.47\,A.$$

All we need to do now is connect an impedance of –30.7 ohms (capacitive reactance) in series with the line at that point. Also note that at this point the current is

$$I = \sqrt{\frac{1500}{75.2}} = 4.46\,A$$

The software module SERIES IMPEDANCE NETWORK can be used to calculate the required component value. In this example, the required capacitor has a value of 1442 pF for a frequency of 3.6 MHz (Fig 6-14). The required voltage rating (RMS) is calculated by multiplying the current through the capacitor times the capacitive reactance, which yields a value of

$$E = I \times Z = 4.46 \times 30.7 = 136.9\,V\ RMS = 193.6\,V\ peak.$$

In the case of a complex load impedance, the procedure is identical, but instead of entering the resistive load impedance (50 ohms in the above example), we must enter the complex impedance.

4.4. High-impedance Matching System

Unbalanced high-impedance feed points, e.g., a half-wave vertical fed against ground, a voltage-fed T-antenna, the Bobtail antenna, etc.) can best be fed using a parallel-tuned circuit on which the 50-ohm cable is tapped for the lowest SWR value. See Fig 6-15, drawings at A, B and C. Symmetrical high-impedance feed points, such as for two half-wave (collinear) dipoles in phase, the bisquare, etc., can be fed directly with a 600-ohm open-wire feeder into a quality antenna tuner, Fig 6-15D.

Another attractive solution is to use a 600-ohm line and stub matching, Fig 6-15E. Assume the feed-point impedance is 5000 ohms. Running the STUB MATCHING software module, we find that a 200-ohm impedance point is located at a distance of 81 degrees from the load. The required 600-ohm stub to be connected in parallel at that point is 14 degrees long (X = 154 ohms). The impedance is now a balanced 200 ohms.

	RECTANGULAR COORDINATES		POLAR COORDINATES		
	REAL PART	IMAG PART	MAGNITUDE	ANGLE	
IMPEDANCE (ohm) =	75.25	30.67	81.26	22.17	O
CURRENT (Amp) =	3.44	2.83	4.46	39.46	L
VOLTAGE (Volt) =	172.12	318.82	362.32	61.64	D
IMPEDANCE (ohm) =	75.25	0.00	75.25	0.00	N
CURRENT (Amp) =	3.44	2.83	4.46	39.46	E
VOLTAGE (Volt) =	259.04	213.25	335.52	39.46	W

CAPACITANCE = 1442 pF   FREQUENCY = 3.60 MHz

X = EXIT   R = RUN   Z = Z-load   E = E-load   I = I-load   F = Freq

Fig 6-14–Calculation of the value of the series element required to tune out the reactance of the load 75.248 + *j* 30.668 ohms. See text for details.

Using a 4:1 balun, this point can now be connected to a 50-ohm feed line.

Let me sum up some of the advantages and disadvantages of both feed systems.

Tuned open-wire feeders
- fewest components, which means the least chance of something going wrong
- likely least losses
- very flexible (can be tuned from the shack)
- open wire lines are mechanically less attractive

Stub matching plus balun and coax line
- coaxial cables are much easier to handle

4.5. Wide-band Transformers

4.5.1. Low-impedance wide-band transformers.

Broadband transformers exist in two varieties: the classic autotransfomer and the transmission-line transformer. The first is a variant of the Variac, a genuine autotransformer. The second is making use of transmission line principles. What they have in common is that they are often wound on toroidal cores. It is not the scope of this book to go into details on this subject. *Transmission Line Transformers* by J. Sevick, W2FMI, and published by the ARRL is an excellent textbook on the subject of transmission-line transformers. It covers all you might need in the field of wide-band RF transformers.

4.5.2. High-impedance wide-band transformer.

If the antenna load impedance is both high and almost perfectly resistive (such as for a half wavelength vertical fed at the bottom), one may also use a broadband transformer such as is used in transistor power amplifier output stages. Fig 6-16 shows the transformer design used by F. Collins, W1FC. Two turns of AWG 12 Teflon-insulated wire are fed through two stacks of 15½ inch (OD) powdered-iron toroidal cores (Amidon T50-2) as the primary low impedance winding. The secondary consists of 8 turns. The turns ratio is 4:1, the impedance ratio 16:1.

The efficiency of the transformer can be checked by terminating it with a high-power 800-ohm dummy load (or with the antenna, if no suitable load is available), and running full power to the transformer for a couple of minutes. Start with low power. Better safe than sorry. If there are signs of heating of the cores, add more cores to the stack. Such a transformer has the advantage of introducing no phase shift between input and output, and therefore can easily be incorporated into phased arrays.

■ 5. 75-OHM CABLES IN 50-OHM SYSTEMS

Lengths of 75-ohm Hardline coaxial cable can often be obtained from local TV cable companies. If very long runs to low-band antennas are involved, the low attenuation of Hardline is an attractive asset. If one is concerned with providing a 50-ohm impedance, a transformer system must be used.

Transformers using toroidal cores (so called ununs) have been described (Ref 1307, 1517, 1518, The 4:1 unun, by Jerry Sevick, W2FMI, *CQ*, Jan 1993, p 30; ARRL publication *Transmission Line Transformers* by J. Sevick, W2FMI).

Ununs have been described for a very wide range of

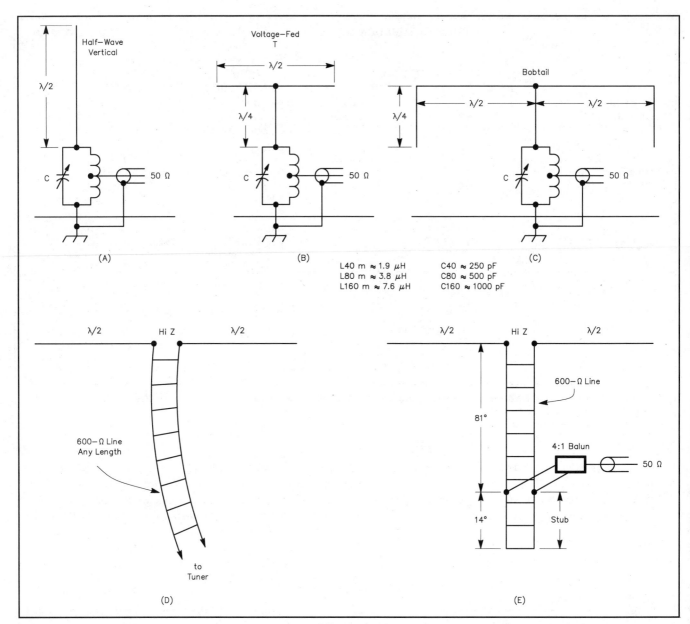

Fig 6-15—Recommended feed methods for high-impedance (2000-5000 ohm) feed points. Asymmetrical feed points can be fed via a tuned circuit. The symmetrical feed points can be fed via an open-wire line to a tuner, or via a stub-matching arrangement to a 4:1 (200- to 50-ohm) balun and a 50-ohm feed line.

impedance ratios. One application is as a matching system for a short loaded vertical. If the short loaded vertical is used over a good ground radial system, its impedance will be lower than 50 ohms. Ununs have been described that will match, e.g., 25 to 50 or 37.5 to 50 ohms.

Transformer systems can also be made using only coaxial cable, without any discrete components. If 60-ohm coaxial cable is available (as in many European countries), a quarter-wave transformer will readily transform the 75 ohms to 50 ohms at the end of the Hardline.

Carroll, K1XX, described the non-synchronous matching transformer and compared it to a stub matching system (Ref. 1318). While the toroidal transformer is broadbanded, the stub and non-synchronous transformers are single-band devices.

Compared to quarter-wave transformers, which need coaxial cable having an impedance equal to the geometric mean of the two impedances to be matched, the non-synchronous transformer requires only cables of the same impedances as the values to be matched (Fig 6-17).

■ 6. THE NEED FOR LOW SWR

In the past, SWR was not understood by many radio amateurs. Unfortunately it still is not. Reasons for low SWR are often false, and SWR is often used as the outstanding parameter telling us all about the performance of an antenna.

Maxwell, W2DU, published a series of articles on the subject of transmission lines. They are excellent reading material for anyone who has more than just a casual interest in antennas and transmission lines (Refs 1308-1311, 1325-1330

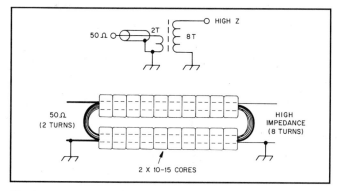

Fig 6-16—A wideband high-power transformer for large transformation ratios, such as for feeding a half-wave vertical at its base (600 to 10,000 ohms), uses two stacks of 10 to 15 half-inch-OD powdered-iron cores (e.g., Amidon T502-2). The primary consists of 2 turns and the secondary has 8 turns (for a 50- to 800-ohm ratio). See text for details.

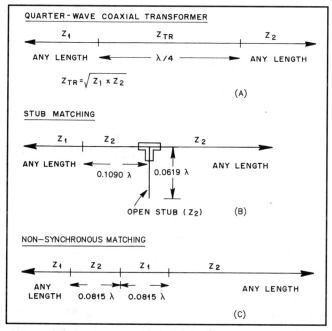

Fig 6-17—Methods of matching 75-ohm cables in 50-ohm systems. The quarter-wave transformer at A requires a cable having an impedance that is the geometric mean of the values being matched. The stub matching system at B and the non-synchronous matching system at C require only cables of the impedances being matched. The stub can be replaced with a capacitor or an inductor. All these matching systems are frequency sensitive.

Z_{TR}—60-ohm line.
Z_1—50-ohm line (or load).
Z_2—75-ohm line.

and 1332). These articles have recently been combined and, with new information added, published as a book, *Reflections: Transmission Lines and Antennas* (ARRL publication).

J. Battle, N4OE, wrote a very instructive article "What is your Real Standing Wave Ratio" (Ref 1319), treating in detail the influence of line loss on the SWR (difference between apparent SWR and real SWR).

Everyone has heard comments like, "My antenna really gets out because the SWR does not rise above 1.5:1 at the band edges." Low SWR is no indication at all of good antenna performance. It is often the contrary. The "antenna" with the best SWR is a quality dummy load. Antennas using dummy resistors as part of loading devices come next (Ref. 663). It may be easily concluded from this that low SWR is no guarantee of radiation efficiency. The reason that SWR has been wrongly used as an important evaluation criterion for antennas is that it can be easily measured, while the important parameters such as efficiency and radiation characteristics are more difficult to measure.

Antennas with lossy loading devices, poor earth systems, high-resistance conductors and the like, will show flat SWR curves. Electrically short antennas should always have narrow bandwidths. If they do not, it means that they are inefficient.

Is too low an SWR dangerous? *"There was this SWR freak who kept climbing his tower, day after day, to prune the antenna matching system. He repeated this again and again, as if he was trying to bring the SWR below 1:1, that important it seemed to him. With all the climbing, one night he fell off his tower and killed himself. So you see, TOO LOW AN SWR CAN KILL."*

■ 7. THE BALUN

Balun is a term coming from the words *bal*anced and *un*balanced. It is a device we must insert between a symmetrical feed line (e.g., an open-wire feeder) and an asymmetric load (e.g., a ground-mounted vertical monopole) or an asymmetric feed line (e.g., coax) and a symmetric load (e.g., a center-fed half-wave dipole). If we feed a balanced feed point with a coaxial feed line, currents will flow on both the outside of the coaxial braid as on the inside (that's where we want to have them). Currents on the outside will cause radiation from the line.

Unbalanced loads can be recognized by the fact that one of the terminals is at ground potential. Examples: the base of a monopole vertical (the feed point of any antenna fed against ground), the feed point of an antenna fed against radials (that's an artificial ground), the terminals of a gamma match or omega match, etc.

Balanced loads are presented by dipoles, sloping dipoles, delta loops fed at a corner, quad loops, collinear antennas, bisquare, cubical quad antennas, split-element Yagis, the feed points of a T match, a delta match, etc.

Many years ago I had an inverted-V dipole on my 25-m tower, and the feed line was just hanging unsupported alongside the tower, swinging nicely in the wind. When I took down the antenna some time later, I noticed that in several places, where the coax had touched the tower in the breeze, holes were burned through the outer jacket of the RG-213, and water had penetrated the coax, rendering it worthless. The phenomena of burning holes illustrates that currents (thus also voltages) are present on the coax if no balun is used. Currents create fields, and fields from the feed line upset the field from the antenna.

Baluns have been described in abundance in the amateur

literature (Refs1504, 1505, 1502, 1503, 1515, 1519, 1520).

- In the simplest form a balun can consist of a number of turns of coaxial cable wound into a close coil. In order to present enough reactance at the low-band frequencies, a fairly large coil is required.
- The newest approach, although introduced by Maxwell, W2DU, several years ago, is to slip a stack of high permeability cores over the outer shield of the coaxial cable at the load terminals. In order to reduce the required ID of the toroids or beads, one can use a short piece of Teflon insulated coaxial cable e.g., RG-141, RG-142 or RG-303, which has an OD of approximately 5 mm (0.2 inch). A balun covering 1.8 to 30 MHz uses 50 no. 73 beads (Amidon no. FB-73-2401 or Fair-Rite no. 2673002401-0) to cover a length of approximately 30 cm (12 inches) of coaxial cable. The stack of beads on the outer shield of the coax creates an impedance of several kilohms, effectively suppressing any current from flowing down on the feed line. Amidon beads type 43-1024 can be used on RG-213 cable. Ten to thirty will be required, depending on the lowest operating frequency.

The two above approaches are the so-called *current* baluns. They are called current-type baluns because even when the balun is terminated in unequal resistances, it will still force equal, opposite-in-phase currents into each resistance.

Current baluns made according to this principle are commercially available from Antennas Etc., PO Box 4215, Andover MA 01810; The Radio Works Inc, Box 6159, Portsmouth VA 23703; and from The Wireman, Inc, 261 Pittman Road, Landrum SC 29356. This last supplier also sells a kit consisting of a length of Teflon coax (RG-141 or RG-303) plus 50 ferrite beads to be slipped over the Teflon coax.

The traditional balun (e.g., the well known W6TC balun) is a *voltage* balun, which produces equal, opposite phase voltages into the two resistances. With the two resistances we mean the two "halves" of the load, which are "symmetrical" with respect to ground (not necessarily in value!). The toroidal-core type baluns as covered in the ARRL publication *Transmission Line Transformers* by J. Sevick, W2FMI, are also voltage-type baluns.

Fig 6-18 shows the construction details for a the W6TC voltage-type balun designed for best performance on 160, 80 and 40 meters, as well as a current-type balun as described in the text above.

We have stated on several occasions that if the reading of an SWR meter changes with its position on the line (small changes in position, not affected by attenuation) this means the SWR meter is not functioning properly. The only other possible reason for a different SWR reading with position on the line is the presence of RF currents on the outside of the coax.

We've touched upon three good reasons for using a balun with a symmetrical feed point:

- we don't want to distort the radiation pattern of the antenna
- we don't want to burn holes in our coax
- we want our SWR readings to be correct

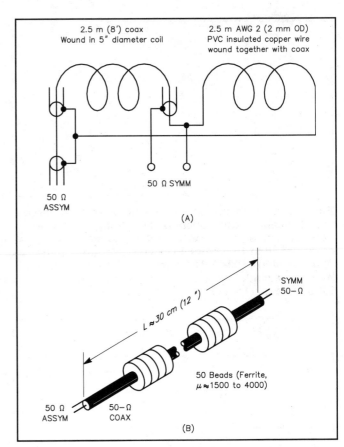

Fig 6-18–At A, details of a W6TC voltage-type balun for 160-40 meters, and at B, a current transformer for 160-10 meters. See text for details.

■ 8. BROADBAND MATCHING

A steep SWR curve is due to the rapid change in reactance in the antenna feed-point impedance as the frequency is moved away from the resonant frequency. There are a few ways to try to broadband an antenna:

• Implement elements in the antenna that will counteract the effect of the rapid change in reactance. The so-called "Double Bazooka" dipole is a well known example. This solution is dealt with in more detail in the chapter on dipoles.

• Instead of using the simple L network, use a multiple-pole matching network which has the property of flattening the SWR curve.

The second solution is covered in great detail in *Antenna Impedance Matching*, by W. N. Caron, published by the ARRL.

ANTMAT is a computer program described in technical Document 1148 (Sep 1987) of the NOSC (Naval Ocean Systems Center). The document describing the matching methodology as well as the software is called "The Design of Impedance Matching Networks for Broadband Antennas." The computer program assists in designing broad-band matching networks. These programs are very useful for designing broadband networks to match, e.g., small whip antennas over a very wide frequency spectrum.

SPECIAL RECEIVING ANTENNAS

■ **1. THE BEVERAGE ANTENNA**

    1.1. Principles

    1.2 Modeling Beverage Antennas

    1.3. Directional Characteristics and Gain

        1.3.1 Influence of length

        1.3.2 Influence of antenna height

        1.3.3 Influence of ground quality

    1.4 Beverage Impedance

    1.5. Terminating the Single-Wire Beverage

    1.6. Ground Systems for Beverage Antennas

    1.7. Feeding the Single-Wire Beverage

    1.8. Sloping Receiving-End Termination

    1.9. Simple Single-Wire Beverage Antenna

    1.10. Bi-directional Beverage Antenna

    1.11. Two-Wire Switchable-Direction Antennas

    1.12. Sloping Two-Wire Beverage Terminations

    1.13. Compensated Ground Wires

    1.14. Designing the Transformers

    1.15. Constructing the Transformers

    1.16. Testing the Transformers

    1.17. Feed Lines

    1.18. Location of the Beverage

    1.19. Mechanical Construction

    1.20. Arrays of Beverages

    1.21. Beverage Performance

    1.22. Electrical Null Steering

    1.23. Preamplifiers for Beverage Antennas

    1.24. The ON4UN Beverage System.

■ **2. SMALL LOOP ANTENNAS**

■ **3. OTHER RECEIVING ANTENNAS**

    3.1. Snake Antenna

    3.2. Low Horizontal Antennas

SPECIAL RECEIVING 7 ANTENNAS

I explained earlier the differences between the main requirements for a receiving and for a transmitting antenna. Efficiency and radiation pattern are the issues with transmitting antennas, while signal-to-noise ratio is the only issue with receiving antennas on the low bands. Only highly directive transmitting antennas such as Yagis, quads or phased verticals will perform adequately as receiving antennas. Verticals are known to be excellent low-angle radiators, and therefore they pick up a lot of man-made noise when used as receiving antennas. They are very prone to rain (and snow) static as well, and they hear equally well (poorly?) in all directions. That's why a good low-band setup, using a vertical transmitting antenna, needs to be complemented with a specific receiving antenna.

■ 1. THE BEVERAGE ANTENNA

The Beverage antenna (named after Harold Beverage, W2BML) made history in 1921. In fact, a Beverage antenna was used in the first transatlantic tests on approximately 1.2 MHz. For many decades, the Beverage antenna wasn't used very much by hams, but in the last 25 years it has gained tremendous popularity with low-band DXers. The early articles on the Beverage antenna (Ref. 1200-1204) are excellent reading material for those who want to familiarize themselves with this unique antenna.

1.1. Principles

Fig 7-1 shows the basic configuration of the Beverage antenna (also called "wave antenna"). It consists of a long wire (typically 1 to 4 wavelengths long) erected at a low height above the ground. The Beverage antenna has very interesting directional properties for an antenna so close to the ground, but it is relatively inefficient. This is why the antenna is primarily used for reception only on the amateur low bands.

The Beverage antenna can be thought of as an open-wire transmission line with the ground as one conductor and the antenna wire as the other. In order to have a unidirectional pattern, the antenna must be terminated at the far end in a resistor equal to the characteristic impedance of the antenna.

If the Beverage antenna is to be used on VLF (where it was originally used), the velocity of propagation in the "two wires" (one is the antenna conductor, the other one is its image in the earth) has to be different, so that the arriving wave front (at zero wave angle for VLF signals) inclines onto the wire and induces an EMF in the wire. Therefore, the ground under the antenna must have rather poor conductivity for best performance.

On the amateur low bands, the situation is different, because the wave angle is not zero. It is typically 10 to 50 degrees for DX signals on 160/80/40 meters. In this case the wave angle of the arriving signal itself is responsible for inducing voltage in the antenna wire, so it is not essential that the antenna be installed over a poorly conducting ground. We will see, however, that the poorer the ground quality, the higher the output of the Beverage antenna.

Some authors have mentioned that the highest useful

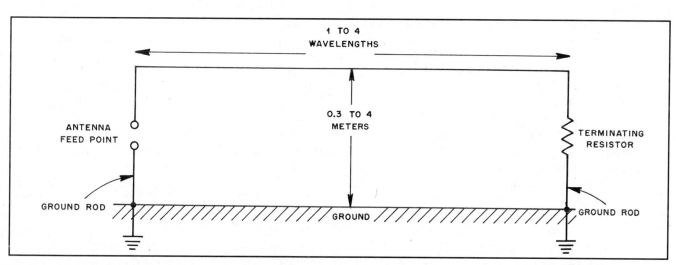

Fig 7-1—The basic Beverage antenna is a straight wire, 1 to 4 wavelengths long, constructed parallel to the ground at a height of 0.01 to 0.03 wavelength. Length limitations are discussed in the text.

frequency for the Beverage is 2 MHz (160 meters). This is not true, and many active users of this fine antenna can testify about its wonderful performance on 80 and even 40 meters! Arrays of Beverage antennas are also used on the HF bands for direction finding and over-the-horizon radar.

In any case, the tilted wave (tilted by the difference of velocity at VLF, and tilted due to the arriving wave angle on the HF bands) will induce signals in the wire. It may seem that the longer the Beverage antenna, the greater the induced signal. This is not the case, however. The gain increases with length, but beyond a certain length, the gain actually begins to drop off. This length limitation varies with the velocity factor of the antenna, but is also dependent on the angle of the incoming signal. The drop in gain is caused by the currents in the wire increasingly lagging the tilted wave in space as the length of the wire is increased (due to the different velocity of propagation in space and in the wire). A point is eventually reached where the current in the wire is more than 90 degrees out of phase with the space wave, and the wave begins to subtract from the signal on the wire, causing a reduction in gain.

The theoretical maximum length for a zero wave angle is:

$$L_{max} = \frac{L \times Vf}{4 \times (1000 - Vf)} \qquad \text{(Eq 7-1)}$$

where

L = wavelength of operation (in meters)
Vf = velocity factor of the antenna (eg 95).

For non zero wave angles, the above equation includes the wave angle factor as follows:

$$L_{max} = \frac{L \times Vf}{4 \times [100 - (Vf \times \cos\alpha)]} \qquad \text{(Eq 7-2)}$$

The maximum length can be determined this way because it is a function of the maximum gain of the antenna. Making the antenna longer will result in reduced output, but the horizontal main lobe can be further narrowed (with substantial sidelobes) and the vertical angle further lowered with greater lengths (at the expense of signal strength). The velocity factor is the ratio of velocity of propagation of the electromagnetic wave in the antenna wire to the velocity of propagation of electromagnetic energy in air. The velocity factor of a Beverage will vary typically from about 90% on 160 meters to 95% on 40 meters. These figures are for a height of 3.0 to 3.5 m (10 to 12 feet). At 1 meter (3.3 ft) height the velocity factor can be much lower (typically 85%). This is a major drawback of very low Beverage antennas.

The velocity of propagation of your Beverage antenna can be determined experimentally as follows:

Measure the physical length of the antenna, then calculate the theoretical wavelength (L_{qw}) and frequency (F_{qw}) on which the antenna is a quarter-wave long (assuming 100% velocity factor). Fill the figures in on the worksheet as shown in Table 7-1. Open one end of the antenna and feed the antenna via a two-turn link from a dip oscillator. Tune through the spectrum starting at approximately 70% of the calculated quarter-wave frequency (approximately 350 kHz in the example case) and note the exact frequency of all the dips up to

Table 7-1

Beverage Antenna Velocity of Propagation Worksheet

Physical antenna length: 200 meters
Calculated ¼ λ L_{qw}: 4 × (300/L) = 600 meters
¼ λ frequency (F_{qw}): 300/600 = 0.5 MHz

Length	Open-End Freq	Shorted-End Freq	Velocity Factory (Dip freq / N × F_{qw})
1 × ¼ λ	0.46	—	0.40 / 1 × 0.5 = 92
2 × ¼ λ	—	0.94	0.94 / 2 × 0.5 = 94
3 × ¼ λ	1.42	—	1.42 / 3 × 0.5 = 95
4 × ¼ λ	—	1.90	1.90 / 4 × 0.5 = 95
5 × ¼ λ	2.38	—	2.38 / 5 × 0.5 = 95
6 × ¼ λ	—	2.87	2.87 / 6 × 0.5 = 96
7 × ¼ λ	3.36	—	3.36 / 7 × 0.5 = 96
8 × ¼ λ	—	3.85	3.85 / 8 × 0.5 = 96
9 × ¼ λ	4.34	—	4.34 / 9 × 0.5 = 96
10 × ¼ λ	—	4.84	4.84 / 10 × 0.5 = 97
11 × ¼ λ	5.34	—	5.34 / 11 × 0.5 = 97
12 × ¼ λ	—	5.83	5.83 / 12 × 0.5 = 97

Example of a worksheet for determining the velocity of propagation of a Beverage antenna. The example is for 200-m long Beverages. A number of resonant frequencies are measured for both open-ended as well as short-circuited far-end conditions.

the maximum frequency of interest. Repeat the same procedure with the antenna end short-circuited to ground. Again note the dip frequencies. Note that the velocity factor changes with frequency of operation.

The antenna from Table 7-1 shows a velocity factor of approximately 95% on 160 meters and 95% on 80 meters. Applying the maximum length formula, we find a maximum length of L_{max} = 480 meters for 80-meter operation and maximum length of 768 meters for 160 meters (for a zero wave angle). If we consider wave angles lower than 20 degrees on 160 meters, the maximum length becomes 214 meters (Equation 2). For 80 meters (assuming a wave angle of 20 degrees), the maximum length is 196 meters. The antenna under evaluation was 200 meters long, which is certainly a good compromise for use on both 160 and 80 meters.

Depending on the ground quality and the wave angle, Beverages as long as 2000 feet have been reported to work very well on 80 and 160 meters.

1.2. Modeling Beverage Antennas

You can do some Beverage modeling with MININEC, but you have to be aware of the shortcoming of MININEC:

While modeling, MININEC assumes a perfect ground right under the antenna. This means that data obtained from modeling with MININEC must be interpreted with caution.

Modeling Beverages with MININEC has the following consequences:

• MININEC works with a 100% velocity factor (because of the perfect ground under the antenna): the gain will increase with length, without reaching a maximum, which is not correct.

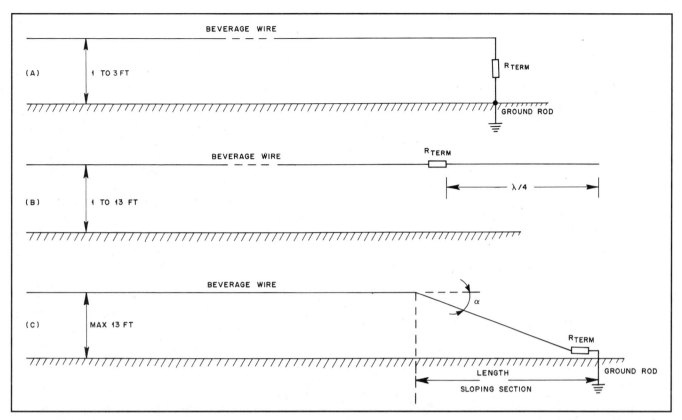

Fig 7-2—Different terminating systems for Beverage antennas. Version A does nothing to eliminate the stray pickup of the vertical downleads and should be used only with very low-to-the-ground antennas. Example B uses a quarter-wave terminating wire, while the sloping termination of figure C is totally broadbanded, and as such is the most favorable solution.

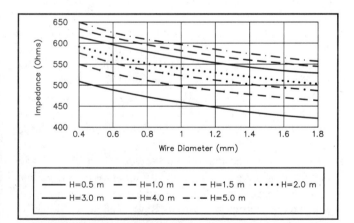

Fig 7-3—Characteristic impedance of the Beverage antenna for different conductor diameters and different antenna heights. The values are calculated from the single-wire feed-line equivalent. In practice over real ground the values are 10% to 30% higher, depending on the ground quality. See text for details.

• MININEC will show an antenna impedance that is typically 10 to 20% lower than the actual impedance over real ground.

• MININEC patterns will show deep nulls in between the different lobes. This is not correct. The various lobes merge into one another due to the real ground conditions.

• Gains reported with MININEC are too high.

Modeling with MININEC

If you want to use MININEC and include the vertical down leads, you will be confronted with the problem of correctly dimensioning the pulses near the right-angle connection. This can be avoided by modeling the Beverage with two quarter-wave terminations as shown in Fig 7-2.

In order to determine how many pulses you need, first model a relatively short (eg 1 wavelength) Beverage, and note the impedance. The resistive part should conform to the values given in Fig 7-3. If the value is very different, then you must increase the number of pulses.

Modeling with NEC2

All Beverages and Beverage patterns described in this chapter were modeled using NEC2, which models over real ground, including in the near field. All Beverages were modeled using a quarter-wave termination in line with the Beverage antenna, connected at both ends (see par. 1.4.)

1.3. Directional Characteristics and Gain

1.3.1. Influence of length.

The chart in Fig 7-4 shows the difference in gain as well as the radiation angle for 2-meter (6.6 ft) high Beverages of various lengths on 80 and 160 meters.

• The gain for the 160-meter Beverage culminates at approximately 5 wavelengths (800 m or 2600 ft!). Beyond that length the gain only drops slightly, but both the wave angle as well as the 3 dB forward lobe beamwidth keeps decreasing.

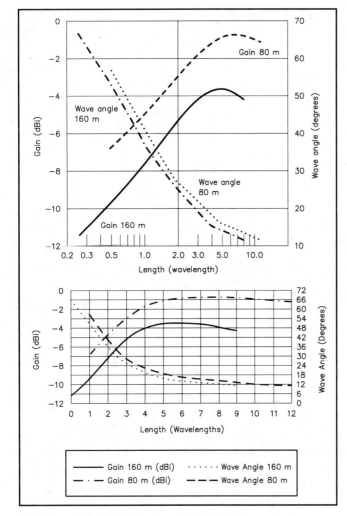

Fig 7-4—Gain (dBd) and peak value of the main radiation angle for a 2-m (6.6 ft) high Beverage antenna over average ground, as a function of antenna length. The antenna is terminated in a 500-ohm resistance in all cases.

• 2 wavelengths seems to be a minimum length for a well performing 160-meter Beverage.

• The gain for the 80-meter Beverage at 2 m height is maximum at a length between 6 and 7 wavelengths (500 m or 1600 ft).

• For covering both 80 and 160 meters, a 500-m Beverage seems to be an excellent compromise, although the compromise is little with a 300-m (1000 ft) long one.

• The reduction in gain for "too long" Beverages is minimal.

• The increase in gain is greatest between 1 and 4 wavelengths. Beyond 4 wavelengths the change in gain is minimal. The forward lobe beamwidth keeps decreasing, however.

The velocity factor can easily be calculated from the chart in Fig 7-4. Let's take the example of the 160-meter Beverage:

• The maximum gain is at 5 wavelengths (from chart).

• This means that at 5 wavelengths the physical length of the antenna is 90 degrees longer than the electrical length of the antenna.

• The physical length is 5 wavelengths or $5 \times 360 = 1800$ degrees.

• The electrical length is $1800 - 90 = 1710$ degrees.

• The velocity factor = $1710 / 1800 = 95\%$.

For the 80-meter case the velocity factor is calculated as 96.3%.

Fig 7-5 shows the radiation patterns over average ground of a Beverage antenna operating on 160 meters for different antenna lengths.

The Beverage must be at least 2 wavelengths long before you get meaningful low-angle radiation from it.

As you can see, Beverages as short as ¼ wavelength show a F/B at a 30 degree wave angle of 20 dB. At the same time the main wave angle is 67 degrees, which is quite high for DX work. If you are forced to use such short Beverage antennas, don't put them too low to the ground. Increasing the height also increases the Beverage output (see par 1.3.2). Note that although the main vertical lobe peaks at 67 degrees, the antenna gain is only down 2 dB at 30 degrees, which still makes it a worthwhile performer at low angles. Such a short Beverage may require a preamplifier, however, due to its low output.

Don't be misled however, and don't think that a Beverage with –12 dBi output (a quarter-wave long Beverage for 160 at 2 m height over good ground) together with a 10 dB preamplifier is as good as a Beverage with –3 dBi (5 wavelengths long) output. The preamp will only serve to compensate for possible losses in the feed line to the Beverage antenna. The preamplifier amplifies noise as well as signal. In addition, if it is not well designed it may have more internally generated noise than the preamp in your receiver so that you will end up with a loss in signal-to-noise ratio.

In practice Beverages as long as 600 m (2000 ft) have demonstrated excellent performance, even on 80 meters. Worth, WB3GCG, has been successful in using eight such Beverages. The length of each Beverage can be switched to 150 m (500 ft), 300 m (1000 ft) or 600 m (2000 ft). Fig 7-6 shows a layout of such a multi-length Beverage. My own experience is that my 300 m (1000 ft) Beverage substantially outperforms shorter ones.

We have seen that all but the very shortest Beverages show one or more minor secondary lobes. We will see later how these lobes (high-angle lobes and back lobes) can be used to make an electrically steerable Beverage antenna, enabling us to get an almost infinite rejection at certain wave angles.

1.3.2. Influence of Antenna Height.

Fig 7-7 shows the radiation patterns for a 330-m (1100 ft) long Beverage operating on 1.83 MHz for heights ranging from 0.5 to 5 meters. Modeling was done over average ground and a terminating resistor of 500 ohms was used in all cases. Note that:

• The difference in gain between a very low (0.5m) and a very high (5 m) Beverage is 4.5 dB.

• The higher the Beverage, the higher the wave angle. For the 0.5-m high antenna, the wave angle is 19 degrees; for the 5-m high antenna the wave angle is 30 degrees.

• The higher the Beverage, the stronger the secondary

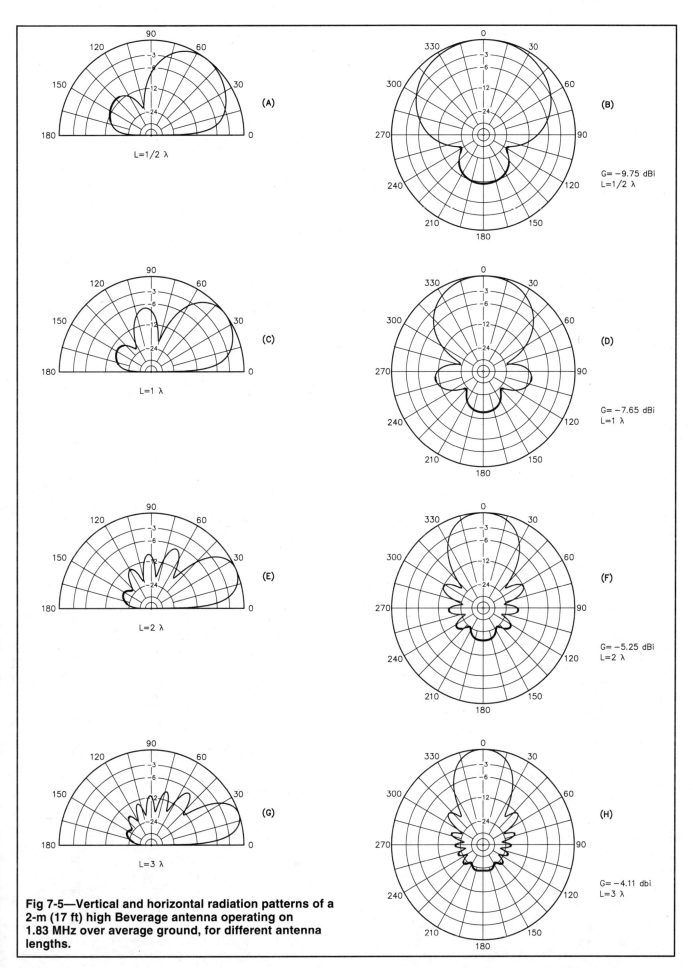

(A) L=1/2 λ

(B) G= −9.75 dBi L=1/2 λ

(C) L=1 λ

(D) G= −7.65 dBi L=1 λ

(E) L=2 λ

(F) G= −5.25 dBi L=2 λ

(G) L=3 λ

(H) G= −4.11 dbi L=3 λ

Fig 7-5—Vertical and horizontal radiation patterns of a 2-m (17 ft) high Beverage antenna operating on 1.83 MHz over average ground, for different antenna lengths.

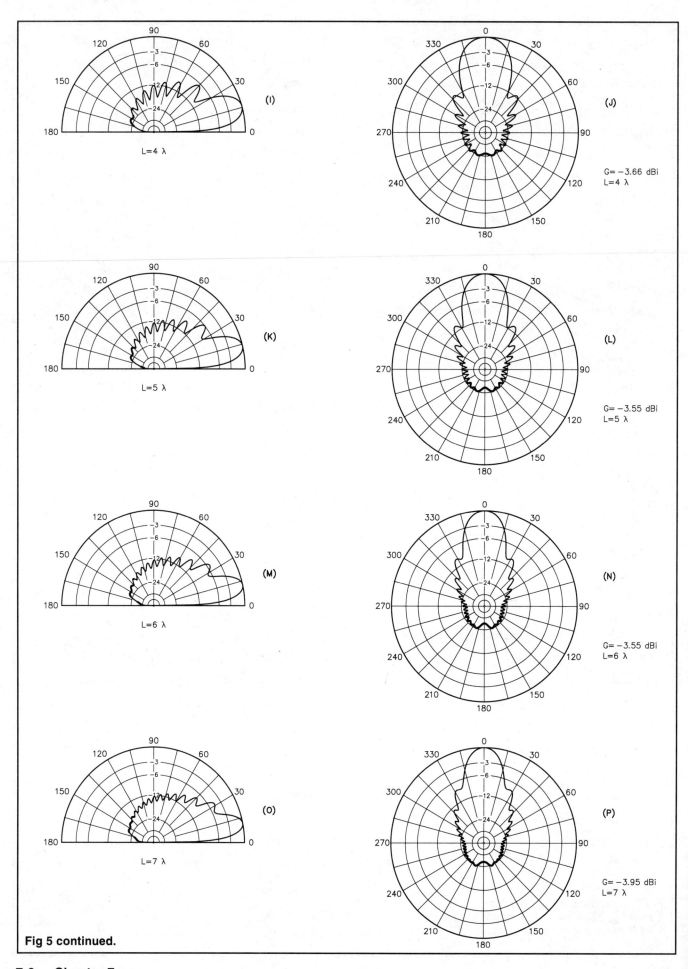

(I) L=4 λ

(J) G= −3.66 dBi
L=4 λ

(K) L=5 λ

(L) G= −3.55 dBi
L=5 λ

(M) L=6 λ

(N) G= −3.55 dBi
L=6 λ

(O) L=7 λ

(P) G= −3.95 dBi
L=7 λ

Fig 5 continued.

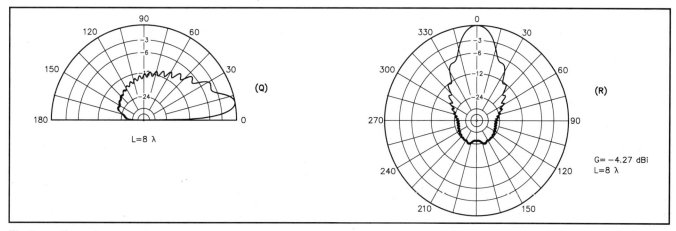

Fig 5 continued.

high-angle radiation lobes. For a 0.5-m high Beverage the second lobe (at 50 to 60 degrees wave angle) is down 8 dB; with the 5-m high Beverage the same lobe is down only 4.5 dB.

•In the horizontal plane the low Beverage also shows a superior directivity pattern as compared to the higher Beverages. This is due to the increasing influence of horizontally polarized signals being picked up by the "high" long wire.

The vertical and horizontal radiation patterns of a 330-m long Beverage antenna at 0.5 m height (1.6 ft), 2 m (6.6 ft) height and 5 m (16 ft) height over average ground are shown in Figs 7-7 and 7-8.

An interesting report was published by the BBC (Ref1257) in 1991. The report describes a method for assessing the performance of a Beverage receiving antenna, using off-air

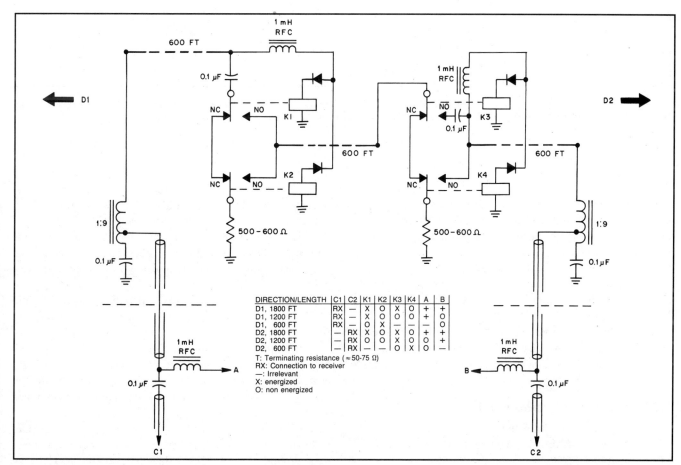

DIRECTION/LENGTH	C1	C2	K1	K2	K3	K4	A	B
D1, 1800 FT	RX	—	X	O	X	O	+	+
D1, 1200 FT	RX	—	X	O	O	O	+	O
D1, 600 FT	RX	—	O	X	—	—	O	O
D2, 1800 FT	—	RX	X	O	X	O	+	+
D2, 1200 FT	—	RX	O	O	X	O	O	+
D2, 600 FT	—	RX	—	—	O	X	O	—

T: Terminating resistance (≈50-75 Ω)
RX: Connection to receiver
—: Irrelevant
X: energized
O: non energized

Fig 7-6—A multi-length Beverage system with direction switching. The control voltages can be supplied to the relays by the circuit shown. As the relays are never simultaneously energized, they can be fed by opposite-polarity voltages on the feed line.

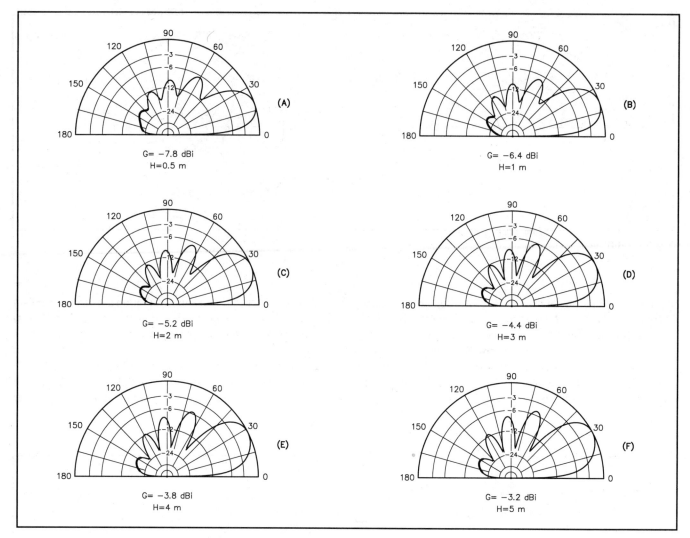

Fig 7-7—Vertical radiation pattern of a 330-m (1100 ft) long Beverage antenna over average ground, at different heights. Modeling is done at 1.83 MHz. The termination resistance is 500 ohms in all cases.

HF broadcast signals. A large number of Beverage antennas are used at the BBC monitoring service receiving site at Crowsley Park near Caversham. The study confirms that low Beverages show better directivity patterns, although the output is down from the higher ones. This is argued to be of lesser importance than the improved directivity.

Conclusion: As on 160 meters, it is not always possible to put up Beverage antennas that are at least 2 wavelengths long. I would suggest, if the antenna is to be used mainly on 160, to put the wire about 4 meters above ground in order to increase the gain somewhat. Raising the height from 2 to 4 meters increases the gain as much as increasing the length from 2 to 4 wavelengths!

1.3.3. Influence of ground quality.

Fig 7-9 shows the radiation pattern of a 330 m (1100 ft) long, 2-meter (6.6 ft) Beverage operating on 160 meters, for different grounds. Note that:

• The better the ground, the lower the output from the antenna.

• The better the ground, the better the low-angle performance. The peak of the main lobe hardly changes (28 to 30 degrees), but the shape of the lobe changes drastically.

• The poorer the ground quality, the less pronounced the nulls will be between the different lobes. This is similar to what we notice with horizontally polarized antennas over real ground.

• The front-to-back ratio as well as the front-to-side ratio of the Beverage remains almost constant for grounds ranging from very good to very poor.

• The vertical radiation angle does not change very much between very good ground and very poor ground (24 to 27 degrees for the 300-m long Beverage at 2 m, modeled for 160 meters). Over salt water the radiation angle becomes much higher.

• The Beverage does not work over sea water. Its output is down almost 20 dB as compared to the same antenna over poor ground. This confirms the observations made by B. Moeller, OZ8BV, that his Beverages near the sea never worked well at all.

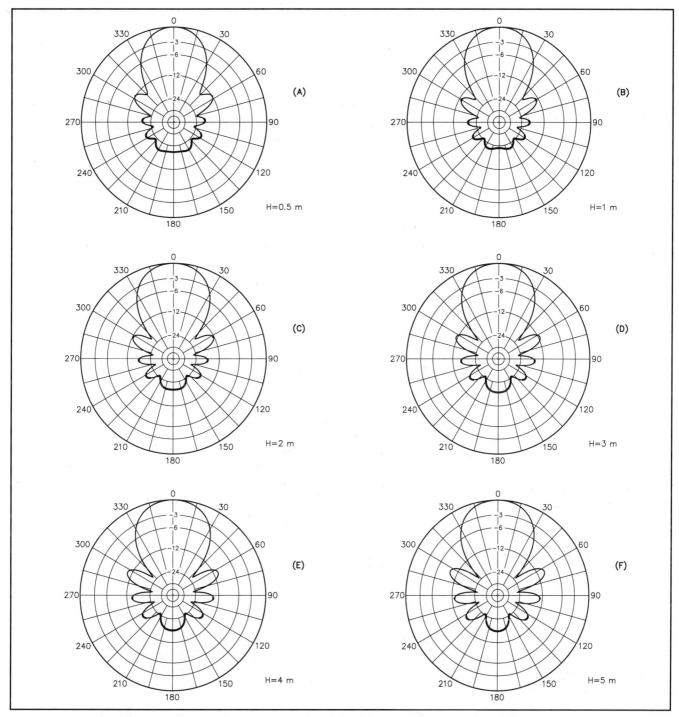

Fig 7-8—Horizontal radiation pattern of a 330-m (1100 ft) long Beverage antenna over average ground, at different heights. Modeling is done at 1.83 MHz. The termination resistance is 500 ohms in all cases.

1.4. Beverage Impedance

Over perfect ground the antenna impedance can be calculated using the formula of the single-wire transmission line over ground:

$$Z = 138 \log (4 \times h / d) \tag{Eq 7-3}$$

where

h = height of wire
d = wire diameter (in the same units).

The theoretical impedance values listed in Fig 7-3 are generated over perfect ground. They are useful for estimating the terminating resistor for a single-wire Beverage and for designing matching transformers and networks. Note that the impedance does not change drastically with height or wire size. Very low Beverages do not have a very low impedance as is sometimes said. Belrose (Ref. 1236) reports impedances varying between approximately 420 ohms and 550 ohms for a 110 m (360 ft) long Beverage at frequencies ranging from 2 to

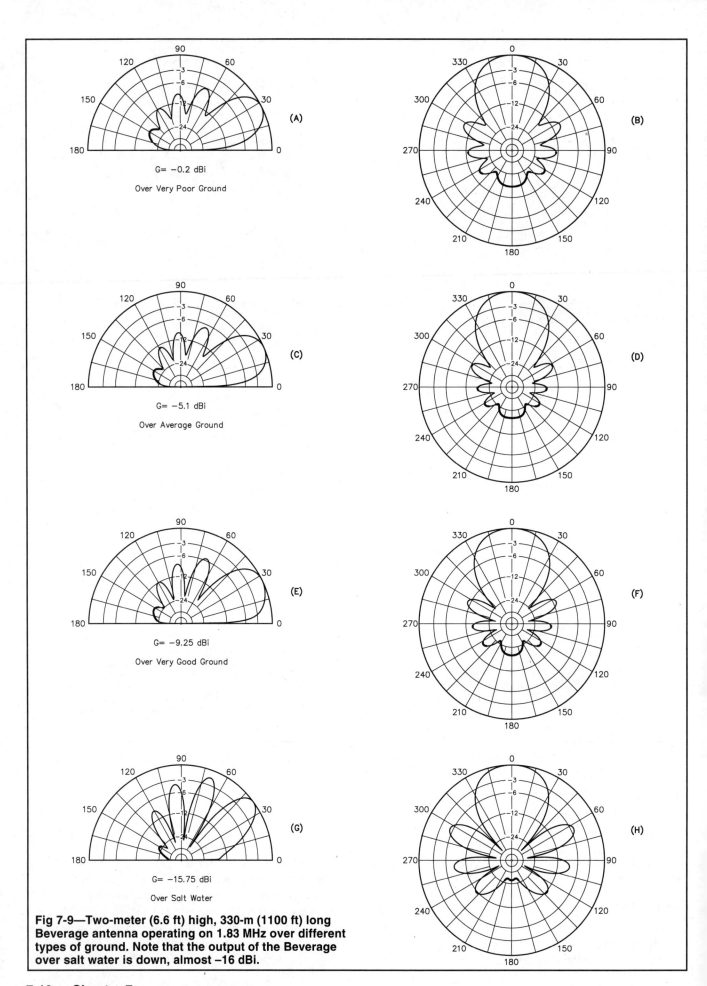

(A) G= −0.2 dBi
Over Very Poor Ground

(B)

(C) G= −5.1 dBi
Over Average Ground

(D)

(E) G= −9.25 dBi
Over Very Good Ground

(F)

(G) G= −15.75 dBi
Over Salt Water

(H)

Fig 7-9—Two-meter (6.6 ft) high, 330-m (1100 ft) long Beverage antenna operating on 1.83 MHz over different types of ground. Note that the output of the Beverage over salt water is down, almost −16 dBi.

10 MHz (height above ground = 1.1 m or 3.6 ft).

Over real ground the impedance appears to be higher than over perfect ground. The following correction figures can be used:

- Good ground: + 12 %
- Average ground: + 20 %
- Very poor ground: + 30 %

as compared to the impedance over perfect ground (Fig 7-3).

The optimum terminating resistor value for a Beverage antenna can also be determined experimentally: Couple a dip meter to one end of the antenna via a two-turn link. Terminate the other end with a 300-ohm resistor and tune the dip meter from 1 to 7 MHz. Measure the depths of the resonant points as you scan through the frequency range. Repeat the same test with a 400-ohm and then a 500-ohm terminating resistor. This process will allow you to find a resistor value for which almost no dips will be found between 1 and 7 MHz. That will be the resistor value for which the antenna is fully aperiodic (nonresonant). The exact impedance can vary greatly with ground conditions (season, humidity and so on).

When using NEC2 to model Beverages over real ground, it appears that the feed-point impedance generally includes some positive reactance (as high as +j100 ohms). B. H. Brunemeier, KG6RT, reports that he obtained the best directivity when terminating the Beverage in a complex load (Ref 1258).

Misek, W1WCR, described the use of wires under the Beverage to stabilize ground conditions (Ref 1206) and to obtain more stable impedances with varying weather conditions.

It is my own experience that the exact value of the terminating resistor is not so critical. I always use a 470- or 560-ohm resistor on all my Beverage antennas.

1.5. Terminating the Single-Wire Beverage

A common way of terminating the single-wire Beverage is to connect the proper terminating resistor between the end of the Beverage and the earth. This, however, is not necessarily the best solution, especially on frequencies higher than the very low ones, where the vertical downlead that connects the Beverage to the terminating resistor becomes a significant part of a wavelength and thus picks up a lot of signal. This effect can greatly impair the front-to-back ratio of the antenna. For Beverages at relatively high heights (1 meter or higher) this is not the most suitable way of terminating the antenna.

Fig 7-2 shows the classic resistor termination system using the vertical downlead as well as alternative systems that eliminate vertical downlead pickup. The quarter-wave termination is essentially a single-band termination. This is the type of termination that I used for modeling the antennas in this chapter (using NEC2). Traps can be included for multiband operation, or alternatively, parallel quarter-wavelength wires for different bands can be used. The disadvantage of this configuration is that it requires an extra quarter wavelength of real estate that does not contribute to the Beverage proper. I have used the sloping termination extensively and found it to work very well. The slope angle should be lower than the

Table 7-2

Wave Angle Versus Slope Length (m) for Beverage Antennas

	Wave Angle					
Beverage Height	10°	15°	20°	25°	30°	35°
0.3 m (1 ft)	1.7	1.2	0.9	0.7	0.6	0.5
1.0 m (3.3 ft)	5.8	3.9	2.9	2.4	2.0	1.7
2.0 m (6.6 ft)	11.5	7.7	5.8	4.7	4.0	3.5
3.0 m (10 ft)	17.3	11.6	8.8	7.1	6.0	5.2

The length of the sloping termination is shown as a function of the antenna height and the lowest wave angle that must be received without loss of gain.

minimum expected arrival angle of the signal. Table 7-2 gives the length of the sloping wire as a function of the minimum wave angle and the Beverage height. To obtain the slope length in feet, multiply the above figures by 3.28 (1 meter = 3.28 feet). For a wave angle of 10 degrees, the amount of extra length required for the sloping section is about ¼ wavelength (on 80 meters). The sloping wire section, however, is part of the antenna proper, and the sloping termination is fully broadbanded. The terminating resistor (approximately 500 ohms) is now connected between the end of the sloping wire and the ground system.

1.6. Ground Systems for Beverage Antennas

The ground system of a Beverage should consist of a ground rod at each end of the antenna. The RF resistance of the ground system at the far end (termination end) of the Beverage does not have to be very low, as the (high) ground resistance is effectively in series with the terminating resistance (approx. 500 ohms). This means that a simple ground rod of a few feet will do the job.

At the receiving end of the Beverage we should pay a little more attention to the ground system, as a high-resistance ground system will dissipate part of the useful RF in the poor ground system. The equivalent ground resistance is in series with the secondary (500-ohm) winding of the matching transformer (see par. 1.6). Assuming we had an equivalent ground resistance of 100 ohms (that's pretty bad!), the loss due to this 100-ohm resistance would be

$$20 \times \left| \log \frac{500}{100 + 500} \right| = 1.6 \text{ dB}$$

This means that whenever possible we should provide a decent RF ground at this point. A ground rod will usually be sufficient in good ground. Where we cannot use a ground rod (rocky ground), we can use a small counterpoise consisting of a large metal screen or made of a number of very short radials laid on the ground. A long radial can be added *in line* with the Beverage wire. Make the long radial a quarter-wave long on the main operating frequency.

Do not lay any long radials on the ground in a direction other than the antenna direction, as this may result in pickup

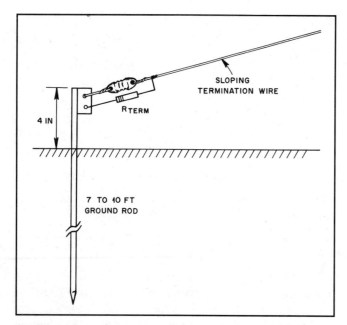

Fig 7-10—The sloping part of the Beverage antenna can be mechanically anchored at the terminating ground rod, via an appropriate insulator. The terminating resistor is connected between the end of the antenna and the ground rod.

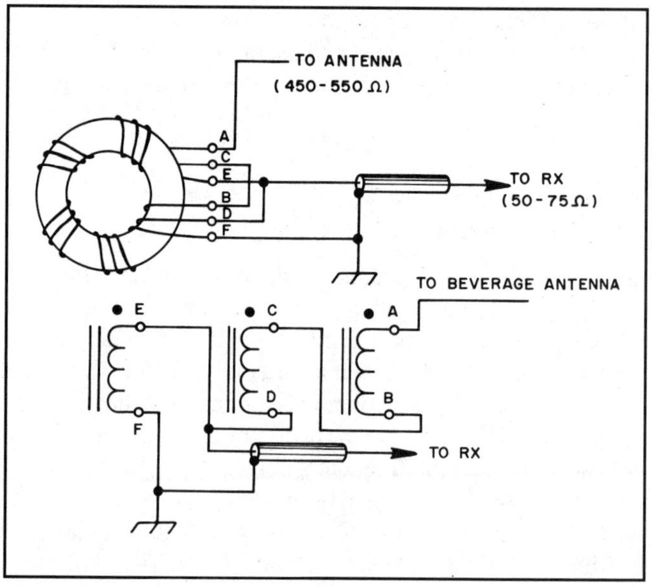

Fig 7-11—The transmission-line transformer consists of three parallel-wound wires, equally spaced across a toroid core. The proper connecting scheme is shown for a 9:1 impedance transformation ratio. The enameled copper wire can be securely fixed to the core using electrical tape or Q-dope.

of signals from unwanted directions.

If the Beverage does not have to be used over a wide frequency range, and where enough room is available, a quarter-wave long termination wire will be a good choice (see Fig 7-2B. A simple trap (using a small coil and capacitor) can be used to make a two-band quarter-wave terminating wire (e.g. for 160 and 80 meters). The disadvantage of this system is that you need the extra space for the terminating wires, which are not part of the antenna itself.

Where a sloping termination is used, the ground rod can extend slightly above ground to act as a mechanical termination post for the sloping wire section (Fig 7-10).

In my location (very good ground) I have been using 60 cm (2 ft) long ground rods with good results. I cannot see any difference when going to a more elaborate ground system.

1.7. Feeding the Single-Wire Beverage

The easiest way to match the Beverage impedance (450 to 600 ohms) to the commonly used coaxial cable (50 or 75 ohms) is to use a wideband toroidal transformer. Such transformers are usually wound on magnetic-material cores. The magnetic material can be either ferrite or powdered iron. Ferrites attain much higher permeability (up to 10,000) than powdered-iron materials (only up to 100), but are less stable at higher frequencies and saturate more easily. For wideband transformers which are not typically confronted with high power, such as in the Beverage antenna situation, ferrites are the most logical approach.

Several core sizes and core materials can be used for this job. As far as the size is concerned, the 0.5-inch cores (or even smaller ones) will do the job if the builder is not tempted to transmit on the Beverage. Larger size cores can be used as

well, and give the added advantage that one can assess the SWR of the transformer. Do this by injecting low power (make sure not to saturate the core!) via a sensitive SWR bridge into the transformer primary and terminating the secondary with a resistor of adequate wattage. When a satisfactory match has been obtained, both the transformer and the terminating resistor can be installed on the Beverage and a new check can be made. Parallel-connected, high-wattage carbon resistors can be used for the terminating resistor. Do not try to use wire-wound resistors; they are inductive at RF. Alternatively, one may use a noise bridge to check the transformer. This approach does not require that you use a large core that is able to withstand the testing power (which may be substantial in order to get a usable SWR bridge reading on 160 meters).

I have been using the high-permeability ferrite material very successfully. To note only one advantage, it is much easier to wind the cores when there are only a few turns! A 9:1 impedance transformer (3:1 turns ratio) will give a more than acceptable match for both 50- and 75-ohm lines. A transmission line transformer using a trifilar winding is well suited to this purpose. The wires can be twisted together at about two or three twists per inch.

Fig 7-11 shows both the schematic and the winding information. Using an Indiana General BBR7731 toroid core, a 50- to 450-ohm transformer would need only three trifilar turns across the core. Multiplying the number of turns by 1.414 would lower the low-frequency limit by a factor of 2. The original BBR7731 cores have been replaced by the cores type MN-8-CX or MN-60. Misek, W1WCR, reports that using a stack of two cores, with the same winding information, yields up to 0.4 dB improvement in insertion loss as compared to using a single core. A stack of two MN-8-CX cores yields a

Table 7-3

Main Winding Data for Beverage Antenna Matching Transformers

Core Material	ID (in)	OD (in)	Height (in)	u_i	A_L Value	Turns Req'd for: 50 Ω	Turns Req'd for: 75 Ω	Ref	Material Type
Ferrite	—	0.500	—	10,000	—	3	4	1	
Ferrite	0.28	0.500	0.188	5000	2750	7	9	2	75,3E2A
Ferrite	0.52	0.825	0.250	5000	2950	7	9	3	75,3E2A
Ferrite	0.75	1.14	0.295	5000	3170	6	8	4	75,3E2A
Ferrite	0.28	0.500	0.188	125	68	44	57	5	61,Q1,4C4
Ferrite	0.52	0.825	0.250	125	73	42	55	6	61,Q1,4C4
Ferrite	0.75	1.14	0.295	125	79	41	53	7	61,Q1,4C4
Iron Powder	0.30	0.500	0.190	10	49	52	67	8	2
Iron Powder	0.495	0.795	0.250	10	55	48	63	9	2
Iron Powder	0.57	1.06	0.437	10	135	31	40	10	2

Numbers for manufacturers are listed in this table under Ref, and are listed in Table 7-4.

transformer with a loss of 0.21 dB on 160 meters, vs 0.51 dB with a single core. On 80 meters the attenuation is 0.07 dB for two stacked cores, and 0.27 dB for a transformer made on a single core.

Table 7-3 gives the winding information for some of the more common core materials and toroids ranging from 0.5- to 1.14-inch outer diameter. One section represents the 50- or 75-ohm winding. The information is typically valid for a

Table 7-4

Manufacturer's Part Numbers for Toroid Cores

Ref	Manufacturer	Core No.
1	Indiana General	BBR-7731, MN-60 02 MN-8-CX
2	Amidon Fair Rite Ferroxcube	FT-50-75 5975000301 768T188 / 3E2A
3	Amidon Fair Rite Ferroxcube	FT-82-75 5975000601 846t250 / 3E2A
4	Amidon Fair Rite Ferroxcube	FT-144-75 595001001 502T300 / 3E2A
5	Amidon Fair Rite Ferroxcube	FT-5-61 5961000301 768T188 / 4C4
6	Amidon Fair Rite Ferroxcube	FT-82-61 5961000601 846t250 / 4C4
7	Amidon Fair Rite	FT-114-61 5961001001
8	Amidon	T-50-2
9	Amdion	T-80-2
10	Amidon	T-106-2

This table shows the manufacturers' part numbers for the cores listed in Table 7-3.

frequency range from 1.8 to 7 MHz. Transformers using high permeability materials and requiring few turns will extend much higher in operating frequency because of the reduced adjacent-turn capacitance. The turns data in the table were derived by calculating the number of turns necessary to yield an impedance equal to three times the primary (50- or 75-ohm) impedance, and for a (minimum) design frequency of 1.8 MHz. The A_L value in Table 7-3 relates the required number of turns for a given core to achieve a given inductance. The relationship is given by:

$$N = 100 \times \frac{L}{A_L} \qquad \text{(Eq 7-4)}$$

where

> N = number of turns
> L = required inductance in μH
> A_L = the appropriate value taken from Table 7-3

The numbers in the column labeled Ref in Table 7-3 refer to Table 7-4, which lists some of the manufacturers and their part numbers. More complete data on toroid cores can be found in *The ARRL Handbook*.

1.8. Sloping Receiving-End Termination

The problems of stray pickup from vertical downleads, as addressed when discussing the Beverage termination, also exist at the "receiving" end of the Beverage. A sloping approach can be followed as earlier explained, and the same figures for angles, lengths and heights apply.

1.9. Simple Single-Wire Beverage Antenna

Fig 7-12 shows a sketch of a simple single-wire Beverage antenna, which consists of a single 3 to 4 m (10 to 13 ft) long support pole from which we slope two 80-meter (262-foot) long wires in one line toward the ground. The slope angle of the wires is only 2.2 degrees, which will certainly allow excellent reception of very low-angle signals. We can use simple ground rods at both ends of the Beverage, letting the ends extend slightly above ground, so that they may be used as end posts for the antenna. Use 2 meters (6.6 ft) as an average height for

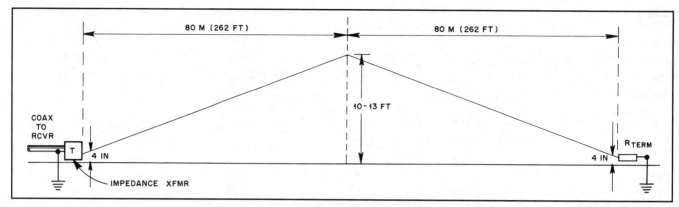

Fig 7-12—The simplest Beverage uses a single central support, while both ends are supported by a ground rod.

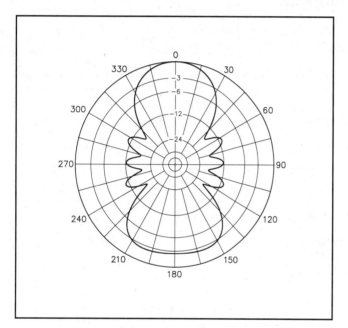

Fig 7-13—Directivity pattern of a 200-m (666 ft) long unterminated Beverage antenna at a height of 2 m (6.6 ft). Note the slight difference in relative gain between the two directions. This is the result of extra losses encountered by the reflected wave.

determining the antenna impedance (and terminating resistor value). Although Beverages by themselves are already quite insensitive to rain (and snow) static, using (PVC) insulated wire will give you a totally quiet receiving antenna even under the worst rain-static conditions.

1.10. Bi-directional Beverage Antenna

When the Beverage antenna is not terminated, the directivity will be essentially bi-directional. Fig 7-13 shows the horizontal directivity pattern for a 1-wavelength long unterminated Beverage antenna. Notice the slight attenuation from the back direction because of the extra loss of the reflected wave in the wire. A method of switching the Beverage from unidirectional to bi-directional is described in Fig 7-14. A relay at the far end of the antenna wire is fed through the antenna wire and the earth return via an RF choke

and blocking capacitors (TV preamplifiers are fed in a similar manner via the coaxial cable).

Two directions can also be obtained from a single-wire Beverage by feeding coax to both ends of the antenna (with the appropriate matching network). In this case, one end is terminated in the shack with an appropriate impedance, while the other is in use for reception. (See Ref 1210.) The "appropriate" terminating impedance can be found as follows. First, determine the characteristic impedance of the Beverage by the method explained earlier in this chapter. Connect an impedance bridge or noise bridge across the high-impedance secondary of the matching transformer. Adjust the terminating impedance at the end of the feed line (inside the shack) until a value is found which is the same as the Beverage impedance. In many cases, the impedance will be close to real, and a simple resistor with a value in the range of 50-75 ohms will provide the proper termination.

1.11. Two-Wire Switchable-Direction Antennas

Instead of erecting one wire, we can put up two wires at a distance of approximately 30 cm (12 inches), as in Fig 7-15. Signals arriving off the back of the antenna (direction B) will induce equal in-phase voltages in both wires. Because of the close spacing of the wires, there is no space diversity effect. At the end of the antenna, one wire is left open, while the other wire is short-circuited to ground. This provokes a 100% reflection of the wave, but with a 180-degree phase reversal. The signals received off the back of the antenna are now fed in a push-pull mode along the open-wire feeders toward the other end of the antenna. At this end a properly designed push-pull transformer (T1) transforms the RF from the push-pull mode (open wire feeder) to the unbalanced coaxial cable impedance. The cold end of the low-Z side of the transformer is connected to the ground system, as well as the center tap of the transformer secondary (via the secondary of transformer T2).

Signals arriving off the front of the antenna (direction A) also induce identical voltages into the parallel wires. At the receiving end, transformer T1 will not produce any output at the low-Z side provided a good balance is achieved in the transformer. However, the currents will produce output at the secondary of transformer T2 (single-ended transformer). Out-

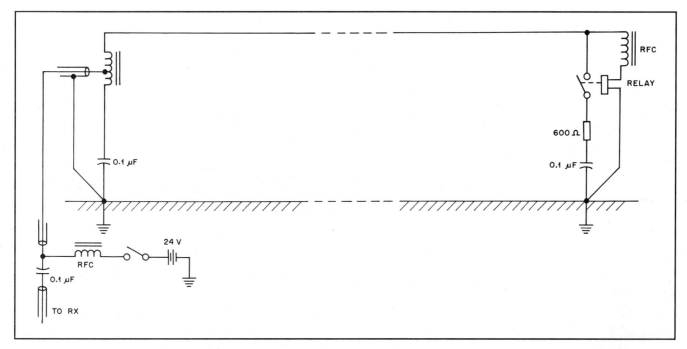

Fig 7-14—Unidirectional/bidirectional Beverage antenna setup. Note that the dc path for feeding the antenna is through ground. The relay should operate from a low voltage (max 24 V) so that dangerous potentials will not be present on the antenna wire.

puts from both directions are simultaneously available from outputs J1 and J2 of this system.

1.12. Sloping Two-Wire Beverage Terminations

In order to avoid stray pickup from the vertical downleads of the earth connections, sloping terminations can be used as explained for the single-wire Beverage antenna. At the far end of the two-wire Beverage, one of the wires is directly connected to the ground rod while the other one is left open (Fig 7-16). At the receiving end, the terminating box containing the two transformers can be housed at ground level.

1.13. Compensated Ground Wires

Where it is impossible to apply the sloping termination approach, there is an alternative ground downlead system that is virtually insensitive to RF pickup. Fig 7-17 shows how the single wire downlead is replaced by a coaxial cable. The outer shield of this cable is shorted to the inner conductor at ground level. Because of the shielding effect of the coaxial cable, no RF signals will be present at the upper end of the cable. However, since the downlead is a transmission line (which is really also the case when a single wire is used), the impedance at the upper end of the cable will be the transformed impedance of the impedance at the bottom end. The inductive reactance of

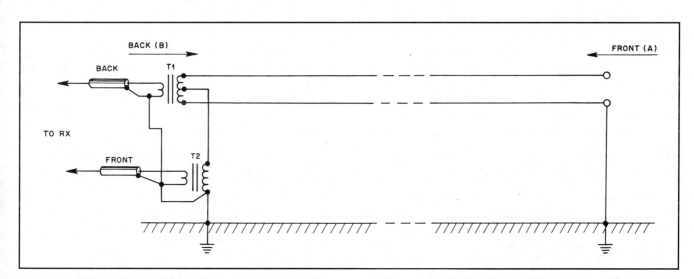

Fig 7-15—Schematic representation of the two-wire Beverage antenna, which allows reception from two directions.

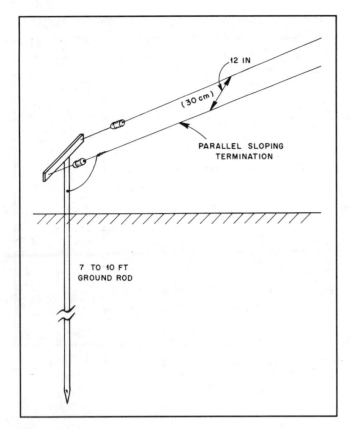

Fig 7-16—Sloping termination for a two-wire Beverage. One wire is connected directly to the ground system, and the other wire is left floating.

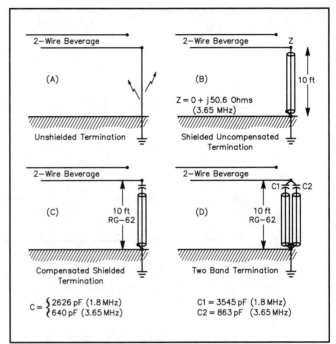

Fig 7-17—Different downlead arrangements. The shielded downlead shown at B does *not* represent a dead short to ground. The inductive reactance present will upset the required phase reversal at the end of the two-wire Beverage. Compensating with a capacitor, as shown at C, will avoid this problem, although only on a single frequency. A two-band version is shown in D. See text for complete details.

the coaxial downlead (assuming a loss-free cable and a perfect short at the bottom end) is given by:

$$Z = 2 \times Z_0 \times \tan L \qquad \text{(Eq 7-5)}$$

where
  Z_0 = characteristic impedance of the coaxial cable
  L = electrical length of the cable

The required capacitive reactance to tune the system is Z.

Table 7-5 shows the relevant values for such compensated downlead structures for 160 and 80 meters and for cable lengths of 2 m (6.6 ft), 3 m (10 ft) and 4 m (13 ft). The values are valid only for RG-62 coaxial cable (95-ohm impedance). This cable was chosen because it has a high velocity factor, resulting in a shorter physical length for a given electrical length. A two-band system can be made by simply paralleling two single-band systems in a manner similar to paralleling two dipoles for different bands. One of the systems will always show an extremely low impedance on the band it has been designed for, so it will effectively short-circuit the impedance of the system designed for the other band. The compensated coaxial cable downlead system can be adjusted in the workshop before installation in the field.

The whole system can be connected in parallel with the input of a receiver, and the capacitor tuned for minimum signal at the desired frequency. The coaxial cable plus capacitor is then used as a parallel trap, effectively shorting the receiver

input on the receiving frequency. An alternative method is to connect the system in parallel with a dummy load that is connected to the transceiver. The internal SWR meters of today's transceivers will indicate the highest SWR when the trap is tuned to resonance. Use a minimum amount of power to protect your final amplifier. See Fig 7-18 for the alignment setup. In the field, the variable capacitor (for 160 meters, a four-gang broadcast variable, plus parallel fixed capacitors) used in the test setup can be replaced by a number of parallel-connected mica capacitors of appropriate value.

7-5

Table 7-5

Compensating Capacitors for Coaxial Downleads

Frequency (MHz)	Height (ft)	Length (degrees)	Top Line Impedance	Required Series Capacitor
1.825	6.6	5.0	16.3	5350
1.825	10.0	7.6	24.6	3545
1.825	13.0	10.2	33.2	2626
3.650	6.6	10.1	33.4	1307
3.650	10.0	15.3	50.6	863
3.650	13.0	20.3	68.2	640

The required values are shown for the compensating capacitor for coaxial downleads, as shown in Fig 7-17.

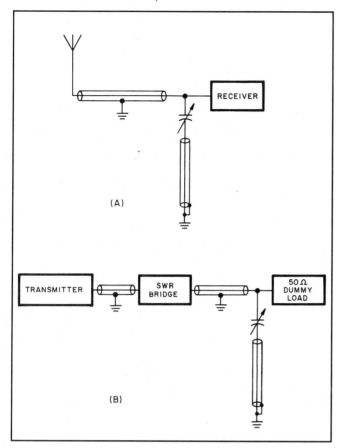

Fig 7-18—The compensated downlead can be connected in parallel with the input of a receiver as shown at A; the capacitor is then adjusted for minimal signal input at the operating frequency. Alternatively, the downlead can be connected in parallel with a dummy load, as shown at B. The capacitor is then adjusted for maximum SWR on the line between the transmitter and the dummy load/downlead combination.

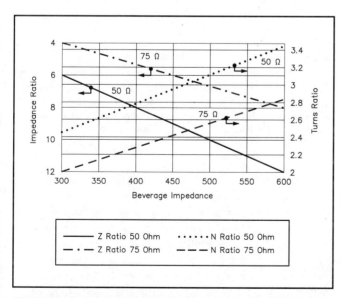

Fig 7-19—Beverage toroidal transformer winding data. Impedance and turns ratios are for transformation of antenna impedances ranging from 300 to 600 ohms, for both 50- and 75-ohm feed line.

7-6

Table 7-6

The Impedance of a Transmission Line Made of Parallel Conductors.

Wire Spacing	For 1.3-mm wire (16 AWG)	For 1.6-mm wire (14 AWG)	For 2.0-mm wire (12 AWG)
25 cm (10 in)	713 ohms	688 ohms	661 ohms
30 cm (12 in)	735 ohms	710 ohms	683 ohms

This is the impedance the two wires exhibit when used to transport the RF energy back to the feed point from the far end.

7-7

Table 7-7

Impedance of a 2-wire Beverage Antenna with 12-inch Spacing Between Wires

Antenna Height	For 1.3-mm wire (16 AWG)	For 1.6-mm wire (14 AWG)	For 2.0-mm wire (12 AWG)
0.3 m (1 ft)	229 ohms	222 ohms	216 ohms
1.0 m (3.3 ft)	298 ohms	292 ohms	295 ohms
2.0 m (6.6 ft)	339 ohms	333 ohms	326 ohms
3.0 m (10 ft)	363 ohms	357 ohms	351 ohms
4.0 m (13.3 ft)	381 ohms	374 ohms	368 ohms

This is the impedance the wires exhibit to ground when used as a Beverage antenna.

1.14. Designing the Transformers

The push-pull impedance of the open wire line is given by:

$$Z = 276 \times \log \frac{2S}{d} \qquad \text{(Eq 7-6)}$$

where

S = spacing between conductors
d = diameter of wires (in the same units).

Table 7-6 gives the impedance of an open-wire transmission line for a range of spacings and wire diameters. The impedance ratios and turns ratios for the transformer T1 are shown in Fig 7-19. The impedance of the parallel wires over ground is given by:

$$Z = 69 \times \log \left[\frac{4h}{d} \sqrt{1 + \frac{(2h)^2}{S}} \right] \qquad \text{(Eq 7-7)}$$

where

S = spacing between wires
d = diameter of wires
h = height of wires above ground (all in the same units)

Table 7-7 lists the range of Beverage antenna impedances for a spacing of 30 cm (12 in.) for three wire sizes and five wire heights. The antenna impedance differs only slightly for the three considered wire diameters.

The transformation ratios (impedance and turns) are

given in Fig 7-19. For all practical purposes, the ratios are the same for other wire sizes. T2 can be wound using the trifilar winding method, although a single winding with a tap also yields very good results. Fig 7-20 shows how transformers T1 and T2 can be wound. For a 50- and 75-ohm primary winding, the number of turns for cores from various suppliers is given in Table 7-3. Using the n-ratio from Fig 7-19 (for T1) and the impedance from Table 7-7 (for T2), the secondary turns can be calculated as follows:

1) For transformer T1 (push-pull transformer).

Inputs:
- Wire size: AWG 14 (1.6 mm diameter)
- Wire spacing: 30 cm (12 in.)
- Coax impedance: 50 ohms

Calculations:
- Push-pull impedance = 710 ohms
- Turns ratio (vs. 50-ohm primary impedance) = 3.8

If we use Indiana General BBR7731 (or the newer MN-8-CX or MN-60) cores, the primary should have three turns for 50-ohm coax (primary) impedance. The secondary should have $3 \times 3.8 = 11$ turns, with a center tap. The primary and secondary turns should be equally spaced around the core. The same number of turns should be used if you use two stacked cores. At the time of this writing, the MN-8-CX cores can be obtained from V. Misek, W1WCR (142 Wason Rd, Hudson, NH 03051; prices: $5 for 4 cores, $8 for 8 cores, $14 for 16 cores).

2) For transformer T2 (single-ended transformer).

Inputs:
- Antenna height: 10 feet (3 meters).

Calculations:
- Antenna impedance = 357 ohms
- Turns ratio (vs. 50-ohm primary impedance) = $\sqrt{\dfrac{357}{50}} = 2.7$

For the same BBR7731 (or single or stacked MN-8-CX or MN-60) cores with three turns for a 50-ohm primary, the secondary should be eight turns. The primary can be tapped at three turns from the cold end of the eight-turn secondary, or it can be wound across the cold end of the secondary. Alternatively, three five-turn parallel windings can be wound in a trifilar fashion (transmission line transformer), whereby we will remove 1.5 turns from the third winding (hot side) to obtain the proper matching ratio. See Fig 7-21 for a possible construction method.

1.15. Constructing the Transformers

After selecting the proper cores and calculating the number of turns for the different windings, the correct enameled wire size should be calculated. The optimum wire size just fills the inside of the toroid core without gaps. To determine the optimum wire diameter, proceed as follows.

Measure the inside diameter of the core (d) and subtract 0.5 mm (0.020 inch). Calculate the inside circumference (d – 0.5) × 3.14 if in mm or (d – 0.020) × 3.14 if in inches and divide the circumference by the total number of turns required for the entire transformer. This calculation gives the maximum

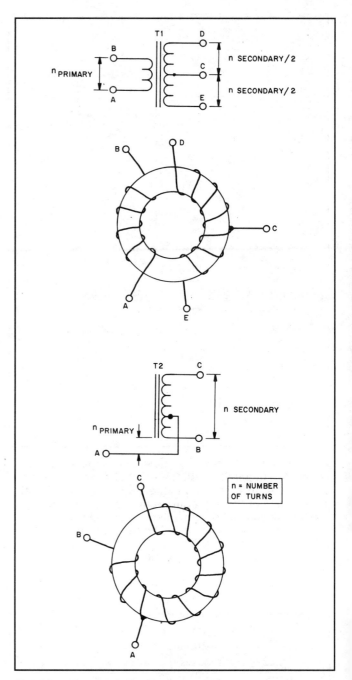

Fig 7-20—Toroidal transformers. The windings of both T1 and T2 should be evenly spaced on the toroidal core. The enameled copper wire can be held on the core with electrical tape or Q dope.

possible wire diameter. If only a small number of turns are to be wound onto a relatively large core, the calculated wire diameter may be rather large, and using such thick wire may cause problems in achieving the proper close-winding on the core. In such a case, a smaller diameter wire must be used, and the turns should be equally spaced around the core. Conversely, when many turns are required (low-permeability material), several layers of wire may be required. The high-end frequency response of such transformers will be restricted due to large inter-winding capacitance. If trifilar windings are used, the three conductors can either be twisted together or laid

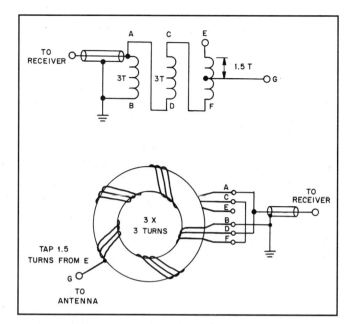

Fig 7-21—By tapping the third winding of the transmission-line transformer, a transformer with any transformation ratio between 4:1 and 9:1 can be made. The example shown is for a transformation ratio of 7:1.

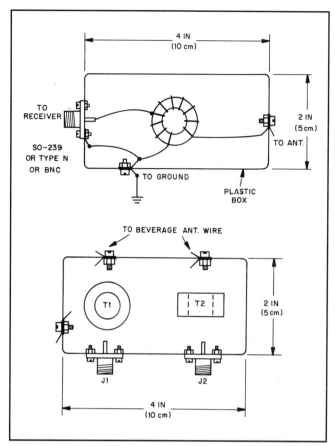

Fig 7-22—Suggested layouts for single and two-wire receiving-end terminations. Plastic boxes are inexpensive and allow simple feedthrough systems to be used (screw and nut), while the toroidal transformers can be secured directly to the plastic material with silicone sealant.

parallel in a closely spaced manner. The group of three wires should be spaced equally around the core (see Fig 7-21). In all cases, using high-permeability material ($\mu = 1000$ to $10,000$) will greatly reduce your efforts in winding the transformers.

Example:

BBR7731 cores measure 5/16 inch (7.9 mm) inner diameter.

T1 needs a total of 13 windings, T2 needs 11.

T1: $(7.9 - 0.5) \times (\pi / 13) = 1.79$ mm
T2: $(7.9 - 0.5) \times (\pi / 11) = 2.11$ mm

It would not be possible to use such thick wire and achieve proper winding results on a small core. AWG 20 enameled wire (approximately 0.8 mm diameter) would be recommended on this core for both T1 and T2.

To house the transformers I have used both aluminum and PVC-type diecast boxes of appropriate size . The PVC boxes are inexpensive and do not need feedthrough standoffs for the output to the Beverage antenna. A stainless steel screw with nuts and bolts mounted right through the plastic wall is all that is needed. Do not economize on coax connectors. One excellent way of waterproofing coaxial connections (and any others) is to squeeze plenty of medical-grade petroleum jelly into both connector parts before mating. Some petroleum jelly can be applied to the box seams to waterproof the whole assembly once the cover has been put on. Petroleum jelly is an excellent electrical insulator (it has a very low dielectric constant similar to Teflon and polyethylene). I have used the same material for protecting non stainless steel antenna hardware. After many years of use in a humid and aggressive climate, the hardware still comes apart with no problems. If the two-wire Beverage is constructed, one may save on coax cable by incorporating a relay in the box, and switching the coax line from direction A to direction B.

The relay can be fed via a single coaxial cable, similar to the way shown in Fig 7-14. Both directions will not be simultaneously available at the receiver site (for electrical null steering purposes). Fig 7-22 shows possible layouts for transformer units for single-wire and two-wire Beverage antennas.

Calibrated and tested toroidal transformers for a 9:1 transformation ratio, wound on a stack of MN-8-CX cores, covering 1 to 10 MHz are available at cost plus shipping (1 transformer = $12, 5 pieces = $50, 10 pieces = $90. Prices include air-mailing worldwide prepaid to J. Devoldere, 215 Poelstraat, B9820 Merelbeke, Belgium).

1.16. Testing the Transformers

The matching transformer for the single-wire Beverage, as well as the single-ended transformer (T2) for the two-wire Beverage, can easily be tested for SWR by terminating the secondary with a terminating resistor (of appropriate wattage) and feeding a small amount of RF into the antenna via a sensitive SWR bridge through the transformer to an appropriate terminating resistor. A more elegant way is to use a noise bridge. Using a noise bridge allows the use of small cores, as very low power will be used when testing. The SWR of the push-pull transformer (T1) can also be tested by connecting two resistors across the secondary to the center tap (each resistor should be equal to half of the impedance of the secondary, which is the impedance of the open-wire line). The balance of the push-pull transformer can be tested by connecting the two secondary outputs together and feeding a small amount of RF from any source (RF generator or dip meter) to this connection. A perfectly balanced transformer should yield no output from this configuration. The physical symmetry of the transformer may be adjusted (slightly adjusting turn spacings on the toroidal core) while performing this test, until the lowest possible signal output is achieved. The balance can be assessed by temporarily disconnecting one of the secondary leads and measuring the signal-strength difference on the receiver. Better than 40-dB difference should be easily obtainable.

1.17. Feed Lines

Stray pickup from an improperly shielded feed-line system can upset all the directional characteristics of an otherwise properly operating Beverage antenna system. As the Beverage antennas will most likely be operated on relatively low frequencies, we need not use a feed line with the lowest possible loss, especially where all but the very longest feed-line runs are being considered. It is still important, however, to use well-shielded coax in order to have a quiet feed system under all circumstances and on all frequencies. I have been using double-shielded RG-214 (same size as RG-8 or RG-213, but with two densely woven copper shields) or ½- to ⅝-inch Hardline on my Beverage systems. All feed systems have proved to be totally quiet. Large coax was used because some of the feed lines are up to 300 m (1000 ft) long. Smaller coax can be used, especially where runs are shorter. Table 6-2 shows the typical losses for common coaxial cables on 1.8, 3.5 and 7 MHz.

Often, 75-ohm CATV-type coax leftovers can be bought at reasonable prices from the local cable company. The flexible coax used for drop lines is good for anything but very long runs. Hardline is the ultimate choice for long runs, as it offers the lowest attenuation and best shielding characteristics.

Four 4-cm (1.5 in.) polyethylene semi-rigid water pipe can be used as a duct for the RG-214 coaxial cables. After installing the feed lines, try to receive signals with the coax connected to the receiver, with both the coax end open and then with it terminated in a resistor equal to the characteristic impedance of the cable. The receiver should be completely dead, even on the medium waves where very strong ground waves can be expected. If not, try grounding the coax shield at the receiver and/or the end of the line, until satisfactory performance is obtained. It is not advisable to suspend the feed line above ground or to hang it between trees. After the feed lines have been tested for stray pickup, connect the termination box with the transformers, and connect the ground lead to the box. Without the Beverage wire(s) connected, the receiver should still be dead on all frequencies. This procedure will prove the performance of a good feed system with no reduction in directivity from stray pickup.

1.18. Location of the Beverage

My own experience with Beverage antennas has been over flat terrain consisting of rich, wet soil. As Beverage antennas receive mainly vertically polarized signals, it is not recommended to run a Beverage antenna wire close to a large vertical transmitting antenna. Large vertical antennas re-radiate strong signals and will upset the directivity pattern of the Beverage antenna if the antennas are separated by less than ¼ wavelength. It is not necessary to have the receiving end close to the station. With a well-shielded, low-loss and well-matched feed line, the receiving end can be many wavelengths away from the shack. Just as it is not recommended to put up a vertically polarized antenna between tall trees, it is not a good idea to run a Beverage antenna through the woods. Many hams have reported satisfactory performance from Beverage antennas strung between trees in the woods; the fact remains, however, that these antennas would probably perform much better if erected in a more appropriate environment. Beverage antennas for different directions may cross each other if the wires are separated by at least 10 cm (4 in.). Beverage antennas should also not be run in close proximity to parallel conductors such as fences, telephone lines, power lines (even if quiet) and the like.

1.19. Mechanical Construction

Almost any type of support will work for a Beverage antenna. For erecting a permanent Beverage I have been using 4-meter (13 ft) lengths of 2.5 cm (1 in.) OD steel water pipe as a support. About 1 m (3 ft) of each pipe is buried in the ground. A polyethylene insulator of the type commonly used for electric fences is mounted at the top of each pipe.

For two-wire Beverages, two such insulators are spaced horizontally 30 cm (12 in.) on a metal crossbar on top of each pipe. See Fig 7-23. The end supports are made from 2-inch OD steel pipe, installed in a small concrete pedestal for added strength and stability. I have used single-strand bronze wire, 14 AWG (1.6 mm OD), which is pulled to approximately 45 kg (100 lb) tension at one end of the total span. Copper-clad steel wire is also a good performer. If ice loading is to be expected, the wire should only be pulled to 14 kg (30 lb.). The sag on the wires will become objectionable for long runs, so that more supports will be required. Where ice loading is not a problem, supports are needed only every 80 to 100 m (260 to 330 ft). This means that a 160 to 200 m (520- to 660-ft) Beverage can be constructed with two end supports and only one intermediate support. If both ends are of the sloping type configuration, no separate supports are needed, and the end of the ground rods can act as mechanical ground posts for the antenna wire(s).

Soft-drawn copper wire cannot be tensioned to any great degree without causing much stretching, and it is not suitable for long unsupported spans of wire. If one does not mind using many supports, a soft wire may be used for the antenna. In any case, do not wrap the antenna wire around trees or branches, as the coils may severely degrade the performance of the antenna. If possible, use insulated wire, as accidental contacts with trees will degrade the performance. In addition the antenna will be completely insensitive to rain and ice static.

In the past years I have been making extensive use of what I call "disposable" Beverage antennas. A number of the

Fig 7-24—Two-meter (6 ft) long bamboo sticks are used as supports on my "disposable" type Beverage antennas.

Fig 7-23—A 3-meter (10 ft) long steel pipe with a 30 cm (12 in.) crossbar at the top is used to support the two-wire Beverage antenna on polyethylene electric-fence insulators.

Beverages I use in the winter have to be taken down in spring time so the farmers can work their fields. Hence, the erecting and dismantling of the Beverage antennas should be easy and fast. For these antennas I use 2.5 m (8 ft) bamboo sticks (they are very cheap) as supports. The bamboos are planted every 30 m (100 ft). For wire I use AWG 20 to 26 (0.4 to 0.8 mm diameter) soft-drawn copper wire. Bare copper wire, enameled copper wire or PVC insulated copper wire all do well. The wire is attached to the top of the bamboo in a small loop made of vinyl tape (Figs 7-24 and 7-25). A 300-m (1000 ft) long Beverage of this type can be erected or dismantled in about 30 minutes.

Do not try to run two Beverage antennas one above the other on the same supports (one firing to the left, one firing to the right). The lower antenna will be screened by the upper one. Side by side is okay though.

1.20. Arrays of Beverages

Although the use of arrays of Beverages is not known to me except as a transmitting antenna (Ref. 1236), arrays of Beverages could easily be implemented, as shown in Fig 7-26. The advantage for a receive-only antenna is not obvious

Fig 7-25—Method of affixing the Beverage wire on the bamboo stick, using a loop made of electrical tape, as shown by Marleen, daughter of ON4UN.

however, as the added gain will inevitably result in a more narrow pattern, which in turn would necessitate more Beverages to cover all directions. Erecting arrays of Beverages for the sake of increased signal output does not seem to be useful either, as the signal produced by a single Beverage two or three wavelengths long is more than adequate on our noisy low-frequency bands. In order to establish a high-quality point-to-point link over distances up to 10,000 km (6,000 miles),

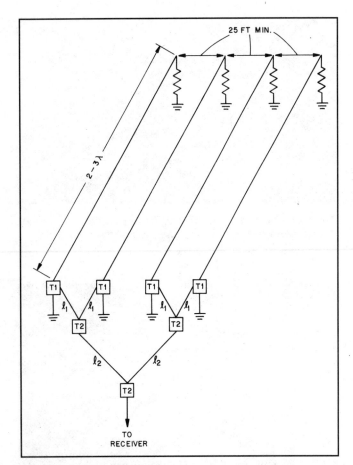

Fig 7-26—Arrays of Beverages can be close spaced as shown (7.5 m or 25 ft recommended). The transformers designated T1 are receiving end transformers; those designated T2 represent 3-dB power splitters (see also Fig 7-27).

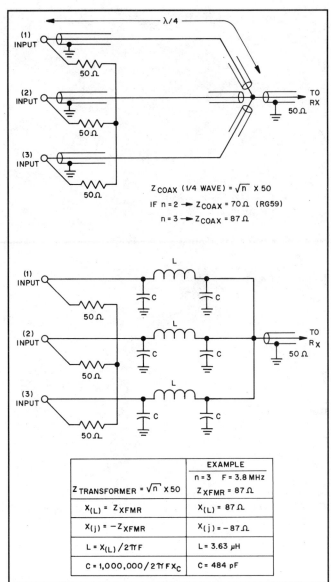

$$Z_{COAX} (1/4\ WAVE) = \sqrt{n} \times 50$$
$$IF\ n = 2 \rightarrow Z_{COAX} = 70\,\Omega\ (RG59)$$
$$n = 3 \rightarrow Z_{COAX} = 87\,\Omega$$

$Z_{TRANSFORMER} = \sqrt{n} \times 50$	EXAMPLE
	n = 3 F = 3.8 MHz
	$Z_{XFMR} = 87\,\Omega$
$X_{(L)} = Z_{XFMR}$	$X_{(L)} = 87\,\Omega$
$X_{(j)} = -Z_{XFMR}$	$X_{(j)} = -87\,\Omega$
$L = X_{(L)}/2\pi F$	$L = 3.63\ \mu H$
$C = 1,000,000/2\pi F X_C$	$C = 484\ pF$

Fig 7-27—Quarter-wave coaxial transformers can be used in a Wilkinson power divider (a 3 dB power splitter or hybrid). Where coaxial cable with the required impedance is not available, the coaxial line can be replaced with a lumped-constant network as shown.

however, a Beverage array would make an exceptionally good low-noise receiving antenna. The outputs from the Beverages can be combined via Wilkinson power dividers. When two Beverages are involved, two 75-ohm quarter-wave transformers can be used to obtain 100-ohm impedances at the junction point. The Wilkinson resistor is $2 \times 50 = 100$ ohms. Where four antennas are involved, cascaded two-input Wilkinson dividers can be used as shown in Fig 7-27. Alternatively, the quarter-wave coaxial transformers can be replaced by a quarter-wave line made of lumped constants, also shown in Fig 7-27 (Ref. 1313). This solution is especially attractive where no coaxial cable with the correct characteristic impedance can be found for the construction of the quarter-wave transformer.

1.21. Beverage Performance

For me, Beverage antennas have undoubtedly been the key to working my last 50 countries on 80 meters. As far as 160 meters is concerned, I would not like to think what it would be without them. Some Beverage users complain that the output from their antennas is too low and they need preamplifiers to boost the signals. If the antenna is properly constructed and has a proper matching transformer, this should not be the case. Beverages at a height of 3 m (10 ft) should produce signals of typically −10 dBi. This is only 1.5 S-units down

from a large vertical. However, as the noise and QRM will be reduced to a much higher degree, the relative gain of a Beverage may be several S-units over a large, low-angle vertical. In every case (when conditions are good), all my Beverage antennas produce atmospheric noise which is substantially higher than the noise floor of the receiver. In most circumstances it has been possible to insert 10 or 20 dB of front-end attenuation on the receiver without degrading the readability of the signal. It goes without saying that in none of these cases a preamplifier was needed or desired. This does not mean that Beverages put up in less than ideal surroundings (in the woods or at very low heights) and fed via less efficient feed lines could not use a little "souping up." In that case, a preamp should be inserted at the receiving end of the antenna, not in the shack.

1.22. Electrical Null Steering

Electrical null steering is a technique used to obtain virtually infinite rejection of an unwanted signal source. This technique is most commonly used with small loop antennas to obtain a unidirectional radiation pattern. Signals from the sense antenna and the loop are combined in the correct phase to achieve a cardioid pattern. The article by Webb, W1ETC, on Electrical Antenna Null Steering (Ref. 1235) is an excellent reference work for understanding the principles of this technique and its limitations. Misek, W1WCR, (Ref 1206) has described in detail the design and the construction of a steerable-wave antenna. I have experimented quite extensively with null steering on Beverage antennas, using the basic setup shown in Fig 7-28. Control of the phasing can be achieved most easily if the Beverage is an exact number of half wavelengths at the operating frequency, because only then will both the forward and backward lobes be available in the shack with phase differences equal to a multiple of 180 degrees (provided the coaxial cables feeding T1 and T2 are of identical electrical length). Fig 7-29 shows how the forward and rearward radiation patterns of a Beverage antenna can be combined to null out a signal source at any angle.

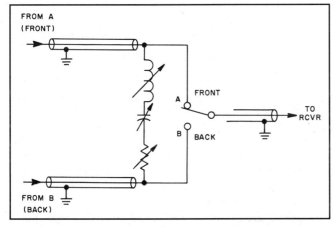

Fig 7-28—Electrical null-steering control for a two-wire Beverage. The outputs from directions A and B are combined via an RLC circuit that provides the correct phasing and amplitude control for null steering. Typical values for the components are: R = 500 ohms, C = 1000 pF max and L = 2 to 10 μH.

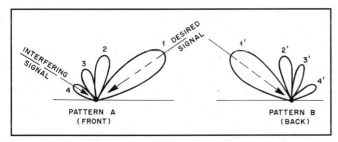

Fig 7-29—The interfering signal which falls in the minor lobe (lobe 4) of the front pattern is combined with the signal produced by lobe 1' from the back pattern. Careful phase and amplitude control can result in total elimination of the interfering signal.

Assume we are receiving a desired signal which is right in the peak of the main lobe (1) of pattern A. At the same time, however, a much stronger interfering signal is being received in the rear lobe (4) of the same pattern. Although this lobe is much smaller (perhaps 20 dB down from the main lobe), the unwanted signal is still so strong that it makes reception of the desired signal impossible. Looking at pattern B (produced by the same antenna in the reverse direction), we now have the offending signal available (at great signal strength) in the forward lobe (1'). If we now combine the signal produced by lobe 4 from the forward pattern (A) with the signal produced by lobe 1' of the rearward pattern (B), and if these signals are equal in amplitude and 180 degrees out of phase with each other, complete cancellation of the offending signal will result. After many hours of experimentation on 80 and 160 meters as well as the top end of the medium-wave broadcast band, the following observations were made:

• Extremely deep nulls (up to 50 dB or better) can be obtained on local (ground wave) broadcast stations in the medium-wave band. Because of the nature of the signals (AM), critical adjustment of both the amplitudes and phasing is possible.

• It becomes much more tricky to null out even a ground-wave SSB or CW signal on 80 meters because of the non-constant amplitude nature of the signals.

• Nulling out sky-wave signals is generally impossible, because they often arrive via multiple paths of varying lengths.

• Nulling out sources of man-made noise can be accomplished quite easily, as these sources are usually vertically polarized and are generated in the vicinity of the receiving antenna.

1.23. Preamplifiers for Beverage Antennas

Although I personally have never yet felt the urge to use a preamplifier on my Beverage antennas, I am aware that numerous hams use them successfully. I have always chosen to feed the terminating points of my Beverages with high quality coaxial cable, showing negligible loss on the low bands (at least RG-214 double shielded, or solid screen CATV line of ½ inch or more). Even with a 300 m (1000 ft) long feed line I feel no need for a preamplifier. These just makes things worse as far as receiver overload is concerned.

The best test to find out whether or not your Beverage antenna needs a preamp is to see if you can hear the receiver internal noise over the atmospheric noise picked up by the antenna. If that is the case, you are ready for a preamp. If not, stay away from a preamp.

Excellent preamplifiers for this purpose have been described in the literature (Ref 257, 267, 1251 and 1254).

1.24. The ON4UN Beverage System

Just as an example, let me explain how I designed the Beverage system at my QTH. Fig 7-30 shows the layout at my QTH. To the north of my property I have a field that measures 150 by 200 m (500 by 660 ft). The friendly neighbor farmer allows me to use the field from mid November until the end of March. I installed four Beverage terminating posts at the four corners of the terrain, and run long coaxial cables (⅝ inch

CATV Hardline) to the four posts. The distance to the farthest post is about 300 m (1000 ft), so a good quality feed line is required, especially as I really don't want to use preamplifiers.

Fig 7-30 shows how 11 different directions are covered basically from one 150 by 200-m (500 by 660-ft) field, with some of the Beverages extending somewhat onto the neighboring fields.

From post #1:
Antenna #1: 180 m (600 ft) long, direction 0 degrees (not much used, right into the aurora belt).
Antenna #2: 300 m (1000 ft) long, direction 30 degrees (Japan, Pacific)
Antenna #3: 300 m (1000 ft) long, direction 70 degrees (Far East, Australia)

From post #2:
Antenna #4: 300 m (1000 ft) long, direction 90 degrees (Central Asia, W6-W7 long path)
Antenna #5: 210 m (700 ft) long, direction 120 degrees (long path W6-W7, Middle East)

From post #3:
Antenna #6: 300 m (1000 ft) long, direction 150 degrees (Indian Ocean, East and South Africa)
Antenna #7: 180 m (600 ft) long, direction 180 degrees (West Africa, South Atlantic)
Antenna #8: 210 m (700 ft) long , direction 220 degrees (South America)

From post #4:
Antenna #9: 200 m (660 ft) long, direction 270 degrees (Northern South America, Caribbean area)
Antenna #10: 240 m (800 ft) long, direction 300 degrees (Southern USA, Central America)
Antenna #11: 240 m (800 ft) long, direction 320 degrees (Northern USA, Pacific).

Switching system: As each post must accommodate three Beverages, a switching arrangement must be provided to switch the three directions. I have developed a small box containing three miniature relays as well as the 9:1 toroidal transformer. The three-position switching logic can be sent from the shack through a single conductor: In position #1 there is no dc voltage on the control line, in position #2 we have a positive voltage and in position #3 we have a negative voltage. As shown in Fig 7-31 the relays for Antennas #1 and #2 have their coils fed via a diode which is connected to pass only positive (relay #1) and only negative (relay #2) voltage. When no voltage is present on the control line, the normally closed contact will select Antenna #3. When a positive voltage is on the control line, Antenna #1 will be selected while #2 and #1 will be grounded. A negative control voltage will select Antenna #2. I do not use a separate control cable, but feed the dc through the coaxial feed line, using small RF chokes and a blocking capacitor to isolate the RF from the dc voltage, as shown in Fig 7-31.

Do not use too small relays. They have to function in the cold under very adverse weather conditions. I must admit I have had quite a few problems with the miniature relays that

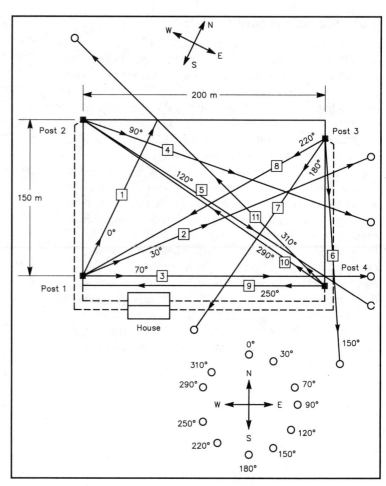

Fig 7-30—Layout of 11 Beverages on a single field, measuring 200 × 150 m (660 × 500 ft). See text for details.

we find on PC boards in present-day equipment. Rather, use over-sized relays if you don't want to have to replace them in the middle of a snowstorm.

Identical terminating boxes are used on all 4 posts. Fig 7-32 shows the switching box in the basement where the four feed lines are merged into a single small coaxial cable going to the receiver.

On the operator table we have a small control box (4 × 8 × 12 cm) containing the power supply (+ and – 24 volt) and a 2-circuit, 12-position rotary switch, with 30-degree steps. Fig 7-33 shows the wiring of the control box.

■ 2. SMALL LOOP ANTENNAS

In the early days of radio, small loop antennas were used extensively as receiving antennas. A small loop antenna is a magnetic antenna, which means that the antenna is excited by the magnetic rather than the electric component of a radio wave. Most other antennas such as dipoles, ground planes, rhombics, Yagis, large loop antennas, and so on, are called electric antennas, responding to the electric component of the wave. Full-size loops (quads and delta loops) are not loop antennas in the strictest sense, but rather an array of close-spaced stacked dipoles. With large loops, the directivity is broadside to the loop plane. With small loops, the directivity

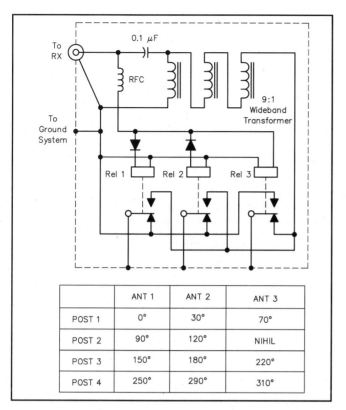

	ANT 1	ANT 2	ANT 3
POST 1	0°	30°	70°
POST 2	90°	120°	NIHIL
POST 3	150°	180°	220°
POST 4	250°	290°	310°

Fig 7-31—Schematic diagram of the receiving-end box which accommodates three Beverage antennas. The dc voltages for the relays are fed through the coaxial cable. Relays are 24 V types. Note that the antennas not in use are grounded.

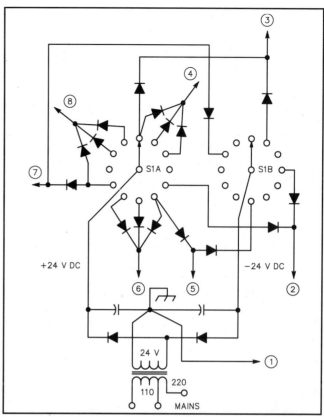

Fig 7-33—Schematic diagram of the control box with the diode switching array and the power supply. The numbers in the schematic correspond with the numbers of the eight-conductor cable used between the control box and the switching box, as shown in Fig 7-32. S1 is a 2-gang, 12-position (12 × 30 degree) rotary switch. All diodes are small power diodes (1 A).

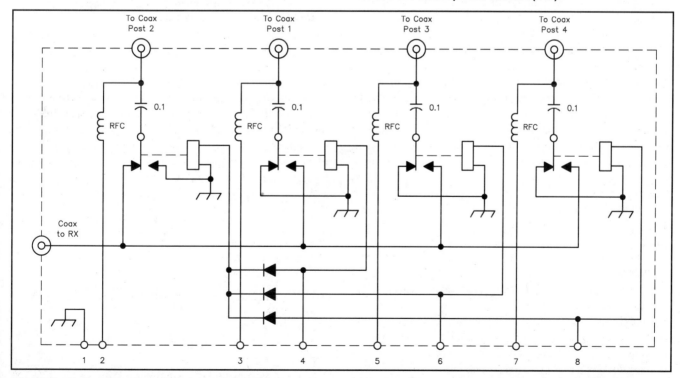

Fig 7-32—Switching box where the four feed lines, running to the four Beverage posts, are switched and merged into a single small coaxial cable going to the receiver. The dc voltages for controlling the four relays are fed to the switching control box on the operator table, together with the dc voltages from the four coaxial lines through a flexible eight-conductor cable.

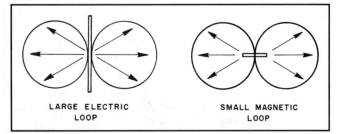

Fig 7-34—Horizontal radiation patterns of a large electric loop (1 wavelength circumference) and a small magnetic loop.

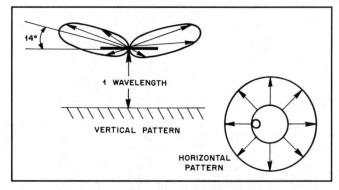

Fig 7-36—Vertical and horizontal radiation patterns of a small loop erected in a plane parallel to the ground. The radiation angle now depends on the height above ground (as with a dipole).

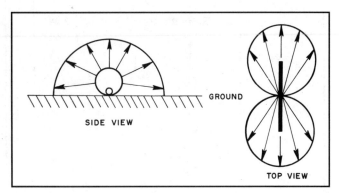

Fig 7-35—Vertical and horizontal radiation patterns of a small loop erected in a plane perpendicular to the ground (classic configuration).

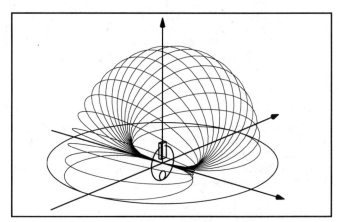

Fig 7-37—Three-dimensional radiation pattern of the magnetic loop erected vertically.

is 90 degrees from this, in the plane of the loop (end-fire). Fig 7-34 shows directivity patterns of both large and small loop antennas.

The windings of a small loop antenna can best be compared to the windings of a transformer. The antenna is tuned to resonance with a tuning capacitor. The energy can then be coupled from the "transformer" by a link, or by an inductive or capacitive tap. Most receiving-only designs use several turns for the loop. The radiation resistance and the loop efficiency are directly proportional to the loop diameter and the number of turns. Receiving-only loops have been described with dimensions ranging from very small to quite large, using a variety of feed systems, and often employing built-in preamps (Ref. 1219, 1226, and 1229). Such receiving-only loops have proved to be especially valuable for reception on 160 meters, where they are often extremely helpful in eliminating local sources of interference.

Loop antennas can show a great deal of horizontal directivity, but when operated vertically (with the plane of the loop perpendicular to the ground) the loop has no vertical directivity at all. See Figs 7-35 and 7-36. This means that the loop receives high- as well as low-angle signals. Its performance is not influenced by the quality of the ground (there is no pseudo Brewster angle involved!). Fig 7-37 shows the three-dimensional radiation pattern of a magnetic loop.

McCoy, W1ICP, described a small, single-turn loop in amateur literature (Ref. 1227). The antenna is a loop for 80 meters, with a diameter of 3.5 m (12 ft), and is resonated by

a series connection of three capacitors with the feed line connected across the middle one (forming a capacitive voltage divider). Other designs of magnetic loops have been published more recently (Ref 1255 and 1250). Ohmic losses appear to be the main problem in obtaining reasonable efficiency, in view of the very low radiation resistance. The radiation resistance of a single turn loop is given by:

$$R_{rad} = 197 \times \left(\frac{C}{\lambda}\right)^4$$

where

C = circumference of the loop
λ = wavelength

For a (quite large) loop with a diameter of 6 m (20 ft) operating on 160 meters, R_{rad} is:

$$197 \times \left(\frac{18.8}{164}\right)^4 = 34 \text{ milohms}$$

The design parameters of a single turn loop are:

$$L_{\mu H} = 2S \times \frac{\ln(S/d) - 1.07}{10}$$

where

$L_{\mu H}$ = inductance of the single-turn coil (loop)
S = circumference of the loop in meters
d = diameter of the loop conductor in meters

Example:

Take a loop of 6-meter diameter, using a 30-mm tube as a conductor:

$$L = 2\pi \times 6 \times \frac{\ln(6/0.03) - 1.07}{10} = 15.9\ \mu H$$

The required capacitor to resonate the loop at a given frequency is:

$$C = \frac{25,300}{f^2 \times L}$$

where

C = tuning capacitance, pF
f = design frequency, kHz
L = inductance of the loop, μH

If we want to resonate the 6 m (diameter) loop (15.9 μH self inductance) on 1.835 kHz, the required capacitor is: 25,300 / (1.835² × 15.9) = 473 pF.

In recent years, Wuertz, DL2FA, Kaeferlein, DK5CZ, and Schwarzbeck, DL1BU (Ref 1218), have experimented extensively with single-turn transmission-type loops (Refs 1215-1217).

Commercial versions of these loops are manufactured by C. Kaeferlein, DK5CZ, and sold worldwide. The largest model (AMA 7) has a diameter of 3.4 meters (11 feet) and is tunable from 1.7 to 8.0 MHz. Table 7-8 shows the main characteristics of this loop antenna, which tunes 160, 80 and 40 meters. The loop has been built for transmitting as well (max. 100 W power), but on 160 meters it would make a rather poor transmitting antenna in view of the intrinsic loss of 10 dB. For receiving, however, this is not important at all.

Note the very low radiation resistance of the loop on 160 meters: 3.5 milohms! This corresponds with a calculated 3 dB bandwidth of just over 2 kHz. Here we come to another advantage of a small loop: The narrow bandwidth adds a high degree of front-end selectivity, which can be an advantage in

reducing intermodulation distortion in the receiver, for instance when strong nearby BC stations are a problem. Although one cannot expect such a small loop antenna to be a competitive transmitting antenna for DX work on the low bands, it can be a worthwhile aid in obtaining better reception. For man-made noise, the electric component of the radiated wave is most often predominant in the near-field. Because a loop responds to the magnetic component of the signal only, loops are much quieter receiving antennas than dipoles or monopoles. Man-made noise sources are almost always of local nature (ground-wave signals), and as such, the signal polarization and the phase are constant (assuming a stationary noise source). These are the necessary prerequisites for achieving a stable null on an interfering signal by orienting the loop in line with the noise source. A practical rejection of 20 dB or better is easily achievable.

When mounted vertically (the classic configuration), the height of the loop above ground does not influence the radiation pattern or the efficiency to any great degree. Poorly conducting ground will not influence the efficiency of a loop, as the magnetic field lines are parallel to the ground. When mounted horizontally (plane of the loop parallel to ground), the horizontal directivity pattern becomes omnidirectional, and the vertical pattern shows a radiation angle which depends on the height of the antenna above ground (the radiation angles given for horizontal dipoles in Fig 8-4 can be used).

Excellent articles have appeared in literature on home building magnetic loops (Ref 1215, 1216, 1219, 1220, 1221, 1229, 1252, 1253, 1254, and 1255). It must be said however, that the problems in constructing an efficient loop for 160 meters are not easy to overcome. Multi-band loops must be small enough to cover the highest frequency with the tuning capacitor set at minimum. For the lowest frequency, the loop may then require a sizable capacitor. Also at the lowest frequency the R_{rad} will be lowest (perhaps 5 to 50 milohms), which means the loss resistance in the loop must be kept very low. Currents as well as voltages involved are very high, even with 100 watts of transmitter power. On the other end the high voltages are not lethal: As soon as you come close to the loop it will be detuned by the proximity effect so that voltages will drop to a low and not dangerous level. Another problem is to have a remotely driven tuning capacitor (which *really must be* a split-stator capacitor if avoiding losses is important) that tunes slowly enough to be practical. Don't forget, we are talking of 3-dB bandwidths of 2 kHz on 160 meters! The AMA 7 magnetic loop antenna, available from Kaeferlein-Electronic DK5CZ, Germany, combines all these requirements in a very well engineered unit. The AMA antennas are also extensively used in commercial service such as in embassies.

Coupling the RF into the loop can be done in different ways. In his commercial brochure, DK5CZ describes an inductively coupled loop, made of coaxial cable. This loop has a diameter of approximately one-fifth of the main loop diameter. Fig 7-38 shows the layout of the coupling loop. Adjusting for lowest SWR is done simply by reshaping the loop inside the large loop. A shape can be found that gives an acceptable SWR over the entire operating bandwidth (eg, 40 through 160 meters for the model AMA7 loop).

7-8

Table 7-8

Main Electrical Characteristics of the AMA 7 Loop for 160 Through 40 Meters.

Tuning range: 1.75 to 8.0 MHz
Power: 100 watts

Band	40 m	80 m	160 m
Gain (dBd)	−0.71	−3.13	−10.2
Efficiency	93%	53%	11%
R_{rad} (milohm)	762	48	3.5
SWR Bandwidth (2:1)	14 kHz	5 kHz	2 kHz

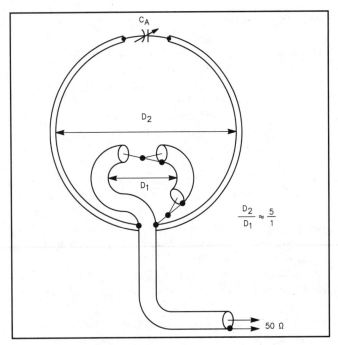

Fig 7-38—Layout of the coupling loop as used by DK5CZ on his AMA magnetic loops. Changing the shape of the small inner loop slightly makes it possible to obtain a nearly 1:1 SWR over the entire spectrum covered. (See Fig 7-40.)

$$\frac{D_2}{D_1} \approx \frac{5}{1}$$

Fig 7-40—The AMA 7 magnetic loop as erected in the front garden at ON4UN. It is located approximately 60 meters (200 ft) from the 160-meter vertical; the large spacing reduces coupling to the vertical.

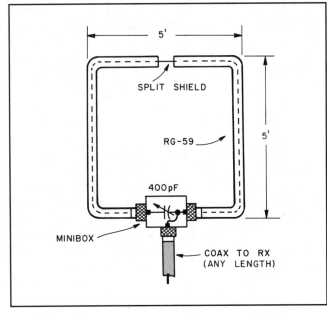

Fig 7-39—Shielded receiving-only loop for 160 meters as described in *The ARRL Antenna Book*, 15th and 16th editions. This is the receiving antenna used by HB9AMO, together with a 15-dB preamplifier.

C. J. Mozzochi, W1LYQ, has been using a loop with a circumference of 24 m (80 ft). He reports excellent results on 160 meters even for transmitting, where he has worked numerous European stations with the loop.

P. Petry, HB9AMO, reports using the shielded loop as described in *The ARRL Antenna Book* (15th edition, pages 5-20 to 5-22; 16th edition, pages 5-19 to 5-20) in conjunction with his 27 m (90 ft) top loaded vertical to bring him well over 200 countries on 160 meters, as well as the all-time number one 160-meter WAZ. He uses a 15-dB preamp to boost the signal. Fig 7-39 shows the dimensions of the loop. For details see the full description in *The ARRL Antenna Book*.

R. C. Fenwick, K5RR, described an array made of two small loops (8.5 m or 28 ft circumference) spaced 18 m (60 ft) and fed via a Wilkinson hybrid coupler and a coaxial delay line (Ref 1248). Fenwick reports a front-to-back ratio of 35 dB on and near the design frequency and nearly 20 dB in a wide range around the design frequency. The output of the array is said to be down approximately 29 dB from a reference vertical.

During the winter of 1992-1993 I installed the AMA 7 loop (1.8 through 7 MHz) in my front garden (see Fig 7-40). The base of the loop is about 1.5 m (5 ft) above ground. The antenna is fed with 30 m (100 ft) of RG-213. The purpose was to evaluate the loop, especially in comparison with the 200- to 300-m long Beverages that I normally use. It immediately became clear that on 160 meters, under all circumstances, the loop is quieter than the quarter-wave transmit antenna, while signals are down 10 to 15 dB (which is really totally irrelevant). On 80 the same is true, but the "loss" vs the vertical is only approximately 1 S-unit. On 40 meters, the loop is down about 10 dB vs the 3-element Yagi. On all three lower bands I have found the loop to be a worthwhile asset in receiving. In no case however, have I found the loop to be as good a receiving antenna as any of my Beverages. The loop is sensitive to rain static, unless it is covered by an insulating material.

Magnetic loops can easily be modeled using MININEC, provided precautions are taken to have enough pulses per side (if a square loop).

■ 3. OTHER RECEIVING ANTENNAS

3.1. Snake Antenna

The snake antenna gets its name from what it looks like: it is usually a coaxial cable just stretched out on the ground like a giant reptile. The antenna is said to have properties similar to those of a genuine Beverage antenna: it receives off the far end of the snake. In amateur literature several versions have been described.

D. DeMaw, W1FB (Ref 1254) described different versions:

1. The far end shorted.

This type of snake consists of a coaxial cable with the end short-circuited. DeMaw states the cable will represent a 50-ohm load at the receiver provided the line is lossy enough (at least 20 dB). Well, that's going to have to be a very long snake, if you know that even a mediocre RG-8 cable exhibits 0.5 dB per 100 ft on 1.8 MHz. Yes, to get the 20-dB attenuation you would need a 4000-ft long snake. DeMaw also says that the velocity factor of the coaxial line should be taken into account when constructing the antenna. I assume the antenna is a traveling wave antenna, so that means it is non resonant. The author also claims that because the antenna is made out of coax with a velocity factor of 0.66, the antenna can be substantially shorter than a Beverage antenna having the same electrical length. I explained in this chapter what makes the velocity factor of the Beverage antenna: it is the ratio of the speed at which the electromagnetic wave travels in the antenna to the speed in the air. It typically ranges from 90 to 95%.

The velocity factor of a coaxial cable is the ratio of the speed at which the electromagnetic wave travels *inside* the coaxial cable, as compared to the speed of the magnetic wave propagating in air. When the coaxial line is laid on the ground to pick up electromagnetic waves, the coaxial line is *not* used in a feed-line mode. The coax shield (braiding) is just used as a conductor that will be exposed to the electromagnetic wave. It will also have a velocity factor, as defined for the Beverage antenna, but it is obvious that there is no relation between the two velocity factors.

DeMaw describes a 1-wavelength long snake. He reports that some users found that the antenna was dead, which it should be. After all, it is a 1-wavelength long transmission line, which means that the far-end short circuit is available right at the receiver input (half-wavelength or multiple of half-wavelength-long transformers are 1:1 transformers). It goes without saying that this kind of snake is an expensive way of short-circuiting the input of the receiver! Or maybe it is a way of testing how "leaky" the cable is. If the receiver is not completely dead, it just means that you have a very poor coaxial cable or your receiver grounding is not effective and you get signals into the receiver through the outer shield of the coaxial cable. DeMaw also states that if the snake is an odd

multiple of quarter waves long, the antenna produces some signals. If so it still proves the line is lossy, because the output should still be dead, this time not because the receiver input is short circuited, but because you have a shielded coaxial line on the input. Maybe you need a better ground system to ground your receiver if the receiver is not dead.

2. The far-end terminated.

DeMaw relates that the 1 wavelength long coax, when terminated in its characteristic line impedance (50 ohms) worked as well as the 5/4-wavelength short-circuited line. This still proves the coaxial cable must be of very poor quality. Remember, this is exactly how we check if our Beverage feed line is of acceptable quality: the cable should be dead (par 1.15)!

3. The third way.

M. Crabtree, ABØX (Ref 1249), reports still another type of "snake" antenna. In this configuration the far end is short-circuited, while at the receiving end only the inner conductor is connected to the receiver and the braid is left floating. That sure makes it an expensive single wire!

4. Variants of the snake

In his article, DeMaw suggests a low-cost snake, made out of a parallel feed line (loudspeaker wires). He terminates the line at the far end in its characteristic impedance and at the receiving end in a 4:1 balun. It is clear that if everything was perfect, this transmission line should be dead as well as with its coaxial counterpart. By the nature of the balanced feed line lying on the ground, there can be a substantial degree of unbalance in the feed line (different and random capacitive coupling). This unbalance will of course cause signal pick-up. This situation is very similar to the situation that exists when we feed a balanced load (a dipole, a quad loop) directly with a coaxial feed line without a form of balun. In this case too we will pick up signals from the feed line (or radiate from the feed line when transmitting).

5. A valid variant?

Instead of using the expensive coaxial cable or loudspeaker cable (however bad the cable quality may be), just buy a spool of insulated hook-up wire (eg #20) and lay it on the ground. This is now a "very low" Beverage, with a characteristic impedance of perhaps a few ohms. Terminate the wire to a ground rod with a low value resistor (try 5 ohms or so), and feed the wire directly to the coaxial cable or better via a 9:1 broadband balun as described for use of a "real" Beverage. But this time make sure you use the transformer correctly (low Z to antenna, high-Z to receiver!).

I have tried a 250-m long insulated wire on the ground, and found it to have directivity characteristics similar to a genuine Beverage, but the output is very low. A preamp may be helpful, but a real Beverage antenna is certainly more helpful.

3.2. Low Horizontal Antennas

Many 160-meter operators have confirmed that a

full-size 1-wavelength long horizontal loop or ½-wavelength long dipole at a height of 3 meters (10 ft) performs as an excellent low-noise receiving antenna, and say it is second only to a real Beverage antenna in that respect. A full-size loop is of course not a "small" antenna, as the circumference of the loop is 160 meters (525 ft). A small city lot will probably not accommodate the loop.

If you use a dipole (which requires half the wire), you can even bend the ends around the property without much loss of efficiency (Ref 1249).

Don't forget, if you have this receiving antenna closer than 1/8 wave from your vertical transmitting antenna, you will have a high degree of mutual coupling between the vertical and the receiving antenna, and the receiving antenna will become almost as noisy as the vertical! One way of overcoming this, even at close spacings, is to detune the vertical (eg disconnect the coax from the vertical if it is a series-fed vertical) during reception. Tall verticals are known to "reradiate" noise into other antennas close by. B. Eldridge, VE7BS, went all the way in that respect and took down his vertical transmitting antennas to reduce noise, knowing that this hurts his transmit situation, but he is convinced that the net balance is favorable. Of course he would like to be able to put up choice Beverages in all directions, which he cannot.

DIPOLE ANTENNAS

■ 1. HORIZONTAL HALF-WAVE DIPOLE

1.1. Radiation Pattern of the Half-wave Dipole in Free Space

1.2. The Half-wave Dipole over Ground

1.2.1. Vertical radiation pattern of the horizontal dipole

1.2.1.1 *Ray analysis*

1.2.1.2 *Vertical radiation pattern equations*

1.2.1.3. *Sloping ground locations*

1.2.1.4. *Antennas over real ground*

- *Radiation efficiency and reflection efficiency*
- *Reflection coefficient*
- *Radiation patterns*
- *Conclusion*

1.2.2. Horizontal pattern of horizontal half-wave dipole

1.3. Half-wave Dipole Efficiency

1.3.1. Radiation resistance

1.3.2. Losses

1.3.2.1. *Dielectric losses in insulators*

1.3.2.2. *Ground losses*

1.4. Feeding the Half-wave Dipole

- *The center-fed dipole*
- *Bandwidth*
- *Broadband dipoles*

1.5. Getting the Full-size Dipole in Your Backyard

■ 2. THE SHORTENED HALF-WAVE DIPOLE

2.1 The Principles

2.2. Radiation Resistance

2.3. Tuning or Loading the Short Dipole

2.3.1. Tuned feeders

2.3.2. Matching at the dipole feed point

2.3.3. Coil loading

2.3.3.1. *Center loading*

- *Procedure*
- *Matching to the feed-line impedance*
- *Comparing losses*

2.3.3.2. *Loading coils away from the center of the dipole*

2.3.4 Linear loading

2.3.5. Capacitive (end) loading

2.3.6. Combined methods

2.4 Bandwidth

2.5 The Efficiency of the Shortened Dipole

■ 3. LONG DIPOLES

3.1. Radiation Patterns

3.2. Feed-point Impedance

3.3. Feeding Long Dipoles

3.3.1. Collinear dipoles (2 half-wave dipoles in phase)

3.3.2. Extended double Zepp

3.4. Three-band Antenna (40, 80, 160 m)

■ 4. INVERTED-V DIPOLE

4.1. Radiation Resistance

4.2 Radiation Patterns and Gain

- *The 90 degree apex angle inverted V*
- *The 120 degree apex angle inverted V*

4.3. Antenna Height

4.4. Length of the Inverted-V Dipole

4.5. Bandwidth

■ 5. VERTICAL DIPOLE

5.1. Radiation Pattern

5.2. Radiation Resistance

5.3. Feeding the Vertical Half-wave Dipole

■ 6. SLOPING DIPOLE

6.1. The Sloping Straight Dipole

- *Radiation patterns*
- *Impedance*

6.2. The Bent-wire Sloping Dipole

- *Feed point*

6.3. Evolution into the Quarter-wave Vertical

6.4. Conclusion

■ 7. MODELING DIPOLES

DIPOLE **8** ANTENNAS

The first antenna most amateurs are confronted with is a dipole. I remember how, as a young boy, I put up my first 20-meter dipole between a second floor window of our house and a nearby structure. It was fed with 75-ohm TV coax, and it worked, whatever that meant. For a while, my whole antenna world was limited to a dipole. But there is more to dipoles.

Although we often think of dipoles as ½-wavelength long, center-fed antennas, this is not always the case. The definition used here is that of a *center-fed radiator with a symmetrical sinusoidal standing-wave current distribution.*

■ 1. HORIZONTAL HALF-WAVE DIPOLE

1.1. Radiation Pattern of the Half-wave Dipole in Free Space

The pattern in the plane of the wire has the shape of a figure 8. The pattern in a plane perpendicular to the wire is a circle (see Fig 8-1). The three-dimensional representation of the radiation pattern is shown in the same figure and is a ring (torus). The gain of this dipole over an isotropic radiator is 2.14 dB. This means that the dipole, at the tip of the ring where radiation is maximum, has a gain of 2.14 dB vs. the theoretical isotropic dipole, which radiates equally well in all directions (its radiation pattern is a sphere).

1.2. The Half-Wave Dipole Over Ground

In any antenna system, the ground acts more or less as an imperfect or lossy mirror that reflects energy. Simplifying, and assuming a perfect ground, we can apply the Fresnel reflection laws, whereby the angles of incident and reflected rays are identical.

1.2.1. Vertical radiation pattern of the horizontal dipole.

The vertical radiation pattern determines the wave angle of the antenna; the wave angle is the angle at which the radiation is maximum. Since obtaining a low angle of radiation is one of the main considerations when building low-band antennas, we will usually consider only the lowest lobe in case the antenna produces more than one vertical lobe. In free space, the radiation pattern of the isotropic antenna is a sphere. As a consequence, any plane pattern of the isotropic antenna in free space is a circle. In free space, the pattern of a dipole in a plane perpendicular to the antenna wire is also a circle. Therefore, if we analyze the vertical radiation pattern of the horizontal dipole over ground, its behavior is similar to an isotropic radiator over ground.

1.2.1.1 *Ray analysis.*

Refer to Fig 8-2. In the vertical plane (perpendicular to the ground), an isotropic radiator radiates equal energy in all directions (by definition). Let us now examine a few typical

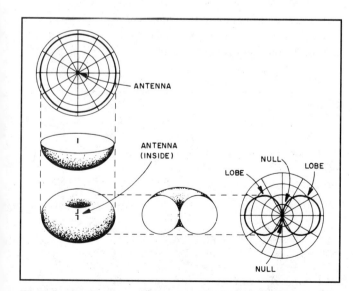

Fig 8-1—Radiation patterns as developed from the three-dimensional pattern of a half-wave dipole in free space.

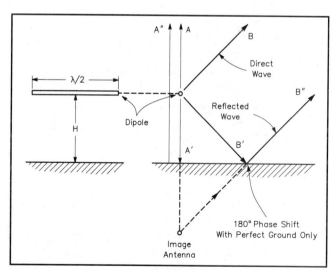

Fig 8-2—Reflection of RF energy by the electrical "ground mirror." The eventual phase relationship between the direct and the reflected horizontally polarized wave will depend primarily on the height of the dipole over the reflecting ground (and to a small degree on the quality of the reflecting ground).

rays. A and A' radiate in opposite directions. A' is reflected by the ground (A") in the same direction as A. B", the reflected ray of B', is reflected in the same direction as B.

The important issue is now the phase difference between A and A", B and B", C and C", etc. Phase difference is made up by path length difference (length is directly proportional to time, as the speed of propagation is constant) plus possible phase shift at the reflection point. Note from Fig 8-2 that horizontally polarized rays undergo a 180-degree phase shift when reflected from perfect ground.

If at a very distant point (in terms of wavelengths) the rays at points A and A" are in phase, then their combined field strength will be at a maximum and will be equal to the sum of the magnitudes of the two rays. If they are out of phase, the resulting field strength will be less than the sum of the individual rays. If A and A" are identical in magnitude and 180 degrees out of phase, total cancellation will occur.

If the dipole antenna is at a very low height (less than a quarter wavelength), A and A" will reinforce each other. Low-angle rays will be almost completely out of phase, resulting in cancellation, and thus there will be very little radiation at low angles. At increased heights, A and A" may be 180 degrees out of phase (no vertical radiation), and lower angles may reinforce each other. In other words, the vertical radiation pattern of a dipole depends on the height of the antenna above the ground.

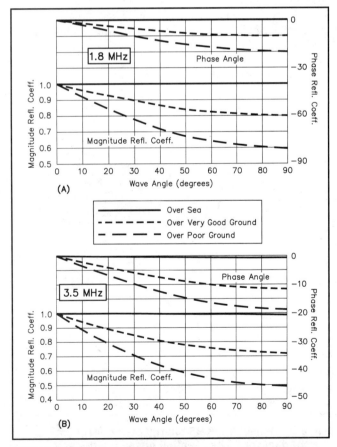

Fig 8-3—Reflection coefficient (magnitude and phase angle) of horizontally polarized waves over three types of ground: sea, average, and very poor. See text for details.

1.2.1.2 *Vertical radiation pattern equations.*

The radiation pattern can be calculated with the following equation.

$$F_\alpha = \sin h \, (h \sin \alpha) \qquad \text{(Eq 8-1)}$$

where

F_α = field intensity at vertical angle α
h = height of antenna, degrees
α = vertical angle of radiation

One wavelength equals 360 degrees. The above equation is valid only for perfectly reflecting grounds. For real ground the formula must be multiplied by the reflection coefficient as shown in Fig 8-3.

The above equation can be rewritten as follows

$$H_1 = \frac{90}{0.366 \, f \sin \alpha} \qquad \text{(Eq 8-2)}$$

where

H_1 = height for first lobe, feet
f = frequency, MHz
α = vertical angle for which the antenna height is sought.

If the height is required in meters, multiply the result by 0.3048 (1 foot = 0.3048 meter). When more lobes are of interest, replace 90 with 270 for the second lobe, with 450 for third lobe, etc. If the nulls are sought, replace 90 with 180 for the first null, with 360 for the second null, etc.

Table 8-1 gives the major lobe angles as well as reflection-point distances for heights ranging from 18 m (60 ft) to 60 m (200 ft) for 40, 80 and 160 meters.

1.2.1.3. *Sloping ground locations.*

In many cases, an antenna cannot be erected above perfectly flat ground. A ground slope (Ref. 630) can greatly influence the wave angle of the antenna. The RADIATION ANGLE HORIZONTAL ANTENNAS module of the NEW LOW BAND SOFTWARE calculates the radiation pattern of dipoles (or Yagis) as a function of the terrain slope.

Table 8-2 shows the influence of the slope angle on the required antenna height for a given wave angle on 80 meters. The table lists the required antenna height and the distance to the reflection point for a horizontally polarized antenna. A

8-1

Table 8-1

Major Lobe Angles and Reflection Point for Various Dipole Antenna Heights

Antenna Height		40 Meters Angle Distance			80 Meters Angle Distance			160 Meters Angle Distance		
(ft)	(m)	(deg)	(ft)	(m)	(deg)	(ft)	(m)	(deg)	(ft)	(m)
60	18	36	83	25	90	0	0	90	0	0
80	24	26	163	50	54	58	18	90	0	0
100	30	20	266	81	40	118	36	90	0	0
120	36	17	391	119	33	187	57	90	0	0
140	42	15	540	148	28	268	82	77	31	9
160	48	13	710	217	24	362	110	59	97	30
180	54	—	—	—	21	467	142	49	154	47
200	60	—	—	—	18	584	178	43	213	66

Table 8-2

Slope Angle Versus Antenna Height at 3.5 MHz

Slope Angle (deg)	20° Wave Angle Height (ft)	20° Wave Angle Distance (ft)	30° Wave Angle Height (ft)	30° Wave Angle Distance (ft)	40° Wave Angle Height (ft)	40° Wave Angle Distance (ft)
35	—	—	—	—	906	10,364
30	—	—	—	—	430	2441
25	—	—	819	9367	275	1029
20	—	—	396	2249	201	553
15	768	8789	258	966	158	340
10	378	2146	192	528	131	227
5	251	937	153	329	113	161
0	189	520	129	224	100	120
−5	153	329	113	161	91	91
−10	131	227	102	121	85	72
−15	116	166	94	94	81	57
−20	107	127	89	75	79	45
−25	101	101	87	61	78	36
−30	97	91	86	49	78	28

positive slope angle is an uphill slope. The results from this table can easily be extrapolated to 40 or 160 meters by simply dividing or multiplying all of the results by 2. For 40 m all dimensions should be halved; for 160 m all dimensions should be doubled. To convert feet to meters, multiply by 0.3048.

1.2.1.4. *Antennas over real ground.*

Up to this point, a perfect ground has been assumed.

Perfect ground does not exist in practical installations, however. Perfect ground conditions are approached only when an antenna is erected over salt water.

Radiation efficiency and reflection efficiency

Contrary to the case with vertical antennas, a horizontal antenna does not rely on the ground for providing a return path for antenna currents. The physical "other half" takes care of that. This means that the ground will not play a role in the radiation efficiency of the antenna. The radiation efficiency is related only to the losses in the antenna itself (conductor, insulator, loading coils, etc), although of course some of the total *radiated* energy can be dissipated in the ground losses.

Both horizontally as well as vertically polarized antennas rely on the ground for reflection of the RF in the so-called Fresnel zone to build up the radiation pattern in combination with the direct wave, as shown in Fig 8-2. The efficiency of the reflection depends on the quality of the ground, and is called the "reflection efficiency."

Reflection coefficient

The reflection from real ground is not like on a perfect mirror. The reflection coefficient is a complex figure that describes the reflection from real ground:

•With a perfect mirror, all energy is reflected. There are no losses; the reflection coefficient is 1.
•With a perfect mirror, the phase of the reflected horizontal wave is shifted exactly 180 degrees vs. the incoming wave.
•With real ground, part of the RF is absorbed, and the reflec-

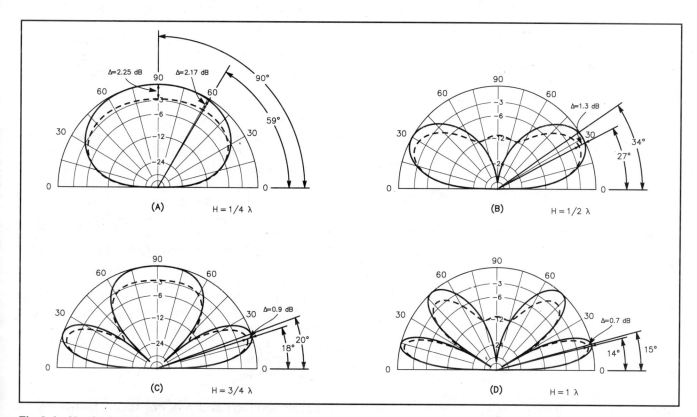

Fig 8-4—Vertical radiation patterns over two types of earth: sea water (solid line in each set of plots) and very poor ground (broken line in each set of plots). The wave angle as well as the gain difference between sea water and poor ground are given for four antenna heights.

tion coefficient magnitude is less than 1.

•With real ground, the phase angle of the reflection is not exactly 180 degrees. Except when the antenna is quite close to the ground the departure is very small, however: a few degrees (0 to 25) for reflection angles (equal to wave angles) between 0 and 90 degrees.

The magnitude of the reflection coefficient, which becomes smaller as the ground quality becomes poorer, is the reason that the dipole over real ground shows less gain than over perfect ground.

The reflection coefficient is a function of reflection angle (equal to the wave angle). The smaller the wave angle, the closer the reflection coefficient will be to 1. This explains why the loss with a dipole (poor ground vs. perfect ground) is higher at high angles (e.g., zenith) than at low angles. See Fig 8-4.

The fact that the dipole over poor ground seems to have a lower radiation angle than over perfect ground is because at lower angles there is less loss. In other words, over poor ground it just has less loss at low angles than at high angles.

The filling in of the deep notch at a 90-degree wave angle for the dipole at ½ wavelength (Fig 8-4B) is because the reflected wave is attenuated (lowest reflection coefficient at 90 degrees) and can no longer cancel the direct wave. The extra phase shift also contributes to this phenomenon, but this could be compensated for by changing the height of the antenna.

Again refer to Fig 8-3, showing the reflection coefficient (magnitude and phase) for a horizontally polarized wave. Information is given for a horizontally polarized antenna over sea, average ground and very poor ground, for both 160 and 80 meters. Eq 8-1 multiplied by this attenuation coefficient gives the vertical radiation pattern over real ground.

Radiation patterns

Fig 8-4 shows vertical patterns of a horizontal dipole over both near-perfect ground (salt water) and desert, the two extremes. Table 8-3 lists the wave angle and the relative loss for a half-wave dipole over 5 different types of ground, and for two antenna heights. Note that for a dipole at ½ wavelength, the peak wave angle drops from 30 degrees over sea water to 26 degrees over desert. At the same time there is a radiation loss of 1.21 dB.

For an antenna at ¼ wavelength height (Fig 8-4), maximum

radiation occurs at 90 degrees over a perfect conductor. Over very poor ground (desert), the maximum radiation is at 59 degrees. This is not because more RF is concentrated at this lower angle, but only because more RF is being dissipated in the poor ground at the 90-degree angle than at 59 degrees (the attenuation coefficient is much higher at 90 degrees than at 59 degrees). The difference, however, between the radiation at 90 and at 59 degrees is very small (0.08 dB). The difference in radiated power at 90 degrees between salt water and a desert type of reflecting ground is 2.25 dB. As 90 degrees is a radiation angle of little practical use, the relatively high loss at the zenith angle does not really bother us.

With a vertical antenna, poor ground results in loss at the low angles in the first place. With horizontal dipoles the loss due to poor ground is in the first place at high angles!

Notice that for a height of ½ wavelength (Fig 8-4B), the sharp null at a 90-degree elevation angle has been degraded to a mere 12-dB attenuation over desert-type ground.

Conclusion

We can conclude that the effects of absorption over poor ground are quite pronounced with low antennas and become less pronounced as the antenna height is increased. Artificial improvement of the ground conditions by the installation of ground wires is only practical if one wants maximum gain at a 90-degree wave angle (zenith) from a low dipole (⅛ to ¼ wavelength height). This can be done by burying a number of wires (½ to 1 wavelength long) underneath the dipole, spaced about 60 cm (2 ft) apart, or by installing a parasitic reflector wire (½ wavelength long plus 5%) just above ground (2 m or 7 ft), about ⅛ to ¼ wavelength under the dipole.

Improving the efficiency of the reflecting ground for low-angle signals produced by high dipoles is impractical and yields very little benefit. The active reflection area can be as far as 10 or more wavelengths away from the antenna!

Dipoles, unlike verticals, do not suffer to a great extent from poor ground conditions. The reason is that for horizontally polarized signals, when reflected by the ground, the phase shift remains almost constant at 180 degrees (within 25 degrees), whatever the incident angle of reflection (equal to the wave angle) may be. For verticals, the phase angle varies between 0 and −180 degrees. For vertical antennas, the pseudo Brewster angle is defined as the angle at which the phase shift at reflection is 90 degrees. This means that there is no pseudo Brewster angle with horizontally polarized antennas such as a dipole, because there never will be a −90 degree phase shift at reflection (the minus sign indicates that the reflected wave is lagging the incident wave).

The effects of this mechanism are proved daily by the fact that on the low bands, big signals from areas with poor ground conditions (mountainous, desert, etc.) are always generated by horizontal antennas, while from areas with fertile, good RF ground, we often hear big signals from verticals and arrays made of verticals.

1.2.2. Horizontal pattern of horizontal half-wave dipole.

The horizontal radiation pattern of a dipole in free space

8-3

Table 8-3

Relative gain (vs dipole over perfect ground) and wave angle(max vertical radiation angle) for ½-λ dipoles at heights of ¼ and ½ λ

	Height = ¼ Wave		Height = ½ Wave	
	Rel. Loss (dB)	Wave Angle (deg)	Rel. Loss (dB)	Wave Angle (deg)
Perfect Ground	0	90	0	30
Sea	−0.05	90	−0.01	30
Very Gd Grnd	−0.57	71	−0.16	29
Aver. Grnd	−1.23	62	−0.52	28
Very Poor Grnd	−2.17	53	−1.21	26

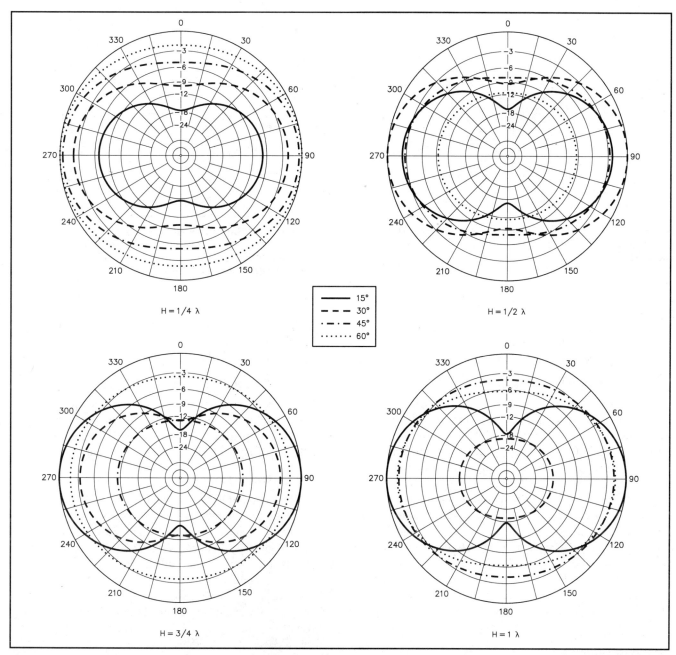

Fig 8-5—Horizontal radiation patterns for ½-wave horizontal dipoles at various heights above ground for wave angles of 15, 30, 45 and 60 degrees (modeled over good ground).

has the shape of a figure 8. The horizontal directivity of a dipole over real ground depends on two factors:

1) Antenna height
2) The wave angle at which we measure the directivity

Fig 8-5 shows the horizontal directivity of half-wave horizontal dipoles at heights of ¼, ½, ¾ and 1 wavelength over average ground. Directivity patterns are included for wave angles of 15 through 60 degrees in increments of 15 degrees. At high angles a low dipole shows practically no horizontal directivity. At low angles, where it has more directivity, the low dipole hardly radiates at all. Therefore, it is quite useless

to put two dipoles at right angles for better overall coverage if those dipoles are at low heights.

At heights of ½ wavelength and more, there is discernible directivity, especially at low angles. Fig 8-6 gives a visual representation of the three-dimensional radiation pattern of a half-wave dipole at ½ wavelength above average ground.

1.3. Half-wave Dipole Efficiency

The radiation efficiency of an antenna is given by the equation

$$Eff = \frac{R_{rad}}{R_{rad} + R_{loss}}$$

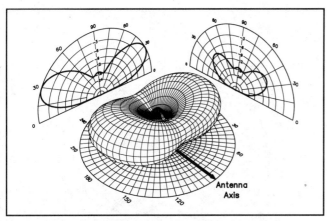

Fig 8-6—Three-dimensional representation of the radiation pattern of a half-wave dipole, ½ wavelength above ground.

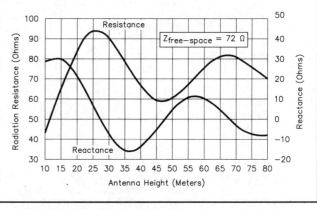

Fig 8-7—Radiation resistance and feed-point reactance of a dipole at various antenna heights. Calculations were done at 3.65 MHz using a 2-mm OD conductor (AWG 12 wire) over good ground.

where

R_{rad} = radiation resistance, ohms
R_{loss} = loss resistance, ohms

1.3.1. Radiation resistance.

The radiation resistance is a fictive resistance in which the same current flows as in the point of the dipole, and whereby this resistor dissipates all the RF applied to it. For a half-wave dipole at or near resonance, the radiation resistance is equal to the real (resistive) part of the feed-point impedance (assuming a perfectly lossless antenna system).

The relationship of the radiation resistance and reactance of a half-wave dipole to its height above ground is shown in Fig 8-7. The radiation resistance varies between 60 and 90 ohms for all practical heights on the low bands. For determining the reactance, the dipole was dimensioned to be resonant in free space (72 ohms). We can conclude that the resonant frequency changes with half-wave-dipole height above ground. Where the reactance is positive, the dipole appears to be too long, and too short where the reactance is negative.

1.3.2. Losses.

The losses in a half-wave dipole are caused by:

• RF resistance of antenna conductor (wire)
• Dielectric losses of insulators
• Ground losses

Table 8-4 gives the effective RF resistance for common conductor materials, taking skin effect into account. The resistances are given in ohms per kilometer. The RF resistance values in the table are valid at 3.8 MHz. For 1.8 MHz the values must be divided by 1.4, while for 7.1 MHz the values must be multiplied by the same factor. The RF resistance of copper-clad steel is the same as for solid copper, as the steel core does not conduct any RF at HF. The dc resistance is higher by 3 to 4 times, depending on the copper/steel diameter ratio. The RF resistance at 3.8 MHz is 18 times higher than for dc (25 times for

7 MHz, and 13 times for 1.8 MHz). Steel wire is not shown in the table; it has a much higher RF resistance. Never use steel wire if you want good antenna performance.

1.3.2.1. *Dielectric losses in insulators.*

Dielectric losses are difficult to assess quantitatively. Care should be taken to use good quality insulators, especially at the high-impedance ends of the dipole. Several insulators can be connected in series to improve the quality.

1.3.2.2. G*round losses.*

Reflection of RF at ground level coincides with absorption in the case of nonideal ground. With a perfect reflector, the gain of a dipole above ground is 6 dB over a dipole in free space (the field intensity doubles, as the same power is now radiated in a half sphere instead of a full sphere).

The ground is never a perfect reflector in real life. Therefore part of the RF will be dissipated in the ground. The effects of power absorption in the real ground have been covered in paragraph 1.2.1.4. and illustrated in Fig 8-4 and Table 8-3.

Attempting to improve ground conductivity for improved performance is a common practice with grounded vertical antennas. One can also improve the ground conductivity with dipoles, although it is not quite as easy, especially if one is

8-4

Table 8-4

Resistance of Various Types of Wire Commonly Used for Constructing Antennas

Wire Diameter	Copper dc (Ω/km)	Copper 3.8 MHz (Ω/km)	Copper-clad dc (Ω/km)	Copper-clad 3.8 MHz (Ω/km)	Bronze dc (Ω/km)	Bronze 3.8 MHz (Ω/km)
2.5 mm (AWG 10)	3.4	61	8.7	61	4.5	81
2.0 mm (AWG 12)	5.4	97	13.8	97	7.2	130
1.6 mm (AWG 14)	8.6	154	22.0	154	11.4	206
1.3 mm (AWG 16)	13.6	246	35.0	246	18.2	328
1.0 mm (AWG 18)	21.7	391	55.6	391	29.0	521

interested in low-angle radiation and if the antenna is physically high. From Table 8-1 we can find the distance from the antenna to the ground reflection point. For the major low-angle lobe this is 36 m (118 ft) for an 80-meter dipole at 30 m (100 ft). Consequently, this is the place where the ground conductivity must be improved. Because of the horizontal polarization of the dipole, any wires that are laid on the ground (or buried in the ground) should be laid out parallel to the dipole. They should preferably be at least 1 wavelength long. However, in view of the small gain that can be realized, especially with high antennas and for low wave angles, it is very doubtful that such improvement of the ground is worth all the effort. The only really worthwhile improvement will be obtained by moving to the sea coast or to a very small island surrounded by salt water. It cannot be emphasized enough, however, that the quality of the reflecting ground with horizontal antennas is of far less importance than with vertical antennas.

The efficiency of low dipoles (¼ wavelength high and less), which essentially radiate at the zenith angle (90 degrees), can be improved by placing wires under the antenna running in the same direction as the antenna.

Practically speaking, one should always use a good solid copper wire (or bronze or copper-clad steel) for the dipole antenna conductor: 2 mm OD (AWG 12) is a good size. Do not use very thin wire. Never use steel wire; its conductivity is extremely poor, especially at high frequencies.

1.4. Feeding the Half-wave Dipole

In general, half-wave dipoles are fed in the center. This, however, is not a must. The Windom antenna is a half-wave dipole fed at approximately ⅙th from the end of the half-wave antenna, with a single-wire feed line. It has been proved (and can be confirmed by modeling) that careful placing of the feed point results in a perfect symmetrical and sinusoidal current distribution in the antenna (Ref 688). The disadvantage of the single-wire fed antenna (Windom) is that the feed line does radiate, and as such distorts the radiation pattern of the dipole. Belrose described a multiband "double Windom" antenna using a 6:1 balun and coaxial feed line in the above-mentioned publication.

The Center-Fed Dipole

The feed point of a center-fed dipole is symmetrical. The antenna can be fed via an open-wire transmission line, if it is to be used on different frequencies (e.g., as two half-waves in phase on the first harmonic frequency), or with a coaxial feed line via a balun. The balun is mandatory in order not to upset the radiation pattern of the antenna. Baluns are covered in detail in the chapter on transmission lines. A current-type balun, consisting of a stack of high-permeability ferrite beads, slipped over the coaxial cable at the load, is recommended. The exact feed-point impedance can be found from Fig 8-7.

Bandwidth

The SWR bandwidth of a full-size half-wave dipole is determined by the diameter of the conductor. Fig 8-8A shows the SWR curves for dipoles of different diameters. Large-conductor diameters can be obtained by making a so-called

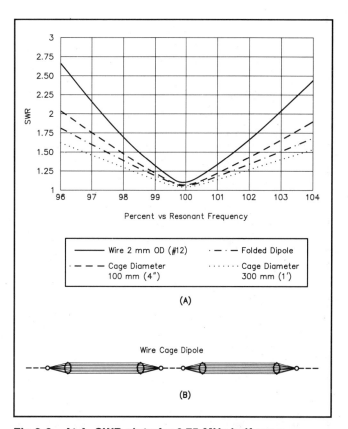

Fig 8-8—At A, SWR plots for 3.75-MHz half-wave dipoles (in free space) of various conductor diameters. The total bandwidth of the 80-meter band (3.5-3.8 MHz) is 8%. The 100-mm (4-inch) and 300-mm (12-inch) diameter conductors can be made as a cage of wires, as shown at B. Note that the SWR bandwidth of a folded dipole is substantially better than for a straight dipole. The spacing between the wires of the folded dipole does not influence the bandwidth to a large extent.

wire-cage (Fig 8-8B). I used the wire-cage approach on my 80-meter vertical, 6 wires forming a 30 cm (12 inch) diameter cage.

A folded dipole shows a much higher SWR bandwidth than a single-wire dipole. A folded dipole for 80 meters, made of AWG no. 12 wire, with a 15 cm (6 in.) spacing between the wires, will cover the entire 80-meter band (3.5-3.8 MHz) with an SWR of approximately 1.75:1, as compared to 2.5:1 for a straight dipole.

Broadband Dipoles

Instead of decreasing the Q factor of the antenna, one can also devise a system whereby the inductive part of the impedance is compensated for as one moves away from the resonant frequency of the antenna. The "double Bazooka dipole" is probably the best known example of such an antenna. In this antenna, part of the radiator is made of coaxial cable, connected in such a way as to present shunt impedances across the dipole feed point when moving away from the resonant frequency. F. Witt, AI1H, covered a similar broadband dipole antenna in detail (Ref 1012). Fig 8-9 shows the dimensions of Witt's 80-meter DX-special antenna, which has been dimen-

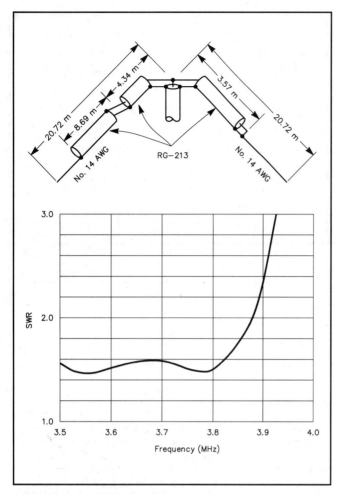

Fig 8-9—Dimensions and SWR curve of the 80 Meter DX Special, a design by F. Witt, AI1H.

sioned for minimum SWR at both the CW as well as SSB end of the band.

Another innovative broadbanding technique was described by M. C. Hatley, GM3HAT (Ref 682).

Of course there is no reason why one could not apply switched inductive or capacitive loading devices, such as described in detail in the chapters on verticals and large loop antennas, although this is seldom done.

1.5. Getting the Full-size Dipole in Your Backyard

The ends of the half-wave dipole can be bent (vertically or horizontally) without much effect on the radiation pattern or efficiency. The tips of the dipoles carry little current; hence, they contribute very little to the radiation of the antenna.

Bending the tips of a dipole is the same as "end loading" the dipole (equal to top-loading with verticals). The folded tips can be considered as capacitive loading devices. For more details see the chapter on vertical antennas (Par 2)

■ 2. THE SHORTENED HALF-WAVE DIPOLE

On the low bands, it is sometimes impossible to use full-size radiators. This section describes the characteristics of short dipoles, and how they can be successfully deployed. Short dipoles are often used as elements in reduced-size Yagis (see the chapter on Yagis) or to achieve manageable dimensions whereby the antenna can be fit into a city lot.

2.1 The Principles

You can always look at a dipole as two back-to-back connected verticals, whereby the "vertical" elements are no longer vertical. Instead of having the ground make the mirror image of the antenna (this is always the case with verticals), we supply the mirror half ourselves.

All principles about radiation resistance and loading of short verticals, as explained in the chapter on vertical antennas, can be directly applied to dipoles as well.

2.2. Radiation Resistance

The radiation resistance of a dipole in free space will be twice the value of the equivalent monopole. For instance, the R_{rad} for the half-wave dipole made of an infinitely thin conductor is approximately 73.2 ohms, which is twice the value of the quarter-wave vertical (36.6 ohms). Over ground, the radiation resistance will also vary in a similar way as the full-size half-wave dipole (see Fig 8-7).

2.3. Tuning or Loading the Short Dipole

Loading a short dipole consists of bringing the antenna to resonance. This means eliminating the capacitive reactance component in the feed-point impedance. Different loading methods yield different values of radiation resistance.

It is not necessary, however, to load a shortened antenna to resonance in order to operate it. You can also connect a feed line to it, directly or via a matching network, without tuning out the capacitive reactance. Therefore you can consider the dipole together with its feed line as the dipole system, and analyze the system of a short dipole to see what the alternatives are. Sometimes this situation is referred to as a dipole with "tuned feeders."

There are different ways to operate the short dipole system:
•Tuned feeders
•Matching at the dipole feed point
•Coil loading to tune out the capacitive reactance
•Linear loading
•Capacitive end loading
•Combined loading methods

2.3.1. Tuned feeders.

Tuned feeders were common in the days before the arrival of coaxial feed lines. Very low-loss open-wire feeders can be made. The Levy antenna is an example of a short dipole fed with open-wire line; its overall length is ¼ wavelength. This antenna (R_{rad} = approximately 13 ohms and X_C = approximately $-j1100$ ohms), can be fed with open-wire feeders (450-600 ohms) of any length into the shack, where we can match it to 50 ohms via an antenna tuner. An outstanding feature of this approach is that the system can be "tuned" from the shack via the antenna tuner, and is not narrow banded, as is the case with loaded elements.

Let us calculate the losses in such a system. The losses of the antenna proper can be assumed to be zero (provided wire elements of the proper size and composition are used). The loss in a flat open-wire feeder is typically 0.01 dB per 100 feet at 3.5 MHz. The SWR on the line will be an unreal value of 280:1 (this value was calculated using the program SWR RATIO which is part of the NEW LOW BAND SOFTWARE. The additional line loss due to SWR for a 30-m (100 ft) long line will be in the order of 1.5 dB (Ref 600, 602). On a line with standing waves, the impedance is different at every point. Slightly changing the feeder length can produce more manageable impedances which the tuner can cope with more easily. This can be done with the software module COAX TRANS-FORMER/SMITH CHART or "IMPEDANCE, CURRENT AND VOLTAGE ALONG FEED LINES." A good antenna tuner should be able to handle this matching task with a loss of less than 0.2 dB. The total system loss depends essentially on the efficiency with which the tuner can handle the impedance transformation. The typical total loss in the system should be under 2.0 dB.

2.3.2. Matching at the dipole feed point.

You can of course install the matching network at the dipole feed point, although this will be highly impractical in most cases. In the case of a vertical antenna this solution is practical, as the feed point is at ground level.

2.3.3. Coil loading.

Loading coils can be installed anywhere in the short dipole halves, from the center to way out near the end. Loading near the end will result in a higher radiation resistance, but will also require a much larger coil, and hence introduce more coil losses.

2.3.3.1. *Center loading.*

The inductive reactance required to resonate the Levy dipole from the previous example is approximately 1100 ohms. To achieve this, two 550-ohm (reactance) coils need to be installed in series at the feed point. We should be able to realize a coil Q (quality factor) of 300.

$$R_{loss} = \frac{550}{300} = 1.83 \text{ ohms}$$

The total equivalent loss resistance of the two coils is 3.66 ohms.

The antenna efficiency will be:

$$Eff = \frac{13}{13 + 3.66} = 78\%$$

The equivalent power loss is $-10 \log (0.78) = 1.08$ dB.

The feed-point resistance of the antenna is $13 + 3.66 \approx 16.7$ ohms at resonance. This assumes negligible losses from the antenna conductor (heavy copper wire). If the use of coaxial feed lines is desired, an additional matching system will be needed to adapt the 15-ohm balanced feed-point impedance to the 50- or 75-ohm unbalanced coaxial cable impedance. The above example was calculated assuming free-space impedances. Over real ground the impedances can be

different, and will vary as a function of the antenna height.

Another way to determine the necessary inductance is to model the antenna using a MININEC program (e.g., ELNEC or MN). Let us work out the example of the ¼-wave long dipole using ELNEC:

Input data:
f = 1.83 MHz
h = 25 m
ℓ_{ant} = ¼ wave

Procedure:

1) Find a dipole length that is resonant at 1.83 MHz. (This turns out to be 80.1 m.) Do not model the dipole at any lower height, as the results obtained with MININEC will be erroneous. It makes no difference what type of earth you model, as MININEC always reports the impedance over a perfect reflector, but do not model the dipole in free space.

2) The ¼-wave-long dipole is half the above length: 40.05 m. Model the dipole again: The impedance is $12.5 - j1094$ ohms.

The required center loading coil has a reactance of 1094 ohms. Assuming a loading-coil Q of 300, the total equivalent loss resistance is 3.64 ohms. The feed point resistance becomes $12.5 + 3.64 = 16.14$ ohms.

Matching to the feed-line impedance

One way of matching this impedance to a 50-ohm feed line is to use a quarter-wave transformer. The required impedance of the transformer is

$$Z_0 = \sqrt{16.14 \times 50} = 28.4 \ \Omega$$

We can "construct" a feed line of 25 ohms (that's close) by paralleling two 50-ohm feed lines. Don't forget you need a 1:1 balun between the antenna terminals and the feed line.

Another attractive way that has been used by a number of commercial manufacturers of short 40-meter Yagis is to use a single central loading coil, on which we install a link in the center. The link turns are adjusted to give a perfect match to the feed line.

Comparing losses

A good current-type balun should account for no more than 0.1 dB of loss. The loading coils (Q factor = 300) give a loss of 1.3 dB. Including 30 m (100 ft) of RG-213 (with 0.23 dB loss), the total system loss can be estimated at 1.63 dB. The resulting efficiency is very close to the result obtained with open-wire feeders.

There are certain advantages and disadvantages to this concept, however. An advantage is that coaxial cable is easier to handle than open-wire line, especially when dealing with rotatable antenna systems.

The high Q of the coils will make the antenna narrow-banded as far as the SWR is concerned. In the case of the open-wire feeders, retuning the tuner will solve the problem. With the coaxial feed line you may still need a tuner at the input end if you want to cover a large bandwidth, in which case the extra losses due to SWR in the coaxial feed line may be objectionable.

Another disadvantage is that the loading-coil solution requires two more elements in the system—the coils. Each element in itself is an extra reliability risk, and even the best loading coils will age and require maintenance.

Instead of modeling the antenna with MININEC, we can calculate the required loading coils as in the following example:

Length of the dipole = 22.5 m
f = 3.8 MHz
Wire diameter = 2 mm OD (AWG no. 12)
Antenna height = 20 m

The full-size dipole length (2.5% shorting factor) is 38.5 m (126.3 ft). We first calculate the surge impedance of the transmission-line equivalent of the short dipole using the equation

$$Z_S = 276 \log \left[\frac{S}{d \times \sqrt{1 + \frac{S}{4h}}} \right] \qquad \text{(Eq 8-3)}$$

where
  S = dipole length = 2250 cm
  d = conductor diameter = 0.2 cm
  h = dipole height = 2000 cm
  Z_S = 1103 ohms

The electrical length of the 22.5-m long dipole is

$$\ell° = 180 \times \frac{22.5}{38.5} = 105.2 \text{ degrees}$$

The reactance of the dipole is given by

$$X_L = Z_S \times \cot \frac{\ell}{2} = 1103 \times \cot 52.6° = 843 \ \Omega$$

Separate MININEC calculations show a reactance of 785 ohms, which is within 7% of the value calculated above.

The required inductance is

$$L = \frac{X_L}{2\pi f}$$

where L is in μH and f is in MHz.

For 3.8 MHz,

$$L = \frac{843}{2\pi \times 3.8} = 32.6 \ \mu H$$

There are two ways of loading and feeding the shortened dipole with a centrally located loading coil:

1) Use a single 33.5-μH loading coil and link couple the feed line to the coil. This method is used by Cushcraft for their shortened 40-meter antennas.

2) The 33.5-μH loading coil can be "opened" in the center where it can be fed via a 1:1 balun.

2.3.3.2. *Loading coils away from the center of the dipole.*

The location of the loading devices has a distinct influence on the radiation resistance of the antenna. This phenomenon is explained in detail in the chapter on short verticals.

Clearly, it is advantageous to put loading coils away from the center, provided the benefit of higher radiation resistance is not counteracted by higher losses in the loading device.

As loading coils are placed farther out on the elements, the required coil inductance increases. With increasing values of inductance, the Q factor is likely to decrease, and the equivalent series losses will increase.

I have calculated the case where the 22.5-meter long dipole (for 3.8 MHz) from Par. 2.3.3.1 was loaded with coils at different (symmetrical) positions along the half-dipole elements. In all cases I assumed a Q factor of 300.

The results of the case are shown in Fig 8-10. The chart includes the reactance value of the required loading coils, the radiation resistance (R_{rad}), and the feed-point impedance at resonance (Z). The radiation efficiency is given by R_{rad}/Z. Note that the efficiency remains practically constant at 88% over the entire experiment range. This means that the advantage we gain from obtaining an increased radiation resistance by moving the coils out on the dipole halves is balanced out by the increased ohmic losses of the higher coil values. In the experiment I assumed a constant Q of 300, which may not be realistic, as it is likely that the Q of the lower inductance coils will be higher than for the higher inductance ones.

The experiment was done in free space. Over real ground the radiation resistance (and Z) will vary to a rather large extent as a function of the height (see Fig 8-7).

We may also conclude that if we can achieve a Q factor which is higher than 300, there will be an advantage in moving the coils out on the elements. We should not expect, however, to see several decibels of difference. The difference will be minute, and theoretical rather than noticeable in practice.

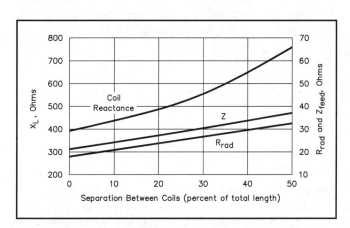

Fig 8-10—Design data for loading a short dipole. The radiation resistance, feed-point impedance at resonance, and the required reactance for the loading coils are given as a function of the separation between the coils (percentage of total dipole length). Calculations are for a coil Q of 100 and a frequency of 3.8 MHz. See text for further details.

Calculating the loading coil value

The method for calculating the loading coil value is described in detail in Par 2.1.3 and 2.6.8 of the chapter on vertical antennas. In short the procedure is as follows:

- Calculate the surge impedance of the wire between the loading coil and the center of the antenna (Z_{S1})
- Calculate the surge impedance of the wire between the loading coil and the tip of the antenna (Z_{S2})
- Calculate the electrical length of the inner length (coil to center) = $\ell 1$
- Calculate the electrical length of the tip (coil to tip) = $\ell 2$
- Calculate the reactance of the $\ell 1$ part using: $X = Z_{S1} \tan (\ell 1)$
- Calculate the reactance of the inner part of the half dipole using: $X1 = +jZ_{S1} \times \tan(\ell 1)$
- Calculate the reactance of the tip using: $X2 = -jZ_{S2}/\tan(\ell 2)$
- Add the reactances (the sum will be a negative value, e.g., −1000 ohms)
- The loading coil will have a reactance with the same absolute value.

It is much faster to use a MININEC-based modeling program, such as MN or ELNEC, to calculate the elements of a short dipole. Results obtained with MININEC match the results obtained by the above procedure.

Fig 8-11 shows the values of the required coils for a dipole (2 mm OD, AWG no. 12 wire, design frequency = 3.6 MHz) as a function of total antenna length (varying from 0.25 to 0.45 wavelength) and loading coil location.

2.3.4 Linear loading.

In the commercial world, we have seen linear loading used on shortened dipoles and Yagis for 40 and 80 meters. Linear loading devices are usually installed at or near the center of the dipole. The required length of the loading device (in each dipole half) will be somewhat longer than the difference between the quarter-wave length and the physical length of the half-dipole. The farther away from the center that the loading device will be inserted, the longer the "stub" will have to be. The "stub" must run in parallel with the antenna wire if we want to take advantage of the radiation off the stub (see the chapter on vertical antennas).

Example: A short dipole for 3.8 MHz is physically 28 meters (91.9 feet) long. The full half-wavelength is 39 meters (128.0 feet). The missing electrical length is 39 − 28 = 11 meters (36.1 feet). It is recommended that the linear loading device be constructed approximately 30% longer than half of this length:

L = 11/2 + 30% = 7 m (23 feet)

Trim the length of the loading device until resonance on the desired frequency is reached. When constructing an antenna with linear-loading devices, make sure the separation between the element and the folded linear-loading device is large enough, and that you use high-quality insulators to prevent arc-over and insulator damage.

Modeling the linear loaded dipole: Modeling antennas which use very close-spaced conductors (e.g., the linear loading device which looks like a stub made of an open-wire

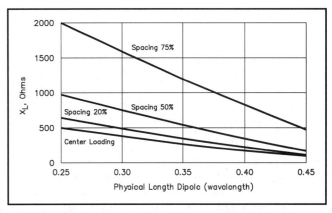

Fig 8-11—Required inductance for loading coils as a function of dipole length and position of the coils. Calculations were made using a 2-mm OD conductor diameter for a design frequency of 3.6 MHz.

transmission line) is very tricky. I would not recommend trying this with MININEC.

2.3.5. Capacitive (end) loading.

Capacitive loading has the advantage of physically shortening the element length at the end of the dipole where the current is lowest (least radiation), and without introducing noticeable losses (as inductors do). End-loaded short dipoles have the highest radiation resistance, and the intrinsic losses of the loading device are negligible. Thus, end or top loading is highly recommended.

Top loading, and the procedures to calculate the loading devices, are covered in detail in the vertical antenna chapter in Par 2.1.2 and 2.6.3.

An example will best illustrate how capacitive loading can be calculated.

Example: A shortened dipole will be loaded for 80 meters. The physical length of the dipole is 18.75 meters (approx. 40% shortening factor).

S = 18.75 m
d = 0.2 cm
h = 20 m

We calculate the surge impedance from Eq 8-3: Z_S = 1084 ohms. The antenna length to be replaced by a disk is

t = 90 degrees × 40% = 36 degrees

This means we must replace the outside 36 degrees of each side of the dipole with a capacitive hat (a half-wave dipole is 180 degrees).

The inductive reactance of the shorted transmission-line equivalent) is given by

$$X_L = +j \frac{Z_S}{\tan t} = +j \frac{1084}{\tan 36°} = +j1492 \, \text{ohms}$$

A capacitive reactance of the same value (but opposite sign) will resonate the "equivalent" transmission line. The required capacitive reactance is $X_C = -j1492$ ohms. The capacitance (f = 3.8 MHz) is

$$C = \frac{10^6}{2\pi f X_C} = 28.1 \, pF$$

The required diameter of the hat disk is given by

D = 2.85 x C

where

    D = hat diameter in cm
    C = the required capacitance in pF

In our example, $D = 2.85 \times 28.1 = 80.1$ cm (31.5 in.).

The above formula to calculate the disk diameter is for a solid disk. A practical capacitive hat can be made in the shape of a wheel with at least four spokes. This design will approach the performance of a solid disk. For ease in construction, the spokes can be made of four radial wires, joined at the rim by another wire in the shape of a circle.

In its simplest form, capacitive end loading will consist of bending the tips of the dipole (usually downward), in order to make the antenna shorter. By doing so we create extra capacitance between those two tips, which will load the antenna (make it electrically longer).

2.3.6. Combined methods.

Any of the loading methods already discussed can be employed in combination. It is essential to develop a system which will give you the highest possible radiation resistance and which employs a loading technique with the lowest possible inherent losses.

Gorski, W9KYZ (Ref 641) has described an efficient way to load short dipole elements by using a combination of linear and helical loading. He quotes a total efficiency of 98% for a two-element Yagi using this technique. This very high percentage can be obtained by using a wide copper strap for the helically wound element, which results in a very low RF resistance. Years ago, Kirk Electronics (W8FYR, SK) built Yagis for the HF bands, including 40 meters, using this approach (fiberglass elements wound with copper tape).

2.4. Bandwidth

The bandwidth of a dipole is determined by the Q factor of the antenna. The antenna Q factor is defined by

$$Q = \frac{Z_S}{R_{rad} + R_{loss}}$$

where

    Z_S = surge impedance of the antenna
    R_{rad} = radiation resistance
    R_{loss} = total loss resistance.

The 3 dB bandwidth can be calculated from

$$BW = \frac{f_{MHz}}{Q}$$

The Q factor (and consequently the bandwidth) will depend on

- The conductor-to-wavelength ratio (influences Z_S)
- The physical length of the antenna (influences R_{rad})
- The type, quality, and placement of the loading devices (influences R_{rad})
- The Q factor of the loading device(s) (influences R_{loss})

- The height of the dipole above ground (influences R_{rad})

For a given conductor length-to-diameter ratio and a given antenna height, the loaded antenna with the narrowest bandwidth will be the antenna with the highest efficiency. Indeed, large bandwidths can easily be achieved by incorporating pure resistors in the loading devices, such as in the Maxcom dipole (Ref 663). The worst-radiating antenna one can imagine is a dummy load, where the resistor can be seen as the ohmic loading device while the radiating component does not exist. Judging by SWR bandwidth, this "antenna" is a wonderful performer, as a good dummy load can have an almost flat SWR curve over thousands of megahertz!

2.5. The Efficiency of the Shortened Dipole

Besides the radiation resistance, the RF resistance of the shortened-dipole conductor is an important factor in the antenna efficiency. Refer to Table 8-4 for the RF resistances of common wire conductors used for antennas. For self-supporting elements, aluminum tubing is usually used. Both the dc and RF resistances are quite low, but special care should be taken to ensure that the best possible electrical RF contact between parts of the antenna is made. Some makers of military-specification antennas go so far as to gold plate the contact surfaces for low RF resistance! As a rule, loading coils are the most lossy elements, and capacitive end loading should always be employed if at all possible. Linear loading is also a better choice than inductive loading. All these aspects are covered in more detail in the chapter on vertical antennas.

■ 3. LONG DIPOLES

Provided the correct current distribution is maintained, long dipoles can give more gain and increased horizontal directivity as compared to the half-wave dipole. The "long" antennas discussed in this paragraph are not strictly dipoles, but arrays of dipoles. They are the double-sized equivalents of the "long-verticals," as covered in the chapter on verticals.

The following antennas are covered:

- Two half-waves in phase
- Extended double Zepp

3.1. Radiation Patterns

Center-fed dipoles can be lengthened to approximately 1.25 wavelengths in order to achieve increased directivity and gain without introducing objectionable side lobes. Fig 8-12 shows the horizontal radiation patterns for three antennas in free space: the half-wave dipole, two half-waves in phase (also called "collinear dipoles"), and the extended double Zepp, which is a 1.25 wavelengths long. Further lengthening of the dipole will introduce major secondary lobes in the horizontal pattern unless phasing stubs are inserted to achieve the correct phasing between the half-wave elements.

As we know, the dipole has 2.14-dB gain over the isotropic antenna (in free space). It is interesting to overlay the patterns of the two "long dipoles" on the same diagram, using the same dB scale; the extended double Zepp beats the dipole with almost 3 dB of gain. Note, however, how much more narrow the forward lobe on the pattern has become. This may altogether be a disadvantage in view of the varying propaga-

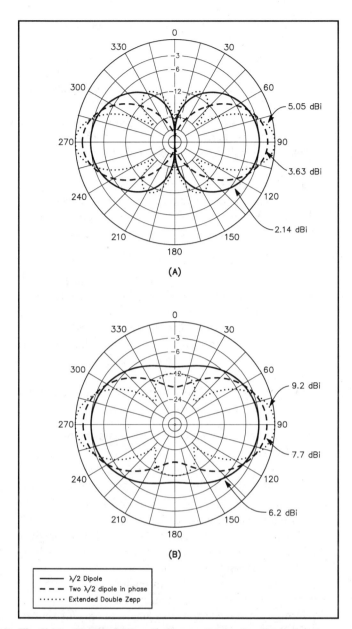

(A)

(B)

Legend:
——— λ/2 Dipole
— — — Two λ/2 dipole in phase
········· Extended Double Zepp

Fig 8-12—Horizontal radiation patterns for three types of "dipoles": the half-wave dipole, the collinear dipole (2 half waves in phase) and the extended double Zepp. At A, the radiation patterns at a 0° wave angle with the antennas in free space. At B, the patterns at a 37° wave angle with the antennas ⅜ λ above good-quality ground. Notice the sidelobes apparent with the extended double Zepp antenna.

tion paths. The two-half-waves antenna sits right between the dipole and the extended double Zepp, with 1.5-dB gain over the half-wave dipole.

Figs 8-13 and 8-14 show the horizontal radiation patterns for the half-waves-in-phase dipole and for the extended double Zepp at various heights and wave angles. As with the half-wave dipole, the vertical radiation pattern depends on the height of the antenna above ground.

3.2. Feed-point Impedance

The charts from Figs 9-8, 9-9, 9-11 and 9-12 can be used for estimating the feed-point impedances of "long" dipoles.

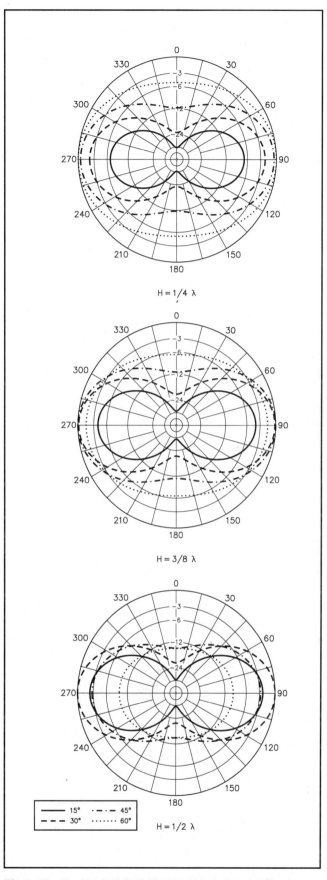

H = 1/4 λ

H = 3/8 λ

Legend:
——— 15°   — · — · 45°
— — — 30°   ········· 60°

H = 1/2 λ

Fig 8-13—Horizontal radiation patterns for collinear dipoles (two half waves in phase) for wave angles of 15, 30, 45 and 60 degrees. As with a half-wave dipole, directivity is not very pronounced at low heights and at high wave angles.

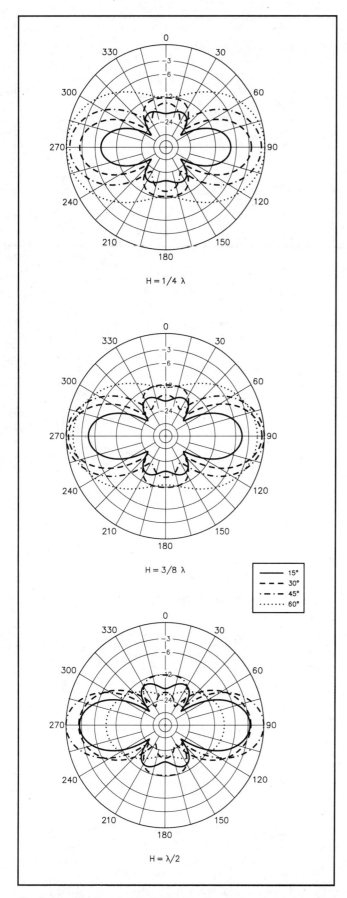

H = 1/4 λ

H = 3/8 λ

	15°
---	30°
-·-·	45°
······	60°

H = λ/2

Fig 8-14—Horizontal radiation patterns for the extended double Zepp for wave angles of 15, 30, 45 and 60 degrees.

The values from the charts that are made for monopoles must be doubled for dipole antennas.

The antennas can also be modeled with MININEC, but care should be taken with the results of long dipole antennas at less than 0.35 wavelength above ground. Remember, too, that (except for free space) MININEC always reports the impedance for the antenna above a perfect ground conductor, but if the height is specified as mentioned above, the results should be reasonably close to the actual impedance over real ground.

Since the center-fed long antennas will not be loaded with lossy elements that would reduce their efficiency, long dipoles can have efficiencies very close to 100% if care is taken to use the best material for the antenna conductor.

3.3. Feeding Long Dipoles

The software module "COAX TRANSFORMER/SMITH CHART" from the NEW LOW BAND SOFTWARE is an ideal tool for analyzing the impedances, currents, voltages and losses on transmission lines. The "STUB MATCHING" module can assist you in calculating a stub-matching system in seconds. In any case, we need to know the feed-point impedance of the antenna. Measuring the feed-point impedance is quite difficult, as you cannot use a noise bridge unless it is specially configured for measuring balanced loads.

3.3.1. Collinear dipoles (two half-wave dipoles in phase).

The impedance at resonance for two half-waves in phase is several thousand ohms. With a 2-mm OD conductor (AWG 12), the impedance is approximately 6000 ohms on 3.5 MHz. The shortening factor (in free space) for that antenna is 0.952. The SWR bandwidth of the two half-waves in phase is given in Fig 8-15. The antenna covers a frequency range from 3.5 to 3.8 MHz with an SWR of less than 2:1.

The antenna can be fed with open-wire feeders into a tuner, or via a stub matching system and balun as shown in Fig 6-15. Using "tuned feeders" with a tuner can of course ensure a 1:1 SWR to the transmitter (50 ohms) at all times.

3.3.2. Extended double Zepp.

The intrinsic SWR bandwidth of the extended double Zepp is much narrower than for the collinear dipoles. For an antenna made out of 2 mm OD wire (AWG 12) and with a total length of 1.24 wavelengths, the feed-point impedance is approximately $200 - j1100$ ohms. The SWR curve (normalized to R_{rad} at the design frequency) is given in Fig 8-15. For lengths varying from 1.24 to 1.29 wavelengths, the radiation resistance will vary from 200 to 130 ohms (decreasing resistance with increasing length). The exact length of the antenna is not critical, but as we increase the length, the amplitude of the sidelobes increases. The magnitude of the reactance will depend on the length/diameter ratio of the antenna: An antenna made of a thin conductor will show a large reactance value, while the same antenna made of a large diameter conductor will show much less reactance.

The impedance of the extended double Zepp also changes with antenna height, as with a regular half-wave dipole. For the

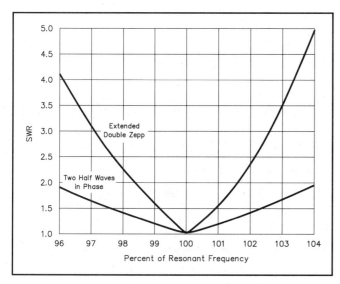

Fig 8-15—SWR curves for an extended double Zepp and for two half waves in phase (collinear array). The calculation was centered on 3.65 MHz using a conductor of 2-mm OD (AWG no. 12), and the results normalized to the radiation resistances. The SWR bandwidth of the collinear array is much higher than for the extended double Zepp.

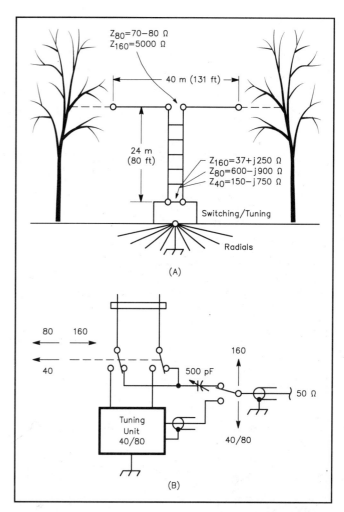

Fig 8-16—Three-band antenna configuration (40, 80 and 160 m). On 40 m the antenna is a collinear (two half waves in phase), on 80 m a half-wave dipole, and on 160 m a top-loaded vertical (T antenna). The bandswitching arrangement is shown at B.

1.24-wavelength-long extended double Zepp, the resistive part changes between 150 and 260 ohms, and settles at 200 ohms at very high elevations.

In principle we can feed this antenna in exactly the same way as the collinear, but as the intrinsic bandwidth is much more limited, it is better to feed the antenna with open-wire lines running all the way into the shack and to the open-wire antenna tuner.

3.4. Three-Band Antenna (40, 80, 160 m)

Refer to the three-band antenna of Fig 8-16. On 40 meters the antenna is a collinear array (two half-waves in phase) at 24 m (80 ft). On 80 meters, it is a half-wave dipole. For 160, we connect the two conductors of the open-wire feeders together, and the antenna is now a flat-top loaded vertical (T-antenna). The disadvantage is that we must install the switch-able tuning network at the base, right under the antenna. Some slope can of course be allowed. As the antenna is a vertical on 160, its performance will largely depend on the quality of the ground and the radial system.

■ 4. INVERTED-V DIPOLE

In the past, the inverted-V shaped dipole has often been credited with almost magical properties. The most frequently claimed "special" property a low radiation angle. Some have more correctly called it a poor man's dipole, as it requires only one high support. Here are the facts.

4.1. Radiation Resistance

The radiation resistance of the inverted-V dipole changes with height above ground (as in the case of a horizontal dipole) and as a function of the apex angle (angle between the legs of the dipole). Consider the two apex-angle extremes. When the

angle is 180 degrees, the inverted V becomes a flat-top dipole, and the radiation resistance (in free space) is 73 ohms. Now take the case where the apex angle is 0 degrees. The inverted-V dipole becomes an open-wire transmission line, a quarter-wavelength long and open at the far end. This configuration will not radiate at all (the current distribution will completely cancel all radiation, as it should in a well-balanced feed line), and the input impedance of the line is 0 ohms (a quarter-wave stub open at the end reflects a dead short at the input). This zero-angle inverted V will have a radiation resistance of 0 ohms and consequently will not radiate at all.

I modeled a range of inverted-V dipoles with different apex angles at different apex heights. This was done using NEC2. Fig 8-17 shows the radiation resistance of the inverted V as a function of the apex angle for a range of angles between 90 degrees and 180 degrees (straight dipole). The curve also shows the physical length which produces resonance (feed point purely resistive). Decreasing the apex angle raises the resonant frequency of the inverted V.

Fig 8-18 shows the feed-point resistance and reactance

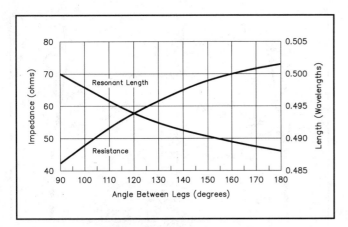

Fig 8-17—Radiation resistance (resistance at resonance) of the inverted-V dipole antenna in free space as a function of the angle between the legs of the dipole (apex angle). Also shown is the physical length (based on the free-space wavelength) for which resonance occurs.

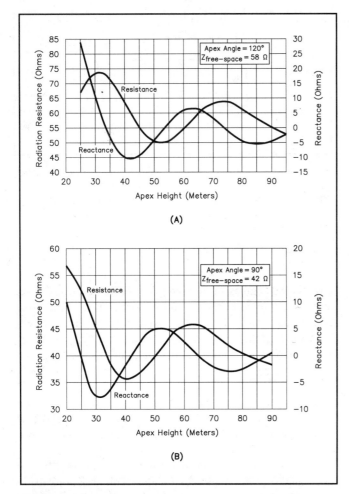

(A)

(B)

Fig 8-18—Impedance (feed-point resistance and reactance) of inverted-V dipoles as a function of height above ground. Analysis frequency is 3.75 MHz, with 2 mm OD wire (AWG no. 12). Resistances at resonance are: 120-degree apex angle, 58 ohms; 90-degree angle, 42 ohms. NEC-2 was used for these calculations, as MININEC is unreliable for doing impedances at low heights.

for inverted-V dipoles with apex angles of 120 and 90 degrees. The antennas were first resonated in free space (zero reactance). Then the reactances were calculated over ground at various heights with the antenna lengths that produced resonance in free space. Notice that the shape of both curves is similar to the shape of the straight dipole curve, Fig 8-7. Bringing the inverted V closer to ground lowers its resonant frequency. This is a fairly linear function between 0.25- and 0.5-wavelength apex height.

4.2. Radiation Patterns and Gain

Previous paragraphs compare the inverted V to a straight dipole at the same apex height. It is clear that the inverted V is a compromise antenna as compared to the straight horizontal dipole. At low heights (0.25 to 0.35 wavelength), the gain difference is minimal, but at heights that produce low-angle radiation the dipole performs substantially better.

The 90-degree apex angle inverted-V dipole

Fig 8-19 shows the vertical and horizontal radiation patterns for inverted Vs with a 90-degree apex angle at different apex heights. Modeling was done over good ground. For comparison, I have included the radiation pattern for a straight dipole at the same (apex) height. In the broadside direction, the inverted-V dipole shows 1 to 1.5 dB less gain than the flat-top dipole, and also a slightly higher wave angle.

The 120-degree apex angle inverted-V dipole

The flat-top dipole is still 0.6 dB better than the inverted V at a height of 0.4 wavelength, 0.7 dB at 0.45 wavelength and 0.8 dB at 0.5 wavelength. In addition, the wave angle for the horizontal dipole is slightly lower than for the inverted V (approx. 3 degrees for heights from 0.35 to 0.5 wavelength). The difference is not spectacular, but it is clear that the inverted-V dipole has no magical properties.

4.3. Antenna Height

In many situations it will be possible to erect an inverted-V dipole antenna much higher than a flat top dipole, in most cases because there is only one high support structure available. In this respect the high inverted V is certainly superior to a low horizontal dipole. The V loses from the dipole at the same apex height, but who's got two such high supports? And are they in the right direction?

4.4. Length of the Inverted-V Dipole

The usual formulas for calculating the length of the straight dipole cannot be applied to the inverted-V dipole. The length depends on both the apex angle of the antenna and the height of the antenna above ground. This effect can be seen from Fig 8-18, which shows the feed-point impedance for inverted Vs of different configurations at different heights.

Closing the legs of the inverted V in free space will increase the resonant frequency. On the other hand, the antenna will become electrically longer when closer to the ground due to the end-loading effect of the ground on the inverted V ends.

4.5. Bandwidth

Fig 8-20 shows the SWR curves for three inverted-V

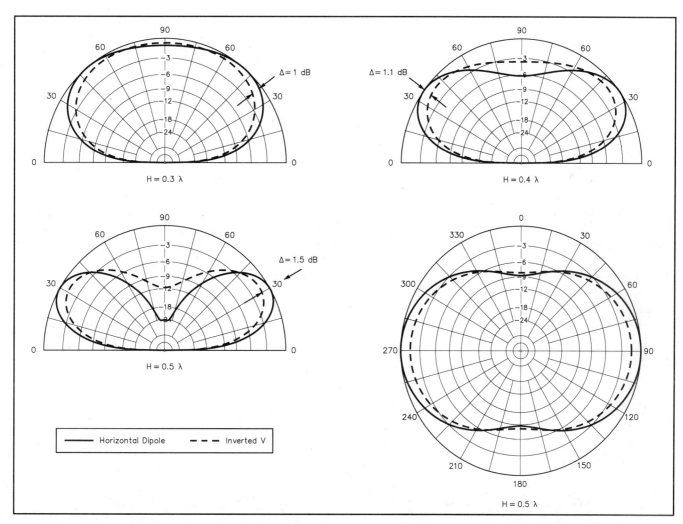

Fig 8-19—Radiation patterns for an inverted-V dipole with an apex angle of 90 degrees. For comparison, the radiation pattern for a horizontal dipole is included in each plot, on the same dB scale. The horizontal pattern is shown for the main wave angles (28° for the straight dipole and 32° for the inverted V). The height of the inverted V is referred to as the height of its apex.

dipoles with different apex angles: 90°, 120° and 180° (flat-top dipole), for a conductor diameter of 2 mm (AWG no. 12) and a frequency of 3.65 MHz. As expected, the SWR bandwidth decreases with decreasing apex angle. The computed figures are for free space. The SWR values from Fig 8-20 are normalized figures. This means that the SWR at resonance is assumed to be 1:1, whatever the impedance (resistance) at resonance is. In practice the SWR will almost never be 1:1 at resonance because the line impedance will be different from the feed-point impedance (see the impedance charts in Figs 8-7 and 8-18).

Over ground the reactive part of the impedance remains almost the same value as in free space (after having re-resonated the inverted V for no reactance at the center frequency). This means that the SWR bandwidth will be largest for heights where the radiation resistance is highest. For the inverted-V dipole this is at an apex height of approximately 0.35 to 0.4 wavelength. Practically speaking, it means that for an apex height of 0.3 to 0.5 wavelength, the SWR curve will be somewhat flatter over ground than in free space.

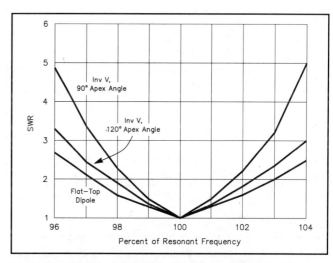

Fig 8-20—SWR curves for three types of free-space half-wave dipoles: the horizontal (flat top) dipole, and inverted-V dipoles with apex angles of 120 and 90 degrees. Each curve is normalized to the feed-point resistance at resonance.

The SWR bandwidth of the inverted V can be increased significantly by making a folded-wire version of the antenna. The feed-point impedance of the folded-wire version is four times the impedance shown in Figs 8-17 and 8-18.

■ 5. VERTICAL DIPOLE

The half-wave vertical is covered in detail in the chapter on vertical antennas. Whereas in that chapter we consider the half-wave vertical mainly as a base-fed antenna, we can of course use a dipole made of wire, and feed it in the center. This is what we usually call a vertical dipole. In most practical cases the half-wave vertical, made of wire, will not be perfectly vertical, but generally slope away from a tall support (tower, building). These sloping half-wave verticals are covered in Par 6.

5.1. Radiation Pattern

Whether the half-wave vertical is base fed or fed in the center, the current distribution is identical, and hence the radiation pattern will be identical. Radiation patterns are shown in Fig 8-21 when the lower end is near the ground. Over sea, the half-wave vertical can yield 6.1-dBi gain, which drops to about 0 dBi over good ground. As with all verticals, it is mainly the quality of the ground in the Fresnel zone that determines how good a low-angle radiator the vertical dipole will be (Ref Par 3 of the chapter on verticals). Half-wave verticals produce excellent (very) low-angle radiation when erected in close proximity to salt water. As a general-purpose DX antenna, the vertical dipole may, however, produce too low an angle of radiation for the run-of-the-mill DX-path.

Raising the half-wave vertical higher above the ground introduces multiple lobes. Fig 8-22 shows the patterns for a half-wave center-fed vertical with the bottom ⅛ wavelength above ground. Note the secondary lobe, which is identical to the lobe we encountered with the extended double Zepp. As a matter of fact, this slightly elevated half-wave vertical is the half-size equivalent of the extended double Zepp antenna.

I also modeled a half-wave vertical on top of a rocky island with very poor ground, 250 m (820 ft) above see level, and some 100 m (330 ft) from the sea. Fig 8-23 shows the

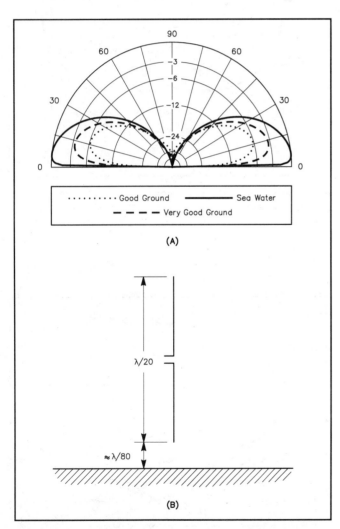

Fig 8-21—At A, vertical radiation patterns over various grounds for a vertical half-wave center-fed dipole with the bottom tip just clearing the ground, as shown at B. The gain is as high as 6.1-dBi over sea, but only 3-dBi over very good ground and 0.2-dBi over good ground. The feed-point impedance is 100 ohms.

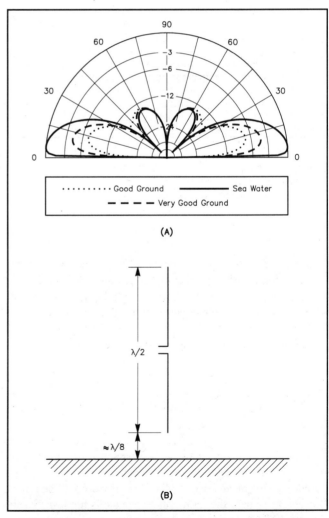

Fig 8-22—At A, vertical radiation patterns of the half-wave vertical dipole with the bottom tip ⅛ wavelength off the ground, as shown at B. This is the vertical equivalent of the extended double Zepp antenna.

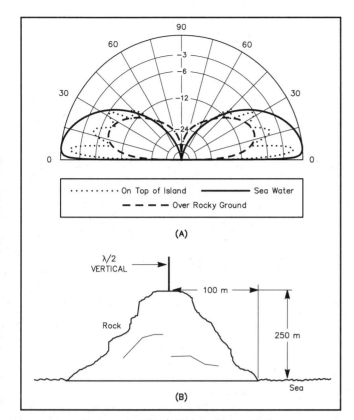

Fig 8-23—At A, the serrated radiation pattern of a half-wave vertical overlooking a slope of very poor ground (e.g. an island with volcanic earth) next to the sea, as shown at B. Because of the antenna height above the sea, multiple lobes show up in the pattern. The radiation patterns of the half-wave vertical at sea level and the pattern over very poor ground are superimposed for comparison.

layout and the radiation pattern. Superimposed on the pattern are the patterns for the same antenna at sea level, as well as over very poor ground. Note that whereas the extra height does not give any gain advantage over sea level, in this case the extra height does help the low angle rays to shoot across the poor ground (the rocky island) and find reflection at sea level some 250 meters below the antenna.

5.2. Radiation Resistance

The radiation resistance of a vertical half-wave dipole, fed at the current maximum (the center of the dipole), is given in Fig 8-24 as a function of its height above ground. The impedance remains fairly constant except for very low heights. No current flows at the tips of the dipole, and hence the small influence of the height on the impedance, except at very low heights where the capacitive effect of the bottom of the antenna against ground lowers the resonant frequency of the antenna.

5.3. Feeding the Vertical Half-wave Dipole

There are two main approaches to feeding a vertical half-wave dipole:

- Base feeding against ground (voltage feeding)
- Feeding in the center (current feeding)

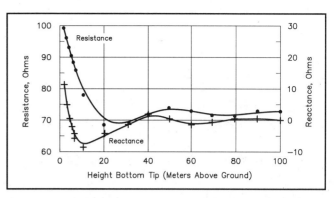

Fig 8-24—Radiation resistance and reactance of the half-wave vertical as a function of height above ground. The height is taken as the height of the bottom tip. Calculations are for a design frequency of 3.5 MHz.

Base feeding is covered in Par 4.4 of the chapter on matching and feed lines. In most cases one will use a parallel tuned circuit on which the coax feed line is tapped. If the vertical is made of a sizable tower, the base impedance may be relatively low (600 ohms), and a broad-band matching system as described in Par 4.5.2 of Chapter 6 on matching and feed lines (the W1FC broadband transformer) may be used.

A center-fed vertical dipole must be fed in the same way as a horizontal dipole. It represents a balanced feed point, and can be fed via an open-wire line to a tuner, or via a balun to a coaxial feed line (see Par 1.4.)

■ 6. SLOPING DIPOLE

Sloping half-wave dipoles are used very successfully by a number of stations, especially near the sea. FK8CP is using a half-wave sloper on 160, with the end of the antenna connected about 15 m above sea level, less than 50 m from the salt water. I8UDB is using a sloper on 160 from his mountaintop QTH near Naples, where the electrical ground is nonexistent, but where the sea is only 100 m away and a few hundred meters below the antenna.

The half-wave sloper radiates a signal with both horizontal and vertical polarization components. Unless it is very high above the ground (e.g., I8UDB), you need not bother with the horizontal component. The low angle will be produced only by the vertical component. All modeling in this section was done on 80 meters, over a very good ground.

6.1. The Sloping Straight Dipole

Due to the weight of the feed line, a sloping dipole will seldom have two halves in a straight line. Let us nevertheless analyze the antenna as if it does.

Radiation patterns

Fig 8-25 shows the radiation patterns of sloping half-wave dipoles for apex angles of 15, 30 and 45 degrees over three types of ground (poor, good and sea). For the dipole with a 45-degree slope angle I include the pattern showing the vertical and the horizontal radiation separately, Fig 8-26. It is obvious that the steeper the slope, the less the horizontal radiation component will be. The high-angle radiation is only

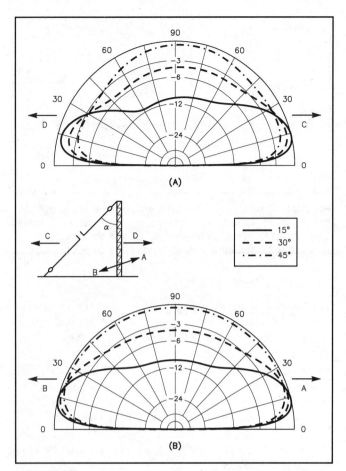

Fig 8-25—Elevation-plane radiation patterns of sloping dipoles with various slope angles. At A, patterns in the plane of the sloper and its support (end-fire radiation), and at B, perpendicular to that plane (broadside radiation). End-fire radiation is 100% vertically polarized, while the broadside radiation contains a horizontal as well as a vertical component. The horizontal pattern shows a very small amount of directivity.

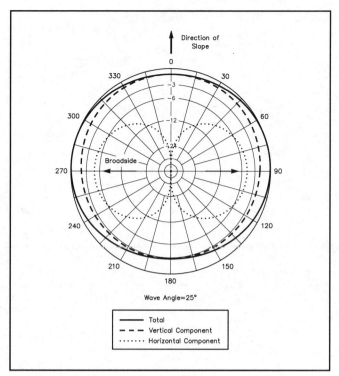

Fig 8-26—Azimuth-plane radiation pattern for the sloping dipole with a 45-degree slope angle, taken at a 25-degree wave angle. Patterns for the vertical and horizontal components of the total are also shown. The directivity is very limited. Actually, the sloping dipole radiates best about 70 degrees either side of the slope direction!

due to the horizontal radiation component. For the vertical component the same rules apply as for the half-wave vertical: In order to exploit the intrinsic very low-angle capabilities, you must have an excellent ground around the antenna. Don't forget, the Fresnel zone (the area where the reflection at ground level takes place) can stretch all the way out to 10 wavelengths or more from the antenna!

Fig 8-26 shows the horizontal pattern for a sloping dipole with a 45-degree slope angle. The sloper is almost omnidirectional, but radiates best broadside (perpendicular to the plane going through the sloper and the support). In the end-fire direction (in the plane of the sloper and its support), it has less than 1 dB F/B at a wave angle of 25 degrees. The antenna radiates a little better in the direction of the slope. The fact that it radiates best in the broadside direction is due to the horizontal component, which only radiates in the broadside direction.

Impedance

The radiation resistance of the sloping dipole with the bottom wire $\frac{1}{80}$ wavelength above ground (1 m for an 80-m

antenna) varies from 96 ohms for a 15-degree slope angle to 81 ohms for a 45-degree slope angle.

6.2. The Bent-Wire Sloping Dipole

Most real-life sloping half-wave dipoles have a bent-wire shape, because of the weight of the feed line. Figs 8-27 and 8-28 analyze a sloping vertical with a slope angle of 20 degrees for the top half of the antenna, and slope angles of 40 and 60 degrees respectively for the bottom half of the dipole. Using a 60-degree slope angle reduces the height requirement for the support.

The sloping dipole with a relatively horizontal bottom quarter-wave wire yields almost the same signal as the straight sloping dipole. It is important to keep the top half of the sloping dipole as vertical as possible. Analysis shows the angle of the bottom half of the antenna is relatively unimportant.

Feed point

Is the feed point of such a bent sloping dipole a symmetrical feed point? Not strictly speaking. If you use such an antenna, don't take any chances. It does not hurt to put a current balun at a load even when the load is nonsymmetric. Use a current type balun to remove any current from the outside of the coaxial cable. A coiled coax or a stack of ferrite beads is the way to go (see the chapter on feed lines and antenna matching).

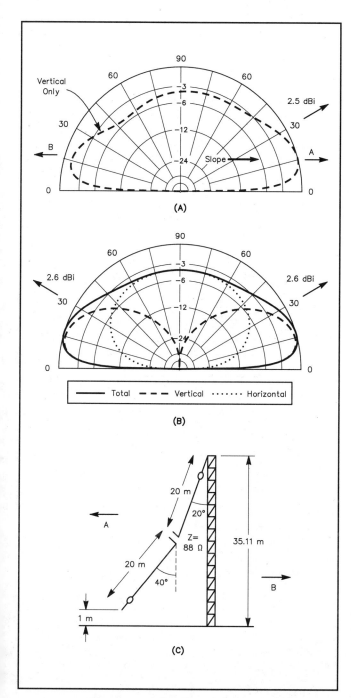

(A)

(B)

(C)

Fig 8-27—At A, "end-fire" and B, "broadside" vertical radiation patterns of a bent-wire half-wave sloper for 3.6 MHz. The horizontal and vertical components of the total pattern are also shown at B. The bottom quarter-wave section slopes at an angle of 40 degrees, as shown at C. Modeling is done over very good ground.

(A)

(B)

(C)

Fig 8-28—A, "end-fire" and B, "broadside" vertical radiation patterns of a 3.6-MHz bent-wire half-wave sloper. The horizontal and vertical components of the total pattern are also shown at B. The bottom quarter-wave section here slopes at an angle of 60 degrees, as shown at C. This configuration and that of Fig 8-27 are just as valid as the configuration using a straight sloper; the loss in gain is negligible. This arrangement requires less support height than that of a straight sloper or that of Fig 8-27.

6.3. Evolution into the Quarter-wave Vertical

We can go one step further and bring the bottom quarter-wave all the way horizontal. If the top half were fully vertical, we now would have a quarter-wave vertical with a single elevated radial. This configuration is described in detail in the chapter on vertical antennas (Fig 9-18).

To transform the half-wave sloper into a quarter-wave vertical, we first replace the sloping bottom half of the antenna with two wires, now called radials. Both radials are "in line" and slope toward the ground, Fig 8-29C. A and B of Fig 8-29 show the radiation patterns for this configuration. Note that the high-angle radiation has been attenuated some 10 dB, and we picked up 0.5 to 0.8 dB of gain. The little horizontally polarized radiation left over is, of course, caused by the sloping

Fig 8-29—Transition from a sloping dipole to a quarter-wave vertical with two radials. At C the bottom half of the dipole is replaced by two quarter-wave wires sloping to the ground; the resulting patterns are shown at A and B. At E the radials are lifted to be horizontal, with the resulting pattern at D. This change eliminates all the horizontal radiation component that was originated by the sloping wires. Analysis frequency: 3.65 MHz. ⟶

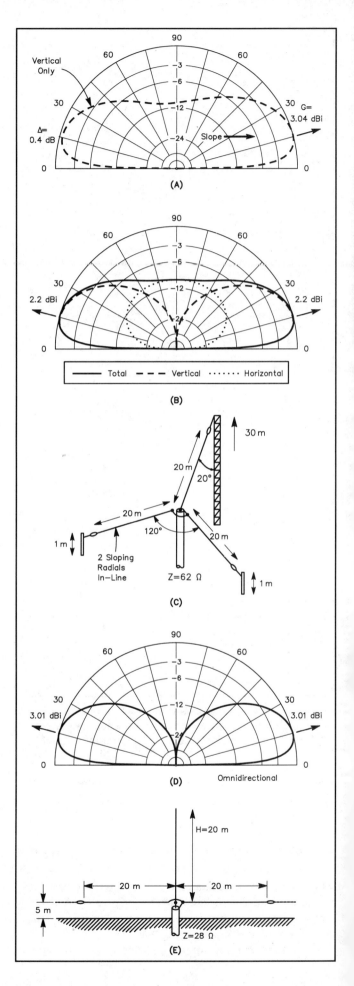

radials. The configuration shows a gain in the direction of the sloping wire of approximately 0.4 dB.

Next we move the radials up, so they are horizontal, and move the antenna down so the base is now 5 m (16 ft) above ground (Fig 8-29E). All the horizontal radiation is gone, and the gain has settled halfway between the forward and the backward gain of the previous model, which was to be expected. We now have a quarter-wave vertical with two radials, which is how the original ground plane was developed (see Par 1.3.3 of the chapter on verticals).

The quarter-wave vertical with two radials definitely has an asymmetrical feed point. However, as the feed line will be exposed to the strong fields of the antenna, and as the feed line will likely be installed on the ground under the two radials, it is strongly recommended that you fully decouple the feed line from the feed point by using a current-type balun (coiled coax or stack of ferrite beads).

6.4. Conclusion

The 6.1-dBi gain can be obtained with a half-wave vertical only over nearly perfect ground (sea). Even over very good ground, the half-wave vertical will not be any better than a quarter-wave vertical (3-dBi gain). This means that unless you are near the sea, you may as well stick with a quarter-wave vertical. The sloping vertical (make the sloping wire as vertical as possible) with two radials (5 m high for 3.6 MHz) will produce as good a signal as a half-wave vertical or sloping half-wave vertical over very good ground. It will, however, only require a 25 m (82 ft) support instead of a 35 (114 ft) or 40 m (131 ft) support for the half-wave vertical.

■ 7. MODELING DIPOLES

MININEC-based modeling programs are well suited for modeling dipoles. Straight dipoles can be accurately modeled with a total of 10 to 20 pulses.

Inverted-V dipoles require more pulses, depending on the apex angle, in order to obtain accurate impedance data. Table 8-5 shows the impedance data for a straight dipole, and Table 8-6 for an inverted-V dipole as a function of the pulses, wires and segments. An inverted V with a 90-degree apex angle requires at least 50 equal-length segments for accurate impedance data. By using the TAPERING technique (see the chapter on Yagi and quad antennas), accurate results can be obtained with a total of only 26 segments. ELNEC (MININEC-based modeling program by W7EL) provides an automatic feature for generating tapered segment lengths, which is a great asset when you model antennas with bent conductors.

Knowing the exact impedance is important only if you

Table 8-5

MININEC Pulses Versus Calculated Impedance for a Straight Dipole Antenna

Pulses	Impedance
5	$71 - j\,14$
10	$67 - j\,26$
20	$68 - j\,28$
30	$68.5 - j\,28$
50	$68.6 - j\,27.3$
80	$68.7 - j\,27.1$
100	$68.7 - j\,27.0$

Table 8-6

MININEC Pulses Vs. Calculated Impedance for an Inverted-V Dipole Antenna

Pulses	Impedance
5	$43.6 - j\,23.7$
10	$44.3 + j\,10.3$
20	$44.6 + j\,28.4$
30	$44.6 + j\,34.3$
50	$44.7 + j\,38.1$
80	$44.7 + j\,39.8$
100	$44.8 + j\,42.0$
20 tapered, min 0.4 m, max 3.0 m	$44.2 + j\,36.1$
26 tapered, min 0.3 m, max 2.0 m	$44.4 + j\,37.6$
26 tapered, min 0.4 m, max 2.0 m	$44.4 + j\,36.3$
28 tapered, min 0.2 m, max 2.0 m	$44.4 + j\,38.9$
46 tapered, min 0.2 m, max 1.0 m	$44.2 + j\,40$

want to calculate the exact resonant length (or frequency) of a dipole, or if the dipole is part of an array.

In order to obtain reliable results, the dipoles should not be modeled too close to ground. For half-wave horizontal dipoles, the antenna should be at least 0.2-wavelength high. For longer dipoles, the minimum height ensuring reliable results is somewhat higher. Vertical dipoles and sloping dipoles (with a steep slope angle) can be modeled quite close to the ground, as there is very little radiation in the near-field toward the ground (a dipole does not radiate off its tips).

The NEC modeling program is required if accurate gain and impedance data are required for dipoles very close to ground.

VERTICAL ANTENNAS

■ **1. QUARTER-WAVE VERTICAL**

1.1. Radiation Patterns

1.1.1. Vertical pattern of monopoles over ideal ground.

1.1.2. Vertical radiation pattern of monopoles over real ground.

The Reflection Coefficient

The Pseudo-Brewster Angle

Ground-Quality Characterization

Brewster Angle Formula

Brewster Angle and Radials

Conclusion

Vertical Radiation Patterns

1.1.3. Horizontal pattern of a vertical antenna.

1.2. Radiation Resistance of Monopoles

1.3. Efficiency of the Monopole Antenna

1.3.1. Conductor RF Resistance

1.3.2. Parallel Losses in Insulators

1.3.3. Ground Losses

The "Artificial" Ground Plane in Free Space

1.3.3.1. *Buried radials.*

Near Field (Radiation Efficiency)

Far Field (Reflection Efficiency)

Quarter-Wave Radials

Two-Wavelength-Long Radials

Sea-Front QTH

Ground Rods

Depth of Buried Radials

Radial Strips Versus Radial Wires

A Radial Plow

An Alternative

1.3.3.2. *Elevated radial systems.*

1.3.3.3. *"Wonder" radials for 160 meters (?).*

1.3.3.4. *Short radials that do work.*

1.3.3.5. *Evaluating the ground system.*

■ **2. SHORT VERTICALS**

2.1. Radiation Resistance

2.1.1. Base loading.

2.1.2. Top loading.

2.1.3. Center loading.

2.1.4. Combined top and base loading.

2.1.5. Linear Loading

2.2. Keeping the Radiation Resistance High

2.3. Keeping Losses Associated with Loading Devices Low

2.4. Short-Vertical Design Guidelines

2.5. SWR Bandwidth of Short Verticals

2.5.1. Calculating the 3 dB bandwidth.

2.5.2. The 2:1 SWR bandwidth.

2.6. Designing Short Loaded Verticals

2.6.1. Base coil loading.

2.6.2. Base linear loading.

2.6.3. Capacitance-hat loading.

2.6.4. Capacitance hat with base loading.

2.6.5. T-wire loading.

2.6.6. Coil Plus Capacitance Hat

Power Dissipation of the Loading Coil

2.6.7. Coil with T wire.

2.6.8. Coil with whip.

2.6.9. Comparing the different loading methods.

Conclusions

■ **3. TALL VERTICALS**

3.1. Vertical Radiation Angle

3.2. Gain

3.3. The Radial System for a Half-Wave Vertical

3.3.1. The near field.

3.3.2. The far field.

3.4. In Practice

■ **4. MODELING VERTICAL ANTENNAS**

Wires and Segments

Modeling Antennas with Wire Connections

Modeling Verticals Including Radial Systems

■ **5. PRACTICAL VERTICAL ANTENNAS**

5.1. Single-Band Quarter-Wave Vertical for 40, 80 or 160

5.2. Top-Loaded Vertical

5.3. Three-Band Vertical for 40, 80 and 160 Meters

5.4. Linear-Loaded Duo-bander for 80/160 Meters

5.5. 80/160 Top-Loaded Vertical with Trap

5.5.1. Isolating traps.

Matching Networks

5.5.2. Shortening/lengthening traps.

5.6. The Self-Supporting Full-Size 160-M Vertical at ON4UN

5.7. The Battle Creek Special Antenna

5.8. Using the Beam Tower as a Low-Band Vertical

The Electrical Length of a Loaded Tower

Measuring the Electrical Length

5.8.1. Gamma and omega matching.

5.8.1.1. *Close spacing versus wide spacing.*

5.8.1.2. *Influence of gamma-wire diameter.*

5.8.1.3. *SWR bandwidth.*

5.8.1.4. *Adjusting the gamma system.*

5.8.1.5. *Using the omega system.*

5.8.1.6. *Conclusion.*

5.8.1.7. *Practical hints.*

5.8.2. The slant-wire feed system.

5.8.3. Modeling shunt fed towers.

■ **6. INVERTED-L ANTENNA**

Tuning Procedure

■ **7. THE T ANTENNA**

7.1. Current-Fed T Antennas

7.2. Voltage-Fed T Antennas

Feeding the Antenna

The Required Ground and Radial System

■ **8. LOCATION OF THE VERTICAL ANTENNA**

■ **9. 160-M DXPEDITION ANTENNAS**

VERTICAL **9** ANTENNAS

The effects of the ground on the radiation pattern and the efficiency of vertically polarized antennas is often not understood, and has not been covered extensively in the amateur literature. The effects are twofold. Near the antenna (in the near field), there is a need for a good ground to collect the antenna return currents without losses. At distances farther away (the far field, or the Fresnel zone), where the wave is reflected from the earth to make up the low-angle radiation, some of the energy will be absorbed by the ground. The absorption is a function of the ground quality and the incident angle. If it were not for these two mechanisms, a very short vertical would radiate a pattern almost identical to a full-size vertical.

Vertical monopole antennas are often called ground-mounted verticals, or simply verticals. They are, by definition, mounted perpendicular to the earth, and they produce a vertically polarized signal. Verticals are very popular antennas for the low-bands, as they can produce very good low-angle radiation without requiring the very high supports needed for horizontal antennas to produce the same low-angle radiation.

■ 1. QUARTER-WAVE VERTICAL

1.1. Radiation Patterns

1.1.1. Vertical pattern of monopoles over ideal ground.

The radiation pattern produced by a ground-mounted quarter-wave vertical antenna is basically half of the radiation pattern of a half-wave dipole antenna in free space (with twice the physical size of the vertical and with symmetrical current distribution). As such, the radiation pattern of a quarter-wave vertical over perfect ground is half of the figure-8 shown for the half-wave dipole in free space. The representation is shown in Fig 9-1.

The relative field strength of a vertical antenna with sinusoidal current distribution and a current node at the top is given by:

$$E_f = k \times I \left[\frac{\cos(L \sin \alpha) - \cos L}{\cos \alpha} \right] \qquad \text{(Eq 9-1)}$$

where

k = constant related to impedance
E_f = relative field strength
α = angle above the horizon
L = electrical length (height) of the antenna
I = antenna current ($\sqrt{P/R}$)

This formula does not take imperfect ground conditions into account, and is valid for antenna heights between 0 and 180 degrees (0 to ½ wavelength). The "form factor" containing the trigonometric functions is often published by itself for use in calculating the field strength of a vertical antenna. If used in this way, however, it appears that short verticals are vastly inferior to tall ones, as the antenna length appears only in the numerator of the fraction.

Replacing I in the equation with the term

$$\sqrt{\frac{P}{R_{rad} + R_{loss}}}$$

gives a better picture of the actual situation. For short verticals, the value of the radiation resistance is small, and this term largely compensates for the decrease in the form factor. This means that for a constant power input, the current into a small vertical will be greater than for a larger monopole.

In practice, however, the current is not determined by just the radiation resistance (R_{rad}), but rather by the sum of the radiation resistance and the loss resistance(s). This is why, with a less-than-perfect ground system and less-than-perfect loading elements (lossy coils in the case of lumped-constant-loaded verticals), the total radiation can be significantly less than in the case of a larger vertical (where R_{rad} is large in

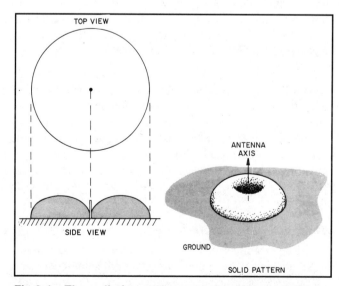

Fig 9-1—The radiation patterns produced by a vertical monopole. The top view is the horizontal pattern, and the side view is the vertical (elevation plane) pattern.

comparison to the ground loss and where there are no lossy loading devices).

Interestingly, short verticals are almost as efficient radiators as are longer verticals, provided the ground system is good and there are no lossy loading devices. When the losses of the ground system and the loading devices are brought into the picture, however, the sum $R_{rad} + R_{loss}$ will get larger, and as a result part of the supplied power will be lost in the form of heat in these elements. For instance, if $R_{rad} = R_{loss}$, half of the power will be lost. Note that with very short verticals, these losses can be much higher.

1.1.2. Vertical radiation pattern of monopoles over real ground.

The final three-dimensional radiation pattern from an antenna is made up of the combination of the direct radiation and the radiation via reflection from the earth. The following explanation is valid *only* for reflection of vertically polarized waves. See Chapter 8 on dipole antennas for an explanation of the reflection mechanism for horizontally polarized waves.

In case of a perfect earth, there is *no* phase shift of the vertically polarized wave at the reflection point. The two waves add with a certain phase difference, due only to the different path lengths. This is the mechanism that creates the radiation pattern. Consider a distant point at a very low angle with the horizon. As the path lengths are almost the same, reinforcement of the direct and reflected wave will be maximum. In case of a perfect ground, the radiation will be maximum at an angle just above zero degrees.

The Reflection Coefficient

Over real earth, reflection causes both an amplitude and a phase change. It is the *reflection coefficient* that describes how the incident (vertically polarized) wave is being reflected. The reflection coefficient of real earth is a complex number, and varies with frequency. In the polar-coordinate system the reflection coefficient consists of:

• The magnitude of the reflection coefficient: It determines how much power is being reflected, and what percentage is being absorbed in the lossy ground. A figure of 0.6 means that 60% will be reflected, and 40% absorbed.

• The phase angle: This is the phase shift that the reflected wave will undergo as compared to the incident wave. Over real earth the phase is always lagging (minus sign). At zero wave angle, the phase is always –180 degrees. This causes the total radiation to be zero (no absorption of reflected wave, and the sum of the incident and reflected waves that are 180 degrees out of phase). At high wave angles, the reflection phase angle will be close to zero (typically –5 to –15 degrees, depending on the ground quality).

The Pseudo-Brewster Angle

The magnitude of the reflection coefficient is minimum at 90 degrees phase angle. This is the reflection-coefficient phase angle at which the so-called *pseudo-Brewster wave angle* occurs. It is called the *pseudo*-Brewster angle because the RF effect is similar to the optical effect from which the term

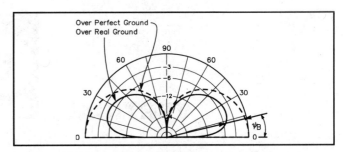

Fig 9-2—Vertical radiation patterns of a quarter-wave monopole over perfect and imperfect earth. The pseudo-Brewster angle is the radiation angle at which the real-ground pattern is 6 dB down from the perfect-ground pattern.

gets its name. At this angle (the pseudo-Brewster angle) the reflected wave changes sign. Below the pseudo-Brewster angle the reflected wave will *subtract* from the direct wave. Above the pseudo-Brewster angle it adds to the direct wave. At the pseudo-Brewster angle the radiation is 6 dB down from the perfect earth pattern (see Fig 9-2).

All this should make it clear that knowing the pseudo-Brewster angle is important for each band at a given QTH. Most of us go to a vertical to achieve good low-angle radiation.

Fig 9-3 shows the reflection coefficient (magnitude and phase) for 3.6 MHz and 1.8 MHz for three types of ground. Over sea water the reflection-coefficient phase angle changes from –180 degrees at a 0-degree wave angle to –0.1 degree at less than 0.5 degree wave angle! The pseudo-Brewster angle is at approximately a 0.2 degree wave angle.

Ground-Quality Characterization

Ground quality is defined by two parameters: the dielectric constant and the conductivity, expressed in millisiemens per meter (mS/m). Table 5-2 shows the characterization of various real-ground types. The table also shows five distinct types of ground, labeled as very good, average, poor, very poor and extremely poor. These come from Terman's classic *Radio Engineers Handbook*, and are also used by Lewallen in his ELNEC modeling program. The denominations and values as listed in Table 5-2 are the standard ground types used throughout this book for modeling radiation patterns.

Brewster Angle Formula

Terman (*Radio Engineers Handbook*) publishes a formula which gives the pseudo-Brewster angle as a function of the ground permeability, the conductivity, and the frequency. The chart in Fig 9-4 has been calculated using the Terman formula. Note especially how salt water has a dramatic influence on the low-angle radiation performance of verticals, where a pseudo-Brewster angle of less than 1 degree (0.2 degree!) exists on the low bands. In contrast, a sandy, dry ground will yield a pseudo-Brewster angle of 13 to 15 degrees on the low bands, and a city (heavy industrial) ground type will yield a pseudo-Brewster angle of no less than nearly 30 degrees on all frequencies! This means that under such circumstances the radiation efficiency for angles under 30 degrees will be severely degraded.

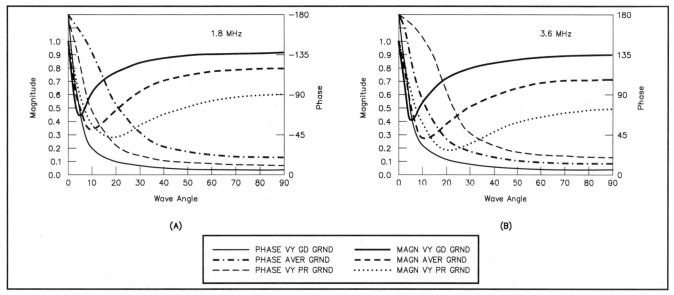

Fig 9-3—Reflection coefficient (magnitude and phase) for vertically polarized waves over three different types of ground (very good, average, and very poor).

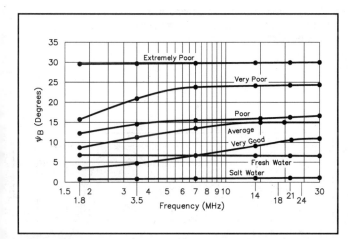

Fig 9-4—Pseudo-Brewster angle for different qualities of reflecting ground. Note that over salt water the pseudo-Brewster angle is constant for all frequencies, at less than 0.1 degree! That's why stations on the seacoast get out so well with vertical antennas.

Brewster Angle and Radials

Is there anything one can do about the pseudo-Brewster angle? Very little. Ground-radial systems are commonly used to reduce the losses in the near field of a vertical antenna. These ground-radial systems are usually quite short (0.1 to 0.5 wavelength), and are too short to improve the earth conditions in the area where reflection near the pseudo-Brewster angle takes place.

For quarter-wave verticals the Fresnel zone (the zone where the reflection takes place) is 1 to 2 wavelengths away from the antenna. For longer verticals (eg, a half-wave vertical) the Fresnel zone will extend up to 100 wavelengths away from the antenna (for the radiation at a wave angle of about ¼ of a degree).

This means that a good radial system (mostly ¼ to max. ½ wavelength long) will improve the efficiency of the vertical in collecting return currents, but will not influence the radiation by improving the reflection mechanism in the Fresnel zone.

In most practical cases the radiation at low angles will be determined only by the "real" ground around the vertical antenna in the so-called Fresnel zone.

Conclusion

This information should make it clear that a vertical may *not* be the best antenna if you are living in an area with very poor ground characteristics. This has been widely confirmed in real life; many top-notch DXers living in the Sonoran desert or in mountainous rocky areas on the West Coast swear by horizontal antennas for the low bands, while some of their colleagues living in flat areas with rich fertile soil, or even better, on such a ground near the sea coast, will be living advocates for vertical antennas and arrays made of vertical antennas.

Vertical Radiation Patterns

It is important to understand that gain and directivity are two different things. A vertical antenna over poor ground may show a good wave angle for DX, but its gain may be very poor. The difference in gain at a 10-degree wave angle for a quarter-wave vertical over very poor ground, as compared to the same vertical over sea-water, is an impressive 6 dB. Fig 9-5 shows the vertical-plane radiation pattern of a quarter-wave vertical over four types of "real" ground:

• Sea.
• Excellent ground.
• Average ground.
• Extremely poor ground.

The patterns in Fig 9-5 are all plotted on the same scale.

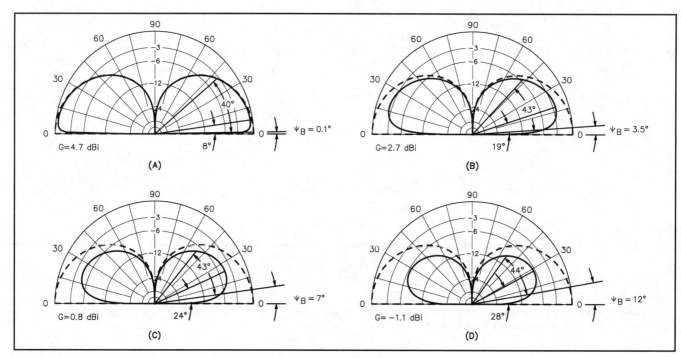

Fig 9-5—Vertical-plane radiation patterns of quarter-wave verticals over four types of ground, in each case using 60 quarter-wave long radials. Modeling was done at 3.5 MHz. The perfect-ground pattern is shown in each pattern as reference (broken line, with a gain of 5.1 dBi), as well as the pseudo-Brewster angle.

A—Over sea.   **C—Over average ground.**
B—Over very good ground.   **D—Over very poor ground.**

1.1.3. Horizontal pattern of a vertical antenna.

The horizontal radiation pattern of both the ground-mounted monopole and the vertical dipole is a circle.

1.2. Radiation Resistance of Monopoles

The radiation resistance value of any antenna depends on where it is fed. I'll call the radiation resistance of the antenna at a point of current maximum as $R_{rad(I)}$ and the radiation resistance of the antenna when fed at its base as $R_{rad(B)}$. For verticals greater than one quarter-wave in height, these two are not the same. Why is it important to know the radiation resistance of our vertical? The information is required to calculate the efficiency of the vertical:

$$Eff = \frac{R_{rad}}{R_{rad} + R_{loss}}$$

The radiation resistance of the antenna plus the loss resistance R_{loss} is the resistive part of the feed-point impedance of the vertical. The feed-point resistance (and reactance) are required to design an appropriate matching network between the antenna and the feed line.

Fig 9-6 shows $R_{rad(I)}$ of monopoles ranging from 20 to 540 degrees. (This is the radiation resistance as referred to the current maximum.) The radiation resistance of a vertical monopole shorter than or equal to a quarter wavelength and fed at its base [thus $R_{rad(I)} = R_{rad(B)}$] can be calculated as follows:

$$R_{rad} = \frac{1450 \, h^2}{\lambda^2} \qquad \text{(Eq 9-2)}$$

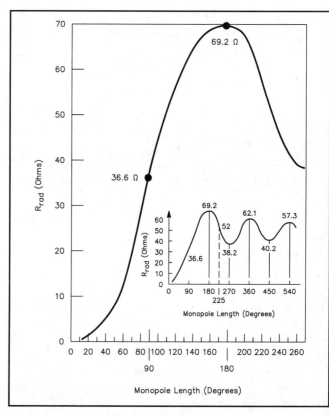

Fig 9-6—Radiation resistances [$R_{rad(I)}$, at the current maximum] of monopoles with sinusoidal current distribution. The chart can also be used for dipoles, but all values must be doubled.

where

h = effective antenna height, meters

λ = wavelength of operation, meters ($300/f_{MHz}$)

The effective height of the antenna is the height of a theoretical antenna having a constant current distribution all along its length, the area under this current distribution line being equal to the area under the current distribution line of the "real" antenna. The formula is valid for antennas with a ratio of antenna length to conductor diameter of greater than 500:1 (typical for wire antennas).

For a full-size, quarter-wave antenna the radiation resistance is determined:

Current at the base of the antenna = 1 A (given)
Area under sinusoidal current-distribution curve = 1 A × 1
   radian = 1 A × 180/π = 57.3 A-degrees
Equivalent length = 57.3 degrees (= 1 radian)
Electrical length = 300/3.8 = 78.95 m
Effective Height = (78.95 × 57.3)/360 = 12.56 degrees

$$R_{rad} = \frac{1450 \times 12.56^2}{78.95^2} = 36.6 \text{ ohms}$$

The same procedure can be used for calculating the radiation resistance of various types of short verticals.

Fig 9-7 shows the radiation resistance for a short vertical (valid for antennas with diameters ranging from 0.1 to 1 degree). For antennas made of thicker elements, Figs 9-8 and 9-9 can be used. These charts are for antennas with a constant diameter.

For verticals with a tapering diameter, large deviations have been observed. W. J. Schultz describes a method for calculating the input impedance of a tapered vertical (Ref 795). It has also been reported that verticals with a large diameter exhibit a much lower radiation resistance than the standard 36.6-ohm value. A. Doty, K8CFU, reports finding values as low as 21 ohms during his extensive experiments on elevated radial systems (Ref 793). I have measured a similar low value on my quarter-wave 160-meter vertical (see paragraph 5.6.) Par 2.1 shows how to calculate the radiation resistance of various types of short verticals.

Longer monopoles are usually not fed at the current maximum, but rather at the antenna base, so that $R_{rad(I)}$ is no longer the same as $R_{rad(B)}$. $R_{rad(B)}$ for long verticals is given in Figs 9-8 and 9-9. (Source: Henney, *Radio Engineering Handbook*, McGraw-Hill, NY, 1959, used by permission.)

$R_{rad(I)}$ is illustrated in Fig 9-10. The value can be calculated from the following formula (Ref. 722):

$$R_{rad(I)} = \varepsilon - 0.7L + 0.1[20 \sin (12.56637 L - 4.08407)] + 45$$

where

  ε = the base for natural logarithms, 2.71828 . . .
  L = antenna length in radians
      (radians = degrees times π/180
      = degrees divided by 57.296).

The length must be greater than π/2 radians (90 degrees).

Fig 9-10C shows the case of a 135-degree (⅜-wavelength) antenna. Disregarding losses, $Rr_{ad(B)} = R_{feed} \approx 300$ ohms, but the value of 2R, the theoretical resistance at the maximum current point, will be lower (57 ohms). If P1 (radiated power) = P2 (power dissipated in 2R), then $R_{rad(I)} = 2R$.

These values of $R_{rad(I)}$ are given in Fig 9-6, while $R_{rad(B)}$ can be found in Figs 9-8 and 9-9.

Figs 9-11 and 9-12 show the reactance of monopoles (at the base feed point) for varying antenna lengths and antenna diameters (source: E. A. Laport, *Radio Antenna Engineering*, McGraw-Hill, NY, 1952, used by permission).

1.3. Efficiency of the Monopole Antenna

The efficiency for short verticals has been defined as

$$Eff = \frac{R_{rad}}{R_{rad} + R_{loss}}$$

For the case of any vertical, short or long, when fed at its base this equation becomes

$$Eff = \frac{R_{rad(B)}}{R_{rad(B)} + R_{loss}} \qquad \text{(Eq 9-3)}$$

The loss resistance of a vertical is composed of:

• Conductor RF resistance.
• Parallel losses from insulators.
• Equivalent series losses of the loading element(s).
• Ground losses.

1.3.1. Conductor RF Resistance

When multisection towers are used for a vertical antenna, care should be taken to ensure proper electrical contact between the sections. If necessary, a copper braid strap should interconnect the sections. Rohrbacher, DJ2NN, provided a formula to calculate the effective RF resistance of conductors of copper, aluminum and bronze:

$$R_{loss} = (1 + 0.1L)\left(f^{0.125}\right)\left(0.5 + \frac{1.5}{D}\right) \times M \qquad \text{(Eq 9-4)}$$

where

  L = length of the vertical, meters
  f = frequency of operation, MHz
  D = conductor diameter, mm (1 inch = 25.4 mm)
  M = material constant (M = 0.945 for copper, 1.0 for bronze, and 1.16 for aluminum)

1.3.2. Parallel Losses in Insulators

Base insulators often operate at low-impedance points. For monopoles near a half-wavelength long, however, care should be taken to use good-quality insulators, as very high voltages can be present. There are many military surplus insulators available for this purpose. For medium- and low-impedance applications, insulators made of nylon stock (turned down to the appropriate diameter) are excellent.

1.3.3. Ground Losses

A large number of articles have been published in the literature concerning ground systems for verticals (Ref. 806 to 822). The reflecting ground plays an important role in determining the effectiveness of a vertical in two very distinct areas:

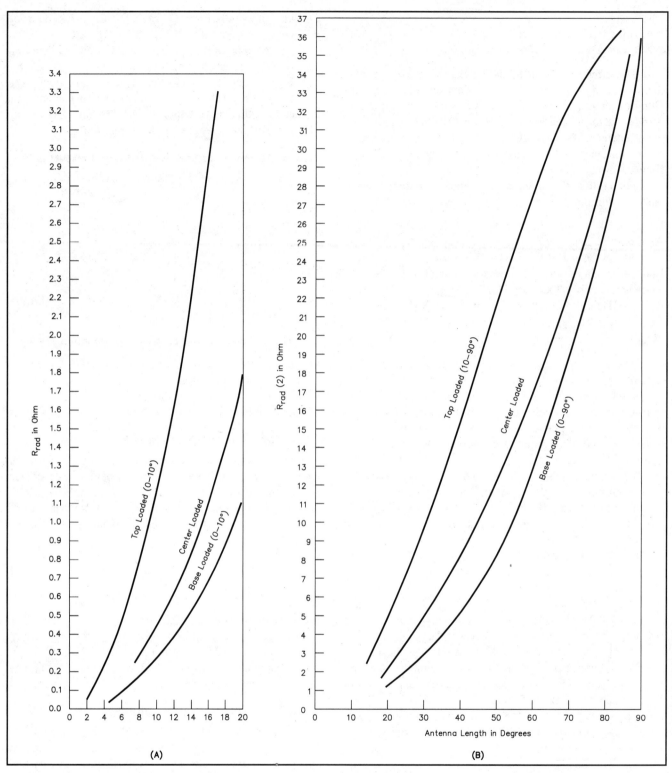

Fig 9-7—Radiation resistance charts (R$_{rad}$) for verticals up to 90 degrees or ¼ wavelength long. At A, for lengths up to 20 degrees, and at B, for greater lengths.

1) In the near field (under the antenna), where the return currents of the antenna are collected: The quality (loss) of the ground will be important as to the efficiency of the antenna (Eq 9-3). In this case we deal with power applied to the antenna that is *not* being radiated (in the far field), but is being dissipated in the lossy ground. In the near field of the antenna we are concerned with the *radiation efficiency*.

2) In the far field (up to many wavelengths away), where the waves are reflected that will combine with the direct wave to form the radiation at low angles: The ground quality in the far field will determine the pseudo-Brewster angle and the low-angle radiation properties of the vertical (see par 4.1.2). In this case we can talk about power that has been radiated from the antenna, but is now being partially absorbed (dissipated) in

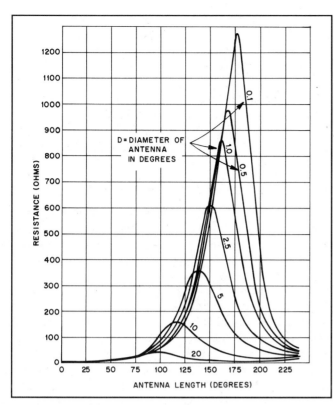

Fig 9-8—Radiation resistances for monopoles fed at the base. Curves are given for various conductor (tower) diameters. The values are valid for perfect ground only.

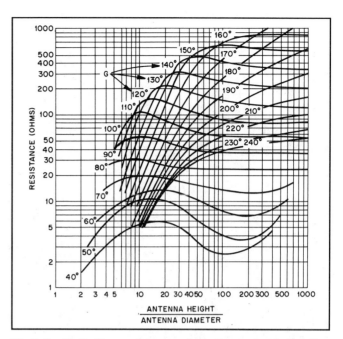

Fig 9-9—Radiation resistances for monopoles fed at the base. Curves are given for various height/diameter ratios over perfect ground.

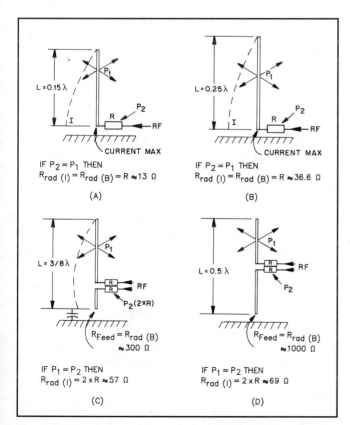

Fig 9-10—Radiation resistance terminology for long and short verticals. See text for details. The feed-point resistances indicated assume no losses.

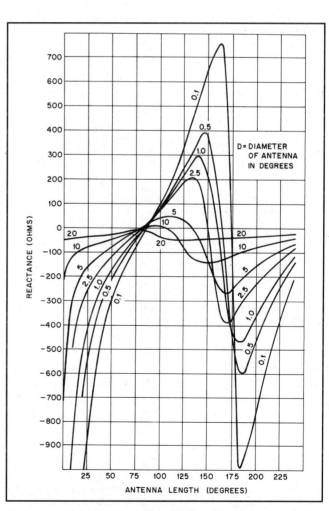

Fig 9-11—Feed-point reactances (over perfect ground) for monopoles with varying diameters.

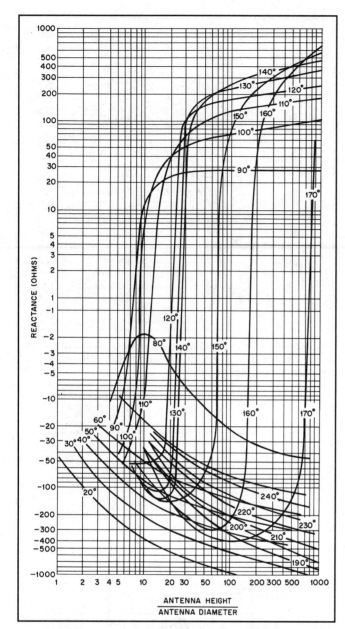

Fig 9-12—Feed-point reactances (over perfect ground) for monopoles with different height/diameter ratios.

9-1

Table 9-1

Optimum Length Versus Number of Radials

Number of Radials	Optimum Length (λ)
4	0.10
12	0.15
24	0.25
48	0.35
96	0.45
120	0.50

This table considers only the effect of providing a low-loss return path for the antenna current (near field). It does not consider ground losses in the far field, which determine the very low-angle radiation properties of the antenna.

the (poor) ground in the far field. These losses are no part of the radiation efficiency of the antenna (Eq 9-3), but are often referred to as the Fresnel zone reflection losses. In the far field (Fresnel zone) we are concerned with the *reflection efficiency* of the antenna.

The effect of ground in these two different zones has been well covered by P. H. Lee, N6PL, in his excellent book, *Vertical Antenna Handbook*, published by *CQ Publishing* (p 81, The effects of earth on the efficiency of radiation and the vertical pattern).

The "Artificial" Ground Plane in Free Space

A vertical on VHF usually employs four radials as a "ground-plane." But in fact, two radials would do the same job. All you need is a quarter-wave wire connected to the feed-line outer conductor in order to have an RF ground at that point. If you had only one radial, it would radiate (a horizontal wave component). Two quarter-wave radials in a straight line have their current distributed in such a way that radiation from the radials is essentially canceled. This is similar to what happens with top-wire loading (T antennas). Using four radials at right angles does just the same.

The story goes that when groundplane antennas were first made available commercially, two extra radials were added because few believed that with only two radials the antenna would radiate equally well in all directions! In the case of a VHF groundplane, there is no "poor ground" involved and all return currents are collected in the form of displacement currents going through the 2 (or 4) radials.

When the vertical is erected on or very near the ground, that "poor" ground must be taken into consideration. There are basically two schools when it comes to designing a good ground-plane system for a vertical:

1) Buried radials, or radials on the ground.
2) Elevated radial system.

1.3.3.1. *Buried radials.*

Dr Brown's original work (Ref. 801) on buried ground radial systems dates from 1937. His classic work led to the still common requirement that broadcast antennas use at least 120 radials, each at least 1 wavelength long.

Near Field (Radiation Efficiency)

With buried radials, the return currents are allowed to enter the earth and are collected with an array of (bare) buried radial wires in the ground. Edward, N2MF, used NEC (Numerical Electromagnetic Code, method of moments) to model the influence of buried radials (Ref. 816). He discovered that for a given number of radial wires, there is a corresponding length beyond which there is no appreciable efficiency improvement. This length is, surprisingly enough, independent of earth conditions. Table 9-1 shows the optimum radial length as a function of the number of radials (within 0.1 dB of maximum gain).

Far Field (Reflection Efficiency)

I modeled a range of situations where a full-size quarter-wave vertical is erected over different types of ground and different radials systems. The results of the analysis are shown in Figs 9-13 through 9-15.

Quarter-Wave Radials

If you have a quarter-wave vertical over very poor ground, changing the number of quarter-wave radials from 30 to 120 will hardly do anything to the radiation pattern. The takeoff angle is 28 degrees, and the pseudo-Brewster angle is between 12 and 14 degrees. There is, however, a signal improvement of 1 dB when going from 30 to 120 radials. If you go from 5 to 120 radials, the improvement is over 3 dB.

Over good ground the situation is similar. The takeoff angle varies between 23 degrees (120 quarter-wave radials) and 24 degrees (30 quarter-wave radials). At the same time the pseudo-Brewster angle varies from 9 to 7 degrees. The signal improvement is 0.7 dB in going from 30 to 120 radials.

Two-Wavelength-Long Radials

If you have only a few radials (30) over very poor ground, it does not pay to make them longer than a quarter-wave. Even with 2-wavelength-long radials, the radiation angle remains unchanged (as compared to quarter-wave-long radials) at 28 degrees. As the number of radials goes up, however, the difference becomes more marked. For 60 radials, the angle has dropped to 25 degrees, for 120 radials to 21 degrees, and for 140 radials to 17 degrees. At the same time the pseudo-Brewster angle drops from 12 to 9, 5.5 and 4.5 degrees! Important is also the signal gain, which is 2.5 dB going from 30 to 250 radials (that's almost like doubling your power!).

Over good ground the situation is similar: no improvement in radiation pattern with only 30 radials. It is remarkable, however, that 240 two-wavelength-long radials produce the same signal over very poor ground as they do over good ground. This proves that for a quarter-wave vertical, the Fresnel zone does not extend much farther than 2 wavelengths.

Sea-Front QTH

I have also modeled an ideal sea-front QTH; the vertical has quarter-wave radials (to take care of collecting the return currents), and from beyond the end of the radials there is nothing but ocean water! Notice that the number of radials does not influence the radiation characteristics whatsoever. From 30 to 120 radials, the takeoff angle remains at 5 degrees, while the pseudo-Brewster angle sits at less than 0.1 degree! At the same time the radiation lobe is within 1 dB from 1.5 to 25 degrees, and within 3 dB from 1 to 40 degrees. There is also no gain change. All this is due to the wonderful conductivity properties of salt water. No wonder such a QTH does wonders (ask B. Moeller, OZ8BV).

In our model the above relative gain figures are caused *only* by the reflection of the waves on an imperfect ground. The effect of current return (antenna efficiency) is *not* taken into account here. In the model it is assumed that the ground resistance in the immediate vicinity of the antenna is perfect. This can be achieved by a number of radials terminating in the sea.

A quarter-wave current-fed vertical was used in the model. The situation can be quite different with other types of vertical, eg, the half-wave vertical (see par 3.3.). Fig 9-16

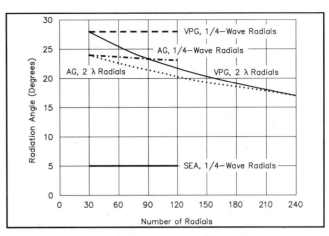

Fig 9-13—Main-lobe peak radiation angle for a quarter-wave vertical over three types of ground: sea, average ground (AG), and very poor ground (VPG), for a varying number of radials of both ¼ and 2 wavelengths. Note that only many very long radials substantially lowers the radiation angle.

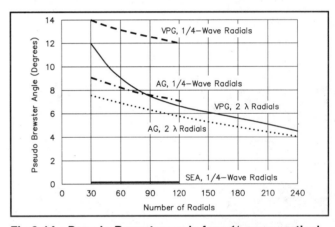

Fig 9-14—Pseudo-Brewster angle for a ¼-wave vertical over three types of ground: sea, average ground (AG), and very poor ground (VPG), for a varying number of radials of both ¼ and 2 wavelengths. Note that only many very long radials substantially lower the pseudo-Brewster angle.

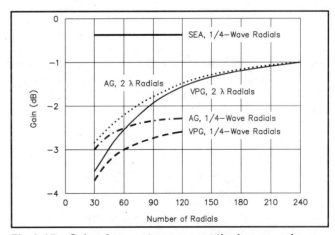

Fig 9-15—Gain of a quarter-wave vertical over various types of ground referenced to the gain over a perfect infinite reflector. The models shown are for three types of ground: sea, average ground (AG), and very poor ground (VPG), and for 30, 60, 120 and 240 radials of both ¼ and 2 wavelengths.

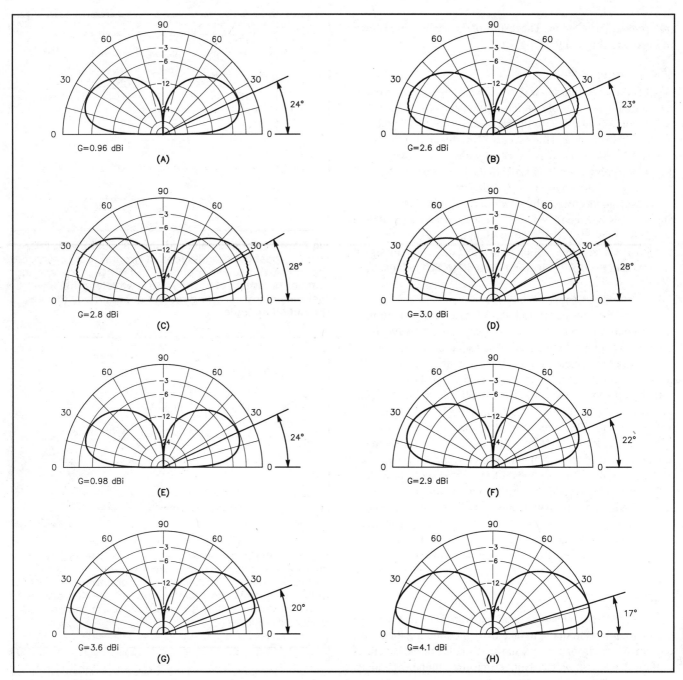

Fig 9-16—Vertical radiation patterns of quarter-wave verticals over average ground for different numbers of radials and different radial lengths. The 0-dB reference is 4.1 dBi for all patterns.

A—4 radials, ¼-λ long.
B—60 radials, ¼-λ long.
C—120 radials, ¼-λ long.

D—240 radials, ¼-λ long.
E—4 radials, 2-λ long.
F—60 radials, 2-λ long.

G—120 radials, 2-λ long.
H—240 radials, 2-λ long.

shows the radiation patterns of quarter-wave verticals over different types of ground and using different radial systems. The general conclusions are the following:

• Very long radials (2 wavelengths) help little unless their number is high (120 or more).

• Long radials will improve only the radiation angle and radiation efficiency (from a far-field ground-loss point of view).

• A sea-front QTH is definitely what everybody wants.

Sectorized radial systems with very long radials (up to 10 wavelengths long) have been evaluated and found to be effective for lowering the wave angle in certain directions. A similar effect occurs when verticals are mounted right at the salt-water line (Ref. the pseudo-Brewster angle). Similar in result to a sectorized radial system is the situation where an elevated radial system is used with only 1 radial (see par 1.3.3.2.).

It has been my experience, which has been confirmed by many others, that using a solid metal plate of reasonable size right under the antenna can result in a notable decrease in ground resistance, and consequently in ground loss. Another possible improvement to an existing radial system has been reported by Sherwood (Ref. 809) and has been used successfully at one time at my QTH. Installing strips of chicken wire, 50 to 100 cm wide (2 to 3 ft), in different directions from the antenna base can significantly reduce the losses of the ground system.

When only a few (fewer than 6) radials are used, the gauge of the wires is important for maximum efficiency. The heavier the better. With many radials, the wire size becomes unimportant since the return current is divided over a large number of conductors.

DXpeditions using temporary antennas just have to take a small spool of no. 24 or 26 (0.5 or 0.4 mm diameter) enameled magnet wire. This is inexpensive, and can be used to establish a very efficient RF ground system.

Only a few of the more fortunate among us have the ability to run any number of radials of great length in all directions, because of the real estate required. In practice, the rule of thumb for designing a good ground system is to use as many radials as possible. Don't bother about very long ones unless you can put in a great number. The addition of a ground screen is definitely to be advocated where space for an elaborate radial system is not available.

Ground Rods

Ground rods are important for achieving a good dc ground, but contribute very little to the RF ground. A ground rod will seldom constitute an acceptable minimum RF ground. An exception exists where no low-resistance ground system is required such as for use in terminating a Beverage antenna.

Depth of Buried Radials

Leo, W7LR (Ref. 808) reports that burying the radials a few inches below the surface does not detract from their performance. C. J. Michaels, W7XC, calculated the depth of penetration of RF current in ground of different properties. He defined the depth of penetration as the depth at which the current density is 37% of what it is at the surface. Under those conditions, for 80 meters, a depth of penetration of an amazing 1.5 m (5 ft) has been calculated for very good ground. For very poor ground the depth reaches 12 m (40 ft)! This tends to confirm that burying the radials will not detract much from their efficiency. Christman confirmed this when modeling his elevated radial systems. He found only hundredths of a dB difference between burying radials at 5 cm (2 in.) or 15 cm (6 in.).

Radial Strips Versus Radial Wires

Sherwood, WB0JGP, has described and compared ground systems consisting of wide strips of ground screens (Ref. 809). Anyone tempted to try the "screen" approach should be warned of one thing: never use steel wire for a buried ground system, whether it be a single wire or chicken wire. Steel is a very poor conductor at RF. The steel wire will also corrode in a very short time, although a thick layer of galvanization may improve the resistance to corrosion.

Fig 9-17—Small home-made radial plow as used by Ghis Penny, ON5NT, for burying the radials in the lawn. That's Heidi, ON5NT's youngest daughter, acting as driver for the wire plow, while the OM himself takes care of the required "horsepower" to cut the slot in the lawn.

A Radial Plow

Many hams will be forced to use a buried radial system. Installing radials can be quite a chore. Hyder, W7IV (Ref. 815) and Mosser, K3ZAP (Ref. 812) have described systems and tools for easy installation of radials. Fig 9-17 shows such a radial plow as made by G. Penny, ON5NT, to bury the radials in his lawn. A small carriage, made of wood, supports a sharp knife which cuts a slot in the ground. A small aluminum feed tube deposits the radial wire at the bottom of the slot, about 5 cm (2 in.) deep. A person sitting on the carriage takes care of the required weight to drive the knife into the ground.

An Alternative

Radials can also be laid on the ground in areas that are suitable. Another neat way of installing radials in a lawn-covered area is to cut the grass really short at the end of the season (October), and lay the radials flat on the ground, anchored here and there with metal hooks. By the next spring, the grass will have covered up most of the wires, and by the end of the following year the wires will be completely covered by the grass. This method also meets the recommendation by Doty, K8CFU, to bury the radials as close as possible to the surface of the ground.

1.3.3.2. *Elevated radial systems.*

A. Doty, K8CFU, concluded from his experimental work (Ref. 807 and 820) that an elevated counterpoise system makes a more efficient ground system than buried bare radials. The reasoning is that in the case of an elevated radial or counterpoise system, the return currents do not have to travel for a considerable distance through high-resistance earth, as is the case when buried radials are used. The article in April 1984 *CQ* also contains a very complete reference list of just about every publication on the subject of radials (72 references!).

Frey, W3ESU, uses the same counterpoise system with his Minipoise short low-band vertical (Ref. 824). He reports that connecting the elevated and insulated radial wires together at the periphery definitely yields improved performance. If a counterpoise system cannot be used, Doty recommends using insulated radials lying right on the ground, or buried as close as possible to the surface.

Quite a few years later, A. Christman, R Redcliff, D. Adler, J. Breakall and A. Resnick used computer modeling to come to conclusions which are very similar to the finding brought forward after extensive field work by A. Doty.

The publication by A. Christman, KB8I, has since become the standard reference work on elevated radial systems (Ref 825).

The results from Christman's study were obtained by computer modeling using NEC-GSD. It is interesting to understand the different steps he followed in his analysis (all modeling was done using "average ground"):

1) Modeling of the quarter-wave vertical with 120 buried radials (5 cm or 2 in. deep). This is the 1937 "Brown" reference.

2) The quarter-wave vertical was modeled using only 4 radials at different radial elevations. For a modeling frequency of 3.8 MHz, Christman found that 4.5 m (15 ft) was the height at which the 4-radial systems equaled the 120-buried-radial systems as far as low-angle radiation performance. It appears that isolating the base of the vertical from the real ground yields a small improvement over the situation where the radials are connected via the support mast to the real ground. If the isolated system is being used, one must isolate the coax feed line by using an RF choke (eg, many turns of coiled up coaxial cable or a stack of ferrite cores or beads over the cable).

Christman's studies also revealed that "as the quality of the soil becomes worse, the elevated radial system must be

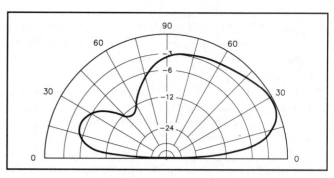

Fig 9-18—Vertical radiation pattern of a quarter-wave vertical with only *one* elevated radial (height 0.05 wavelength).

raised progressively higher above the earth to reach performance on par with that of the reference 120-buried-radial vertical monopole. If the soil is highly conductive, the reverse is true."

The elevated-radial approach has become increasingly popular with low-band DXers since the publication of the above work, and represents a viable alternative to digging and plowing, especially where the ground is unfriendly for such operations.

Fig 9-18 shows the vertical radiation pattern of a vertical with one quarter-wave elevated radial (height of antenna base = 0.05 wavelength). This vertical with a single elevated radial has the same gain (in its favored direction) as a ground-mounted vertical with 120 buried radials!

D. Schoen, N2KK/6, has built a 4-square array using an elevated radial system, and reports that after having initially used the array with just 4 radials, the addition of more radials has yielded a net improvement on angle of radiation.

It should be clear that the elevated radial system is a valid alternative for a system of buried radials in its task to efficiently collect the return currents of the vertical. However, the formation of the low-angle radiation is also accomplished at greater distances from the vertical (typically up to 2 wavelengths away for a quarter-wave vertical). Therefore, in addition to the elevated radial system, the "real" ground will also play an important role in achieving good low-angle radiation.

1.3.3.3. *"Wonder" radials for 160 meters (?).*

R. Artigo, KN6J, has published a mysterious wonder solution to the space problem of full-size quarter-wave radials for 160 meters (*CQ*, June 92, p 57). He makes his radials of old coax cable, fashioning each one into a quarter-wave resonant line, making the velocity factor of the line work for him. For ordinary cable the velocity factor is 0.66, so a radial for 1.85 MHz is only about 88 ft long. He leaves the end of each radial unshorted, while the shields of the radials are connected to a ground rod at the antenna base.

What happens in reality? The shield of the coax will be exposed to the field of the antenna, and will take care of the return currents. The electrical length of the shield of the coax is *not* related to the velocity factor of the feed line when used as a transmission line. The open-circuited quarter-wave line represents at the antenna-base end a short circuit, which means

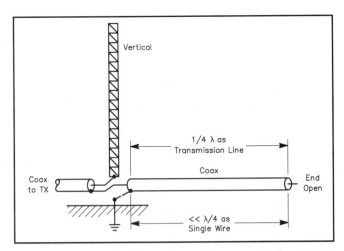

Fig 9-19—Representation of the short radials described by Artigo, KN6J. It is clear that the radial is not ¼ wave long, but only ¼ wave times the velocity factor of the coaxial cable (0.25 × 0.66 = 0. 165 wavelength). The velocity factor of the cable (shield) used as a single wire is *not* the same as the velocity factor of the cable used as a transmission line. The velocity factor of the "wire" is between 95 and 98%.

Fig 9-20—Walter Skudlarek, DJ6QT, inspecting some of the radials used on the 160-meter vertical at ON4UN. Half of the radials are buried (where the garden is), and half are just lying on the ground in the back of the garden behind the hedge (where the XYL can't see the mess from the house!). In total, some 250 radials are used, ranging from 15 m (50 ft) to 75 m (245 ft).

that the radial is connected to both the ground rod and the antenna base (see Fig 9-19).

1.3.3.4. *Short radials that do work.*

As explained above, radials provide a low-impedance ("short") point to connect the outer conductor of our coaxial feed line. This low-impedance point can be obtained by using a plane—many radial wires (buried or elevated), or in its simplest form by one or preferably two (in-line) elevated radials. They must be a quarter-wave long in order to provide the low impedance. If there is not enough space for installing straight quarter-wave radials, several ways exist to stay within limited space and still get the necessary low-impedance point:

• Fold back the ends of the radials.
• Load the radials with coils in order to make them resonant at the operating frequency.

In order to calculate the loading-coil value, you can consider the radial to be a vertical and follow the procedure as outlined in par 2.6.8. Practically speaking, you can grid-dip a couple of radial wires connected as a dipole in order to bring them to the correct frequency.

1.3.3.5. *Evaluating the ground system.*

The classic way to evaluate the losses of a ground system is to measure the feed-point resistance of the vertical while steadily increasing the number of radials. The feed-point resistance will drop consistently and will approach a lower limit when a very good ground system has been installed. Be aware, however, that the intrinsic ground conductivity can vary greatly with time and weather, so it is recommended that you do such a test in a very short time frame in order to minimize the effects of varying environmental factors on your tests (Ref. 818, 819).

Radiation resistance can be measured with a noise bridge or an antennascope with an appropriately expanded scale (Ref. 105, 1600, 1601, 1607). Antennas shorter or longer than a quarter wavelength are first resonated (loaded) to the operating frequency if an antennascope is used. With a noise bridge, direct resistance and reactance measurement can be made on any frequency within the range of the receiver used.

For calculating the antenna efficiency, Table 9-2 shows the equivalent resistance of buried radial systems in good-quality ground. For poor ground, higher resistance can be expected, especially with only a few radials. The situation is similar to the far-field evaluation. It does not pay off to install just a few long radials. For a given length of available radial wire, it is better to use many shorter radials than just a few long ones (also see Table 9-1).

Periodic visual inspections of the radial system for broken wires and loose or corroded connections etc will assure continued efficient operation. Fig 9-20 shows DJ6QT examining the radials of the ON4UN 160-meter vertical.

■ 2. SHORT VERTICALS

Short verticals can be "loaded" to be resonant at the desired operating frequency. Different loading methods are covered in this section, and the radiation resistance for each

Table 9-2

Equivalent Resistances of Buried Radial Systems

Number of Radials

Radial Length (λ)	2	15	30	60	120
0.15	28.6	15.3	14.8	11.6	11.6
0.20	28.4	15.3	13.4	9.1	9.1
0.25	28.1	15.1	12.2	7.9	6.9
0.30	27.7	14.5	10.7	6.6	5.2
0.35	27.5	13.9	9.8	5.6	2.8
0.40	27.0	13.1	7.2	5.2	0.1

The values in the body of this table are in ohms, and are valid for "good" ground.

type is calculated. Design rules are given, and practical designs are worked out for each type of loaded vertical. The design of loading coils is covered in detail. The different methods are compared as to their efficiency.

Short verticals have been described in abundance in amateur literature (Ref 771, 794, 746, 7793 and 1314).

The radiation pattern of a short vertical is essentially the same as for a full-size quarter-wave vertical. Fig 9-21 shows the vertical radiation patterns of a range of short verticals over perfect ground, as calculated using ELNEC. Notice that the gain is essentially the same in all cases (the theoretical difference is less than 0.5 dB).

A short (shorter than ¼ wave) monopole exhibits an impedance with a real part that is smaller than 36.6 ohms, and in addition a reactive part that is capacitive. Loading a short vertical means canceling the reactive part of the impedance (it brings the antenna to resonance). The simplest way is to add a coil at the base of the antenna, a coil with an inductive reactance equal to the capacitive reactance shown by the short vertical. This is the so-called base-loading method. Fig 9-22 shows a number of classic loading schemes for short verticals, along with the current distribution along the antenna. Remember from par 1.2. that the radiation resistance is a measure of the area under the current distribution curve. Also remember from par 1.3. that the radiation efficiency is given by

$$Eff = \frac{R_{rad}}{R_{rad} + R_{loss}}$$

It is clear now that the real issues with short verticals are *efficiency* and *bandwidth*. Let us examine these issues in detail.

With short verticals the numerator of the efficiency formula decreases in value (smaller R_{rad}), and the term R_{loss} in the denominator is likely to increase (losses of the loading devices such as coils). This means we have two terms which tend to decrease the efficiency of loaded verticals. Therefore maximum attention must be paid to these terms by
• Keeping the radiation resistance as high as possible.
• Keeping the losses of the loading devices as low as possible.

2.1. Radiation Resistance

The procedure for calculating the radiation resistance was explained in par 1.2., where we found that R_{rad} for a

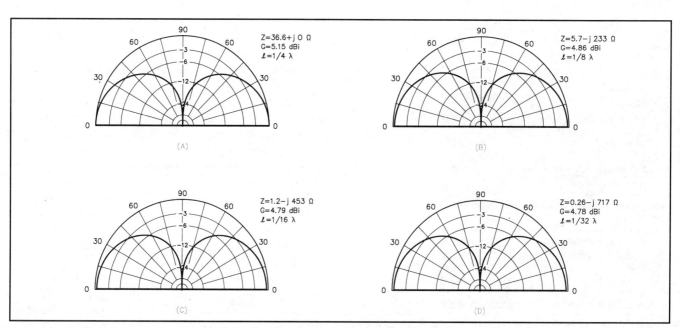

Fig 9-21—Elevation-plane radiation patterns and gain (dBi) of verticals with different heights. The 0-dB reference for all patterns is 5.2 dBi. Note that the gain as well as the shape of the radiation patterns remain practically unchanged with height differences. The patterns were calculated with ELNEC over perfect ground, using a modeling frequency of 3.5 MHz and a conductor diameter of 2 mm.

A—Height = ¼ λ.
B—Height = ⅛ λ.
C—Height = 1/16 λ.
D—Height = 1/32 λ.

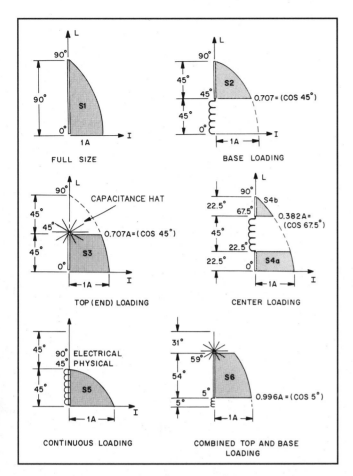

Fig 9-22—Short loaded verticals with their current distribution. The radiation resistance is proportional to the area under the current-distribution curve. The efficiency is also proportional to the radiation resistance. See text for details.

quarter-wave vertical is 36.6 ohms. We will now analyze the following types of short verticals:

1) Base-loaded vertical.
2) Top-loaded vertical.
3) Center-loaded vertical.
4) Vertical with helical loading.
5) Base plus top-loaded vertical.
6) Linear loading.

2.1.1. Base loading.

Base loading consists of adding a loading coil at the base of the monopole. The base-loaded monopole shown in Fig 9-23C is physically 50% shorter than the full-size, quarter-wave monopole. Base loading makes it electrically the same size.

The radiation resistance can be calculated as defined in par 1.2. A trigonometric expression which gives the same results is given below (Ref. 742).

$$R_{rad} = 36.6 \times \frac{(1 - \cos L)^2}{\sin^2 L} \qquad \text{(Eq 9-5)}$$

where L = the length of the monopole.

According to this formula, the radiation resistance of the base-loaded vertical (50% size reduction) is 6.28 ohms.

Hall, K1TD, derived another equation (Ref. 1008):

$$R_{rad} = \frac{L^{2.736}}{6096} \qquad \text{(Eq 9-6)}$$

where L = electrical length of the monopole in degrees.

This very simple formula yields accurate results for monopole antenna lengths between 70 and 100 degrees, but should be avoided for shorter antennas. A practical design example is described in par 2.6.1.

2.1.2. Top loading.

The patent for the top-loaded vertical was granted to a Simon Eisenstein of Kiev, Russia, in 1909. Fig 9-24 is a copy of the original patent application, where one can see a combined loading coil plus top-hat loading configuration. The resulting current distribution is also shown.

Top loading is achieved by one of the following methods (see Fig 9-25):

- Capacitance top hat: in the shape of a disk, or the spokes of a wheel at the top of the shortened vertical. Details of how to design a vertical with a capacitance hat are given in par 2.6.3.
- Flat-top wire loading (T antenna): The flattop wire is symmetrical with respect to the vertical. Equal currents flowing outwards in both flattop halves essentially cancel the radiation from the flattop wire. For design details see par 2.6.5.
- Coil with capacitance hat: In many instances a loading coil is used in combination with a capacitance hat to load a short monopole. This may be necessary, as otherwise an unusually large capacitance hat may be required to establish resonance at the desired frequency.
- Coil with flattop wire: This loading method is similar to the coil with capacitance hat (see par 2.6.7. for design example).
- Inverted L: This configuration is not really a top-loaded vertical, as the horizontal loading wire radiates along with the vertical mast to produce both vertical and horizontal polarization. Inverted-L antennas are covered separately in paragraph 8.9.
- Coil with wire: This one is not really a loaded short vertical, but a form of a loaded inverted L.

For calculating the radiation resistance of the top-loaded vertical, it is irrelevant which of the above loading methods is used. For a given vertical height, all produce the same radiation resistance. However, when we deal with efficiency (where both R_{rad} and R_{loss} are involved) the different loading methods may behave differently (different loss resistances).

The radiation resistance can be calculated as defined in par 1.2. A trigonometric expression which gives the same results is given below (Ref. 742 and 794):

$$R_{rad} = 36.6 \times \sin^2 L \qquad \text{(Eq 9-7)}$$

where L is the length of the monopole.

The 50% shortened monopole with pure end loading (Fig 9-23C) has a radiation resistance of

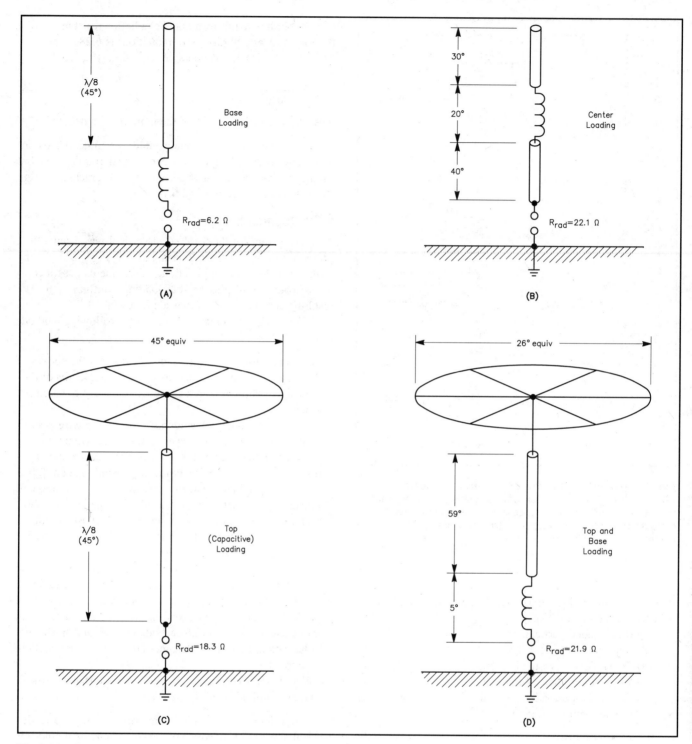

Fig 9-23—Four of the most common types of loading used to resonate short verticals. When comparing the R_{rad} of the four examples, be sure to also consider the differences in the physical lengths of the radiators; they are not all equal.

$R_{rad} = 36.6 \times \sin^2 45° = 18.3$ ohms

The radiation resistance of top-loaded verticals can be read from the charts in Figs 9-26 and 9-27. For top-loaded verticals, use only the 0% curves.

2.1.3. Center loading.

The center-loaded monopole of Fig 9-23B is loaded with

a coil positioned along the mast. The antenna section above the coil is often called the whip.

Inputs:

- Length of mast below the coil = 40 degrees
- Length of mast (whip) above the coil = 30 degrees

The radiation resistance can be calculated as defined in par 1.2. A trigonometric expression which gives the same

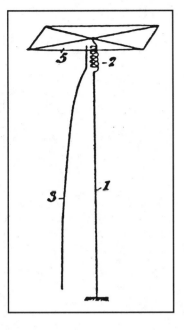

Fig 9-24—Replica of the patent application of August 10, 1909, showing the original drawing of the top-loaded vertical.

results is given below (Ref 742 and 7993):

$$R_{rad} = 36.6 \times (1 - \sin t2 + \sin t1)^2 \qquad \text{(Eq 9-8)}$$

where

t1 = length of vertical below loading coil (40°)
t2 = 90° – length of vertical above loading coil
 (= whip, 30°) = 60°

Using this formula, R_{rad} is calculated as = 22.1 ohms.

2.1.4. Combined top and base loading.

Top and base loading are frequently used together, as shown in Fig 9-23D. Top loading is often done with capacitance-hat loading, in many cases combined with a loading coil or a flat-top wire. If a wide frequency excursion is required (eg, 3.5 to 3.8 MHz), one can load the vertical to resonate at 3.8 MHz using the top-loading technique. When operating on 3.5 MHz, a little base loading is added to establish resonance at the lower frequency. Perfectionists could use a motor-

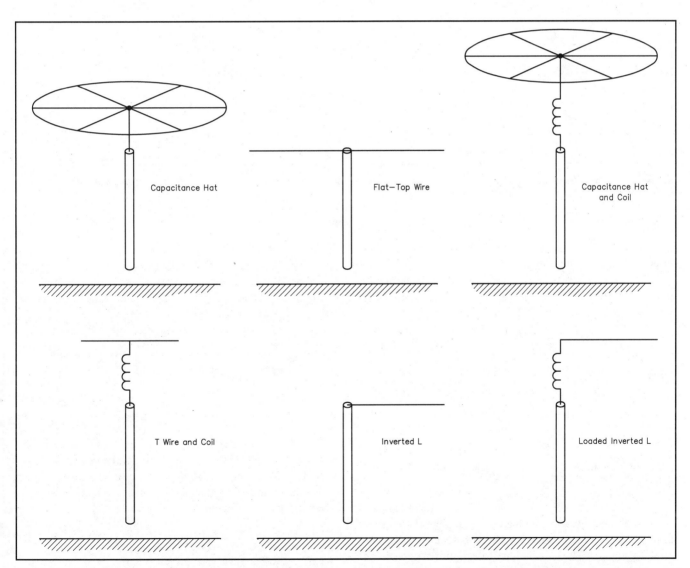

Fig 9-25—Common types of top loading for short verticals. The inverted L and loaded inverted L are not true verticals, as their radiation contains a horizontal component.

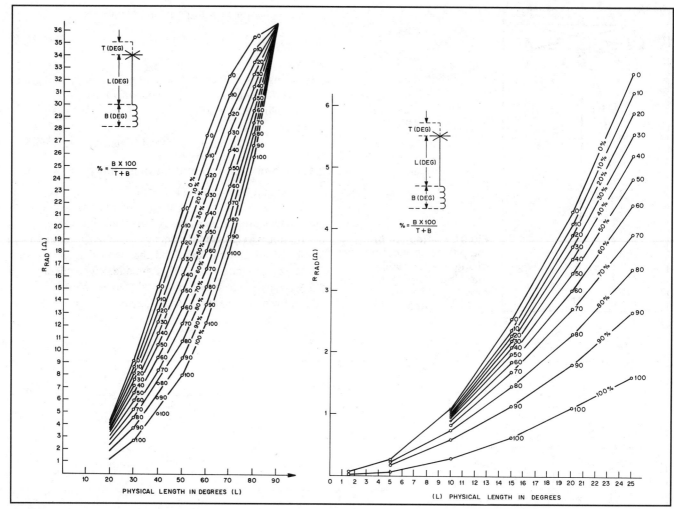

Fig 9-26—Radiation resistances of a monopole with combined top and base loading. Use the chart at B for shorter monopoles to obtain better accuracy.

driven inductor for tuning the vertical exactly to resonance anywhere in the band.

The radiation resistance can be calculated as defined in par 1.2. A trigonometric expression which gives the same results is given below (Ref 742 and 7993):

$$R_{rad} = 36.6 \frac{(\sin t1 - \sin t2)^2}{\cos^2 t2} \qquad \text{(Eq 9-9)}$$

where

t1 = electrical height of vertical mast
t2 = electrical length of base loading coil

In our example shown in Fig 9-23D, t1= 59 degrees and t2 = 5 degrees.

$$R_{rad} = 36.6 \frac{(\sin 59° - \sin 5°)^2}{\cos^2 5°} = 21.9 \text{ ohms}$$

Fig 9-26 shows the radiation resistance for monopoles with combined top and base loading. The physical length of the antenna (L) plus top loading (T) plus base loading (B) must total 90 degrees. The calculation of the required capacitance and the dimensions of the capacitance hat are explained further in par 2.6.3.

2.1.5. Linear Loading

Designing linear-loaded elements can best be done graphically as shown in Fig 9-27. Let us use as an example the vertical monopole of Fig 9-27A, 28 meters long (92 feet), and linearly loaded for 1.8 MHz.

A quarter-wave vertical (90 electrical degrees, using a 96% shortening factor) for 160 meters measures

$$\frac{300 \times 0.96}{1.8 \times 4} = 40 \text{ m}$$

and 28 meters represents $90 \times \frac{28}{40} = 63$ degrees.

The remaining $90 - 63 = 27$ degrees is made up by a linear loading device, which is simply a folded length of radiator.

B and C of Fig 9-27 show the current distribution for the antenna. Assuming an antenna current of 1 A at the feed point, the current can be calculated at key points:

At 13.5 degrees: I(a) = cos 13.5 = 0.972 A
At 27.0 degrees: I(b) = cos 27 = 0.891 A
At 40.5 degrees: I(c) = cos 40.5 = 0.760 A

The folded linear-loading "stub" may look like an open-

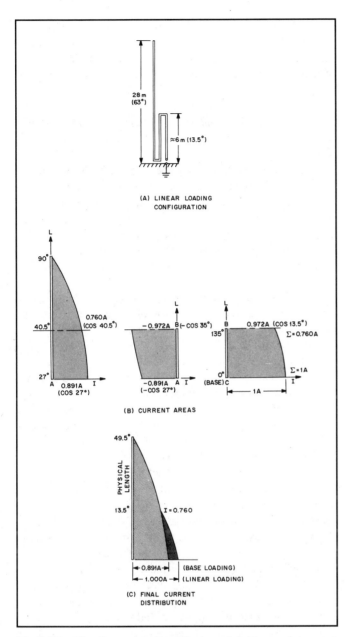

Fig 9-27—The linear loading device at A is merely a part of the antenna folded back on itself in order to shorten the physical length of the antenna. At B is the graphical representation of the area under the current distribution curve for a linear-loaded vertical. The shaded area in C represents the increase in radiation resistance over the base-loaded equivalent. Since no coils are used in this form of loading, linear loading can be used with almost no loss.

wire transmission line, but, whereas in an open transmission line with a fully balanced load the currents in the two wires are equal in magnitude but 180 degrees out of phase and hence produce no radiation, in the case of a linear loading stub the radiation is not canceled out. To assess the effect of radiation from the linear-loading stub we analyze the area under the current distribution (Fig 9-27). Summing the areas under the current distribution along the two wires of the loading stub yield the effective area that is responsible for radiation from

the loading stub, and hence for an increase in radiation resistance.

Summing the currents at these points: I_{total} at 40.5 degrees from the top = 0.760 − 0.972 + 0.972 = 0.760 A. I_{total} at base of antenna = 0.891 − 0.891 + 1.0 = 1.0 A. Fig 9-27C shows the resulting total current distribution.

Area of the top section =

$$\int_{40.5}^{90} \cos L \, dL = \sin 90 - \sin 40.5$$

$$= 0.35 \times \frac{180 \text{ degrees}}{\pi \text{ radians}} = 20.1 \text{ A - degrees}$$

Equivalent length of the top section = $\frac{20.1}{0.760}$ = 26.44 degrees

Area of the bottom section:

Average width of the trapezoid = $\frac{1.0 + 0.76}{2}$ = 0.880

S2 = 13.5 degrees × 0.880 = 11.88 A-degrees
Equivalent length of the bottom section = 11.88 degrees
Total effective height = 26.44 + 11.88 = 38.32 degrees

Electrical length = $\frac{300}{3.8}$ = 78.95 m

Effective height = $\frac{78.95 \times 38.32}{360}$ = 8.40 m

From Eq 9-2, $R_{rad} = \frac{1450 \times 8.40^2}{78.95^2}$ = 16.4 ohms

Let us compare linear loading with base loading for the same antenna structure. Using Eq 9-5:

$$R_{rad} = 36.6 \frac{(1 - \cos 63)^2}{\sin^2 63} = 13.7 \text{ ohms}$$

Thus it is clear that linear loading has two advantages over base loading:
1) The radiation resistance is slightly higher with linear loading.
2) Linear loading can be done with much lower loss than a (large) base-loading coil.

The linear-loading technique described above is used with great success on the Hy-Gain 402BA shortened 40-meter beam, where linear loading is used at the center of the dipoles. It is also used successfully on the KLM 40- and 80-meter shortened Yagis and dipoles, where linear loading is applied at a certain distance from the center of the elements.

2.2. Keeping the Radiation Resistance High

The rule for keeping the radiation resistance high is simple:

• Use as long a vertical as possible (up to 90 degrees).
• Use top loading.

Fig 9-26 gives the radiation resistance for monopoles with combined base and top loading. The graphs clearly show the tremendous advantage of top loading.

The values of R_{rad} given in these figures can be used for antennas with diameters ranging from 0.1 to 1 degree (360 degrees = 1 wavelength). Sevick, W2FMI (Ref.818), obtained very similar results experimentally, while the values in the figures mentioned above were derived mathematically.

2.3. Keeping Losses Associated with Loading Devices Low

- Capacitance hat: The losses associated with a capacitance hat are negligible. When applying top-capacitance loading, especially on 160 meters, the practical limitation is likely to be the size (diameter) of the top hat. Therefore, when designing a short vertical, it is wise to start by dimensioning the top hat.
- T-wire top loading: This method is lossless, as with the capacitance hat. It may not always be possible, however, to have a perfectly horizontal top wire.
- Linear loading: Linear loading systems can be made virtually loss free, just as a capacitance hat. Linear loading does not have to be implemented at the bottom end of the vertical. Applying it higher up on the vertical does, however, make it necessary to electrically open up the vertical at the point of loading.
- Loading coil: Loading coils are intrinsically lossy devices. The equivalent series loss resistance is given by:

$$R_{loss} = \frac{X_L}{Q} \qquad (Eq\ 9\text{-}10)$$

where

X_L = inductive reactance of the coil
Q = Q (quality) factor of the coil

Q factors of 200 to 300 are easy to obtain without special precautions. Well-designed and carefully built loading coils can yield Q factors of up to 800 (see par 2.6.6.).

Base loading requires a relatively small coil, so the Q losses will be relatively low, but the R_{rad} will be low as well. See par. 2.6.2. for practical design examples with real-life values.

Top loading requires a large-inductance coil, with correspondingly larger losses, while in this case the R_{rad} is much higher (see par. 2.6.6 to 2.6.9 for practical design values).

2.4. Short-Vertical Design Guidelines

From the above considerations we can conclude the following:

- Make the "short" vertical physically as long as possible.
- Make use of top loading (capacitance hat or T wire) to achieve the highest radiation resistance possible, if necessary in combination with a small amount of coil loading if you cannot achieve enough top loading with the hat or T wire alone.
- Use linear loading instead of a base-loading coil whenever possible to reduce losses.
- Use the best possible ground system (radials or a counterpoise).
- Try to avoid loading coils, or design and build them with great care (high Q).

Though we may be able to build small verticals with low intrinsic losses, it may not always be possible to improve the ground resistance to a point where the loaded verticals achieve a good efficiency. Small loaded verticals will often be imposed by area restrictions, which may also mean that an extensive and efficient ground (radial) system will be excluded. Keep in mind that with short, loaded verticals, the ground system is even more important than with a full-size quarter-wave vertical.

It is a widespread misconception that vertical antennas don't require much space. Nothing is farther from the truth. Verticals take a lot of space! A good ground system for a short vertical takes much more space than a dipole, unless you live right at the coast, over salt water, where you might get away with a simple ground system. By the way, the salt water is why short, loaded verticals produce such excellent signals on many DXpeditions.

Another common misconception is that folded elements increase the radiation resistance of an antenna, and thus increase the system efficiency. However, the radiation resistance of a folded element is not the same as its feed-point resistance. The folding of the element transforms the feed-point impedance to a higher value, which may be advantageous from an ease-of-feeding standpoint. A folded monopole with two equal-diameter legs will show a feed-point impedance with the resistive part equal to $4 \times R_{rad}$. The higher feed-point impedance does not help to reduce the losses due to low radiation resistance, however, since with the folded element the lower feed current now flows in one more conductor, totaling the same loss. In a folded monopole, the same current ends up flowing through the lossy ground system, resulting in the same loss whether a folded element is used or not. Reasoning by extremes, it is obvious that it is impossible to obtain a better efficiency by using an impedance step-up configuration. There is no "free lunch" in the world of antennas, either!

One way to improve the radiation efficiency of a vertical over poor ground is to replace the single radiating element with several close-spaced verticals, all fed in phase.

2.5. SWR Bandwidth of Short Verticals

2.5.1. Calculating the 3 dB bandwidth.

One way of defining the Q factor of a vertical is (Ref. Par 2.10.2):

$$Q = \frac{Z_{surge}}{R_{rad} + R_{loss}} \qquad (Eq\ 9\text{-}11)$$

Z_{surge} is the characteristic impedance of the antenna seen as a short single-wire transmission-line. The surge impedance is given by:

$$Z_{surge} = 60\left[\ln\left(\frac{4h}{d}\right) - 1 \right] \qquad (Eq\ 9\text{-}12)$$

where

h = antenna height (length of transmission line)
d = antenna diameter (transmission line diameter)
and where values for h and d are in the same units

The 3 dB bandwidth is given by:

$$BW_{3dB} = \frac{f}{Q} \qquad \text{(Eq 9-13)}$$

where f = the operating frequency.

Example:

Assume a top-loaded vertical measuring 30 m (100 ft), with a diameter of 25 cm (10 in.) and a capacitance hat that resonates the vertical at 1.835 MHz.

Using Eq 9-12: Z_{surge} = 310 ohms
The electrical length of the vertical is

$$\frac{1.835}{300 \times 0.96} \times 30 \text{ m} \times 360° = 68.8 \text{ degrees}$$

Using Eq 9-7, R_{rad} = 31.8 ohms.

R_{ground} = 10 ohms (average ground system)

Using Eq 9-11: $Q = \frac{310}{31.8 + 10} = 7.42$

Using Eq 9-13: $BW_{3dB} = \frac{1.835}{7.42} = 0.247$ MHz

2.5.2. The 2:1 SWR bandwidth.

A more practical way of knowing the SWR bandwidth performance is to model the antenna at different frequencies, using eg, MININEC. The Q of the vertical is a clear indicator of bandwidth. Antenna Q and SWR bandwidth are discussed in Chapter 5, par 2.10.1.

A large-diameter conductor (eg, tower sections) gives a much better bandwidth than a wire. Ground losses also increase the SWR bandwidth (and reduce the Q factor). Table 9-3 shows the results obtained by modeling full-size quarter-wave verticals of various conductor diameters. Both the perfect as well as the real ground case are calculated. The vertical with a folded element clearly exhibits a larger SWR bandwidth than the single-wire vertical. Note that with a tower-size vertical (25 cm or 10 in. diameter), both the CW as well as the phone DX portions of the 80-meter band are well covered. If a wire vertical is planned (eg, suspended from trees), the folded version is to be preferred. Matching can easily be done with an L network.

It is evident that loaded verticals exhibit a much narrower bandwidth than their full-size quarter-wave counterparts. With the shorter verticals, the ground plays a very important role in the bandwidth of the antenna. Table 9-4 shows the calculated impedances and SWR values for short top-loaded verticals. The same equivalent ground resistance of 10 ohms (used in Table 9-3) has a very drastic influence on the bandwidth of the very short vertical. Note the drastic drop in Q and the increase in bandwidth with the 10-ohm ground resistance.

It is clear that two factors will definitely influence the SWR bandwidth of a vertical of a given length: the conductor diameter, and the total loss resistance. It should also be clear that we only want to use the first parameter to increase the bandwidth. If we want to use the second parameter (loss resistance), we can use a dummy load for an antenna; that's the antenna with the largest SWR bandwidth (and the worst radiating efficiency).

If you use a coil for loading a vertical (center or top loading), you will understand that for a given antenna diameter, the bandwidth will decrease up to a point as the antenna is shortened and the missing part is partly or totally replaced

9-3

Table 9-3

Quarter-Wave Verticals on 80 Meters

Z_t, SWR_t and Q_t indicate the theoretical figures assuming zero ground loss. Z_g, SWR_g and Q_g values include an equivalent ground resistance of 10 ohms.

diameter vertical		2 mm (0.08")	40 mm (1.6")	250 mm (10")
3.5 MHz	Z_t =	31.6 − j35.9	31.4 − j23.5	31.1 − j16.7
	Z_g =	41.6 − j35.9	41.4 − j23.5	41.1 − j16.7
	SWR_t =	2.8:1	2.0:1	1.7:1
	SWR_g =	2.2:1	1.7:1	1.5:1
3.65 MHz	Z_t =	35.9	35.9	35.9
	Z_g =	45.9	45.9	45.9
	SWR_t =	1:1	1:1	1:1
	SWR_g =	1:1	1:1	1:1
3.8 MHz	Z_t =	40.0 + j35.5	40.9 + j24.5	41.1 + j16.6
	Z_g =	50.0 + j35.5	50.9 + j24.5	51.1 + j16.6
	SWR_t =	2.5:1	1.9:1	1.6:1
	SWR_g =	2.1:1	1.7:1	1.4:1
	Q_t =	12.1	8.1	5.6
	Q_g =	9.5	6.4	4.4

9-4

Table 9-4

Verticals with 40-mm OD for 80 Meters

Z_t, SWR_t and Q_t are the values for a zero ohm ground resistance. Z_g, SWR_g and Q_g relate to an equivalent ground resistance of 10 ohms.

Frequency		⅛ wave long (9.9 m) (28.4 ft)	³⁄₁₆ wave long (12.6 m) (41.3 ft)
3.5 MHz	Z_t =	5.37 − j340	9.3 − j237
	Z_g =	15.37 − j340	19.3 − j237
	SWR_t =	15.7:1	6.0:1
	SWR_g =	3.6:1	2.7:1
3.65 MHz	Z_t =	5.9 − j319	10.3 − j217
	Z_g =	10.5 − j319	20.3 − j217
	SWR_t =	1:1	1:1
	SWR_g =	1:1	1:1
3.8 MHz	Z_t =	6.47 − j299	11.4 − j198
	Z_g =	16.47 − j299	21.4 − j198
	SWR_t =	12.3:1	4.9:1
	SWR_g =	3.3:1	2.4:1
	Q_t =	42	23
	Q_g =	15	12

by a loading coil. Then with more shortening, the bandwidth will begin to increase again as the influence of the equivalent resistive loss in the large coil begins to affect the bandwidth of the antenna.

If you measure an unusually broad bandwidth for a given vertical design, you should suspect a poor-quality loading coil or some other lossy element in the system (did you forget a ground system, or maybe did you forget to connect it?).

2.6. DESIGNING SHORT LOADED VERTICALS

Let us review some practical designs of short loaded verticals (Ref 794).

2.6.1. Base coil loading.

Assume a 24 m (79 ft) vertical having a diameter of 25 cm or 10 in., which we use as a ⅜-wavelength vertical on 80 meters. We want to resonate it on 160 m using a base-mounted loading coil (Fig 9-28). The length of the vertical on 160 meters is 53.5 degrees. Let us now calculate the surge impedance of the short vertical using Eq 9-12:

$$Z_{surge} = 60 \left[\ln \left(\frac{4 \times 2400}{25} \right) - 1 \right] = 297 \text{ ohms}$$

Calculation of the loading coil:

The capacitive reactance of the short vertical is:

$$X_C = \frac{Z_{surge}}{\tan t} \qquad \text{(Eq 9-14)}$$

where t = the electrical length of the vertical in degrees (24 m is 53.5 degrees).

In this example, $X_C = \dfrac{297}{\tan 53.5} = 220$ ohms.

Since X_L must equal X_C,

$$L = \frac{X_L}{2\pi f} = \frac{220}{2\pi \times 1.83} = 19.1 \text{ }\mu H$$

Let us assume a Q factor of 300, which is easily achievable:

$$R_{loss} = \frac{X_L}{Q} = \frac{220}{300} = 0.73 \text{ ohm}$$

This value of loss resistance is reasonably low, especially when you compare it with the value of R_{rad} (calculated using Eq 9-5):

$$R_{rad} = 36.6 \frac{(1 - \cos 53.5)^2}{\sin^2 53.5} = 9.3 \text{ ohms}$$

ELNEC also calculates R_{rad} as 9.3 ohms.

The radiation resistance is effectively in series with the ground-loss resistance. Assuming 60 ⅛-wavelength radials over good ground, which turns out to yield an equivalent loss resistance of about 10 ohms, the feed-point impedance will be approximately 20 ohms. The efficiency will be 50%.

2.6.2. Base linear loading.

Par 2.1.5. explains why a linear loading stub is better than

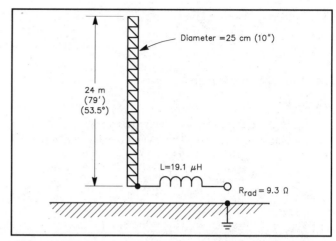

Fig 9-28—Base-loaded tower for 160 meters. See text for details on how to calculate the radiation resistance as well as the value of the loading coil. The loss resistance is effectively in series with the radiation resistance. With 60 ⅛-wavelength radials over good ground, the feed-point impedance will be approximately 20 ohms and the radiation efficiency about 50%.

a regular base-loading coil. The physical length of the linear-loading device required to bring the shortened vertical to resonance is typically 10 to 20% longer than the missing electrical length. A practical example is elaborated in Fig 9-27.

For 5 years I used such a vertical, where the linear loading system was made of two aluminum tubes, 2 cm (0.8 in.) in diameter, spaced approximately 25 cm (10 in.), and 6 meters (20 ft) long. The linear-loading device was spaced about 8 inches from the vertical. The easiest way to tune the system is to provide a movable shorting bar near the top of the device. Moving the bar changes the resonant frequency of the loaded vertical.

I. Payne, VE3DO, has reported great success with the linear loading on his 28.5-m (94 ft) vertical. Fig 9-29 shows details of the professional work he has done on his linear-loaded vertical.

2.6.3. Capacitance-hat loading.

Consider the design of a 30-m (98 ft) vertical that we want to load with a capacitance hat to resonate on 1.83 MHz. The electrical length of the 30-m vertical is 67 degrees. We will replace the missing 23 degrees with a capacitance hat (Fig 9-32).

First we calculate the surge impedance of the short vertical using Eq 9-12. Take a vertical diameter of 25 cm (10 in.). The surge impedance is

$$Z_{surge} = 60 \left[\ln \left(\frac{4 \times 3000}{25} \right) - 1 \right] = 310 \text{ ohms}$$

The electrical length of the capacitance top-hat is calculated as follows:

$$X_C = \frac{Z_{surge}}{\tan t} \qquad \text{(Eq 9-15)}$$

where

X_C = reactance of the capacitance hat, ohms

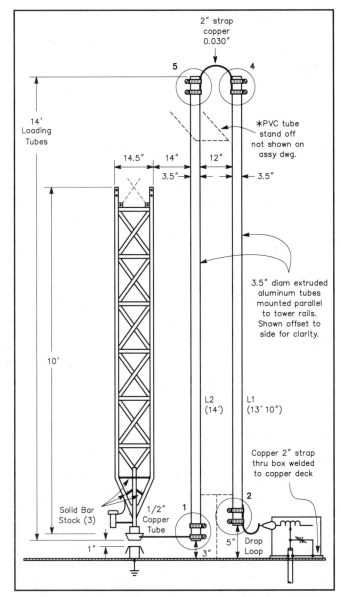

Fig 9-29—Sketch of the linear loading device used by VE3DO on his 28.5-m (94 ft) vertical.

> t = electrical length of the top hat = 23 degrees
> Z_{surge} = 310 ohms

(Eq 9-15 has the same form as Eq 9-14, but the definitions of terms are different.)

$$X_c = \frac{310}{\tan 23°} = 730 \text{ ohms}$$

$$C_{pF} = \frac{10^6}{2\pi f X_C} = \frac{10^6}{2\pi \times 1.83 \times 730} = 119 \text{ pF}$$

The diameter of a solid-disk capacitance hat is given by:

$$D = C \times 1.12 \qquad\qquad \text{(Eq 9-16)}$$

where

> D = hat diameter, inches (1 inch = 2.54 cm)
> C = hat capacitance, pF

In this example C = 119 pF, and D works out to be 133 inches = 3.38 m.

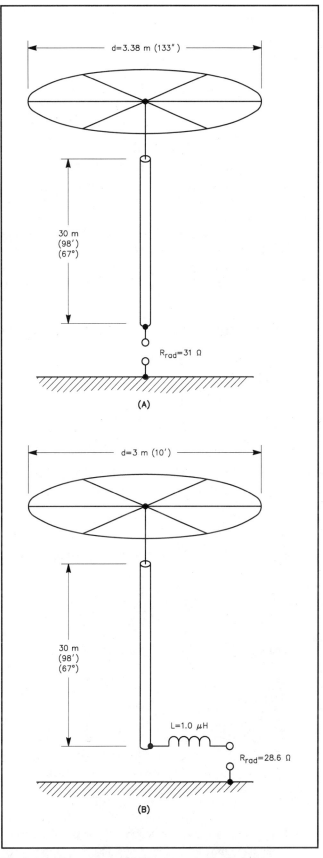

Fig 9-32—Examples of 160-meter verticals using capacitance hats. At A, the hat is dimensioned to tune the vertical to resonance at 1830 kHz. The antenna at B uses a capacitance hat of a given dimension, and resonance is achieved by using a small amount of base loading.

This formula is valid only for a solid disk of limited dimensions. For a different construction (eg, common wheel-type construction used on HF) the capacitance will be lower, and must be determined by experimentation or by accurate modeling. In this example we will continue to assume a solid-disk capacitance hat.

Notice that the conductor diameter has a great influence on the surge impedance. The same vertical made of 5-cm (2 inch) tubing has a surge impedance of 407 ohms.

2.6.4. Capacitance hat with base loading.

Consider the design of the same 30 m (98 ft) vertical with a 3-m diameter (10 ft) solid-disk capacitance hat for 1.83 MHz as shown in Fig 9-32B. The diameter of the vertical is 25 cm (10 in.). We know from the example under 2.6.3. that this hat will be slightly too small to achieve resonance on 1.83 MHz. We will add some base loading to tune out the remaining capacitive reactance at the base of the vertical. That can be referred to as "fine tuning" of the antenna. Purists may motorize the coil. The coil will normally also merge with the coil of the L network that could be used to match the vertical to the feed line.

The capacitance of a solid-disk hat is given by Eq 9-16, rewritten as:

$$C = \frac{D}{1.12}$$

In this example, $C = \frac{120 \text{ inches}}{1.12} = 107 \text{ pF}$.

The capacitive reactance of the hat is 813 ohms at 1.83 MHz.

Next we calculate the surge impedance:

$$Z_{surge} = 60\left[\ln\left(\frac{4 \times 3000}{25}\right) - 1\right] = 310 \text{ ohms}$$

The electrical length of the capacitance top-hat is calculated using Eq 9-15, rewritten as:

$$\tan t = \frac{Z_{surge}}{X_C} \text{ or } t = \arctan \frac{Z_{surge}}{X_C}$$

$$t = \arctan \frac{310}{813} = 20.9 \text{ degrees}$$

For a thinner radiator, the electrical length of the hat would be higher

$$\left(\arctan \frac{407}{813} = 26.6 \text{ degrees for d} = 2 \text{ inches}\right)$$

The electrical length of our example vertical radiator is 67 degrees, and the top-hat capacitance is 20.9 degrees. Since the sum of the two is 87.9 degrees, another 2.1 degrees of loading is required to make a full 90 degrees. The best solution would be to include a loading coil or a linear-loading device just under the capacitance hat, but this is not always possible. Let us calculate the required loading coil for mounting at the base of the short vertical:

To do this calculation, we must first calculate the surge impedance of the vertical (with its capacitance top hat). The surge impedance was calculated above as 310 ohms. The capacitive reactance is calculated using Eq 9-14:

$$X_C = \frac{Z_{surge}}{\tan t} = \frac{310}{\tan 87.9°} = 11.4 \text{ ohms}$$

Since X_L must equal X_C,

$$L = \frac{X_L}{2\pi f} = \frac{11.4}{2\pi \times 1.83} = 1.0 \text{ μH}$$

The coil can be calculated using the program module available on the NEW LOW BAND SOFTWARE.

Let's see what the equivalent series loss resistance of the coil will be, in order to assess how much the base-loading coil influences the radiation efficiency of the system. We will assume a coil Q of 200. Using Eq 9-10 we calculate:

$$R_{loss} = \frac{X_L}{Q} = \frac{11.4}{200} = 0.06 \text{ ohm}$$

This negligible loss resistance is effectively in series with the ground-loss resistance.

Calculation of radiation resistance using Eq 9-9:

$$R_{rad} = 36.6 \frac{(\sin t1 - \sin t2)^2}{\cos^2 t2} = 36.6 \frac{(\sin 67° - \sin 2.1°)^2}{\cos^2 2.1°} = 28.6 \text{ ohms}$$

With an equivalent ground resistance of 10 ohms, the efficiency of this system (Eq 9-3) is:

$$\text{Eff} = \frac{R_{rad}}{R_{rad} + R_{loss}} = \frac{28.6}{28.6 + 10 + 0.06} = 74\%$$

2.6.5. T-wire loading.

To bring a short vertical to ¼-wave resonance, the total T-wire length should be about twice the length of the missing portion of the vertical mast. Fig 9-33 shows a typical configuration of a T antenna. Two existing supports, such as trees, are used to hold the flattop wire. Try to keep the vertical wire as far as possible away from the supports, as power will inevitably be lost in the supports if close coupling exists.

Fig 9-34 shows a design table that was derived using the ELNEC modeling program. The dimensions can easily be extrapolated to other design frequencies.

In practice the T-shaped loading wires will often be downward-sloping wires. In this case the radiation resistance will be slightly lower due to the vertical component from the downward-sloping current being in opposition with the current in the short vertical.

2.6.6. Coil Plus Capacitance Hat

Let's work out an example of a 12-m (40 ft) mast, 5 cm (2 in.) OD, with a 48-inch (1.2 m) diameter capacitance hat above the loading coil (Fig 9-35). The length of the mast is 26.3 degrees.

The capacitance of the top hat, by rearranging Eq 9-16, is:

$$C = \frac{D}{1.12} = \frac{48}{1.12} = 43 \text{ pF}$$

$$X_C = \frac{10^6}{2\pi \times 1.8 \times 43} = 2056 \text{ ohms}$$

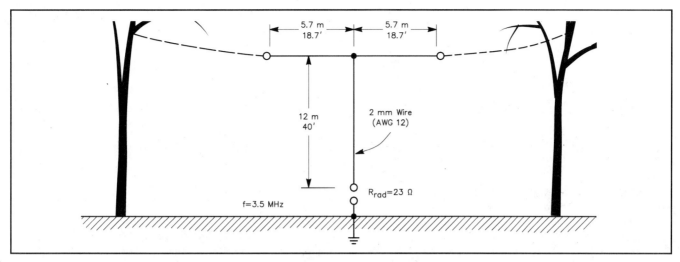

Fig 9-33—Typical setup of a current-fed T antenna for the low bands. Good-quality insulators should be used at both ends of the horizontal wire, as high voltages are present.

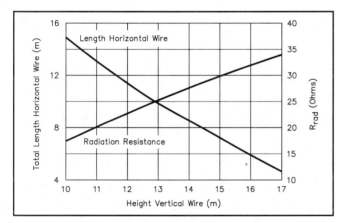

Fig 9-34—Design chart for a wire-type quarter-wave current-fed T antenna made of 2-mm OD wire (AWG 12) for a design frequency of 3.5 MHz. For 160 meters the dimension should be multiplied by a factor of 1.9.

The surge impedance of the vertical mast is calculated using Eq 9-12:

$$Z_{surge} = 60\left[\ln\left(\frac{4 \times 1200}{5}\right) - 1\right] = 352 \text{ ohms}$$

Let us look at the vertical as a short-circuited line having a characteristic impedance of 352 ohms. The input impedance of the short-circuited transmission line is given by:

$$Z = X_L = +jZ_0 \tan t \qquad \text{(Eq 9-17)}$$

where

> Z = input impedance of short-circuited line
> Z_0 = characteristic impedance of the line (352 ohms)
> t = line length, degrees

Thus,

$$Z = 352 \tan 26.3° = 174 \text{ ohms}$$

This means that the mast, as seen from above, has at the top an inductive reactance of 174 ohms. The capacitive reactance from the top hat is 2056 ohms. This means that the

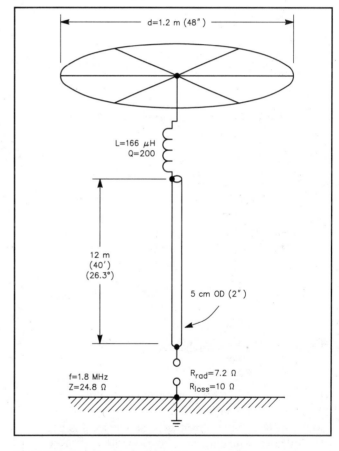

Fig 9-35—Top-loaded vertical for 160 meters, using a combination of a capacitance hat and a loading coil. See text for details.

loading coil, installed at the top of the mast, will need to have a reactance of 2056 – 174 = 1882 ohms.

$$L = \frac{1882}{2\pi \times 1.8} = 166 \text{ μH}$$

Assuming you build a loading coil of such a high value with a Q of 200, the equivalent series loss resistance is:

$$\frac{1882}{200} = 9.4 \text{ ohms}$$

Using Eq 9-7, we calculate the radiation resistance of the 12-m-long top-loaded vertical:

$$R_{rad} = 36.6 \times \sin^2 26.3° = 7.2 \text{ ohms}$$

Notice that if we want to use the loss resistance of the (top) loading coil for determining the efficiency (or the feed-point impedance) of the vertical, we must transpose the loss resistance to the base of the vertical. This can be done by multiplying the loss resistance of the coil times the square of the cosine of the height of the coil. In our example the loss resistance transposed to the base is:

$$Loss_{base} = Loss_{coil} \times \cos^2 h = 9.4 \times \cos^2 26.3° = 7.6 \text{ ohms}$$
(Eq 9-18)

Assuming a ground loss of 10 ohms, the efficiency of the antenna is:

$$\frac{7.2}{7.2+10+7.6} = 29\%$$

If there were no coil loss, the efficiency would be 42%. This brings us to the point of power-handling capability of the loading coil.

Power Dissipation of the Loading Coil

Let us calculate how much power is dissipated in the loading coil for an input power to the antenna of 1500 W. The base feed impedance is the sum of R_{rad}, R_{ground} and R_{coil}. This sum is = 7.2 + 10 + 7.6 = 24.8 ohms.

The base current is:

$$I_{base} = \sqrt{\frac{1500}{24.8}} = 7.78 \text{ A}$$

The resistance loss of the loading coil is 9.4 ohms. The current at the position of the coil (26.3 degrees above the feed point) is:

$$I_{coil} = 7.78 \times \cos 26.3° = 6.97 \text{ A}$$

The power dissipated in the coil is:

$$I_{coil}^2 \times R_{coil} = 6.97^2 \times 9.4 = 457 \text{ W}$$

This is an extremely high figure, and it is unlikely that we can construct a coil that will be able to dissipate this amount of power without failing (melting!). In practice this means that we will have to do one of the following things if we want the loading coil to survive:

• Run lower power. For 100 W of RF, the power dissipated in the coil is 30 watts, for 200 watts it is 61 watts, for 400 watts it is 122 watts. Let us assume that 150 W is the amount of power that can safely be dissipated in a well-made coil. In that case a maximum input power of 492 W can be allowed to the vertical (assumed coil Q = 200).
• Use a coil of lower inductance and use more capacitive loading (with a larger hat or longer T wires). To allow a power input of 1500 watts, and assuming a ground loss of 10 ohms and a coil Q of 200, the maximum value of the

loading coil for 150-W dissipation is 42.1 µH. This value is verified as follows (the intermediate results printed here are rounded):

The reactance of the coil is $X_L = 2\pi \times 1.8 \times 42.1 = 476$ ohms.
The R_{loss} of the coil is 476/200 = 2.4 ohms.
Transposed to the base, $R_{loss} = 2.4 \times \cos^2 26.3° = 1.9$ ohms

$$I_{antenna} = \sqrt{\frac{1500}{7.2+10+1.9}} = 8.9 \text{ A}$$

This current, transposed to the coil position, is
8.9 × cos 26.3° = 7.9 A.

$$P_{coil} = 7.9^2 \times 2.4 = 150 \text{ W.}$$

This is only about ¼ the original 166-µH coil inductance needed to resonate the antenna at 1.8 MHz. This smaller coil will require a substantially larger capacitance hat to resonate the antenna on 160 meters. T wires would also be an appropriate way to tune the antenna to resonance.

• Make a coil with the largest possible Q. If we change the coil with a Q of 200 in the above example to 300 and run 1500 W, then the maximum coil inductance is 63.1 µH. The calculation procedure is identical to the above example:

The reactance of the coil is XL = $2\pi \times 1.8 \times 63.1 = 714$ ohms.
The R_{loss} of the coil is 714/300 = 2.4 ohms.
Transposed to the base, $R_{loss} = 2.4 \times \cos^2 26.3° = 1.9$ ohms

$$I_{antenna} = \sqrt{\frac{1500}{7.2+10+1.9}} = 8.9 \text{ A}$$

This current, transposed to the coil position, is
8.9 × cos 26.3° = 7.9 A.

$$P_{coil} = 7.9^2 \times 2.4 = 150 \text{ W.}$$

This means that an increase of Q from 200 to 300 allows us to use a loading coil of 63.1 µH instead of 42.1 µH, resulting in the same power being dissipated in the coil. As you can see, the inductance is inversely proportional to the Q.

Notice that the ground loss resistance also has a great influence on the power dissipated in the loading coil. Staying with the same example as above (Q = 300, L = 63.1 µH), the power loss in the coil for a ground-loss resistance of 1.0 ohm (excellent ground system) is:

$$I_{base} = \sqrt{\frac{1500}{7.2+1+1.9}} = 12.2 \text{ A}$$

$$P_{coil} = (12.2 \times \cos 26.3°)^2 \times 2.4 = 284 \text{ W}$$

The better the ground system, the more power will be dissipated in the loading coil.

C. J. Michaels, W7XC, investigated the construction and the behavior of loading coils for 160 meters (Ref 797). In the above examples we have assumed Q factors of 200 and 300. The question is, how can we build loading coils having the highest possible Q? Michaels comes to the following conclusions:

• For coils with air dielectric, the L/D (length/diameter) ratio should not exceed 2:1.
• For coils wound on a coil form, this L/D ratio should be 1:1.

- Long, small-diameter coils are no good.
- The highest Q that can be achieved for a 150-μH loading coil for 160 meters is approximately 800. This can be done with a square coil (15 cm long by 15 cm diameter or 6×6 in.), using approx. 35 turns of AWG no. 7 (3.7 mm) wire (air wound), or a coil of 30 cm length by 15 cm diameter (12×6 in.), wound with 55 turns of AWG no. 4 (5.1 mm diameter) wire.
- Coil diameters of 10 cm (4 in.) wound with AWG wire nos. 10 to 14 can yield Q factors of 600, while coil diameters of 5 cm (2 in.) wound with BSWG no. 20 to 22 will not yield Q factors higher than approximately 250. These smaller wire gauges should not be used for high-power applications.

You can use some very common sense and simple test methods for selecting an acceptable plastic coil-form material:

- High-temperature strength: Boil a sample for ½ hour in water, and check its rigidity immediately after boiling, while still hot.
- Check the loss of the material by inserting a piece inside an air-wound coil, of which the Q is being measured. There should be little or no change in Q.
- Check water absorption of the material: Soak the plastic for 24 hours in water, and repeat the above test. There should be no change in Q.
- Dissipation factor: Put a sample of the material in the microwave oven, together with a cup of water. Run the oven until the water is boiling. The sample should not get appreciably warm.

2.6.7. Coil with T wire.

A coil with T-wire configuration is essentially the same as the one described under 2.6.6. In case of a capacitance hat we would normally adjust the resonant frequency by pruning the value of the loading coil or by adding some reactance (inductor for positive or capacitor for negative) at the base of the antenna. In case of a T-loading wire it is easier to tune the vertical to resonance by adjusting the length of the T wire.

Fine tuning can also be done by changing the "slope" angle of the T wires. If the T wires are sloped downward the resonant frequency goes up, but also the radiation resistance will drop somewhat. Fig 9-36 shows two examples of practical designs. In the example of the guyed vertical shown in Fig 9-36B, changing the slope angle by dropping the wires from 68 degrees (end of T wires at 12 m height) to 43 degrees (end at 9 m height) raises the resonant frequency of the antenna from 1.835 kHz to 1.860 kHz. Note, though, that with this change the radiation resistance drops from 10.1 ohms to 8.3 ohms!

The larger the value of the coil, the lower the efficiency will be. The equivalent loss resistance of the coil and the transposed loss resistance required to calculate the efficiency and the feed impedance of the vertical can be calculated as

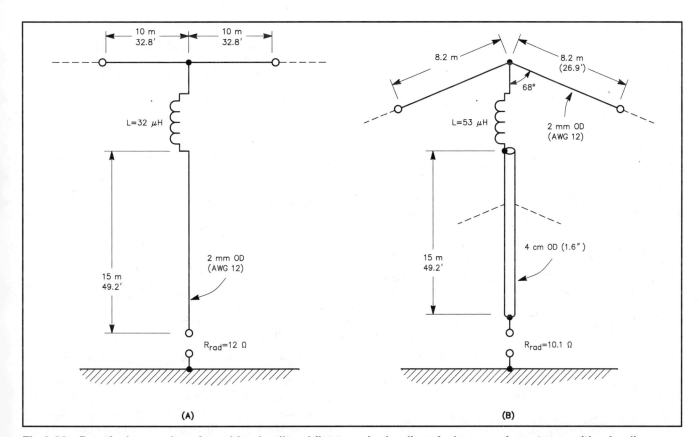

Fig 9-36—Practical examples of combined coil and flat-top wire loading. A shows a wire antenna with a loading coil at the top of the vertical section (no space for longer top-load wires). B shows a loaded vertical mast (4 cm or 1.6-in. OD) where two of the top guy wires, together with a loading coil, resonate the antenna at 1.835 MHz. The remaining guy wires are made of insulating material (eg, Kevlar, Phylistran, etc).

shown in par 2.6.6. As explained in par 2.6.6., we should avoid having a coil of more than approximately 75 µH inductance.

2.6.8. Coil with whip.

Now we consider a vertical antenna loaded with a whip and a loading coil, as in Fig 9-37. Let's work out an example:

Mast length below the coil = 18.16 m = 40 degrees
Mast length above the coil (whip) = 4.54 m = 10 degrees
f_{design} = 1.835 MHz
Mast diameter = 5 cm (2 in.)
Whip diameter = 2 cm (0.8 in.)

Calculate the surge impedance of the bottom mast section using Eq 9-12:

$$Z_{surge} = 60 \left[\ln\left(\frac{4 \times 1816}{5} \right) - 1 \right] = 377 \text{ ohms}$$

Looking at the base section as a short-circuited line with an impedance of 377 ohms, we can calculate the reactance at the top of the base section using Eq 9-17:

$$Z = X_L = +j377 \tan 40 = +j316 \text{ ohms}$$

Calculate the surge impedance of the whip section, again using Eq 9-12:

$$Z_{surge} = 60 \left[\ln\left(\frac{4 \times 454}{2} \right) - 1 \right] = 349 \text{ ohms}$$

Let us look from the coil at the whip as an open-circuited line having a characteristic impedance of 349 ohms. The input impedance of the open-circuited transmission line is given by:

$$Z = X_C = -j \frac{Z_0}{\tan t} \qquad \text{(Eq 9-19)}$$

Calculate the reactance of the whip:

$$Z = X_c = \frac{349}{\tan 10°} = -j1979 \text{ ohms}$$

Sum the reactances:

$$X_{tot} = +j316 - j1979 = -j1663 \text{ ohms}$$

This reactance is tuned out with a coil having a reactance of +j1663 ohms:

$$L = \frac{X_L}{2\pi f} = \frac{1663}{2\pi \times 1.835} = 144 \text{ µH}$$

Assuming you build the loading coil with a Q of 300, the equivalent series loss resistance is

$$\frac{1663}{300} = 5.5 \text{ ohms}$$

The coil is placed at a height of 40 degrees. Transpose this 5.5-ohm loss to the base using Eq 9-18:

$$Loss_{base} = 5.5 \times \cos^2 40 = 3.2 \text{ ohms}$$

Calculate the radiation resistance using Eq 9-8:

$$R_{rad} = 36.6 \times (1 - \sin 80 + \sin 40)^2 = 16 \text{ ohms}$$

Assuming a ground resistance of 10 ohms, the efficiency of this antenna is:

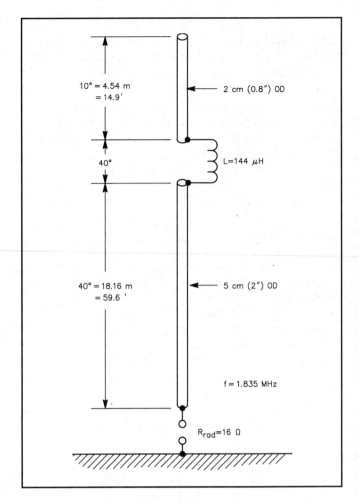

Fig 9-37—Practical example of a vertical loaded with a coil and whip. The length and diameter of the whip are kept within reasonable dimensions that can be realized on top of a loading coil without guying.

$$\frac{16}{16 + 10 + 3.2} \times 100 = 55\%$$

I modeled the same configuration using ELNEC and found the following results:

Required coil = 1650 ohms reactance = 143 µH
R_{rad} = 20 ohms

The R_{rad} is 25% higher than what we found using Eq 9-8. This formula uses a few assumptions such as equal diameters for the mast section above and below the coil, which is not the case in our design. This is probably the reason for the difference in R_{rad}.

2.6.9. Comparing the different loading methods.

In order to get a fair idea of how the different loading methods work, let's compare verticals of identical physical lengths over a relatively poor ground. Where one cannot erect a full-size vertical, it will often be the case that an elaborate radial system won't be possible either. That's why we'll use a rather high ground resistance in our comparative study.

The study is based upon the following assumptions:

- Physical antenna length = 45 degrees ($\frac{1}{8}$ wavelength).
- L = 20.5 m = 67 ft.
- Design frequency = 1.83 MHz.
- Antenna diameter = 0.1 degree on 160 meters = 4.55 cm = 1.8 in.
- Ground-system loss resistance = 15 ohms.

Quarter-wave full size:
R_{rad} = 36 ohms
R_g = 15 ohms
$R_{ant\ loss}$ = 0 ohms
Z_{feed} = 51 ohms
Eff = 71%
Loss = 1.5 dB

Base loading:
R_{rad} = 6.2 ohms
R_g = 15 ohms
Coil Q = 300
L_{coil} = 34 µH
$R_{coil\ loss}$ = 1.3 ohms
Z_{feed} = 22.5 ohms
Eff = 28%
Loss = 5.6 dB

Top-loaded vertical (capacitance hat or T-wire)
R_{rad} = 18 ohms
R_g = 15 ohms
Z_{feed} = 33 ohms
Eff = 55%
Loss = 2.6 dB

Top-loaded vertical (coil with capacitance hat at top)
R_{rad} = 18 ohms
R_g = 15 ohms
Diameter of capacitance hat: 3 m or 10 ft
L_{coil} = 37 µH
Coil Q = 200
$R_{coil\ loss}$ = 2.1 ohms
$R_{coil\ loss}$ transposed to base = 1 ohm
Z_{feed} = 34 ohms
Eff = 53%
Loss = 2.8 dB

Top-loaded vertical (coil with whip)
R_{rad} = 12.7 ohms
R_g = 15 ohms
Length of whip = 10 degrees (4.55 m on 1.83 MHz)
L_{coil} = 150 µH
Coil Q = 200
$R_{coil\ loss}$ = 8.6 ohms
$R_{coil\ loss}$ transposed to base = 5.8 ohms
Z_{feed} = 33.5 ohms
Eff = 38%
Loss = 4.2 dB

Conclusions

With an average or poor ground system (15 ohms), a $\frac{1}{8}$-wavelength vertical with capacitance top loading is only 1.1 dB down from a full-size $\frac{1}{4}$-wave vertical. Over a better ground the difference is even less. If possible, stay away from loading schemes that use a coil.

■ 3. TALL VERTICALS

In this section verticals that are substantially longer than $\frac{1}{4}$-wavelength are analyzed, especially their behavior over different types of ground. Is the very low wave angle, computed over ideal ground, ever realized in practice?

I will tackle the myth of voltage-fed antennas not requiring an elaborate ground system. Long verticals require an even better radial system and an even better ground quality in the Fresnel zone to achieve their low angle and gain potential.

In earlier sections of this chapter, short verticals are dealt with in detail, mostly for 160 meters. On higher frequencies, taller verticals are quite feasible. A full-size quarter-wave radiator on 80 meters is only approximately 19.5 m (64 ft) in height. Long verticals are considered to be the $\frac{1}{2}$-wave or $\frac{5}{8}$-wave variety. Verticals that are slightly longer than a quarter-wave (up to 0.35 wavelength) do not fall in the *long vertical* category.

3.1. Vertical Radiation Angle

Fig 9-38 shows the vertical radiation patterns of two long verticals of different lengths. These are analyzed over an identical ground system consisting of average earth with 60 quarter-wave radials. A quarter-wave vertical is included for comparison.

Note that going from a quarter-wave vertical to a half-wave vertical drops the radiation angle from 26 to 21 degrees. More important, however, is that the 3-dB vertical beamwidth drops from 42 to 29 degrees. Going to a $\frac{5}{8}$-wave vertical drops the radiation angle to 15 degrees with a 3-dB beamwidth of only 23 degrees. But notice the high-angle lobe showing up with the $\frac{5}{8}$-wave vertical. If we make the vertical still longer, the low-angle lobe will disappear and be replaced by a high-angle lobe. A $\frac{3}{4}$-wave vertical has a radiation angle of 45 degrees.

Whatever the quality of the ground is, the $\frac{5}{8}$-wave vertical will always produce a lower angle of radiation and also a more narrow vertical beamwidth. The story gets more complicated, though, when one compares the efficiency of the antennas.

3.2. Gain

I have modeled both a $\frac{1}{4}$-wave as well as a $\frac{5}{8}$-wave vertical over different types of grounds, in each case using a realistic number of 60 quarter-wave radials. Fig 9-5 shows the patterns and the gains in dBi for the quarter-wave vertical, and Fig 9-39 shows the results for the $\frac{5}{8}$-wave antenna.

Over a perfect (ideal) ground, the $\frac{5}{8}$-wave vertical has 3.0 dB more gain than the quarter-wave vertical at a 0-degree wave angle. Note the very narrow lobe width and the minor high-angle lobe (broken-line patterns in Fig 9-39).

Over sea-water the $\frac{5}{8}$ wave has lost 0.8 dB of its gain already, the $\frac{1}{4}$-wave only 0.4 dB. The $\frac{5}{8}$-wave vertical has an extremely low wave angle of 5 degrees and a vertical beamwidth of only 17 degrees. The $\frac{1}{4}$ wave has an 8-degree take off angle, but a 40-degree vertical beamwidth.

Over very good ground, the $\frac{5}{8}$-wave vertical has now lost

5.0 dB, the quarter wave only 1.9 dB. The actual gain of the ¼ wave equals the gain of the ⅝ wave! Note also that the high-angle lobe of the ⅝ wave becomes more predominant as the quality of the ground decreases.

Over average ground the situation becomes really poor for the ⅝-wave vertical. The gain has dropped 7.3 dB, and the secondary high-angle lobe is only 4 dB down from the low-angle lobe. The quarter-wave vertical has lost 2.6 dB versus the ideal ground, and now shows 2.0 dB *more* gain than the ⅝-wave vertical!

Over very poor ground the ⅝-wave vertical has lost 6.6 dB from the perfect-reflector situation, and the ¼ wave vertical only 3.0 dB. Note that the ⅝ wave vertical seems to pick up gain as compared to the situation over average ground. From Fig 9-39 it is clear that this is because the radiation at lower angles is now attenuated to such a degree that the radiation from the high-angle lobe (60 degrees) becomes very dominant. Note also that the intensity of the high-angle lobe hardly changes form the perfect ground situation to the situation over very poor ground. This is because the reflection for this very high angle takes place right under the antenna, where the ground quality has been improved by the 60 quarter-wave long radials.

I am sure this must come as a surprise to most. How can we explain this? An antenna that intrinsically produces a very low angle (as seen from the perfect ground model), relies on reflection at great distances from the antenna to produce the low angle. At these distances, radials of limited length do not play any role in improving the ground. With poor ground, a great deal of the power that is sent at a very low angle to the ground-reflection point is being absorbed in the ground rather than reflected. This means that from a Fresnel zone reflection point of view, the long vertical requires a better ground than the quarter-wave vertical in order to realize its full potential as a low angle radiator.

3.3. The Radial System for a Half-Wave Vertical

Here comes another surprise. A terrible misconception about voltage-fed verticals is that they do not require a good ground nor extensive radial system.

3.3.1. The near field.

It is true that if you measure the current going into the ground at the base of a half-wave vertical, this current will be very low (theoretically zero). With quarter-wave and shorter verticals, the current in the radials increases in value as you get closer to the base of the vertical. That's why, for a given amount of radial wire, it is better to use many short radials than just a few long ones.

With voltage-fed antennas, the earth current will increase as you move away from the vertical. Brown (Ref 7997) has calculated that the highest current density exists at approximately 0.35 wavelength from the base of the voltage-fed half-wave vertical. Therefore it is clear that it is even more important to have a good radial system with a voltage-fed antenna such as the voltage-fed T or the half-wave vertical. It is also clear that these verticals require longer radials to do their job

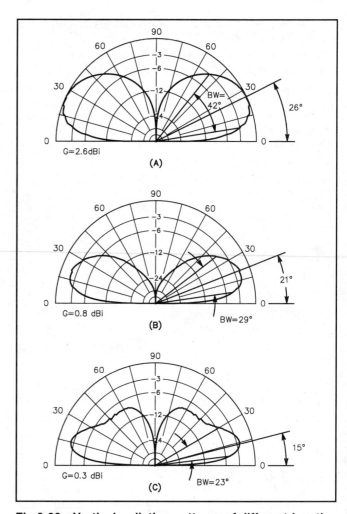

Fig 9-38—Vertical radiation patterns of different-length verticals over average ground, using 60 quarter-wave radials. The 0-dB reference for all patterns is 2.6 dBi.
A—¼ wavelength vertical.
B—½ wavelength.
C—⅝ wavelength.

efficiently than is the case with current-fed verticals.

3.3.2. The far field.

In the far field, the requirement for a good ground with a long vertical is much more important than for the quarter-wave vertical. I have modeled the influence of the ground quality on the gain of a vertical by the following experiment.

- I compared three antennas: a quarter-wave vertical, a voltage-fed quarter-wave T (also called an inverted vertical), and a half-wave vertical.
- I modeled all three antennas over average ground.
- I put them in the center of a disk of perfect conducting material and changed the diameter of the disk to find out at what distance the Fresnel zone is situated for the three antennas.

The results of the experiment are shown in Fig 9-40. Let us analyze those results.

- With a disk ¼ wave in radius (equal to a large number of

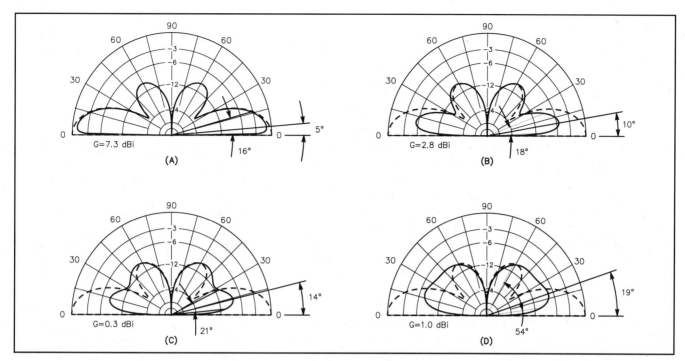

Fig 9-39—Vertical radiation pattern of the 5/8-wave vertical over different types of ground. In all cases, 60 quarter-wave radials were used. The theoretical perfect ground pattern is shown in each case as a reference (broken line, with a gain of 8.1 dBi). Compare with the patterns and gains of the quarter-wave vertical, modeled under identical circumstances (Fig 9-5).
A—Over sea.
B—Over very good ground.
C—Over average ground.
D—Over very poor ground.

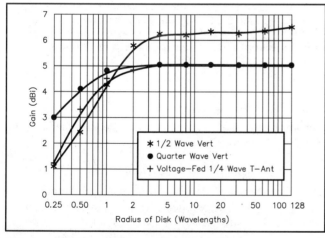

Fig 9-40—Gain of three types of verticals over a perfectly conducting disk of varying radius. The ground beyond the disk is of good quality. This means that the half-wave vertical requires 0.6-wavelength-long radials to perform as well as the quarter-wave vertical with ¼-wave radials. Be aware that the radiation angle of the half-wave vertical will be much lower, however.

¼-wave radials) the quarter-wave current-fed vertical is almost 2 dB better than the voltage-fed quarter-wave and the half-wave vertical.

• The quarter-wave vertical remains better than the other antennas up to a disk size of 1.5 wavelengths in diameter.

This means that over good ground you must be able to put out radials at least 2 wavelengths long with a ½-wave vertical before the half-wave vertical will show any gain over the quarter-wave current-fed vertical.

• The voltage-fed quarter-wave (voltage-fed T) equals the current-fed quarter-wave for a disk size of at least 2 wavelengths in diameter. This is because the current maximum is at the top of the antenna, which means that for a given radiation angle (the wave angle), the Fresnel zone (the place where the wave hits the ground to be reflected) is much farther away from the base of the vertical than is the case with a quarter-wave current-fed vertical. In other words, there is no advantage in using such a voltage-fed quarter-wave antenna.

• For both the voltage- and the current-fed quarter-wave vertical, the Fresnel zone is situated up to approximately 4 wavelengths away from the vertical. For the ¼-wave vertical, the Fresnel zone stretches out to at least 100 wavelengths.

3.4. In Practice

On 40 meters, a height more than ¼ wavelength (10 m or 33 ft) should be easy to install in most places. In many cases it will be the same vertical that is used as a quarter-wave on 80 meters.

I have been using a ⅝-wavelength vertical for 40 meters (equals ³⁄₁₀ wave on 80) for more than 20 years with good success. It does not compete with a Yagi at 100 feet or better, but with separate receiving antennas (Beverages), it has always been a relatively good performer. Now that I have been using a 3-element Yagi at 30 meters for a few years, I know, however, that the solution was far from ideal.

The lower angle of radiation is certainly an advantage on the higher bands (10 through 20 meters) and is certainly a positive asset on 40, but I had the saddening experience that a ⅝-wavelength vertical is too long a vertical radiator for the average DX paths on 80 meters (see par 9.6).

The base resistance, $R_{rad(B)}$, and feed-point reactance for monopoles is given in Figs 9-8 and 9-11 as a function of the conductor diameter in degrees, and in Figs 9-9 and 9-12 as a function of the antenna length-to-diameter ratio. The graphs are accurate only for structures with rather large diameters (not for single-wire structures) and of *uniform* diameter. A conductor diameter of 1 degree equals 833/f (MHz) in mm or 32.8/f (MHz) in inches.

■ 4. MODELING VERTICAL ANTENNAS

ELNEC as well as other versions of MININEC are well suited to do your own vertical antenna modeling. Be aware, however, that all MININEC-based antenna modeling programs assume a perfect ground for computing the impedance of the antenna. You cannot use these programs to assess the efficiency of the vertical, where we have defined efficiency as

$$\frac{R_{rad}}{R_{rad} + R_{losses}}$$

MININEC will show the influence of the reflecting ground (in the far field) to make up the (low-angle) radiation pattern of the vertical antenna.

If you want to include the losses of the ground, you can insert a resistance at the feed point, having a value equivalent to the assumed loss resistance of the ground (see Table 9-2).

Wires and Segments

A wire is a straight conductor, and is part of the antenna (or the total antenna). A segment is a part of the wire. Each wire can be broken up into several segments, all having the same length. Each segment has a different current. The more segments a wire has, the closer the current (pulse) distribution will come to the actual current distribution. There are limits, however.

- Many segments take a lot of computing time.
- Each segment should be at least 2.5 times the wire diameter (according to MININEC documentation).

There is no general rule as to the minimum number of segments that should be used on a wire. The only rule is the cut-and-try rule, whereby you gradually increase the number and look for the point where no further significant changes in the results are observed.

Fig 9-41 shows the example of a straight vertical for 80 meters (19 m long). This antenna consists of a single wire. In order to evaluate the effect of the wire length, I broke it up into several segments, going from 5 segments to 150 segments. Gain and pattern are very close with only 5 segments. For impedance calculations at least 20 sections are required in order to obtain a reasonably accurate result. The table also shows an example of too many segments (for the vertical

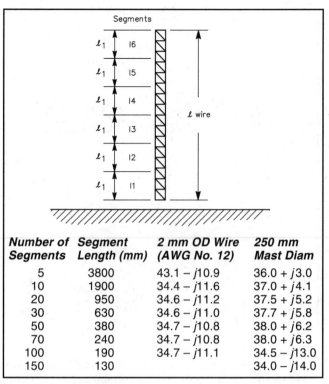

Number of Segments	Segment Length (mm)	2 mm OD Wire (AWG No. 12)	250 mm Mast Diam
5	3800	43.1 − j10.9	36.0 + j3.0
10	1900	34.4 − j11.6	37.0 + j4.1
20	950	34.6 − j11.2	37.5 + j5.2
30	630	34.6 − j11.0	37.7 + j5.8
50	380	34.7 − j10.8	38.0 + j6.2
70	240	34.7 − j10.8	38.0 + j6.3
100	190	34.7 − j11.1	34.5 − j13.0
150	130		34.0 − j14.0

Fig 9-41—MININEC analysis of a straight 19-m vertical antenna as shown in the drawing. The analysis frequency is 3.8 MHz. MININEC impedance results are shown as a function of the number of segments in the table. Note that for reliability with a "thick" vertical (200 mm or 8 in.), the maximum number of segments (in this case segments = pulses) is 70. The MININEC documentation states that the segment length should be greater than 2.5 times the wire diameter (2.5 × 200 mm = 500 mm). In this particular case errors occur when the segment length is smaller than the wire diameter.

measuring 250 mm in diameter). As the segment length becomes very short in comparison to the wire diameter, the result becomes totally erroneous.

Modeling Antennas with Wire Connections

When the antenna consists of several straight conductors, things become more complicated. Fig 9-42 shows the example of a 27-m vertical tower (250 mm OD), loaded by two sloping top-hat wires, measuring 2 mm OD (AWG no.12).

The standard approach is to have 3 wires, one for each of the three antenna parts, and divide the three conductors into a number of segments (which are always of equal length inside each wire).

To obtain reliable results, one must make sure that the lengths of the segments near the junction are similar. The table in Fig 9-42 shows the impedance obtained for the top-loaded vertical with different numbers of segments. A large number of segments on the vertical mast (eg, 35 segments, which results in a segment length of 770 mm), together with a small number of segments on the sloping wires, give an unreliable result, while a good result is obtained with a total of just 9 segments if the lengths are carefully matched. The segment

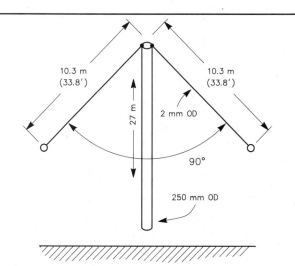

Fig 9-42—Impedances calculated by MININEC for a top-loaded 1.8-MHz vertical, using a 250 mm OD mast and two 2-mm OD slant loading wires. The segment lengths are indicated in mm. A large number of segments on all wires always gives more reliable results, provided the segment length is not very different. Judicious choice of segment length on the different wires can also yield very accurate results with a small number of total segments. In order to obtain accurate impedance results using MININEC, the wire sections near the acute-angle wire junctions must be short.

Vertical Mast			Slant Wires				
No. of Segments	Segment Length (min.)	Segment Length (max.)	No. of Segments	Segment Length (min.)	Segment Length (max.)	Total Pulses	Impedance
3	9000	9000	3	3765	3765	9	9.0 – j184.0
5	5400	5400	5	2260	2260	1	14.2 – j107.0
10	2700	2700	10	1130	1130	3	16.2 – j83.5
20	1350	1350	20	565	565	6	16.6 – j87.1
30	900	900	30	437	437	9	16.7 – j77.0
40	625	625	40	282	282	120	16.6 – j76.5
50	540	540	50	226	226	150	16.8 – j76.3
10	2700	2700	5	2260	2260	15	16.8 – j78.6
6	4500	4500	2	5650	5650	10	16.8 – j80.4
5	5400	5400	2	5650	5650	9	16.7 – j80.7
35	770	770	2	5650	5650	39	14.9 – j103.0

f = 1.8 MHz
length of vert mast = 27 m
slant wire = 10.3 m

tapering technique, as described in Chapter 14 on Yagis and quads, can also be used to minimize the number of segments and improve the accuracy of the results.

Modeling Verticals Including Radial Systems

MININEC does not analyze antenna systems with horizontal wires close to the ground. Therefore, modeling ground systems as part of the antenna requires the "professional" NEC software. NEC-2, which is generally available, will model radials over ground. NEC-3 will model buried radials, but this version of the software is not (yet) available to the general public (US military classified).

■ 5. PRACTICAL VERTICAL ANTENNAS

A number of practical designs of verticals for 40, 80 and 160 meters are covered in this section, as well as dual and triband systems. A number of practical matching cases are solved, and the component ratings for the elements are discussed. All the L networks have been calculated using the L-NETWORK DESIGN module from the NEW LOW BAND SOFTWARE.

5.1. Single-Band Quarter-Wave Vertical for 40, 80 or 160

The length of a resonant full-size quarter-wave vertical

depends on its physical diameter. Fig 9-43 shows the physical shortening factor of a quarter-wave resonant antenna as a function of the ratio of antenna length to antenna diameter. The required physical length is given by:

$$\ell_{meters} = \frac{74.95}{f_{MHz}} \times p$$

or

$$\ell_{feet} = \frac{245.9}{f_{MHz}} \times p$$

where

ℓ = length (height) of the vertical
p = correction factor (from Fig 9-43)
f_{MHz} = design frequency in MHz

Quarter-wave verticals are easy to match to 50-ohm coaxial feed lines. The radiation resistance plus the usual earth losses will produce a feed-point resistance close to 50 ohms.

If you don't mind using a matching network at the antenna base, and if you can manage a few more meters of antenna height, extra height will give you increased radiation resistance and higher efficiency. The feed-point impedance can be found in the charts of Figs 9-8, 9-9, 9-11 and 9-12.

Consider the following examples (see Fig 9-44):

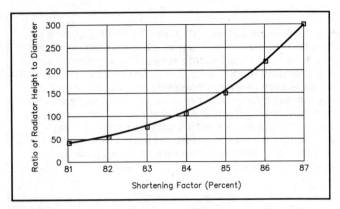

Fig 9-43—Graph showing the amount a quarter-wave vertical must be shortened for resonance as a function of the length-to-diameter ratio.

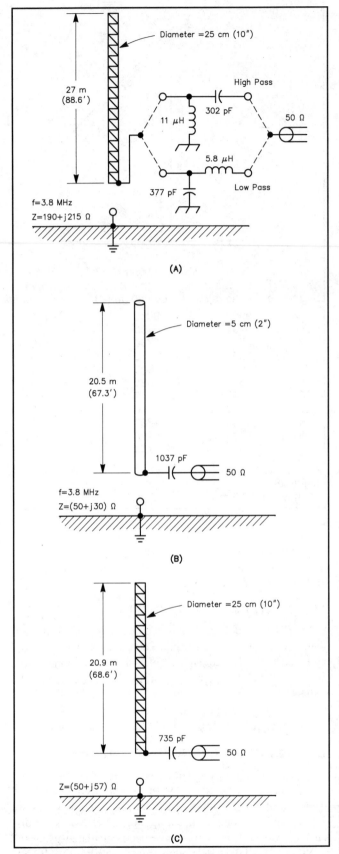

Fig 9-44—Three different 80-meter verticals that are longer than ¼ wavelength, together with their matching networks. Designs at B and C are dimensioned in such a way that the resistive part of the impedance is 50 ohms, in which case the matching network consists of only a series capacitor. The difference between B and C is the diameter of the vertical. In all cases a perfect ground (zero loss) is assumed.

Example 1:

Tower height = 27 meters (88.6 ft)
Tower diameter = 25 centimeters (10 in.)
Design frequency = 3.8 MHz

From the appropriate charts or through modeling we find:

R = 185 ohms
X = +j 215 ohms

Let's assume we have a pretty good ground radial system with an equivalent ground resistance of 5 ohms. We calculate the matching L network with the following values:

Z_{in} = 190 + j215 ohms
Z_{out} = 50 ohms

The values of the matching network were calculated for 3.8 MHz. The two matching-network alternatives (low- and high-pass) are shown in Fig 9-44A. The low-pass filter network gives a little additional harmonic suppression, while the high-pass assures a direct dc ground for the antenna, and some rejection of medium-wave broadcast signals.

Example 2:

This time we are setting out to build a vertical that is a little longer than a quarter-wave, so the resistive part of the feed-point impedance (at the design frequency) will be exactly 50 ohms. In this case the matching network will consist of a simple series capacitor to tune out the inductive reactance of the feed-point impedance.

We use ELNEC to design two models:

• Vertical mast diameter = 5 cm (2 in.), length = 20.5 m (67.3 ft), Z = 50 + j39 ohms (see Fig 9-44B). The matching network consists of a series capacitor with a capacitance of 39 ohms at 3.8 MHz. The value of the capacitor is:

$$C = \frac{10^6}{2\pi \times 3.8 \times 39} = 1073 \text{ pF}$$

• Vertical mast diameter = 25 cm (10 in.), length = 20.9 m (68.6 ft), Z = 50 + j57 ohms (see Fig 9-44C). The series-matching capacitor has a value of 735 pF.

Note that for the above examples we assumed a zero

ground loss. The values of the series-matching capacitor can also be calculated using the SERIES IMPEDANCE module of the NEW LOW BAND SOFTWARE package.

5.2. Top-Loaded Vertical

The design of loaded verticals has been covered in great detail in paragraph 2.6. Capacitance-hat top loading and wire top loading are quite easily realized from a mechanical point of view. It is more difficult to insert a husky loading coil in a vertical antenna. In addition, because of their intrinsic losses, loading coils are always a second choice when it comes to loading a short vertical.

A wire-loaded vertical for 160 m is described in par 6.5. as part of an 80/160-m duo-band system.

5.3. Three-Band Vertical for 40, 80 and 160 Meters

A ⅝-wavelength vertical for 40 meters produces a very low angle of radiation, which can be used advantageously when working long-haul DX on that band. The condition for producing a very low angle, and for being an efficient radiator, is to erect the antenna over excellent ground.

The length of a ⅝-wavelength-long vertical made of 25-cm (10 in.) diameter mast on 7.05 MHz is 24 meters (79 ft). On 3.65 MHz, this antenna is approximately 0.3 wavelength long (3.65 MHz was chosen because this antenna will easily cover 3.5-3.8 MHz with less than 2:1 SWR). On 160 meters the antenna is only about 0.15 wavelength long.

The feed-point impedances can again be found in the charts of Figs 9-8, 9-9, 9-11 and 9-12. I also modeled the antenna with MININEC. The impedance of the 24-m vertical (25 cm tower diameter) on the different bands is:

40 m: $99 - j255$ ohms
80 m: $77 + j98$ ohms
160 m: $9.3 - j255$ ohms

Linear loading will add approximately 0.7 ohm to the radiation resistance on 160 meters. The feed-point impedance becomes: $10 + j0$ ohms.

For calculating the three-band switchable matching networks, we assume using radials of 20-meter length. The equivalent ground-loss resistance for this radial system is estimated at 10 ohms for 160 meters, 6 ohms for 80 meters and 0.5 ohm on 40 meters (see Table 9-2). The antenna with its 3-band switchable matching system, comprising three L networks, is shown in Fig 9-45.

5.4. Linear-Loaded Duo-bander for 80/160 Meters

Full-size, quarter-wave verticals (40 m or 131 feet on 160 m) are out of reach for all but a few amateurs. Often an 80/160-meter duo-band vertical will be limited to a height of around 100 feet (30.5 meters). This represents an electrical length of 140 degrees at 3.65 MHz and 70 degrees on 160 meters. We can determine R and X from Figs 9-9 and 9-11 or through modeling:

80 meters: $Z = 280 + j278$ ohms
160 meters: $Z = 17 - j102$ ohms

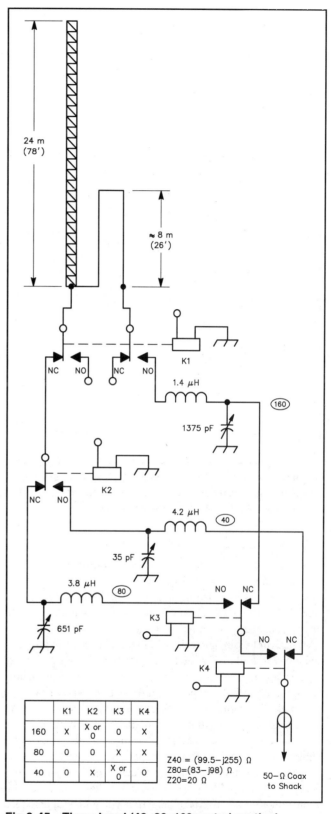

	K1	K2	K3	K4
160	X	X or O	O	X
80	O	O	X	X
40	O	X	X or O	O

$Z40 = (99.5 - j255)\ \Omega$
$Z80 = (83 - j98)\ \Omega$
$Z20 = 20\ \Omega$
50-Ω Coax to Shack

Fig 9-45—Three-band (40, 80, 160-meter) vertical system. The vertical is ⅝ wave long on 40 meters. (Longer would introduce too much high-angle radiation). On 160 m, the vertical is resonated using a linear-loading device. The switchable matching network consists of three L networks. For calculations, a real ground was assumed with an equivalent loss resistance of 10, 6 and 0.5 ohms respectively on 160, 80 and 40 meters.

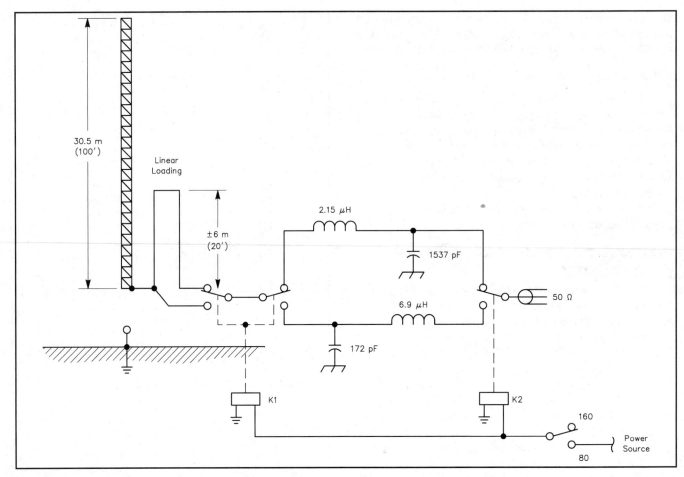

Fig 9-46—Two-band (80 and 160-m) vertical system using linear loading to bring the antenna to resonance on 160 meters. The values of the L networks were calculated assuming an equivalent ground-loss resistance of 10 and 5 ohms respectively on 160 and 80 meters.

Fig 9-46 shows the antenna configuration together with the switchable matching system. For calculating the L network for 160 meters, we assume that the linear loading device will add 1 ohm to the radiation resistance. The assumed ground-loss resistance is 10 ohms on 160 and 5 ohms on 80 meters.

Linear loading provides a higher radiation resistance and ensures low coil loss, as no large-value inductors are required in the matching network. The exact length of the linear loading device must be found experimentally, but a good starting point is to make the loading device as long as the antenna would have to be extended to make it a full quarter-wavelength long. An antennascope is a good instrument to prune the length of a linear loading device. The antennascope will only produce a full null when the measured impedance is purely resistive. Keep changing the length of the loading device until a complete null is obtained. At the same time you will be able to read the radiation resistance of the antenna on 160 m from the scale of the instrument. Deduct the theoretical value of the vertical (17 + 1 ohms) and you will have the value of the equivalent ground-loss resistance.

Fig 9-46 shows the two-band L-network matching device for the 160/80-meter antenna. If the vertical is made from lattice-type tower sections, the linear loading device can be made of two 1-inch aluminum tubes spaced about 12 inches

(30 cm) apart and about the same distance from the tower. Fig 9-29 shows the linear loading device on VE3DO's 27-m (88.6 ft) vertical.

5.5. 80/160 Top-Loaded Vertical with Trap

Traps are frequency-selective insulating devices, and are incorporated in radiating elements to adapt the electrical length of the element depending on the frequency for which the element is being used.

Commercial multiband antennas make frequent use of traps. Home-made antennas use the technique much more infrequently. There are two types of commonly used traps:

• Isolating traps
• Shortening/lengthening traps

5.5.1. Isolating traps.

An isolating trap is a parallel-tuned circuit that represents a high impedance at the design frequency, effectively decoupling (by its high impedance) the "outer" section of the radiator from the "inner" section.

A good isolating trap therefore will meet the following specifications:

• It represents a high impedance on the design frequency.

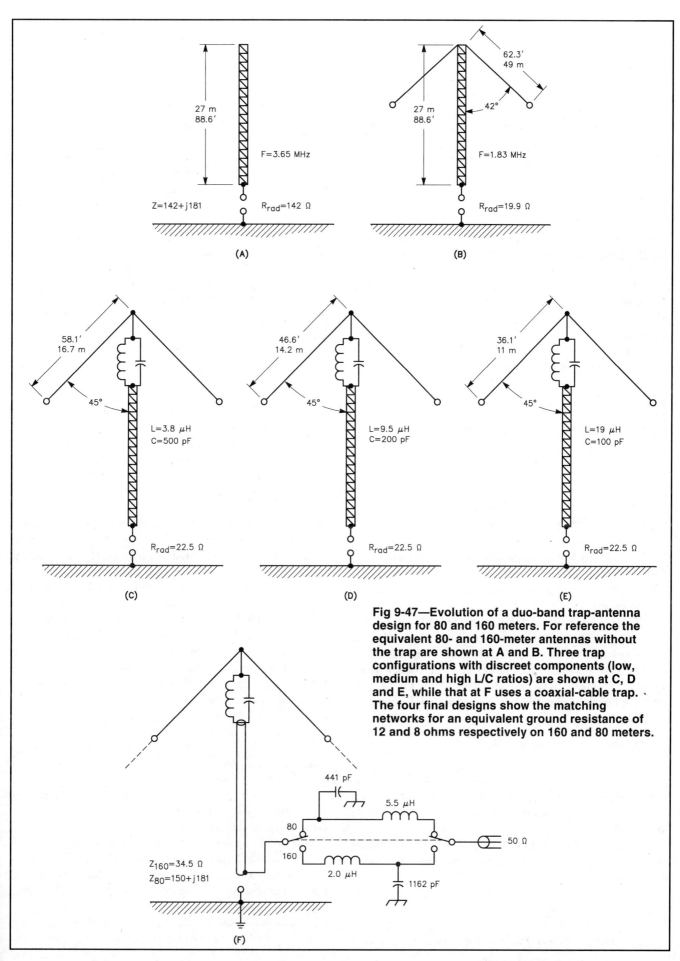

Fig 9-47—Evolution of a duo-band trap-antenna design for 80 and 160 meters. For reference the equivalent 80- and 160-meter antennas without the trap are shown at A and B. Three trap configurations with discreet components (low, medium and high L/C ratios) are shown at C, D and E, while that at F uses a coaxial-cable trap. The four final designs show the matching networks for an equivalent ground resistance of 12 and 8 ohms respectively on 160 and 80 meters.

- It represents as low a Q as possible, together with the high impedance.
- It represents as low a series inductance as possible on the frequencies where the trap is not resonant (minimize inductive loading).

An effective way of making one's own traps is to build a trap of coaxial cable. Several articles describe in detail how to make these traps (Ref 684, 662 and 689). The Battle Creek Special (par 8.7) uses the coax-cable trap very successfully to make an outstanding 3-band (40, 80, 160 m) compact inverted L.

The example in Fig 9-47 shows a 27-m (88.6 ft) vertical mast, measuring 25 cm (10 in.) in diameter. We want to use this mast on 80 meters and load it to resonance on 160 meters using two flat-top wires. The trap at the top of the vertical will isolate the loading wires from the mast when operating on 80 meters; it will have to be resonant on 80 meters. Let us design a system that covers 3.5 to 3.8 MHz and see what the performance will be when compared to two monoband systems using basically the same configuration.

Resonance of the trap at 3.65 MHz can be obtained by an unlimited number of L/C combinations:

$$f_{res} = \frac{10^3}{2\pi\sqrt{L \times C}}$$

where f is in MHz, L in μH and C in pF.

Let us evaluate three different L/C ratios that resonate at 3.65 MHz:

L = 3.8 μH, C = 500 pF (X = 87 ohms)
L = 9.5 μH, C = 200 pF (X = 218 ohms)
L = 19 μH, C =100 pF (X = 436 ohms)

As standards of comparison we'll use the stand-alone 27-meter tower (no trap, no flat-top wires) on 80 meters, and the same 27-m tower with two sloping flat-top wires on 160 meters. The dimensions of the 5 different configurations are shown in Fig 9-47.

The impedance at 1.835 (resonance with the loading wires, Fig 9-47B) is 22.5 ohms. At 3.65 MHz (Fig 9-47A) the R_{rad} is 142 ohms (Z = 142 + j181). Here we see the advantage of a vertical that is slightly longer than a quarter-wave: improved efficiency. The estimated ground loss for 60 quarter-wave radials (8 ohms on 80 meters) hardly influences the efficiency:

$$Eff = \frac{142}{142 + 8} = 95\%$$

Fig 9-48 shows the influence of the slope angle of the top wires on the resonant frequency. The values are for a 27-m (88.6 ft) vertical with two sloping loading wires, 19 m (62 ft) long.

On 160 meters the ground loss of 60 ⅛-wave radials (estimated at 12 ohms) will have a substantial influence in the efficiency:

$$Eff = \frac{22.5}{22.5 + 12} = 65\%$$

The three different trap solutions have a significant

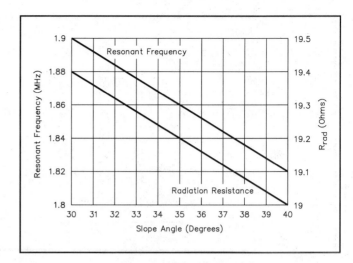

Fig 9-48—This chart shows the variation in resonant frequency and radiation resistance for a 27-m (88.6 ft) vertical with 19.5-m (64 ft) long sloping top-load wires, as a function of the slope angle. Varying the angle from 30 to 40 degrees shifts the resonant frequency by 80 kHz.

influence on the SWR-bandwidth behavior of the antenna. The influence of the L/C ratio is the opposite on 80 m from what it is on 160. The low-L, high-C solution (3.8 μH and 500-pF) yields the highest bandwidth on 160, and the lowest bandwidth on 80 meters. The opposite is also true. With L = 19 μH and C = 100 pF, the SWR curve on 80 is almost as flat as for the reference antenna (just the 27-m vertical with no trap nor loading wire).

The bandwidth results for the different designs are shown in Fig 9-49 for both 80 and 160 meters. I have calculated the theoretical bandwidth, excluding the ground losses, as well as the practical bandwidth, including ground losses.

Solution two (9.5 μH and 200 pF, Fig 9-47D) is certainly an excellent compromise if both bands are to be treated with equal attention. The reactance of the circuit for these LC values is X = 218 ohms. Assuming an equivalent series loss resistance of 1 ohm, we end up with a Q factor of 218/1= 218.

For the parallel capacitor we must use a high-voltage transmitting type (doorknob) ceramic capacitor. The winding data for the coil can be calculated using the COIL module of the NEW LOW BAND SOFTWARE.

Example: The 9.5-μH coil can be wound on a 5-cm (2 in.) coil form, with close-wound turns of 3-mm OD double-enameled wire, giving a coil length of 5 cm (2 in.). The square form will yield a good Q.

In practice you will need slightly less inductance to establish resonance of the trap at 3.65 MHz because of the self-capacitance of the coil. After winding the coil, connect the 200-pF doorknob in parallel (it can be inserted inside the coil form), and grid dip the parallel circuit. Use a receiver to monitor the grid-dip frequency accurately. Remove turns until you obtain resonance at the desired frequency. When all is done, coat the assembly generously with Q-dope.

If we use the coax-cable trap as described by C. Sommer, N4UU (Ref 662), we have a reactance of 173 ohms using

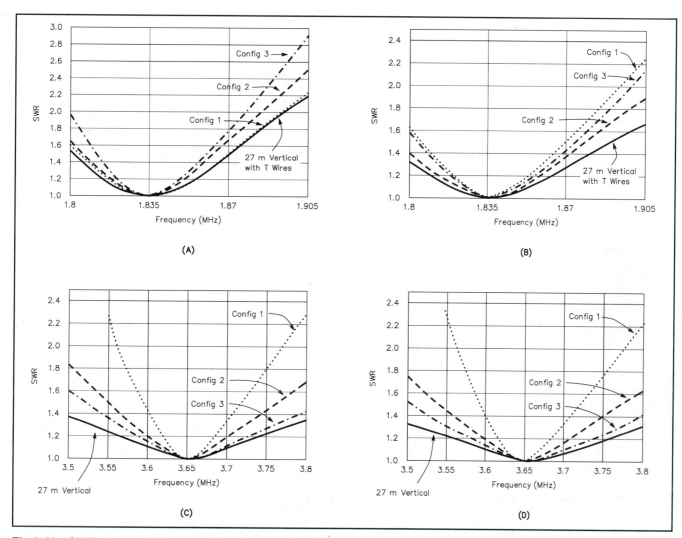

Fig 9-49—SWR curves for 80 and 160 meters for the different antenna configurations of Fig 9-47. Config 1 refers to Fig 9-47C, Config 2 to Fig 9-47D, and Config 3 to Fig 9-47E. The curves are plotted for perfect ground (at A and C) as well as for real ground (at B and D). Note the increased bandwidth on 160 meters caused by the ground losses and the low R_{rad}. On 80 meters the ground losses have almost no influence due to the high R_{rad}.

RG-58 cable to make the coil. This means that the inductance of the trap is

$$L = \frac{173}{2\pi \times 3.65} = 7.5 \ \mu H$$

The equivalent capacitance of the coax trap will be 252 pF. In practice, 14 close-wound turns of RG-58 cable on a 5-cm-diameter (2 in.) coil form, connected as shown in Fig 9-50, will yield a trap with resonance near 3.65 MHz.

Matching Networks

The impedances to be matched are:

80 meters (3.65 MHz): $150 + j181$ ohms
160 meters (1.835 MHz): $34.5 + j0$ ohms

The values and the wiring of the switchable network are shown in Fig 9-47F.

5.5.2. Shortening/lengthening traps.

If the isolating trap principle were to be used on a triband

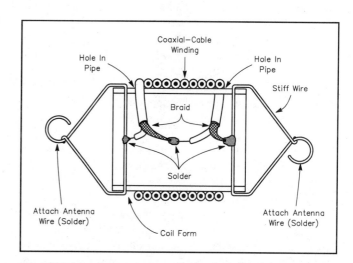

Fig 9-50—Cutaway view of the coaxial-cable trap wound on plastic tubing. At the position of the last turn you can drill 4 holes around the circumference of the coil form. That will help you in pruning the trap to the desired resonant frequency.

antenna, it would require two isolating traps. Three-band trap Yagis of early days (early sixties) indeed used two traps on each element half, the inner one being resonant on the highest band, the outer one on the middle band. Modern trap-design Yagis only use a single trap in each element half to achieve the same purpose. Y. Beers, WØJF, wrote an excellent article covering the design of these traps (Ref 680). In this design, the trap is not resonant on the high-band frequency, but somewhere in between the low and the high band. In the balanced design described by Y. Beers, the frequency at which the trap is resonant is the geometrical mean of the two operating frequencies (equal to the square root of the product of the two operating frequencies). For an 80/160 meter vertical, the trap would be resonant at:

$$f = \sqrt{1.83 \times 3.65} = 2.58 \text{ MHz}$$

The principle is that, on a frequency below the trap resonant frequency, the trap will show a positive reactance (acts as an inductor), while above the resonant frequency the trap acts as a capacitor. A single parallel-tuned circuit can be designed which inserts the necessary positive reactance (at the lowest frequency) and negative reactance (at the highest frequency) . In the balanced design the absolute value of the reactances is identical for the two bands; only the sign is different. There are 5 variables involved in the design of such a trap system: the two operating frequencies, the trap resonant frequency, the total length, and the L/C ratio used in the trap parallel circuit. The design procedure and the mathematics are covered in detail in the above-mentioned article.

5.6. The Self-Supporting Full-Size 160-M Vertical at ON4UN

A full-size quarter-wave vertical antenna for 160 meters is just about the best transmitting antenna you can have on that band, with the exception of an array made of full-size verticals. I use a 32-m (105 ft) triangular self-supporting tower, measuring 1.8 m (6 ft) across at the base, and tapering to 20 cm (8 in.) at the top. I knew that the taper would make the tower electrically shorter than if it had a constant diameter, so that had to be accounted for. On top of the tower I mounted a 7-m-long mast. It is steel at the bottom and aluminum at the top, tapering from 50 mm (2 in.) OD to 12 mm (0.5 inch) at the top.

In order to make up for the shortening due to the tower taper, I knew I had to install a capacitance hat somewhere near the top of the tower. The highest point I could do this was at 32.5 m (107 ft). I decided to try a disk with a diameter of 6 m (20 ft), because I had 6-m long aluminum tubing available. Two aluminum tubes were mounted at right angles, the ends being connected by copper wire to make a square. Fig 9-51 shows the vertical.

I hoped I would come close to an electrical quarter-wave on 160 m, and fortunately the antenna resonated on exactly 1830 kHz. In the beginning I had the tower insulated at the base, and was able to measure its impedance—approximately 20 ohms, where 36 ohms would be expected with a zero-ohm earth system resistance. Such a low radiation resistance has been reported in the literature, and must be due to the large tower cross-section. Originally I suspected mutual coupling

Fig 9-51—Self-supporting 39.5 m (130 ft) quarter-wave vertical for 160 meters at ON4UN. The base is 1.8 m (6 ft) wide and the tower tapers to just a few inches at the top. The tower is shunt fed with a gamma match and also serves as a support for an 80-meter 4-element square array made of quarter-wave verticals, supported from sloping caternary lines running from the 160-m tower.

with one (or both) of two other towers, but decoupling or detuning those towers did not change anything.

Fig 9-52 shows the radiation resistance of a quarter-wave vertical over a radial system consisting of 60 quarter-wave radials, measured as a function of the diameter of the vertical. From the graph, we see that for a height/diameter ratio of 44 (eg, a self-supporting tower with a diameter of 1 m operating at 1.83 MHz) shows a radiation resistance of approximately 20 ohms. The classic 36 ohms applies for a very thin conductor!

After a series of unsuccessful attempts to use the vertical on 80 meters, I grounded the tower and shunt fed it using a gamma match. A tap at 8 m (26 ft) height, and a 500-pF series capacitor provided a 1:1 SWR on top band, and a 2:1 SWR bandwidth of 175 kHz. The gamma wire is approximately 1.5 m (5 ft) from the tower. This vertical really plays extremely well. I use quite an extensive radial system, consisting of

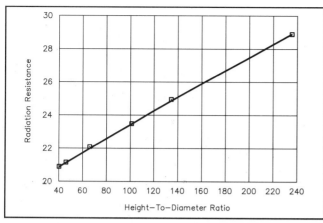

Fig 9-52—Showing the feed-point resistance of a resonant quarter-wave vertical over 60 quarter-wave radials, as a function of the conductor diameter. Verticals made of a large-diameter conductor, such as a tower, exhibit much lower feed-point resistances than encountered with wire verticals.

Fig 9-54—R. Vermet, ON6WU, with his professional antenna measuring setup, tuning the new vertical at ON4UN. An HP network analyzer is used which directly produces a Smith Chart. Although such sophisticated test equipment is not necessary to tune a vertical, it is very instructive to know the impedance of the vertical over a wide frequency range. Coupling with other structures (towers) on certain frequencies can easily be identified as irregularities in the impedance (admittance) curve.

Fig 9-53—Giving out new countries and chasing new countries on 160 meters are not the only hobbies for Rudi, DK7PE (left) and ON4UN, who are ready to go on a bike trip. In the background is the base of the ON4UN 160-meter vertical showing the cabinet that houses the matching circuitry for the 160-meter vertical and the 4-square 80-meter system.

assistance of ON6WU and his professional-grade test equipment. See Fig 9-54.

5.7. The Battle Creek Special Antenna

Everyone familiar with DX operating on 160 meters has heard about the Battle Creek Special and its predecessor, the Minooka Special. These antennas are transportable verticals, for operating on the low bands (40, 80 and 160 meters). The Minooka Special (Ref 761) was designed by B. Boothe, W9UCW, for B. Walsh, WA8MOA, to take on his trips to Mellish Reef and Heard Island many years ago.

Basically the antennas were designed to complement a triband Yagi on DXpeditions to provide excellent 6-band coverage for the serious DXpeditioner. The original Minooka was a 40- through 160-meter antenna, using an L network for matching and an impressively long 160-meter loading coil near the top. W0CD built a very rugged and easily transportable version of the Minooka Special, but soon found out that the slender loading coil simply melted when the antenna was taking high power for longer than a few seconds. No wonder! It was more than 100 cm (3.3 ft) long with a diameter of only 27 mm (1.06 in.) Michaels, W7XR, later calculated the Q factor of the coil to be around 20! That's an equivalent loss resistance of 100 ohms!

W0CD improved the antenna both mechanically and electrically. Instead of developing a better loading coil, he simply did away with the delicate part, and replaced the loading coil with a loading wire. His design uses two sloping wires, one for 80 meters and one for 160, which now makes it really an inverted L, but nothing would prevent you from using a T-shaped loading wire as described in par 2.6.5.

The new design, named the Battle Creek Special, takes

approximately 250 radials ranging from 18 m (60 ft) to 75 m (250 ft) in length. The tower now also supports a 4-square sloping quarter-wave vertical array as described in the chapter on vertical arrays.

Fig 9-54 shows the base of the vertical and the cabinet housing the series capacitor for the 160-m gamma match as well as the hybrid coupler for the 80-meter 4-square array. Information about the ON4UN vertical was obtained with the

1.5 kW of RF on SSB or CW without any problem for several minutes. For continuous-duty digital modes the RF output should not exceed 600 W. A coax-cable 80-meter trap isolates the loading wires for 80 and 160. The Battle Creek Special has been reported by the 3Y5X DXpedition operators to outperform commercially available verticals such as the Butternut with the 160-meter option by a solid 2 S units!

The section below the 40-meter trap is 9.75 m (32 ft) long, which makes it a full-size quarter-wave on that band. The SWR bandwidth is less than 2:1 from 7 to 7.3 MHz.

On 80 meters the 14 m (46 ft) of tubing below the 80-meter trap, together with the loading wire, make it an inverted L. The antenna will cover 3.5 to 3.6 MHz with an SWR of less than 2:1. On 3.8 MHz the antenna is "too long," but a simple series capacitor of 300 to 500 pF will reduce the SWR to a very acceptable level (typically 1.5:1).

On 160 meters the entire vertical antenna plus the top-loading wire make it a quarter-wave L antenna. The SWR is typically 2:1 over 20 kHz, indicating a feed-point impedance of approximately 25 ohms (depending to a large extent on the quality of the radial system).

There are several ways to obtain a better match to the feed line. WØCD uses an unun with a 2.5:1 impedance ratio (see also Chapter 6 on feed lines and matching), which is switched in the circuit on 160 m, and out of the circuit on 80 and 40 meters. The unun is an unbalanced-to-unbalanced wideband toroidal transformer. Another alternative is to use an L network. A simple tunable L network that has been especially designed for matching "short" 160-meter loaded verticals is shown in Figs 9-55 and 9-56. The L network was made by ON7TK and has been traveling around the world on several DXpeditions (A61, 9K2, FOØC, etc).

WØCD recommends using at least 30 radials, each of 20 m (66 ft) length. I would consider this a bare minimum. The Battle Creek Special is not for sale, but is available for loan to DXpeditions to rare countries. Interested and qualified DXpeditioners should contact WØCD, K8GG or W8UVZ for further details. The antenna was used at Bouvet on 80 and 160 meters in 1989/90, and during the DXpeditions to ZSØZ, 7P8EN, AH1A and many other locations with great success.

The entire antenna, with its base, guy-wires and radials is packed in a strong wooden case for safe transport to the remotest DXpedition spot. The package weighs 30 kg (66 lb). Fig 9-57 shows W8UVZ and K8GG with the wooden crate containing the Battle Creek Special. Fig 9-58 shows the 80-meter coax-cable trap.

WØCD also developed a wire version for attachment to trees or other tall structures. Fig 9-59 shows the 40- and 80-meter traps as designed and made by WØCD (Ref 662 and 689). Both the wire and the tubing version of the Battle Creek should provide inspiration for those who are looking for a compact but effective transportable 160-meter antenna.

5.8. Using the Beam Tower as a Low-Band Vertical

The tower supporting the HF antennas can make a very good loaded vertical for 160 meters. A 24-m (79 ft) tower with a triband or monoband Yagi, or a stack of Yagis, will exhibit

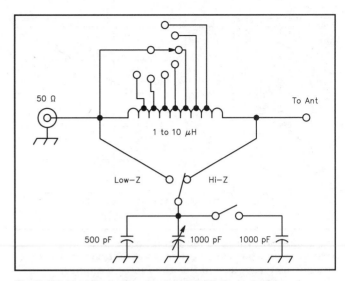

Fig 9-55—L network to be used with inverted-L antennas and other loaded 160-meter verticals. With the component values shown, impedances in the range 20 − j100 to 100 + j100 can easily be matched on 160 meters.

Fig 9-56–The L network of Fig 9-55 is contained in a small plastic housing. This particular unit was built by ON7TK and used on several DXpeditions (A61, 9K2, FOØC).

an electrical length on 160 meters between 90 and 150 degrees. These are lengths that are very attractive for low-angle work on 160.

The Electrical Length of a Loaded Tower

Fig 9-59A can be used to assess the electrical length of a tower loaded with a Yagi antenna. The chart shows the situation for a tower, with a diameter of 30 cm (12 in.), loaded with five different Yagis, ranging from a 3-element, 20-m Yagi to a 3-element 40-m full-size Yagi.

A 24-m (80-ft) tower, loaded with a 5-element, 20-m Yagi (15-m or 46-ft boom), will have an electrical length of 103 degrees on 1.825 MHz. The effect of capacitive top

Fig 9-57—W8UVZ (left) and K8GG (right) with the wooden crate containing the Battle Creek Special, a 3-band (160, 80 and 40-m) vertical. The wooden crate was designed especially to ensure safe transportation of the antenna to the most remote parts of the world.

Fig 9-58—Eighty-meter coax-cable trap as used by WØCD in the Battle Creek Special 160/80/40-m 3-band vertical.

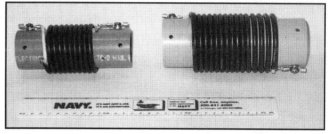

Fig 9-59—Traps for 40 and 80 meters, developed by WØCD for the wire version of the Battle Creek Special.

loading depends to a great extent on the diameter of the tower under the capacitance hat. The capacitance hat (the Yagis) will have a greater influence with "slim" towers than with towers having a large diameter. If we increase the tower diameter to 60 cm (2 ft), this will shorten the electrical length between 4 and 7 degrees (4 degrees for the tower loaded with the 3-element, 20-meter Yagi, and 7 degrees for the tower loaded with the 40-m, 3-element full-size Yagi).

W. J. Schultz, K3OQF, published the mathematical derivation of the shunt fed top-loaded vertical (Ref 7995).

Measuring the Electrical Length

A second and very practical method of determining the resonant length of a tower system was given by DeMaw, W1FB (Ref. 774). A shunt-fed wire is dropped from the top of the tower to ground level, and a small 2- or 3-turn loop between the end of the wire and ground is used for coupling to a dip meter (Fig 9-60). The lowest dip found is then the resonant frequency of the tower/beam. The electrical length at the design frequency is then given by:

$$l° = 90 \frac{f_{design}}{f_{resonant}}$$

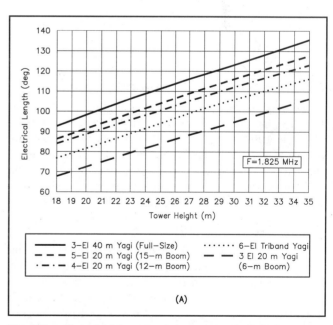

Fig 59A—Electrical length of a tower loaded with a Yagi antenna. The chart is valid for 160 m (1.825 MHz) and a tower diameter of 30 cm (12 in.). For a larger tower diameter, the electrical length will be shorter (4 to 7 degrees for a tower measuring 60 cm—24 in.—in diameter.

Therefore, if $f_{resonant} = 1.6$ MHz and $f_{design} = 1.8$ MHz, then $\ell^\circ = 101$ degrees.

5.8.1. Gamma and omega matching.

There are many approaches to matching a loaded, grounded tower. Two popular methods are:

• Slant-wire shunt feeding.
• Gamma- or omega-match shunt feeding.

DeMaw uses the shunt-fed wire and matches the bottom end via a T network. An L network should work just as well. The impedance at the bottom of the shunt-fed wire can be measured with a noise bridge. The L-network design program may be useful once again in this situation.

Gamma and omega matching techniques are most widely used on loaded towers. The design of gamma matches has been described in the literature (Ref. 1401, 1414, 1421, 1426 and 1441).

Fig 9-61 shows the height of the gamma-match tap as well as the value of the gamma capacitor for a range of antenna lengths varying from 60 degrees to 180 degrees. The chart was developed using a gamma wire of 10 mm (0.4 in.) diameter. There are three sets of curves, for three different wire spacings.

5.8.1.1. *Close spacing versus wide spacing.*

The wider the spacing, the shorter the gamma wire needs to be. Shorter gamma wires will logically show less inductive reactance, which means that the series capacitor will be larger in value.

Electrically very long verticals will require a tap which is 20 to 30 m (65 to 100 ft) up on the tower. The required series capacitor will be small in value (typically 100 to 150 pF). There will be a very high voltage across capacitors of such small value.

In case the required gamma-wire length is longer than the physical length of the tower, an omega match will be required (see par 5.8.1.5).

5.8.1.2. *Influence of gamma-wire diameter.*

The gamma-wire diameter has little influence on the length of the gamma wire (position of the tap on the tower). A larger diameter wire will require a somewhat shorter gamma wire. The wire diameter has a pronounced influence on the required gamma capacitor. It also has some influence on the SWR bandwidth of the antenna system, but less than most believe.

5.8.1.3. *SWR bandwidth.*

Tables 9-5 and 9-6 show the feed-point impedance and the SWR versus frequency for a vertical of 100 degrees electrical length, fed with a gamma match. A spacing of 50 cm (20 in.) is used in Table 9-5, and 150-cm (59 in.) spacing in Table 9-6. Wire diameters of 2 mm (AWG 12), 10 mm (0.4 in.), 50 mm (2 in.) and 250 mm (10 in.) are included. The 2-mm (AWG 12) wire is certainly not responsible for a narrow bandwidth. It does not seem worth using a "wire cage" gamma wire to improve the bandwidth.

For loaded towers that are much longer, the bandwidth

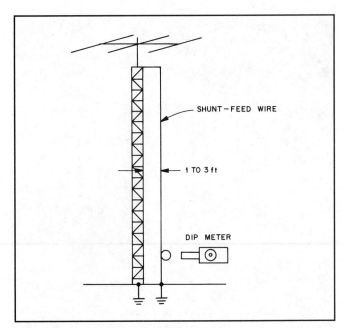

Fig 9-60—A method of "dipping" a tower with a shunt-feed wire connected to the top.

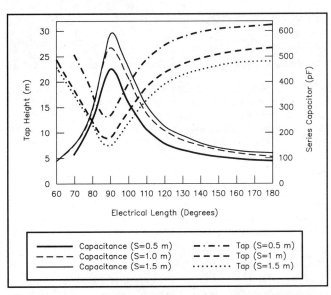

Fig 9-61—Tap height and values of the gamma series capacitor for a shunt-fed tower at 1.835 MHz. The tower diameter is 250 mm (10 in.), and the gamma wire has a diameter of 10 mm (0.4 in.). Three sets of curves are shown, for three spacings (S). The spacing is the distance from the wire to the tower center.

behavior is quite different. The longer the electrical length of the vertical, the narrower the SWR bandwidth. Table 9-7 shows the feed-point impedance and the SWR for a vertical of 150 degrees electrical length, fed with a gamma match and a gamma wire of both 10 mm (0.4 in.) and 250 mm (10 in.) OD. In contrast with the effect on the shorter vertical (100 degrees), the wire diameter now has a pronounced influence on the bandwidth. The 10-mm wire yields a 70-kHz bandwidth, the 250-mm wire cage almost 130 kHz. As can be seen from the impedance values listed in Table 9-7, it is

Table 9-5

Gamma-Match Data for a Shunt-Fed Tower with 50-cm Gamma-Wire Spacing

Tower electrical height = 100 degrees

Tower diameter = 250 mm (10 in.)

	1.730	1.765	1.800	1.835	1.870	1.905	1.940 MHz

Gamma-wire diameter = 2 mm (AWG 12); tap height = 19.5 m (64.0 ft)

R	80.6	66.8	56.5	50.0	43.3	39.2	36.0
X	+330	+338	+350	+363	+377	+392	+407
SWR	2.0	1.7	1.3	1.0	1.4	2.0	2.8

Gamma-wire diameter = 10 mm (0.4 in.); tap height = 19.8 m (65.0 ft)

R	82.9	68.6	58	50	44.8	40.6	37.4
X	+250	+257	+267	+278	+291	+303	+316
SWR	1.9	1.6	1.3	1.0	1.3	1.8	2.4

Gamma-wire diameter = 50 mm (2 in.); tap height = 20.0 m (65.6 ft)

R	80.8	66.9	56.9	50.0	44.3	40.3	37.3
X	+164	+171	+179	+188	+198	+208	+218
SWR	1.8	1.5	1.2	1.0	1.3	1.6	2.1

Gamma-wire diameter = 250 mm (10 in); tap height = 20.2 m (66.3 ft)

R	78.8	65.5	56	50	44	41	38.3
X	+75	+82	+90	+98	+105	+113	+121
SWR	1.8	1.5	1.2	1.0	1.2	1.5	1.8

Table 9-6

Gamma-Match Data for a Shunt-Fed Tower with 150-cm Gamma-Wire Spacing

Tower electrical height = 100 degrees

Tower diameter = 250 mm (10 in.)

	1.730	1.765	1.800	1.835	1.870	1.905	1.940 MHz

Gamma-wire diameter = 2 mm (AWG 12); tap height = 11.9 m (39.0 ft)

R	86.8	71.0	59.0	50.0	43.7	38.8	35.0
X	+226	+229	+36	+244	+53	+262	+272
SWR	1.8	1.5	132	1.0	1.2	1.6	2.1

Gamma-wire diameter = 10 mm (0.4 in.); tap height = 12.0 m (39.4 ft)

R	87.8	71.7	59.8	50.0	44.4	39.5	35.7
X	+179	+181	+187	+195	+203	+212	+220
SWR	1.8	1.5	1.3	1.0	1.2	1.6	2.0

Gamma-wire diameter = 50 mm (2 in.); tap height = 12.0 m (39.4 ft)

R	87.0	71.0	59.0	50.0	44.3	39.5	35.8
X	+1230	+132	+137	+44	+152	+159	+166
SWR	1.8	1.5	1.2	1.0	1.2	1.5	1.8

Gamma-wire diameter = 250 mm (10 in); tap height = 11.9 m (39.0 ft)

R	85.2	69.6	58.3	50	44	39.4	36
X	+79	+82	+87	+93	+100	+106	+112
SWR	1.8	1.5	1.2	1.0	1.2	1.5	1.7

the large variation in reactance that is responsible for the steep SWR curve. This can easily be overcome by using a motor-driven variable capacitor. The 150-degree-long antenna with a 10-mm-OD gamma wire shows an SWR of less than 1.3:1 over more than 200 kHz, if a variable capacitor with a tuning range of 100 to 175 pF is used. A high-voltage vacuum variable is a must.

This simple way of obtaining a very flat SWR curve does not apply to the shorter verticals (90-110 degrees), where a much larger variation of the resistive part of the impedance is responsible for the SWR. Fig 9-62 shows SWR curves for gamma-fed towers of varying electrical length, using a 10-mm OD gamma wire, spaced 150 cm (59 in.) from the tower.

5.8.1.4. *Adjusting the gamma system.*

The easiest way to fine-tune the gamma-matching system is to vary the spacing of the gamma wire.
Example:

For a vertical with 100 degrees electrical length and a tower diameter of 250 mm (10 in.), we install the tap at 14 m (46 ft). At that point the spacing is 1 m (3.3 ft). Changing the spacing at ground level has the following influence:

Spacing = 0.5 m (20 in.): Z = 38 + j206 ohms
Spacing = 0.75 m (30 in.): Z = 44.8 + j298 ohms
Spacing = 1.0 m (39 in.): Z = 49.3 + j211 ohms
Spacing = 1.25 m (49 in.): Z = 56.4 + j213 ohms
Spacing = 1.5 m (59 in.): Z = 61.5 + j214 ohms

This demonstrates how fine-tuning can easily be done on the gamma matching system.

Table 9-7

Gamma-Match Data for a Shunt-Fed Tower with 150-cm Gamma-Wire Spacing

Tower electrical height = 150 degrees

Tower diameter = 250 mm (10 in.)

	1.730	1.765	1.800	1.835	1.870	1.905	1.940 MHz

Gamma-wire diameter = 10 mm (0.4 in.); tap height = 25.9 m (85.0 ft)

R	43.1	45.2	47.7	50.0	54	58	62.7
X	+567	+597	+628	+661	+697	+736	+778
SWR	6.0	3.5	1.9	1.0	2.0	3.7	6.3

Gamma-wire diameter = 250 mm (10 in.); tap height = 24.8 m (81.4 ft)

R	41.5	43.8	46.6	50	54	58.54	64.0
X	+286	+303	+320	+340	+362	+384	+409
SWR	3.2	2.2	1.5	1.0	1.5	2.2	3.2

5.8.1.5. *Using the omega system.*

If you can use a gamma, I would not advise an omega system. The omega match requires one more component, which means additional losses and additional chances for a component breakdown. It is possible, however, to use a gamma-rod (wire) length that is up to 50% shorter than the length shown in Fig 9-61 when an omega match is employed. In this case a parallel capacitor will be required between the bottom end of the gamma wire and ground.

The 100-degree-long vertical requires a 14-m-long (45.9 ft) gamma wire, with 100-cm (39 in.) gamma-wire (OD 10 mm or 0.4 in.) spacing. If we shorten the gamma wire to 8 m (26.2 ft), the impedance becomes $14.1 + j127$ ohms. This can be matched to 50 ohms using an L network. One of the solutions of this L network consists of two capacitors: the well-known parallel and series capacitor of the omega matching system.

To calculate the omega system, the following procedure should be used:

- Model the vertical with the "short" gamma rod. Make sure you use enough segments (pulses). For 160 meters, segment lengths of 100 cm (40 in.) gives good results. Note the input impedance, which will be lower than 50 ohms, and inductive).
- Use the L NETWORK module of the NEW LOW BAND SOFTWARE to calculate the capacitance of the parallel and the series capacitor.

In our above example, the 8-m-long (26.2 ft) gamma wire requires a parallel capacitor of 369 pF and a series capacitor of 323 pF.

If you have a physically short tower with a lot of loading, it may be that the required tap height is greater than your tower height. In this case an omega match is the only solution (if you have already tried a larger spacing).

Example: See Fig 9-63. The tower was "dipped" and the

electrical length turned out to be 140 degrees. The physical height is 24 m (78.7 ft). Fig 9-61 shows a required gamma-wire length of 30 m for a 2-mm OD gamma wire and a 50-cm spacing. In this case we will connect the gamma wire at the top of the tower (h = 24 m or 78.7 ft). Using MININEC, we calculate the feed-point impedance as $Z = 17.2 + j579$ ohms. From the L NETWORK software module, the capacitor values are calculated as $C_{par} = 62$ pF, $C_{series} = 88$ pF. Note that these very low-value capacitors will carry very high voltages across their terminals with high power.

This L network is a very high-Q network. Table 9-8 lists the impedances at the end of the gamma wire before and after transformation by the capacitors of the omega-match system (an L network using two capacitors). Note the very narrow bandwidth of this extremely high-Q matching system. If we adjust the omega capacitors for a 1:1 SWR on 1835 kHz, the 2:1 bandwidth will be typically 20 kHz! If we make the series capacitor adjustable (60 to 120 pF), we can tune the antenna to an SWR of less than 1.5:1 over more than 200 kHz.

5.8.1.6. *Conclusion.*

If you have an electrically long vertical, it pays to use a large-diameter cage-type gamma wire and a large wire-to-tower spacing. Making the series capacitor remotely tunable will certainly make the antenna much more broadbanded. Do not shorten the gamma wire unless required because of the physical length of the tower.

Fig 9-64 shows the correct wiring of both the gamma and omega matching networks on a loaded tower. Notice the

---

Table 9-8

Omega-Match Data for a Shunt-Fed Tower with 50-cm Wire Spacing

Tower electrical height = 140 degrees
Omega-wire diameter = 2 mm (AWG 12)

	1.730	1.765	1.800	1.835	1.870	1.905	1.940 MHz
Gamma-wire diameter = 2 mm (AWG 12); tap height = 24.0 m (78.7 ft)							
R	16.0	16.3	16.7	17.2	17.9	18.6	19.3
X	+514	+535	+552	+579	+603	+629	+650
With parallel capacitor of 62 pF added							
R	37.4	40.7	44.8	50.0	56.8	65.3	74.7
X	+785	+845	+910	+986	+1073	+1178	+1287
With fixed series capacitor of 88 pF added							
R	37.4	40.7	44.8	50.0	56.8	65.3	74.7
X	−261	−180	−95	0	+106	+228	+348
SWR	38.0	17.9	5.9	1.0	5.8	17.9	35
With variable series capacitor, 50 to 125 pF (adjusted to cancel inductive reactance)							
R	37.4	40.7	44.8	50.0	56.8	65.3	74.7
X	0	0	0	0	0	0	0
SWR	1.3	1.2	1.1	1.0	1.1	1.3	1.5

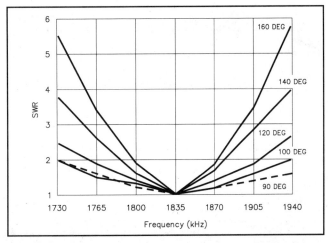

Fig 9-62—SWR curves for gamma-fed towers using a 10-mm OD (0.4 in.) gamma wire and a spacing of 50 cm (20 in.), for electrical tower lengths varying from 90 to 160 degrees. The SWR bandwidth of the longer vertical can be "tuned" to a very low SWR over a wide bandwidth by using a motor-driven variable series capacitor.

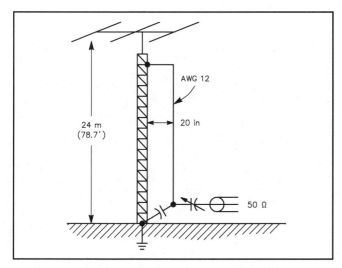

Fig 9-63—A shunt-fed tower using an omega matching system. The tower is electrically 140 degrees long. An omega match is required, as the tower is physically too short to accommodate a gamma match with a 2-mm gamma wire. Table 9-8 lists the impedances at the end of the gamma wire before and after transformation by the capacitors of the omega match system.

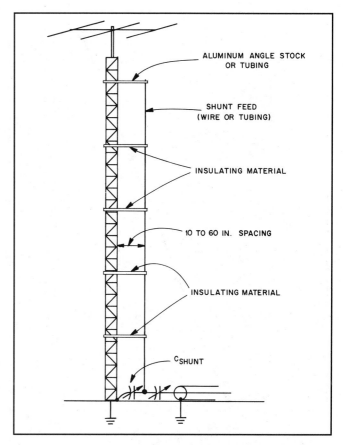

Fig 9-64—The omega matching system (a gamma match with an additional shunt capacitor) adds a great deal of flexibility to the shunt-fed-tower arrangement. In order to maintain maximum bandwidth, make the gamma wire as long as possible. If the antenna is electrically longer than 120 degrees, a variable series capacitor will make it possible to obtain a very low SWR over a very wide bandwidth.

correct connection of the shunt capacitor in the case of the omega match.

The same principles can of course be applied to 80 meters, although it is probable that a tower of reasonable height, loaded with a Yagi antenna, will result in too long an antenna for operation on 80 meters.

5.8.1.7. *Practical hints.*

All cables leading to the tower and up to the rotator and antennas should be firmly secured to a tower leg, preferably on the inside of the tower. All leads from the shack to the tower base should be buried underground in order to provide sufficient RF decoupling. A stack of ferrite beads (similar to those used on current baluns) can be used to decouple RF from any conductors.

If there is still RF on some of the cables, you may wish to coil up a length of the cable where it enters the shack. Care should be taken to ensure good electrical continuity between the tower sections, and between the rotator, the mast, and the tower. Large braid (such as the flattened braid from old coax or a piece of car-battery cable) can provide the necessary electrical contact and physical flexibility. The gamma rod can be supported with sections of plastic pipe, attached to the tower with U bolts or stainless-steel radiator hose clamps. If the tower is a crank-up type, heavy, insulated copper wire can be used for the gamma element. As with any vertical, this system requires the best possible ground system for optimum low-angle radiation and efficiency. The longer the electrical length of the loaded tower, the better the quality of the ground will need to be to achieve the potential low-angle radiation.

5.8.2. The slant-wire feed system.

The slant-wire feed system is very similar to the gamma feed system. The feed wire is attached at a certain height on the

tower and slopes at an angle to the ground, where a series capacitor tunes out the reactance. The advantage of this system is that a match can be obtained with a lower tap point, which makes in possible to avoid using an omega match on physically short towers. The disadvantage is that the slant wire feed also radiates a horizontally polarized component.

The slant-wire feed system can easily be modeled using MININEC, just as the gamma and omega matching systems.

5.8.3. Modeling shunt fed towers.

MININEC can be used for modeling the gamma, omega and slant-wire matching systems on shunt-fed grounded towers. Satisfactory results are obtained using the following guidelines:

• The horizontal wire connecting the gamma wire to the tower has one segment (the length of the segment is the spacing from the gamma wire to the tower).
• Use approximately the same segment lengths on all wires of the antenna.

Do not try to model the capacitance top load. It is much easier to first "dip" the tower (see Fig 9-60), calculate the electrical length of the loaded tower, and then use an equivalent straight

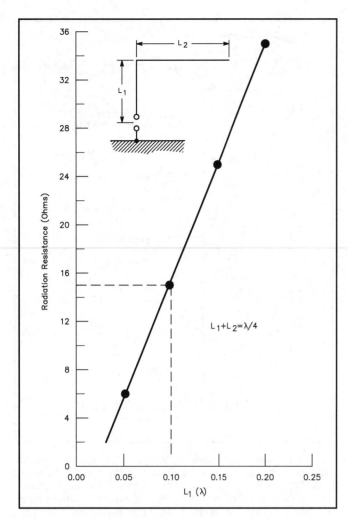

Fig 9-65—Radiation resistance of inverted-L antenna as a function of the lengths of the horizontal wire versus the vertical conductor.

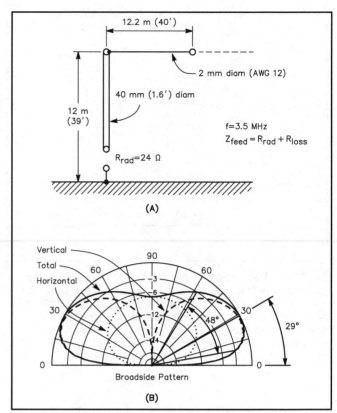

Fig 9-66— At A is a 3.5-MHz inverted L with a 12-m (39 ft) vertical mast. The vertical radiation pattern is shown at B. The pattern has both vertically and horizontally polarized components, and these components are also plotted at B. The pattern is generated over average ground, using 60 quarter-wave radials. Note that the angle of maximum radiation is 29 degrees, not bad for a DX antenna.

tower to do the gamma-match modeling.

Example:

The tower dips at 1.42 MHz. The required operating frequency is 1.835 MHz. The electrical length is

$$90 \times \frac{1.835}{1.42} = 116 \text{ degrees}.$$

The physical length of a quarter-wave tower (250 mm OD or 10 in. section) is 39 m (128 ft). The equivalent tower length for 116 degrees is

$$39 \times \frac{116}{90} = 50.3 \text{ m (165 ft)}.$$

Now model a vertical with a wire diameter of 250 mm (10 in.) of 50.3 m length.

According to Fig 9-61, the tap will be at a height of between 17 and 25 m (56 to 82 ft), depending on the wire spacing.

■ 6. INVERTED-L ANTENNA

The-ever-so popular inverted L is analyzed in this section

and a few practical designs, such as the well-known AKI Special, are given particular attention.

The inverted L is a popular antenna, especially on 160 meters. These antennas are not truly verticals, as part of the antenna is horizontal and radiates a horizontally polarized wave. Most inverted Ls are of the quarter-wave variety, although this does not necessarily need to be the case. The vertical portion of an inverted L can be put up alongside a tower supporting HF antennas. In such a setup one must take care that the tower (plus antenna) does not resonate near the design frequency of the inverted L. The longer the vertical part of the antenna, the better the low-angle radiation characteristics of the antenna and the higher the radiation resistance (see Fig 9-65). The horizontal part of the antenna accounts for the high-angle radiation that the antenna produces. If you are looking for an antenna that radiates reasonably well at both low and high angles, an inverted L may be an excellent choice for you. Since it is a loaded monopole, an inverted L requires a good ground system for optimum low-angle radiation. Fig 9-66 shows the vertical and horizontal radiation patterns for a practical design of an inverted-L antenna for 3.5 MHz, one having a 12 m (39 ft) vertical mast. Notice how the vertical part of the antenna takes care of the low-angle radiation, while

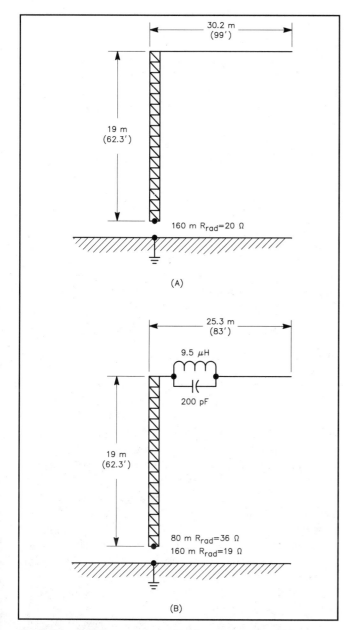

Fig 9-67—A shows an inverted-L antenna for 160 meters, using a 19-m vertical tower. To cover both 80 and 160 meters, a trap can be installed at the top of the tower as shown at B. With the trap installed, the loading wire is shorter, because the trap shows a positive reactance (loading effect) on 160 meters. See also Figs 9-47 and 9-49.

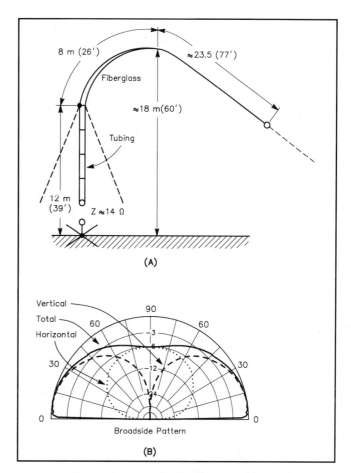

Fig 9-68—The AKI Special, a typical DXpedition type 160-m inverted L. A collapsible fiberglass fishing rod (available in Europe in lengths of up to 12 m or 39 ft) is used on top of a 12-m aluminum mast. A no. 12 wire is attached to the rod, and slopes to a distant point to make the sloping (horizontal) part of the antenna. The radiation pattern is over salt water. (That's where the island DXpeditioners put these antennas.)

the horizontal part assures high-angle output. The radiation pattern shown is for the direction perpendicular to the plane of the inverted L.

An inverted L is also an attractive solution for the operator who needs to use an 80-meter vertical antenna as a support for a 160-meter antenna (Fig 9-67A). The easiest solution is to insert a trap at the top of the 80-meter vertical. The exact L/C ratio is not important, but influences the length of the loading wire and the SWR behavior of the antenna on both 80 and 160 meters. See also Figs 9-47 and 9-49.

A second alternative, shown in Fig 9-67B, uses an 80-m trap to isolate the horizontal part of the 160-m inverted-L

antenna when operating on 80 meters (Ref 659). The trap can be a coax-cable trap as explained in paragraph 5.5.

The inverted L has been extensively described in amateur literature as the better antenna for producing a low-angle signal on top-band (Ref 798 and 7994).

The AKI Special is a DXpedition-style inverted L, as used by Aki Nago, JA5DQH, during his operation on 160 meters from several rare DX spots. From Kingman Reef (May 1988), Nago used the inverted L as shown in Fig 9-68. The vertical part is made of a 12-m (39 ft) aluminum mast, which is extended by an 8-m-long (26 ft) fiberglass fishing rod, to which a copper wire has been attached. From the tip of the (bent) fishing rod, the sloping wire extends another 23.5 m (77 ft), to be terminated with a fishing line supported by a 10-ft pole at some distance. Aki used about 800 m (2600 ft) of radials running into the Pacific ocean. A very similar 160-meter antenna was successfully used from Palmyra during the same DXpedition trip in 1988, and during a more recent DXpedition to Ogasawara by JA5AUC. The calculated radiation resistance of this antenna is approximately 14 ohms. The main radiation angle (over sea water) is 10 degrees, but due to the relatively long horizontal (sloping) wire, the radiation at higher angles is only slightly suppressed.

Tuning Procedure

When cutting the length of the sloping wire, cut it at first a little long (2 m or 6 or 7 ft too long). Put up the antenna, and connect a noise bridge between the antenna base and the ground radials. Set the reactance dial exactly to zero. Now tune the receiver until you find a frequency where the noise is minimum. Adjust the noise bridge resistance potentiometer. Repeat the procedure until a perfect balance (zero noise) is achieved. Keep the reactance dial at zero at all times. The frequency will likely be too low, eg, 1750 kHz. Shorten the wire progressively until the noise bridge is in balance at the desired operating frequency. Now read the resistance value off the scale. If it is between 35 and 70 ohms, the SWR will be pretty acceptable (1.5:1) and you may want to feed the antenna directly with 50-ohm feed line. From the difference between the R value and the calculated 14 ohms radiation resistance, you can calculate the effective ground-loss resistance of the ground (radial) system. If the feed-point impedance is above 50 ohms, you really need to improve the radial system. For 50 ohms the efficiency would be 14/50 = 28%. Any value higher than 50 ohms would indicate an even lower efficiency. If you want a perfect match you can use an L network, as described in paragraph 6.7.

■ 7. THE T ANTENNA

The current-fed T antenna is a top-loaded short vertical, as covered earlier in this chapter. The voltage-fed T antenna is given special attention here, as well as the different top-loading structures.

7.1. Current-Fed T Antennas

T-wire loading (flat-top wire) is covered in detail in par 2.1.2 and par 2.6.5 for dealing with top loading of short verticals. The advantage of the horizontal T-wire loading system over the inverted-L system is that the top-wire does not contribute to the total radiation pattern. Fig 9-69 shows a practical design where a 12 m long vertical is loaded with a horizontal top-load wire to achieve resonance at 3.5 MHz. The R_{rad} of this design is approximately 23.5 ohms.

7.2. Voltage-Fed T Antennas

Voltage-fed T antennas are loaded vertical antennas with a current minimum at ground level. A specific case consists of a quarter-wave vertical, loaded with a half-wave top wire. Fig 9-70 shows the configuration of this antenna, and the current distribution. In this case, the impedance at the base of the antenna is high and purely resistive. The current maximum is at the antenna top. The antenna is sometimes called an inverted vertical, as it has its current maximum at the top. As the radiation resistance at the base is very high, it has the advantage of good efficiency over a poor ground. In theory, the current in both halves of the flat-top wire is such that radiation from that wire is zero. (In practice there is a very small amount of horizontal radiation.) The disadvantage of this construction is that the antenna requires a very long flat-top wire. Fig 9-70

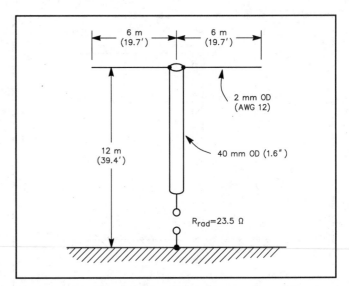

Fig 9-69—T-wire loaded current-fed quarter-wave antenna for 3.5 MHz.

also shows the dimensions for such a vertical, for a practical design on 3.5 MHz.

Hille, DL1VU, dramatically improved the T antenna by folding the half-wave flat-top section in such a way that the radiation from the flat-top section is effectively suppressed. Fig 9-71 shows the configuration of this antenna. It can easily be proved that the area under the current distribution line for the central part (which is 1/12 wavelength long) is the same as the area for the remaining part of the loading device (which is 1/6 wavelength long). Because of the way the wires are folded, the radiation from the horizontal loading device is effectively canceled.

The latest design of a T-type top-load by Hille requires only a single quarter-wave flat top. In order to cancel all possible horizontal radiation from this flat-top wire, the quarter-wave is folded back as shown in Fig 9-72. Notice that the top load is asymmetrical.

A single quarter-wave flat top acts as a short circuit at the top of the vertical, the same way as radials provide a low-impedance attachment point for the outer conductor of the coax feed line in the case of a groundplane (vertical) antenna.

Hille also described a vertical with a physical length of only 0.39 wavelength, using the quarter-wave-long top-load wire configuration as described above (Ref 7991). This antenna produces the same field strength as a 5/8-wave (0.64 wavelength) vertical antenna.

The T antenna can also be seen as a bobtail curtain antenna with the two vertical end sections missing (see Fig 12-18). As such, this antenna is a poor performer with respect to the bobtail antenna, where the directivity and gain is obtained through the use of three vertical elements.

Feeding the Antenna

The voltage-fed T antenna can best be fed by means of a parallel tuned circuit (see Fig 9-70). You can either tap the coax on the coil for the lowest SWR point or tap the antenna near the top of the coil. Either method is valid.

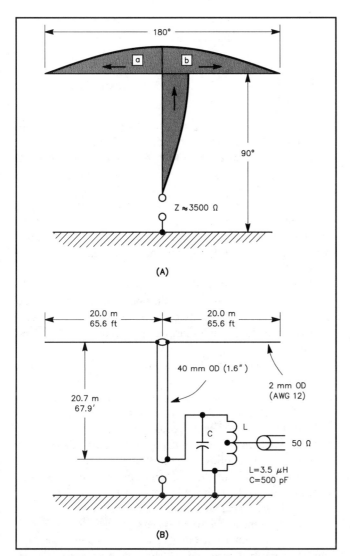

Fig 9-70—Voltage-fed 80-m quarter-wave vertical (also called inverted vertical), using a ½-wavelength long top-loading wire. The T wire has a twofold function—providing a low impedance at the top of the vertical, and having a configuration whereby horizontally polarized radiation is essentially canceled (area a = area b, hence no radiation).

    C—500 pF.
    L—3.5 μH.

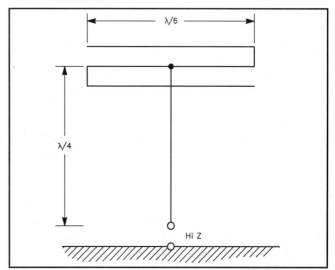

Fig 9-71—Voltage-fed quarter-wave T antenna with the ½-wave flat-top wire folded to have a total span of only ⅙ wavelength. The current distribution in the folded top-load is such that radiation from the top-load is effectively canceled. The advantage of this design over the original voltage-fed T antenna is that it requires a much smaller (shorter) top-load space.

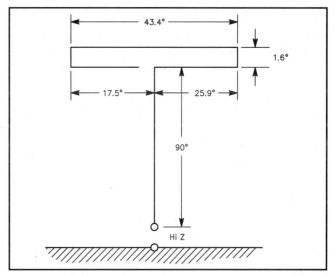

Fig 9-72—Voltage-fed T antenna with a quarter-wave long top load, arranged in such a way that there is no radiation from the flat top section.

The Required Ground and Radial System

The ground and radial requirements are identical to those required for a half-wave vertical (see par 3.3.).

■ 8. LOCATION OF THE VERTICAL ANTENNA

Let's tackle the so-often-asked question, "Will a vertical work in my particular location?" Verticals for working DX on the low bands are certainly not space-saving antennas, but to the contrary, require a lot of space and a good ground. Many low-band DXers have wondered why some verticals don't work well at all, while others work "like gangbusters." The poor performers generally have the poor locations. To repeat, a vertical is not a space-saving antenna! A good vertical takes a lot of real estate. In addition it must be real estate with a good RF ground!

The standard for buried radials is that for best radiation efficiency you need 120 half-wave radials. This means that for 80 meters, you need about an 80 × 80-meter (265 × 265 ft) lot in which to place all the radials. The radials are there to provide a low-resistance return path for the antenna current in order to achieve a good efficiency. You can do as well with just a few elevated quarter-wave radials, as far as the radiation efficiency is concerned.

The area beyond the ends of the radials is at least as important, because that's where the low-angle reflection at ground level takes place (the Fresnel zone). This is where the reflection efficiency is determined.

Fig 9-73 shows how much clearance a current-fed quarter-wave vertical should have for adequate performance. Assuming a quarter-wave vertical with an excellent ground system, the wave angle can be as low as 20 to 25 degrees. RF radiated from the top of the quarter-wave vertical at an angle of −25 degrees will hit the ground about ½ wavelength away from the base, reflecting at an angle of 25 degrees (the main wave angle). Here you can see that the 1-wavelength-long radials start having an influence on the very low-angle radiation behavior of verticals.

Up to ½ wavelength away from the vertical, most of the reflection will take place that is responsible for the 25-degree radiation (main angle) of a quarter-wave vertical. Therefore, beyond this point, a clear path should be provided for these low-angle rays in order to obtain maximum low-angle radiation. It is clear that for even lower angles of radiation, the ground at even greater distances becomes important. As explained earlier, this is of course very much more so with "long" verticals (eg, half-wave vertical) where the Fresnel reflection takes place up to 100 wavelengths away from the antenna (for wave angles down to ¼ degree).

From Fig 9-73 you can see that this means no structures taller than the antenna should be closer than 1 wavelength away from a quarter-wave vertical. Smaller interfering and absorbing obstacles can be a little closer, as long as the size remains small enough to refrain from interfering with the low-angle energy reflected from the ground within ½ wavelength from the base of the vertical.

For a ¼-wavelength vertical, the maximum height of a neighboring obstacle can be calculated with the following formulas.

$$h_{max\ (feet)} = \left(D - \frac{468}{f}\right)\tan\alpha$$

or

$$h_{max\ (meters)} = \left(D - \frac{143}{f}\right)\tan\alpha$$

where

D = distance of the obstacle from the antenna base, same units as h

f = frequency, MHz

α = wave angle, degrees (25 degrees is a good rule of thumb)

This means, for instance, that at a point 60 m (196.9 ft) from a 3.5-MHz antenna, the maximum height of a structure should be limited to 9.1 m or 30 ft. What about trees closer in? Trees are reasonably good conductors and can be very lossy elements in the near field of a radiator. A case has been reported in the literature where a quarter-wave vertical with an excellent ground system showed a much lower radiation resistance than expected. It was found that trees in the immediate area were coupling heavily with the vertical and were causing the radiation resistance of the vertical to be very low. Under such circumstances of uncontrolled coupling into very lossy elements, far from optimum performance can be expected. Of course if the trees are short in relation to the (quarter) wavelength, it is reasonable to assume that the result of such coupling will be minimal.

Even though neighboring structures such as trees may not be resonant, they will always absorb some RF to an unknown degree. Other objects that are very likely to affect the performance of a vertical are nearby antennas and towers. Mutual coupling can be considered the culprit if the radiation resistance of the vertical is lower than expected. Another way of checking for coupling with other antennas is to alternately open- and short-circuit the suspected antenna feed lines while watching the SWR or the radiation resistance of the vertical antenna. If there is any change, you are in trouble.

It may come as a surprise that a vertical is so demanding of space. Most amateur verticals are not anywhere near ideal, and good performance can still be obtained from practical setups, but the builder of a vertical should understand which factors are important for optimum performance, and why.

■ 9. 160-M DXPEDITION ANTENNAS

I have talked at great length with well-known

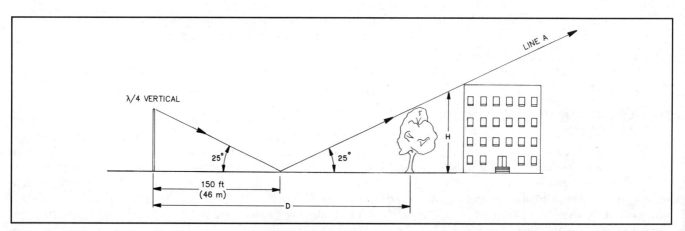

Fig 9-73—Clearance required for a good layout of a vertical antenna. The dimensions are given for 3.5 MHz. For 160 m, all dimensions should be multiplied by 1.9. All neighboring structures should fall below line A. See text for discussion.

DXpeditioners who have been especially successful on the low bands. I'd like to share the following rules with candidate DXpeditioners with respect to the low bands.

If you're on an island, erect the station on that side of the island where you will have the most difficult path or where you are facing the most stations (eg, if you are on an island in the South Indian Ocean, try a shore on the northwest side of the island, looking into both Europe and North America). By all means erect the antenna very close to the salt water, or over (or in) the salt water. This will help you lower the pseudo-Brewster angle, and assure a good low-angle take-off.

Unless you have a very tall support of at least 30 meters (100 ft), use a vertical. Good choices are the Battle Creek Special, the AKI Special, or any inverted L, for which you should try to make the vertical part as long as possible. The vertical section should be at least 15 m (50 ft) tall. If there are some trees, you may try to climb a tall tree, and use a collapsible fiberglass fishing rod (they exist in 40 ft lengths) to extend the effective support height. Use as many radials as you can, and let them run into the salt water. Very thin wire is just fine. A small spool of no. 28 enameled copper wire (magnet wire) can hold a lot of wire and takes little space. Don't bother putting up a Beverage near the sea; it won't work well. Anyhow, it's unlikely you will have to deal with a lot of local QRM or man-made noise.

If there is a tall support, you may want to use a sloping half-wave vertical, especially if you are near the sea (see Chapter 8 on dipole antennas). The sloping vertical builds up its image as far as 100 wavelengths away from the antenna. If there is no salt water nearby and ground conductivity is poor, use a high support for an inverted-V dipole. Don't try an inverted V or any other horizontally polarized antenna at a height of 15 meters (50 ft) or less. All you will get is very high angle radiation.

Here is a hint I got from Rudi, DK7PE: If you are on a DXpedition in a country with a substantial tourist business, choose the tallest hotel (Hiltons, Sheratons or Intercontinentals are usually doing well in this respect). Slope a dipole from the top of the building to some distant point and let the feed line come to your room, which can be a few stories below the roof. Make the dipole as vertical as possible. This is by far the best antenna if you are in such a situation.

DK7PE proved it during his operation from D2CW (August 92) where he had his sloping dipole attached some 60 meters (200 ft) above the street level, facing north, and within 1 wavelength of the South Atlantic ocean. Rudi's signals were always S9 in Europe on 160. During his more recent operation from Ethiopia and Eritrea (9F2CW), he proved it again. Rudi's total antenna system for his DXpeditions (covering 160 through 10 meters) can be packed in a very small handbag. The RG-58 cable takes up 80% of the volume. The antenna consists of precut lengths of flexible insulated wire, with small insulators and a variety of alligator clips that let him change bands. On the higher bands he can configure the wire into a 2-element Yagi.

R. E. Tanaka, 9M2AX, well-known 160-meter operator from the Far East, sent me the sketches of the antennas he is using in 9M2 as well as when he operated from 9M8AX. The antennas Ross was using can be put up at any tall hotel, and should be excellent suggestions for 160-meter DXpeditioners. Figs 9-74 and 9-75 show the layouts of the two antenna setups and their radiation patterns. The radial system covering only one quadrant (90 degrees) results in a significant high-angle

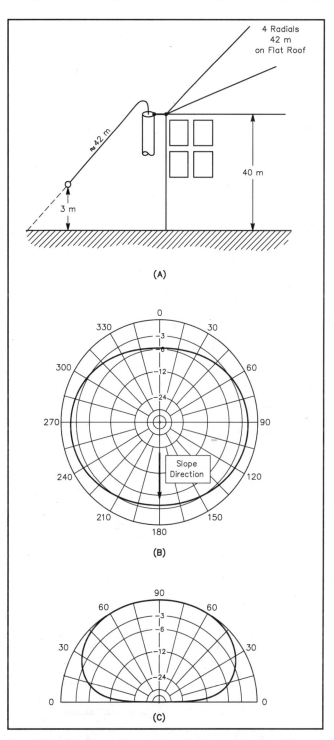

Fig 9-74—Configuration and radiation patterns of the inverted quarter-wave sloper antenna used by 9M2AX. The azimuth pattern is shown at B for an elevation angle of 30°, and at C is the elevation pattern. (The elevation pattern is taken in the 90-270° direction as displayed in the azimuth pattern.) Note the relative high amount of high-angle radiation. Using just two radials in line would improve this situation considerably.

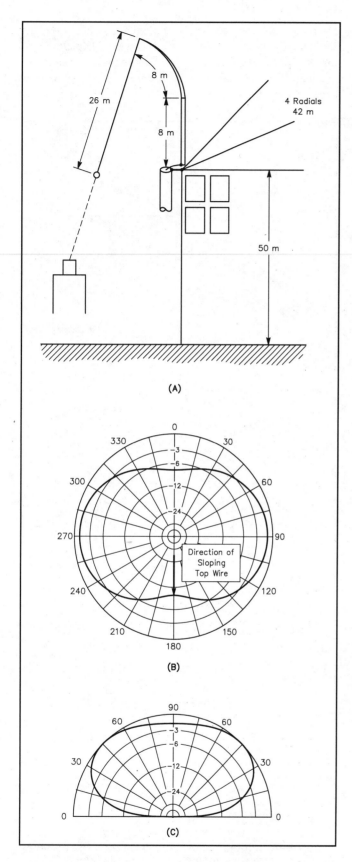

(A)

(B)

(C)

radiation component with the 9M2AX version. The low-angle radiation is very pronounced as well. From modeling, the "inverted sloping wire vertical" from the 9M2 QTH has a feed-point impedance of approximately 75 ohms. The 9M8AX configuration is an inverted L with a sloping flat-top. The calculated impedance from modeling is nearly 60 ohms. This antenna has better low-angle radiation than the 9M2AX version, which is normal. In order for the 9M2AX version to eliminate the high angle radiation, it would be necessary to install just two radials (in line with one another), so that the radiation from these wires would be canceled. The radials are *not* there to provide a ground plane, but are merely serving to provide a low-impedance point to which to connect the outer shield of the feed line. One quarter-wave radial would serve that purpose, but would radiate a lot of horizontal component. Two radials in line would provide a low impedance point just as well, but not radiate any high-angle horizontal component.

Fig 9-75—Configuration and radiation patterns of the inverted quarter-wave sloper antenna used by 9M2AX during his expedition from East Malaysia (Sarawak) as 9M8AX. The azimuth pattern is shown at B, and the elevation pattern at C. (The elevation pattern is taken in the 90-270° direction as displayed in the azimuth pattern.) The antenna was installed on the edge of a 50 m (164 ft) high flat roof. Four quarter-wave long radials were laid on the roof. The metal mast plus the fiberglass rod are 16 m (52 ft) long. The sloping wire was adjusted for minimum SWR at resonance.

LARGE LOOP ANTENNAS

- **1. QUAD LOOPS**
  - **1.1. Impedance**
  - **1.2. Square Loop Patterns**
    - 1.2.1. Vertical polarization.
    - 1.2.2. Horizontal polarization.
    - 1.2.3. Vertical versus horizontal polarization.
  - **1.3. A Rectangular Quad Loop**
  - **1.4. Loop Dimensions**
  - **1.5. Feeding the Quad Loop**

- **2. DELTA LOOPS**
  - **2.1. Vertical Polarization**
    - 2.1.1. How it works.
    - 2.1.2. Radiation patterns.
      - 2.1.2.1. *The equilateral triangle.*
      - 2.1.2.2. *The compressed delta loop.*
      - 2.1.2.3. *The bottom-corner-fed-delta loop.*
  - **2.2. Horizontal Polarization**
    - 2.2.1. How it works.
    - 2.2.2. Radiation patterns.
  - **2.3. Vertical versus Horizontal Polarization**
    - *Over very poor ground*
    - *Over very good ground*
    - *Conclusion*
  - **2.4. Dimensions**
  - **2.5. Feeding the Delta Loop**
  - **2.6. Gain and Radiation Angle**
  - **2.7. Modeling Loops**

- **3. LOADED LOOPS**
  - **3.1 CW and SSB 80-meter Coverage**
    - 3.1.1. Inductive loading.
    - 3.1.2. Capacitive loading.
    - 3.1.3. Bandwidth.
  - **3.2. Reduced-size Loops**

- **4. BI-SQUARE**

- **5. THE HALF LOOP**
  - **5.1 The Low-Angle Antenna**
  - **5.2 High-Angle Operation**

- **6. THE HALF SLOPER**

LARGE LOOP 10 ANTENNAS

The delta loop antenna is a superb example of a high-performance compromise antenna. The single-element loop antenna is almost exclusively used on the low bands, where it can produce low-angle radiation, requiring only a single quarter-wave high support. We will see that a vertically polarized loop is really an array of two phased verticals, and that the ground requirements are the same as for any other vertically polarized antenna.

Loop antennas have been popular with 80-meter DXers for the last 25 years or so. Resonant loop antennas have a circumference of 1 wavelength. The exact shape of the loop is not particularly important. In free space, the loop with the highest gain, however, is the loop with the shape that encloses the largest area for a given circumference. This is a circular loop, which is difficult to construct. Second best is the square loop (quad), and in third place comes the equilateral triangle (delta) loop (Ref 677).

The maximum gain of a full-wave loop over a half-wave dipole in free space is approximately 1.35 dB. Delta loops are used extensively on the low bands at apex heights of ¼ to ⅜ wavelength above ground. At such heights the vertically polarized loops far outperform dipoles or inverted-V dipoles for low-angle DXing, assuming good ground conductivity.

Loops are generally erected with the plane of the loop perpendicular to the ground. Whether or not the loop produces a vertically or a horizontally polarized signal (or a combination of both) depends only on how (where) the loop is being fed.

Sometimes we hear about horizontal loops. These are antennas with the plane of the loop parallel to the ground. Such horizontal loops have the reputation of being excellent low-noise receiving antennas. On transmit they produce exclusively high-angle radiation.

■ 1. QUAD LOOPS

Belcher, WA4JVE, Casper, K4HKX (Ref 1128), and Dietrich, WAØRDX (Ref 677), have published studies comparing the horizontally polarized quad loop with a dipole. A horizontally polarized quad loop antenna (Fig 10-1A) can be seen as two short, end-loaded dipoles, stacked a quarter-wavelength apart, with the top antenna at ¼ wavelength and the bottom one just above ground level. There is no broadside radiation from the vertical wires of the quad because of the current opposition in the vertical members. In a similar manner, the vertically polarized quad loop (Fig 10-1B) consists of two top-loaded, quarter-wave vertical dipoles, spaced ¼-wavelength apart. Fig 10-1 shows how the current distribu-

tion along the elements produces cancellation of radiation from certain parts of the antenna, while radiation from other parts (the horizontally or vertically stacked short dipoles) is reinforced.

The square quad can be fed for either horizontal or vertical polarization merely by placing the feed point at the center of a horizontal arm or at the center of a vertical arm. At the higher frequencies in the HF range, where the quads are typically ½ to several wavelengths high, quad loops are usually fed to produce horizontal polarization, although there is no specific reason for that except maybe from a mechanical

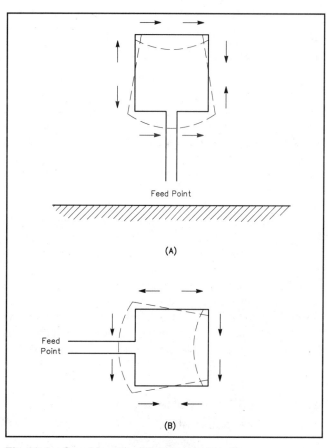

Fig 10-1—Quad loops with a 1-wavelength circumference. The current distribution is shown for (A) horizontal and (B) vertical polarization. Note how the opposing currents in the two legs results in cancellation of the radiation in the plane of those legs, while the currents in the other legs are in phase and reinforce one another in the "broadside" direction (direction perpendicular to the plane of the antenna).

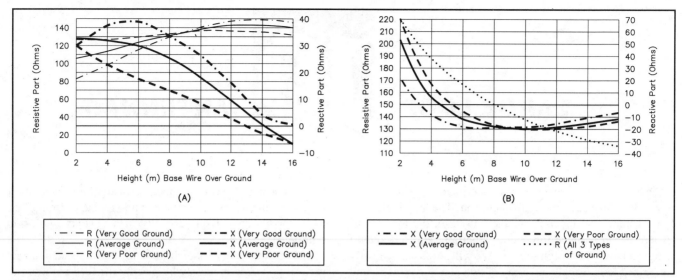

Fig 10-2—Radiation resistance and feed-point reactance for square loops at different heights above real ground. The loop was first dimensioned to be resonant in free space (reactance equal zero), and those dimensions were used for calculating the impedance over ground. At A, for horizontal polarization, and at B, for vertical polarization. Analysis was with NEC at 3.75 MHz.

standpoint. Polarization by itself is of little importance at HF, because it becomes random after ionospheric reflection.

1.1. Impedance

The radiation resistance of an equilateral quad loop in free space is approximately 120 ohms. The radiation resistance for quad loops as a function of their height above ground is given in Fig 10-2. The impedance data were obtained by modeling an equilateral quad loop over three types of ground (very good, average, and very poor ground) using NEC. MININEC cannot be used for calculating loop impedances at low heights (see Par 2.7).

The reactance data can assist you in evaluating the influence of the antenna height on the resonant frequency. The loop antenna was first modeled in free space to be resonant at 3.75 MHz, and the reactance data was obtained with those loop dimensions.

For the vertically polarized quad loop, the resistive part of the impedance changes very little with the type of ground under the antenna. The reactance is influenced by the ground quality, especially at lower heights. For the horizontally polarized loop, the radiation resistance is noticeably influenced by the ground quality, especially at low heights. The same is true for the reactance.

1.2. Square Loop Patterns
1.2.1. Vertical polarization.

The vertically polarized quad loop, Fig 10-1B, can be considered as two shortened top-loaded vertical dipoles, spaced ¼-wavelength apart. Broadside radiation from the horizontal elements of the quad is canceled, because of the opposition of currents in the vertical legs. The wave angle in the broadside direction will be essentially the same as for either of the vertical members. The resulting radiation angle will depend on

the quality of the ground up to several wavelengths away from the antenna, as is the case with all vertically polarized antennas.

The quality of the reflecting ground will also influence the gain of the vertically polarized loop to a great extend. The quality of the ground is as important as it is for any other vertical antenna. This means that vertically polarized loops close to the ground will not work well over poor soil.

Fig 10-3 shows both the azimuth and elevation radiation patterns of a vertically polarized quad loop with a top height of 0.3 wavelength (bottom wire at approximately 0.04 wavelength). This is a very realistic situation, especially on 80 meters. The loop radiates an excellent low-angle wave (lobe peak at approximately 21 degrees) when operated over average ground. Over poorer ground, the wave angle would be closer to 30 degrees. The horizontal directivity, Fig 10-3C, is rather poor, and amounts to approximately 3.3 dB of side rejection at any wave angle.

1.2.2. Horizontal polarization.

A horizontally polarized quad loop antenna (two stacked short dipoles) produces a wave angle that is dependent on the height of the loop. The low horizontally polarized quad (top at 0.3 wavelength) radiates most of its energy right at or near the zenith angle.

Fig 10-4 shows directivity patterns for a horizontally polarized loop. The horizontal pattern, Fig 10-4C, is plotted for a wave angle of 30 degrees. At low wave angles (20 to 45 degrees), the horizontally polarized loop shows more front-to-side ratio (5 to 10 dB) than the vertically polarized rectangular loop.

1.2.3. Vertical versus horizontal polarization.

Vertically polarized loops should be used only where

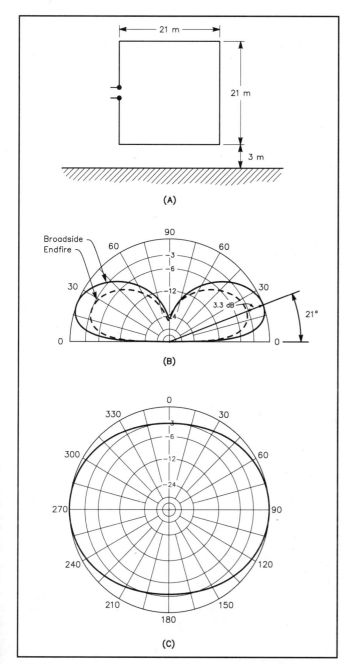

Fig 10-3—Shown at A is a square loop, with its elevation-plane pattern at B and azimuth pattern at C. The patterns are generated for good ground. The bottom wire is 0.0375 wavelength above ground (3 m or 10 ft on 80 meters). At C, the pattern is for a wave angle of 21 degrees.

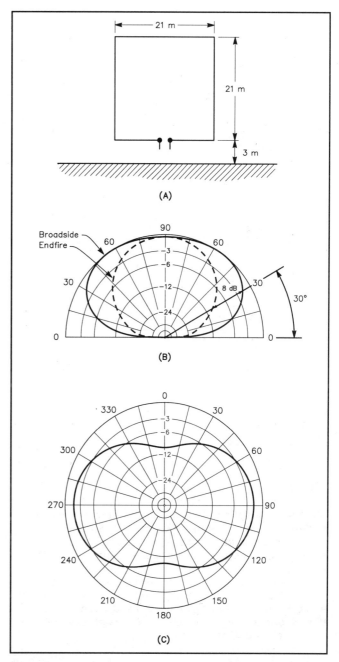

Fig 10-4—Azimuth and elevation patterns of the horizontally polarized quad loop at low height (bottom wire 0.0375 wavelength above ground). At a wave angle of 30 degrees the loop has a front-to-side ratio of approximately 8 dB.

very good ground conductivity is available. Installing radials under the loop does not pay off unless they are many wavelengths long. From Fig 10-5A we learn that the gain of the vertically polarized quad loop, as well as the wave angle, does not change very much as a function of the antenna height. This makes sense, as the vertically polarized loop is in the first place two phased verticals, each with its own radial. However, the gain is drastically influenced by the quality of the ground. At low heights, the gain difference between very poor ground and

very good ground is a solid 5 dB! The wave angle for the vertically polarized quad loop at a low height (bottom wire at 0.03 wavelength) varies from 25 degrees over very poor ground to 17 degrees over very good ground.

For the horizontally polarized quad loop, things are very different. The wave angle is very dependent on the antenna height, but not so much by the quality of the ground. At very low heights, the main wave angle varies between 50 and 60 degrees (but is rather constant all the way up to 90 degrees), but

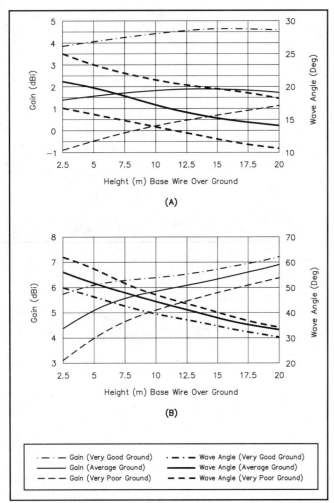

(A)

(B)

—·—·— Gain (Very Good Ground)	—··—··— Wave Angle (Very Good Ground)
—————— Gain (Average Ground)	—————— Wave Angle (Average Ground)
— — — — Gain (Very Poor Ground)	— — — — Wave Angle (Very Poor Ground)

Fig 10-5—Radiation angle and gain of the horizontally and the vertically polarized square loops at different heights over good ground. At A, for vertical polarization, and at B, for horizontal polarization. Note that the gain of the vertically polarized loop never exceeds 4.6 dBi, but its wave angle is low for any height (14 to 20 degrees). The horizontally polarized loop can exhibit a much higher gain provided the loop is very high. Modeling was done over average ground for a frequency of 3.75 MHz, using NEC.

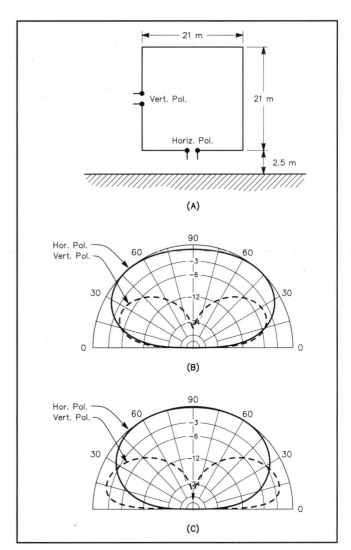

Fig 10-6—Superimposed (same dB scale) patterns for horizontally and vertically polarized square quad loops (shown at A) over very poor ground (B) and very good ground (C). In the vertical polarization mode the ground quality is of utmost importance, as it is with all verticals; see also Fig 10-14.

these are rather useless radiation angles for DX work.

As far as gain is concerned, there is a 2.5-dB gain difference between very good and very poor ground, which is only half the difference we found with the vertically polarized loop. Comparing the gain to the gain of the vertically polarized loop, we see that at very low antenna heights the gain is about 3-dB better than for the vertically polarized loop. But this gain exists at a high wave angle (50 to 90 degrees), while the vertically polarized loop at very low heights radiates at 17 to 25 degrees.

Fig 10-6 shows the vertical-plane radiation patterns for both types of quad loops over very poor ground and over very good ground on the same dB scale. For more details see Par 2.3.

1.3. A Rectangular Quad Loop

A rectangular quad loop, with unequal side dimensions,

can be used with very good results on the low bands. An impressive signal is generated by 5NØMVE from Nigeria with such a loop antenna. The single quad loop element is strung between two 30-meter (100 ft) high coconut trees, some 57 meters (190 ft) apart in the bushes of Nigeria. 5NØMVE uses this configuration and feeds the loop in the center of one of the vertical members. He first tried to feed it for horizontal polarization but he says it did not work well. The vertical and the horizontal radiation patterns for this quad loop over good ground are shown in Fig 10-7. The horizontal directivity is approximately 6 dB (front-to-side ratio).

I have analyzed the antenna. It is significant that even in free space, the impedance of the two varieties of this rectangular loop are not the same. When fed in the center of a short (27-m) side, the radiation resistance at resonance is 44 ohms. When fed in the center of one of the long (57-m) sides, the resistance is 215 ohms. Over real ground the feed-point imped-

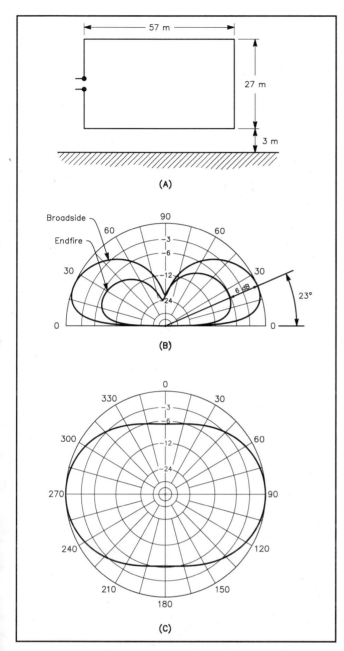

Fig 10-7—At A, a rectangular loop with its baseline approximately twice as long as the vertical height. At B and C, the vertical and horizontal radiation patterns, generated over good ground. The loop was dimensioned to be resonant at 1.83 MHz. The azimuth pattern at C is taken at a 23-degree wave angle.

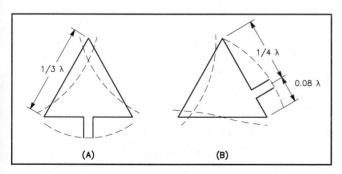

Fig 10-8—Current distribution for equilateral delta loops fed for (A) horizontal and (B) vertical polarization.

ance is different in both configurations as well; depending on the quality of the ground, the impedance varies between 40 and 90 ohms.

1.4. Loop Dimensions

The total length for a resonant loop is approximately 5 to 6% longer than the free-space wavelength.

1.5. Feeding the Quad Loop

The quad loop feed point is symmetrical, whether you feed the quad in the middle of the vertical or the horizontal wire. A balun must be used. Baluns are described in Chapter 6 on matching and feed lines.

Alternatively one could use open-wire feeders (450-ohm line). The open-wire-feeder alternative has the advantage of being a lightweight solution. With a tuner you will be able to cover a wide frequency spectrum with no compromises.

■ 2. DELTA LOOPS

Just as the inverted-V dipole has been described as the poor man's dipole, the delta loop can be called the poor man's quad loop. Because of its shape, the delta loop with the apex on top is a very popular antenna for the low bands; it needs only one support.

In free space the equilateral triangle produces the highest gain and the highest radiation resistance for a three-sided loop configuration. As we deviate from an equilateral triangle toward a triangle with a long baseline, the effective gain and the radiation resistance of the loop will decrease (bottom-corner-fed delta loop). In the extreme case (where the height of the triangle is reduced to zero), the loop has become a half-wavelength-long transmission line that is shorted at the end, which shows a zero-ohm input impedance (radiation resistance), and thus zero radiation (well-balanced open-wire line does not radiate).

Just as with the quad loop, we can switch from horizontal to vertical polarization by changing the position of the feed point on the loop. For horizontal polarization the loop is fed either at the center of the baseline or at the top of the loop. For vertical polarization the loop should be fed on one of the sloping sides, at ¼ wavelength from the apex of the delta. Fig 10-8 shows the current distribution in both cases.

2.1. Vertical Polarization

2.1.1. How it works.

Refer to Fig 10-9. In the vertical-polarization mode the delta loop can be seen as two sloping quarter-wave verticals (their apex touching at the top of the support), while the baseline (and the part of the sloper under the feed point) takes care of feeding the "other" sloper with the correct phase. The second sloping vertical is also fed via the top (both sloping verticals are connected at the top). This top connection can be left open without changing anything to the operation of the delta loop. The same is true for the baseline, where the middle of the baseline can be opened without changing anything. These two points are the high-impedance points of the antenna. Either the apex or the center of the baseline must be "shorted," however, in order to provide feed voltage to the

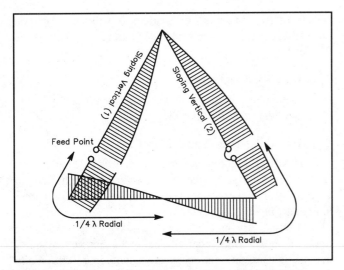

Fig 10-9—The delta loop can be seen as two quarter-wave sloping verticals, each using one radial. Because of the current distribution in the radials, the radiation from the radials is effectively canceled. Either point A or point B may be left open. One of the two must remain closed, however.

"other half" of the antenna. Normally we use a fully closed loop in the standard delta loop, although for single-band operation this is not strictly necessary.

Assume we construct the antenna with the center of the horizontal bottom wire open. Now we can see the two half baselines as two quarter-wave radials, one of which provides the necessary low-impedance point for connecting the shield of the coax. The other "radial" is connected to the bottom of the second sloping vertical, which is the other sloping wire of the delta loop.

This is similar to the situation encountered with a ¼-wave vertical using a single elevated radial (see Chapter 9 on vertical antennas). The current distribution in the two quarter-wave radials is such that all radiation from these radials is effectively canceled. The same situation exists with the voltage-fed T antenna (see Chapter 9), where we use a half-wave flat-top (equals two quarter-wave radials) to provide the necessary low-impedance point to raise the current maximum to the top of the T antenna.

The vertically polarized delta loop is really an array of two quarter-wave verticals, with the high-current points spaced 0.25 to 0.3 wavelength, and operating in phase. The fact that the tops of the verticals are close together does not influence the performance to a large degree. The reason is that the current near the apex of the delta is at a minimum (it is *current* that takes care of radiation!).

Considering a pair of phased verticals, we know from the study on verticals that the quality of the ground will be very important as to the efficient operation of the antenna:

• This does not mean that the delta loop requires radials. It has two elevated radials that are an integral part of the loop and take care of the return currents (radiation efficiency).

• As with all vertically polarized antennas, however, the qual-

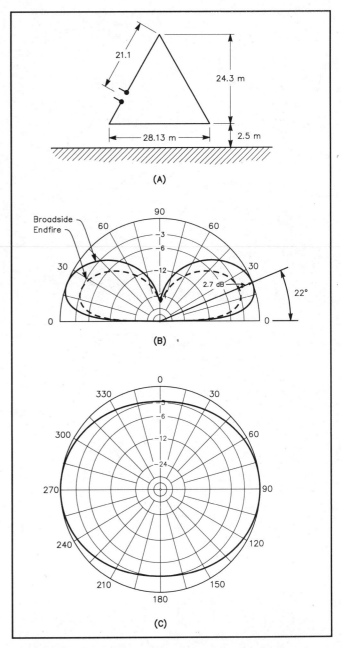

Fig 10-10—Configuration and radiation patterns for a vertically polarized equilateral delta loop antenna. The model was calculated over good ground, for a frequency of 3.8 MHz. The wave angle for the azimuth pattern at C is 22 degrees.

ity of the ground within a radius of several wavelengths will determine the low-angle radiation of the loop antenna (reflection efficiency).

Refer to Chapter 9 on verticals for more details on this topic (see pseudo-Brewster angle).

2.1.2. Radiation patterns.

2.1.2.1. *The equilateral triangle.*

Fig 10-10 shows the configuration as well as both the broadside and the end-fire vertical radiation patterns of the

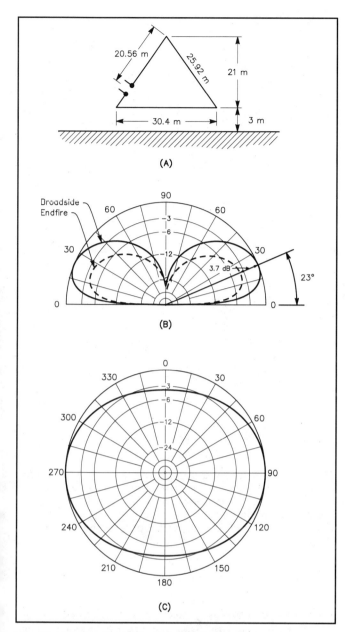

Fig 10-11—Configuration and radiation patterns for the "compressed" delta loop, which has a baseline slightly longer than the sloping wires. The model was dimensioned for 3.8 MHz to have an apex height of 24 m (79 ft) and a bottom wire height of 3 m (10 ft). Calculations are done over good ground at a frequency of 3.8 MHz. The azimuth pattern at C is for a wave angle of 23 degrees. Note that the correct feed point remains at ¼ wavelength from the apex of the loop.

vertically polarized equilateral-triangle delta loop antenna. The model was constructed for a frequency of 3.75 MHz. The baseline is 2.5 m (8 ft) above ground, which puts the apex at 26.83 m (88 ft). The model was made over good ground. The delta loop shows nearly 3 dB front-to-side ratio at the main wave angle of 22 degrees. With average ground the gain is 1.3 dBi.

2.1.2.2. *The compressed delta loop.*

Fig 10-11 shows an 80-meter delta loop with the apex at

24 m (79 ft) and the baseline at 3 m (10 ft). This delta loop has a long baseline of 30.4 m (99.7 ft). The feed point is again located ¼ wavelength from the apex.

The front-to-side ratio is 3.8 dB. The gain with average ground is 1.6 dBi. In free space the equilateral triangle gives a higher gain than the "flat" delta. Over real ground and in the vertically polarized mode, the gain of the flat delta loop is 0.3 dB better than the equilateral delta, however. This must be explained through the fact that the longer baseline yields a wider separation of the two "sloping" verticals, yielding a slightly higher gain.

For a 100-kHz bandwidth the SWR raises to 1.4:1 at the edges. The 2:1-SWR bandwidth is approximately 175 kHz.

2.1.2.3. *The bottom-corner-fed delta loop.*

Fig 10-12 shows the layout of the delta loop being fed in one of the two bottom corners. The antenna has the same apex and baseline height as the loop described in Par 2.1.2.2. Because of the "incorrect" location of the feed point, cancellation of radiation from the base wire (the two "radials") is not 100% effective, resulting in a significant horizontally polarized radiation component. The total field has a very uniform gain coverage (within 1 dB) from 25 degrees to 90 degrees. This may be a disadvantage as to the rejection of high-angle signals when operating DX at low wave angles.

Due to the incorrect feed-point location, the end-fire radiation (radiation in line with the loop) has become asymmetrical. The horizontal radiation pattern shown in Fig 10-12D is for a wave angle of 29 degrees. Note the deep side null (nearly 20 dB) at that wave angle. The loop actually radiates maximum signal approximately 18 degrees off the broadside direction.

All this is to explain that this feed-point configuration (in the corner of the compressed loop) is to be avoided, as it really deteriorates the performance of the antenna.

2.2. Horizontal Polarization
2.2.1. How it works.

In the horizontal polarization mode, the delta loop can be seen as a stack of an inverted-V dipole on top of a very low dipole with its ends bent upward to connect to the tips of the inverted V. The loop will act as any horizontally polarized antenna over real ground; its wave angle will depend on the height of the antenna over the ground.

2.2.2. Radiation patterns.

Fig 10-13 shows the vertical and the horizontal radiation patterns for an equilateral-triangle delta loop, fed at the center of the bottom wire. As anticipated, the radiation is maximum at zenith. The front-to-side ratio is around 3 dB for a 15- to 45-degree wave angle. Over average ground the gain is 2.5 dBi.

Looking at the pattern shape, one would be tempted to say that this antenna is no good for DX. So far we have only spoken about relative patterns. What about real gain figures from the vertically and the horizontally polarized delta loops?

2.3. Vertical versus Horizontal Polarization

Fig 10-14 shows the superimposed elevation patterns for

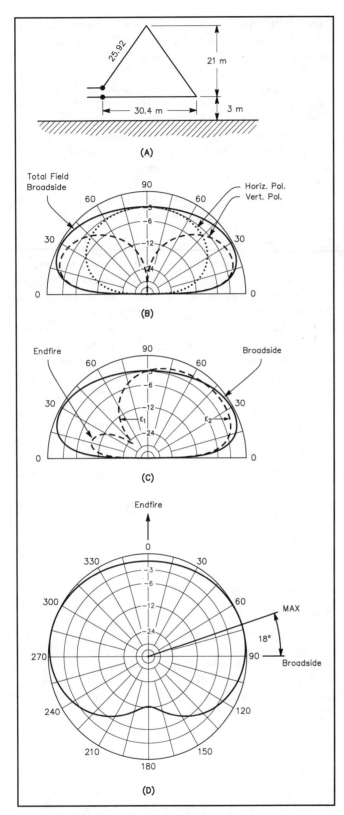

Fig 10-12—Configuration and radiation patterns for the compressed delta loop of Fig 10-11 when fed in one of the bottom corners at a frequency of 3.75 MHz. Improper cancellation of radiation from the horizontal wire produces a very strong high-angle horizontally polarized component. The delta loop now also shows a strange horizontal directivity pattern (at D), the shape of which is very sensitive to slight frequency deviations. This pattern is for a wave angle of 29 degrees.

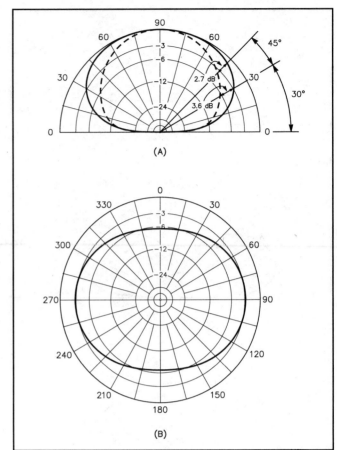

Fig 10-13—Vertical and horizontal radiation patterns for an 80-meter equilateral delta loop fed for horizontal polarization, with the bottom wire at 3 m (10 ft). The radiation is essentially at very high angles, comparable to what can be obtained from a dipole or inverted-V dipole at the same (apex) height.

vertically and horizontally polarized low-height equilateral-triangle delta loops over two different types of ground (same dB scale).

MININEC-based modeling programs cannot be used to compute the gain figures of these loops, as impedance and gain figures are incorrect for very low antenna heights (see Par 2).

Over Very Poor Ground

The horizontally polarized delta loop is better than the vertically polarized loop for all wave angles above 35 degrees. Below 35 degrees the vertically polarized loop takes over, but quite marginally. The maximum gain of the vertically and the horizontally polarized loops differs by only 2 dB, but the big difference is that for the horizontally polarized loop, the gain occurs at almost 90 degrees, while for the vertically polarized loop it occurs at 25 degrees.

One might argue that for a 30-degree wave angle, the horizontally polarized loop is as good as the vertically polarized loop. It is clear, however, that the vertically polarized antenna gives good high-angle rejection (rejection against local signals), while the horizontally polarized loop will not.

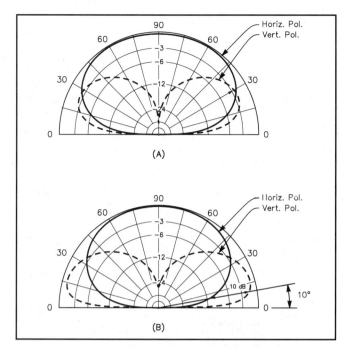

Fig 10-14—Radiation patterns of vertically and horizontally polarized delta loops on the same dB scale. At A, over very poor ground, and at B, over very good ground. These patterns illustrate the tremendous importance of ground conductivity with vertically polarized antennas. Over better ground, the vertically polarized loop performs much better at low radiation angles, while over both good and poor ground the vertically polarized loop gives good discrimination against high-angle radiation. This is not the case for the horizontally polarized loop.

Over Very Good Ground

The same thing that happens with any vertical happens with our vertically polarized delta: The performance at low angles is greatly improved with good ground. The vertically polarized loop is still better at any wave angle under 30 degrees

than when horizontally polarized. At a 10-degree radiation angle the difference is as high as 10 dB.

Conclusion

Over very poor ground, the vertically polarized loops do not provide much better low-angle radiation when compared to the horizontally polarized loops. They have the advantage of giving substantial rejection at high angles, however.

Over good ground, the vertically polarized loop will give up to 10-dB gain as compared to the horizontally polarized loop, in addition to its high-angle rejection.

2.4. Dimensions

The resonant length of the resonant delta loop is approximately 1.05 to 1.06 wavelength. When putting up a loop, cut the wire at 1.06 wavelength, check the frequency of minimum SWR (it is always the resonant frequency), and trim the length.

The wavelength is given by

$$\lambda_{meters} = \frac{299.8}{f_{MHz}}$$

or

$$\lambda_{feet} = \frac{983.59}{f_{MHz}}$$

2.5. Feeding the Delta Loop

The feed point of the delta loop in free space is symmetrical. At high heights above ground the loop feed point is to be considered as symmetrical, especially when we feed the loop in the center of the bottom line (or apex), because of its full symmetry with respect to the ground.

Fig 10-15 shows the radiation resistance and reactance for both the horizontally and the vertically polarized equilateral delta loops as a function of height above ground. At low heights, when fed for vertical polarization, the feed point is to be considered as asymmetric, whereby the "cold" point is the

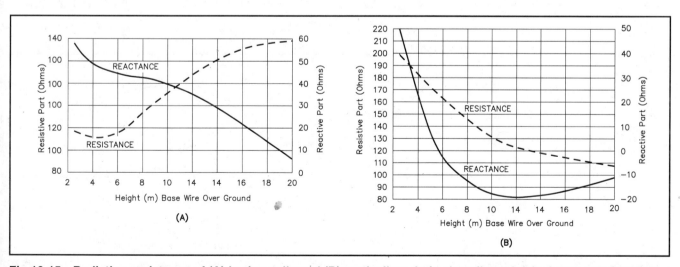

Fig 10-15—Radiation resistance of (A) horizontally and (B) vertically polarized equilateral delta loops as a function of height above average ground. The delta loop was first dimensioned to be resonant in free space (reactance equal zero). Those dimensions were then used for calculating the impedance over real ground. Modeling was done at 3.75 MHz over good ground, using NEC.

point to which the "radials" are connected. The center conductor of a coax feed line goes to the sloping vertical section. Many users have, however, used (symmetric) open-wire line to feed the vertically polarized loop (eg, 450-ohm line).

Most practical delta loops show a feed-point impedance between 50 and 100 ohms, depending on the exact geometry and coupling to other antennas. In most cases the feed point can be reached, so it is quite easy to measure the feed-point impedance using, eg, a good-quality noise bridge connected directly to the antenna terminals. If the impedance is much higher than 100 ohms (equilateral triangle), feeding via a 450-ohm open-wire feeder may be warranted. Alternatively, one could use an unun (unbalanced-to-unbalanced) transformer, which can be made to cover a very wide range of impedance ratios (see Chapter 6 on feed lines and matching). With somewhat compressed delta loops the feed-point impedance usually turns out between 50 and 100 ohms. Feeding can be done directly with a 50-ohm or a 70-ohm coaxial cable, or with a 50-ohm cable via a 70-ohm quarter-wave transformer (Z_{ant} = 100 ohms).

To keep RF off the feed line it is best to use a balun, although the feed point of the vertically polarized delta loop is not strictly symmetrical. A stack of toroidal cores on the feed line near the feed point, or a coiled-up length of transmission line (making an RF choke) will also be useful. For more details refer to Chapter 6 on feed lines and matching.

2.6. Gain and Radiation Angle

Fig 10-16 shows the gain and the main-lobe radiation angle for the equilateral delta loop at different heights. The values were obtained by modeling a 3.8-MHz loop over average ground using NEC.

2.7. Modeling Loops

Loops can be well modeled with MININEC when it comes to radiation pattern generation. Because of the inherent acute angles at the corners of the delta loop, special attention must be paid as far as the length of the wire segments near the corners. Wire segments that are too long near wire junctions

with acute angles will cause pulse overlap (the total conductor will look shorter than it actually is). The wire segments need to be short enough in order to obtain reliable impedance results. Wire segments of 20 cm (8 in.) length are in order for an 80-meter delta loop if accurate results are required. To limit the total number of pulses, the segment-length tapering technique can be used: The segments are shortest near the wire junction, and get gradually longer away from the junction. ELNEC has a special provision which automatically generates tapered wire segments (Ref 678).

At low heights (bottom of the antenna below approximately 0.2 wavelength), the gain and impedance figures are incorrect. The gain is too high, and the impedance too low. This is because MININEC calculates using a perfect ground under the antenna. Correct gain and impedance calculations at such low heights require modeling with NEC. All gain and impedance data listed in this chapter were obtained by modeling with NEC.

■ 3. LOADED LOOPS

3.1 CW and SSB 80-Meter Coverage

An 80-meter delta loop or quad loop will not cover 3.5 through 3.8 MHz with an SWR below 2:1. There are two ways to achieve a wide-band coverage:

1) Feed the loop with an open-wire line (450 ohms to a matching network).

2) Use inductive or capacitive loading on the loop to lower its resonant frequency.

3.1.1. Inductive loading.

For the principles you can refer to the detailed treatment of short verticals in Chapter 9 on vertical antennas.

There are three principles:

• The required inductance of the loading devices (coils or stubs) to achieve a given downward shift of the resonant frequency will be minimum if the devices are inserted at the current maximum (similar to base loading with a vertical).

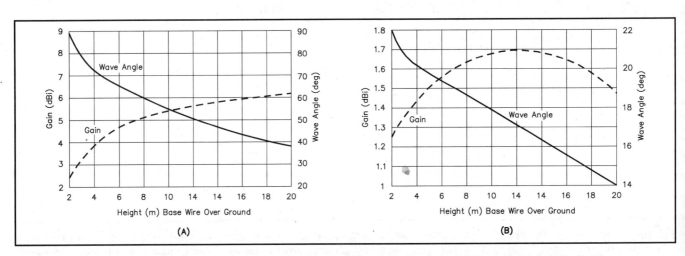

Fig 10-16—Gain and radiation angle of (A) horizontally and (B) vertically polarized equilateral delta loops as a function of the height above ground. Modeling was done at 3.75 MHz over average ground, using NEC.

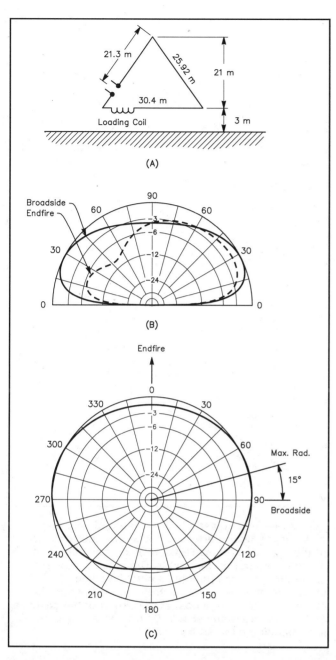

(A)

(B)

(C)

Fig 10-17—To shift the resonant frequency of the delta loop from 3.75 MHz to 3.55 MHz, a loading coil (or stub) is inserted in one bottom corner of the loop, near the feed point (A). This has eliminated the reactive component, but has also upset the symmetrical current distribution in the bottom wire. Vertical patterns are shown at B, and the horizontal pattern at C for a 27-degree wave angle. As with the loop shown in Fig 10-12, high-angle radiation (horizontal component) has appeared, and the horizontal pattern exhibits a notch in the endfire direction. Maximum radiation is again slightly off from the broadside direction.

At the current minimum, the inductive loading devices will not have any influence. This means that for a vertically polarized delta loop, the loading coil (or stub) cannot be inserted at the apex of the loop, nor in the middle of the bottom wire.

- Do not insert the loading devices in the radiating parts of the loop. Insert them in the part of which the radiation is canceled. For example, in a vertically polarized delta loop, the loading devices should be inserted in the bottom (horizontal) wire near the corners.
- Always keep the symmetry of the loop intact, including after having added a loading device.

From a practical (mechanical) point of view it is convenient to insert the loading coil (stub) in one of the bottom corners. Fig 10-17A shows the loaded compressed delta loop (same physical dimensions as the loop in Fig 10-11), where we have inserted a loading inductance in the bottom corner near the feed point.

A coil with a reactance of 240 ohms (on 3.5 MHz) or an inductance of 10.9 µH will resonate the delta on 3.5 MHz. The 100-kHz SWR is 1.5:1. Note again the high-angle fill in the broadside pattern (no longer symmetrical baseline configuration), as well as the asymmetrical front-to-side ratio of the loop. The 10.9-µH coil can be replaced with a shorted stub. The inductive reactance of the closed stub is given by

$$X_L = Z \tan \ell$$

where

Z = characteristic impedance of stub (transmission line)
ℓ = length of line, degrees
X_L = inductive reactance

From this, $\ell = \arctan \left(\dfrac{X_L}{Z} \right)$

In our example:

X_L = 240 ohms
Z = 450 ohms

$$\ell = \arctan \left(\frac{240}{450} \right) = 28 \text{ degrees}$$

Assuming a 95% velocity factor for the transmission line, we can calculate the physical length of the stub as follows:

$$\text{Wavelength} = \frac{299.8}{3.5} = 85.66 \text{ m} = 360 \text{ degrees}$$

$$\text{Length} = 85.66 \times 0.95 \times \frac{28}{360} = 6.33 \text{ m (20.76 ft)}$$

B and C of Fig 10-17 show the radiation patterns resulting from the insertion of a single stub (or coil) in one of the bottom corners of the delta loop. The insertion of the single loading device has broken the symmetry in the loop, and the bottom wire now radiates as well, upsetting the pattern of the loop.

This can be avoided by using two loading coils or stubs, located symmetrically about the center of the baseline. The example in Fig 10-18A shows two stubs, one located in each bottom corner of the loop. Each loading device has an inductive reactance of 142 ohms. For 3.5 MHz this is

$$\frac{142}{2\pi \times 3.5} = 6.46 \text{ µH}$$

A 450-ohm short-circuited line is 3.96 m (12.99 ft) long. The corresponding radiation patterns in Fig 10-18 are now

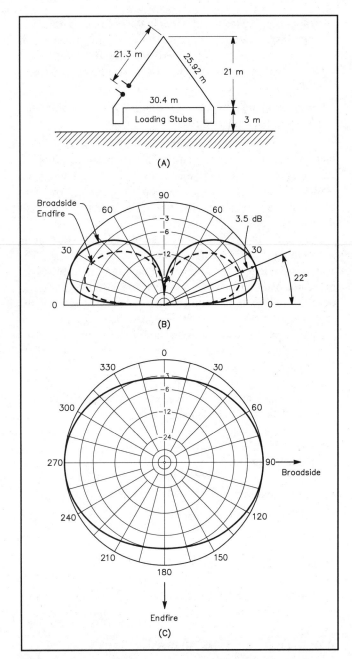

Fig 10-18—The correct way of loading the delta loop is to insert two loading coils (or stubs), one in each bottom corner. This keeps the current distribution in the baseline symmetrical, and preserves a "clean" radiation pattern in the horizontal as well as the vertical plane. The horizontal pattern at C is for a wave angle of 22 degrees.

fully symmetrical, and the annoying high-angle radiation is totally gone.

The 100-kHz SWR is 1.45:1. The 2:1 SWR bandwidth is 170 kHz.

Fig 10-19 shows the practical arrangement that can be used for installing the switchable stubs at the two delta-loop bottom corners. A small plastic box is mounted on a piece of epoxy printed-circuit-board material that is also part of the guying system. In the high-frequency position the stub should be completely isolated from the loop. Use a good-quality

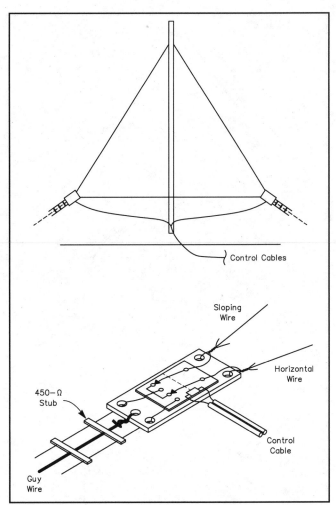

Fig 10-19—Small plastic boxes, mounted on a piece of glass-epoxy board, are mounted at both bottom corners of the loop, and house DPDT relays for switching the stubs in and out of the circuit. The stubs can be routed along the guy lines (guy lines must be made of insulating material). The control-voltage lines for the relays can be run to a post at the center of the baseline and from there to the shack. Do not install the control lines parallel to the stubs.

open-wire line and DPDT relay with ceramic insulation. The stub can be attached to the guy lines, which must be made of insulating material.

3.1.2. Capacitive loading.

We can also use capacitive loading in the same way that we employ capacitive loading on a vertical. Capacitance loading has the most effect when applied at a voltage antinode.

This capacitive loading is much easier to install than the inductive loading, and requires only a single-pole (high-voltage!) relay to switch the capacitance wires in or out of the circuit. **Keep the ends of the wires out of reach of people and animals, as extremely high voltage is present.**

Fig 10-20 shows different possibilities for capacitance loading on both horizontally and vertically polarized loops. If installed at the top of the delta loop as in Fig 10-20C, a 9-m (29.5 ft) long wire inside the loop will shift the 3.8-MHz loop

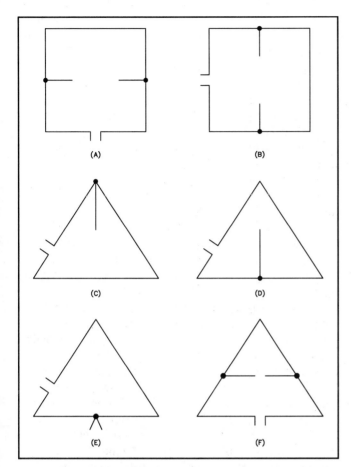

Fig 10-20—Various loop configurations and possible capacitance loading alternatives. Capacitance loading must be applied at the voltage maximum points of the loops to have maximum effectiveness. The loading wires carry very high voltages, and good insulators should be used in their installation.

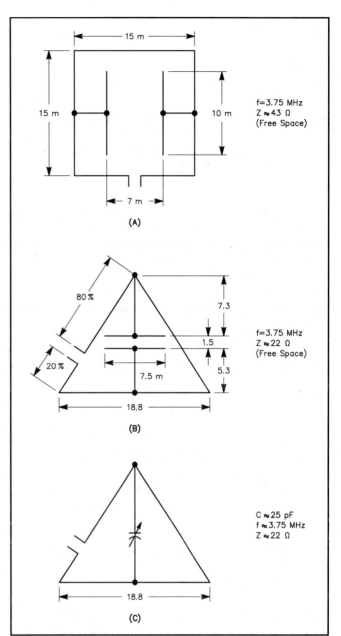

Fig 10-21—Capacitive loading can be used on loops of approximately ⅔ full size. See text for details.

from Fig 10-11 to resonance at 3.5 MHz. For installation at the center of the baseline, you can use a single wire (Fig 10-20D), or two wires in the configuration of an inverted V (Fig 10-20E). Several wires can be connected in parallel to increase the capacitance. (**Watch out, as there is very high voltage on those wires while transmitting!**)

The same symmetry guidelines should be applied as explained in Par 3.1 in order to preserve symmetrical current distribution.

Adjustment

Once the loop has been trimmed for resonance at the high end of the band, just clip a length of wire at the voltage point and check the SWR to see how much the resonant frequency has been lowered. It should not take you more than a few iterations to determine the correct wire length. If a single wire tuns out to require too much length, connect two or more wires in parallel, and fan out the wire ends to create a higher capacitance.

3.1.3. Bandwidth.

By using one of the above-mentioned loading methods and a switching arrangement, a loop can be made that covers the entire 80-m band with an SWR below 2:1.

3.2. Reduced-Size Loops

Reduced-size loops have been described in amateur literature (Ref 1115, 1116, 1121, 1129). Fig 10-21 shows some of the possibilities of applying capacitance loading to loops, whereby a substantial shift in frequency can be obtained. G3FPQ uses a reduced-size 2-element 80-m quad that makes use of capacitance-loaded square elements as shown in Fig 10-21A. The loading wires are supported by the fiberglass spreaders of the quad.

It is possible to lower the frequency by a factor of 1.5 with this method, without lowering the radiation resistance to an unacceptable value (a loop dimensioned for 5.7 MHz can be loaded down to 3.8 MHz).

The triangular loop can also be loaded in the same way, although the mechanical construction may be more complicated than with the square loop.

In principle, we can replace the parallel wires with a (variable) capacitor. This would allow us to tune the loop. The example in Fig 10-21C requires approximately 30 pF to shift the antenna from 5.7 to 3.8 MHz. Beware, however, that extremely high voltages exist across the capacitor. It would certainly not be over-engineering to use a 50 kV or higher capacitor for the application.

■ 4. BI-SQUARE

The bi-square antenna has a circumference of 2 wavelengths and is opened at a point opposite the feed point. A quad antenna can be considered as a pair of shortened dipoles with ¼-wavelength spacing. In a similar way, the bi-square can be considered as a lazy-H antenna with the ends folded vertically, as shown in Fig 10-22. Not many people are able to erect a bi-square antenna, as the dimensions involved on the low bands are quite large.

In free space the bi-square has 3-dB gain over two half-wave dipoles in phase (collinear), and almost 5 dB over a single half-wave dipole. Over real ground, with the bottom

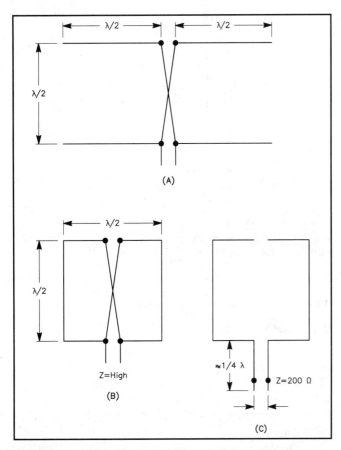

Fig 10-22—The bi-square antenna is a lazy-H antenna (two half-wave collinear dipoles, stacked ½ wavelength apart and fed in phase), with the ends of the dipoles bent down (or up) and connected together. The feed-point impedance is high and the array can best be fed via a quarter-wave stub arrangement.

wire ⅛ wave above ground (10 m or 33 ft for an 80-meter bi-square), the gain of the bi-square is the same as for the two half-wave dipoles in phase. The bottom two half waves do not contribute to low-angle radiation of the antenna.

The bi-square has the advantage over two half-waves in phase that the antenna does not exhibit the major high-angle sidelobe that is present with the collinear antenna when the height is over ½ wavelength. Fig 10-23 shows the radiation patterns of the bi-square and the collinear with the top of the antenna ⅝-wavelength high. Notice the cleaner low-angle pattern of the bi-square. Of course one could obtain almost the same result by lowering the collinear from ⅝ to ½ wavelength height!

The bi-square can be raised even higher in order to further lower the wave angle without introducing high-angle lobes, up to a top height of 2 wavelengths. At that height the wave angle is 14 degrees, without any secondary high-angle lobe. With the top at ⅝ wavelength, the wave angle is 26 degrees.

In order to exploit the advantages of the bi-square antenna, you need quite impressive heights on the low bands. N7UA is one of the few stations using such an antenna, and he is producing a most impressive signal on the long path into Europe on 80 meters. With a proper switching arrangement, the antenna can be made to operate as a full-wave loop on half the frequency (eg, 160 meters for an 80-meter bi-square).

The feed-point impedance is high (a few thousand ohms), and the recommended feed system consists of 600-ohm line with a stub to obtain a 200-ohm feed point. By using a 4:1 balun, a coaxial cable can be run from that point to the shack. Another alternative is to run the 600-ohm line all the way to the shack into an open-wire antenna tuner.

■ 5. THE HALF LOOP

The half loop was first described by Belrose, VE2CV (Ref 1120 and 1130). This antenna, unlike the half sloper, cannot be mounted on a tall tower supporting a quad or Yagi. If this was done, the half loop would shunt-feed RF to the tower and the radiation pattern would be upset. This can be avoided by decoupling the tower using a quarter-wave stub (Ref 1130). The half loop as shown in Fig 10-24 can be fed in different ways.

5.1. The Low-Angle Antenna

For low-angle radiation the feed point can be at the end of the sloping wire (with the tower grounded), or else at the base of the tower (with the end of the sloping wire grounded). The radiation pattern in both cases is identical. The front-to-side ratio is approximately 3 dB, and the antenna radiates best in the broadside direction (the direction perpendicular to the plane containing the vertical and the sloping wire).

There is some pattern distortion in the end-fire direction, but the horizontal radiation pattern is fairly omnidirectional. Most of the radiation is vertically polarized, so the antenna requires a good ground and radial system, as for any vertical antenna. As such, the half loop does not really belong to the family of large loop antennas, but as it is derived from the full-size loop, it is treated in this chapter rather than as a top-loaded short vertical.

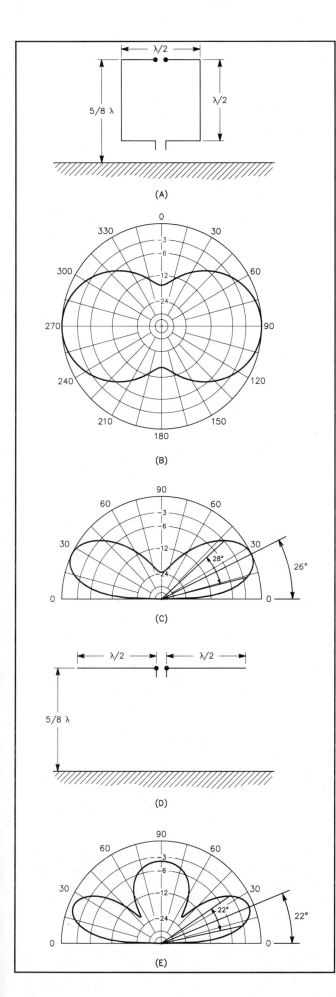

(A)

(B)

(C)

(D)

(E)

Fig 10-23—The bi-square antenna (A) and its radiation patterns, (B and C). The azimuth pattern at B is for a wave angle of 25 degrees. At D, two half waves in phase and at E, its radiation pattern. Note that for a top-wire height of ⅝ wave, the bi-square does not exhibit the annoying high-angle lobe of the collinear antenna.

The exact resonant frequency depends to a great extent on the ratio of the diameter of the vertical mast to the slant wire. The dimensions shown in Fig 10-24 are only indicative. Fine-tuning the dimensions will have to be done in the field.

5.2. High-Angle Operation

The half delta loop antenna can also be used as a high-angle antenna. In that case you must isolate the tower section from the ground (use a good insulator because it now will be at a high-impedance point) and feed the end of the sloping wire. Alternatively, you can feed the antenna between the end of the sloping wire and ground, while insulating the bottom of the tower from ground. Using the same dimensions that made the low-angle version resonant no longer produces resonance in these configurations.

Fig 10-25 shows the low-angle configurations with the radiation patterns. Note that the alternative where the end of the slant wire is fed against ground produces much more high-angle radiation than the alternative where the bottom end of the tower is fed. In both cases, the other end of the aerial is left floating (not connected to ground).

Dimensional configurations other than those shown in the relevant figures can be used as well, with, eg, a higher tower section and a shorter slant wire. If you move the end of the sloping wire farther away from the tower, you will need to decrease the height of the tower to keep resonance, and the radiation resistance will decrease. This will, of course, adversely influence the efficiency of the antenna. If the bottom of the sloping wire is moved toward the tower, the length of the vertical will have to be increased to preserve resonance. When the end of the sloping wire has been moved all the way to the base of the tower we have a quarter-wave vertical with a folded feed system. The feed-point impedance will depend on the spacing and the ratio of the tower diameter to the feed-wire diameter.

Compared to a loaded vertical, this antenna has the advantage of giving the added possibility for switching to a high-angle configuration. For a given height, the radiation resistance is slightly higher than for the top-loaded vertical, whereby there is no radiation from the top load. The sloping wire in this half-loop configuration adds somewhat to the vertical radiation, hence the increase (10% to 15%) in R_{rad}.

Being able to feed the antenna at the end of the sloping wire may also be an advantage: This point may be located at the transmitter location, so the sloping wire can be directly connected to an antenna tuner. This would enable wide-band coverage by simply retuning the antenna tuner. Switching from a high- to a low-angle antenna in that case consists of shorting the base of the tower to ground (for low-angle radiation).

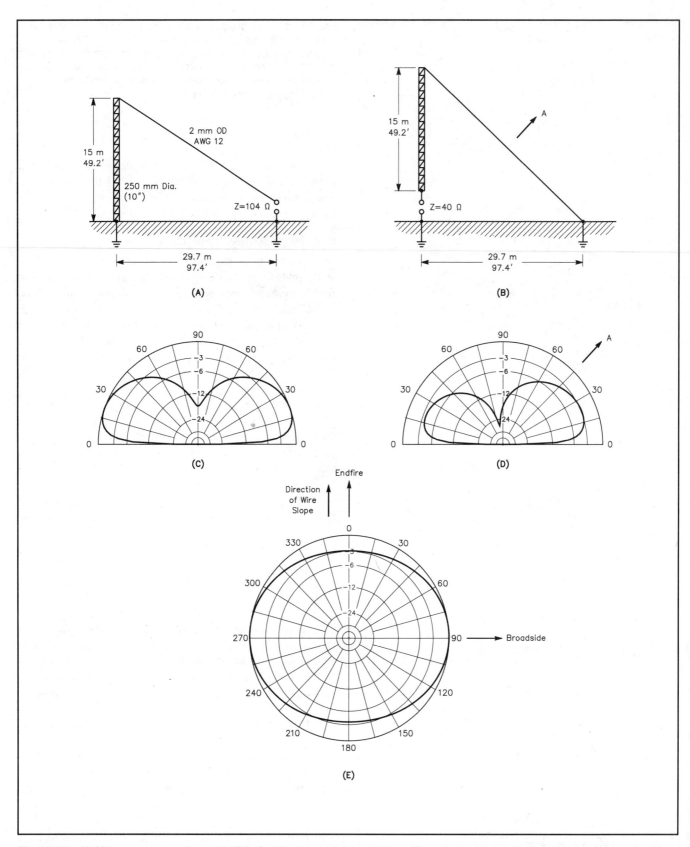

Fig 10-24—Half-loop antenna for 3.75 MHz fed for low-angle radiation. The antenna can be fed at either end against ground (A and B). The grounded end must be connected to a good ground system, as must the ground-return conductor of the feeder. Radials are essential for proper operation. Note that while the feed-point locations are different, the radiation patterns do not change.

C—Broadside vertical pattern.
D—Endfire vertical pattern.
E—Azimuth pattern, for a wave angle of 20 degrees.

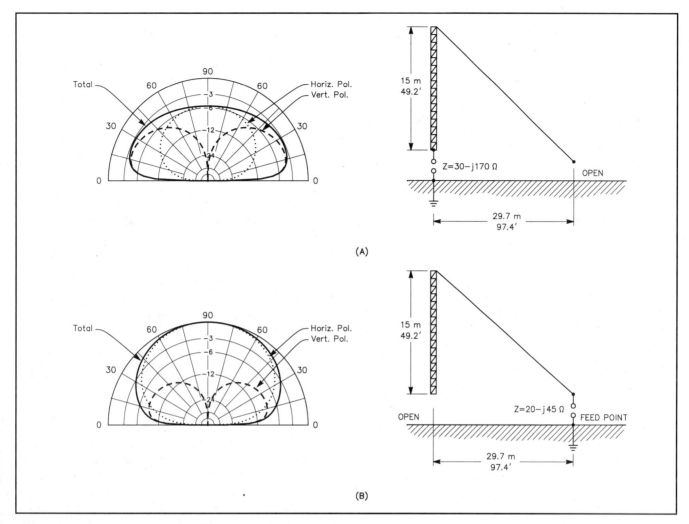

Fig 10-25—High-angle versions of the half delta loop antenna for 3.75 MHz. As with the low-angle version, the antenna can be fed at either end (against ground). The other end, however, must be left floating. The two different feed points produce different high-angle patterns as well as different feed-point impedances.

■ 6. THE HALF SLOPER

Although the so-called half sloper of Fig 10-26A may look like a half delta, it really does not belong with the loop antennas. As we will see, it is rather a loaded vertical with a specific matching system and current distribution.

Quarter-wave slopers are the typical result of ingenuity and inventiveness. Many DXers, short of space for putting up large, proven low-angle radiators, have found their half-slopers to be good performers. Of course they don't know how much better other antennas might be, as they have no room to try them. Others have reported that they could not get their half-sloper to resonate on the desired frequency (that's because they gave up trying before having found the proverbial needle in the haystack). Of course resonating and radiating are two completely different things. It's not because you cannot make the antenna resonant that it will not radiate well. Maybe you need a matching network?

To make a long story short, half slopers seem to be very unpredictable. There are a large number of parameters (different tower heights, different tower loading, different slope

angles, and so forth) that determine the resonant frequency and the feed-point impedance of the sloper.

Unlike the half delta loop, the half sloper is a very difficult antenna to analyze from a generic point of view, as each half sloper is different from any other.

Belrose, VE2CV, thoroughly analyzed the half sloper using scale models on a professional test range (Ref 647). His findings were confirmed by DeMaw, W1FB (Ref 650). Earlier, Atchley, W1CF, reported outstanding performance from his half sloper on 160 meters (Ref 645).

I have modeled an 80-meter half sloper using MININEC. After many hours of studying the influence of varying the many parameters (tower height, size of the top load, height of the attachment point, length of the sloper, angle of the sloper, ground characteristics, etc), I came to the following conclusion:

• The so-called half sloper is made up of a vertical and a slant wire. Both contribute to the radiation pattern. The radiation pattern is essentially omnidirectional. The low-angle radiation comes from the loaded tower, the high-angle radiation

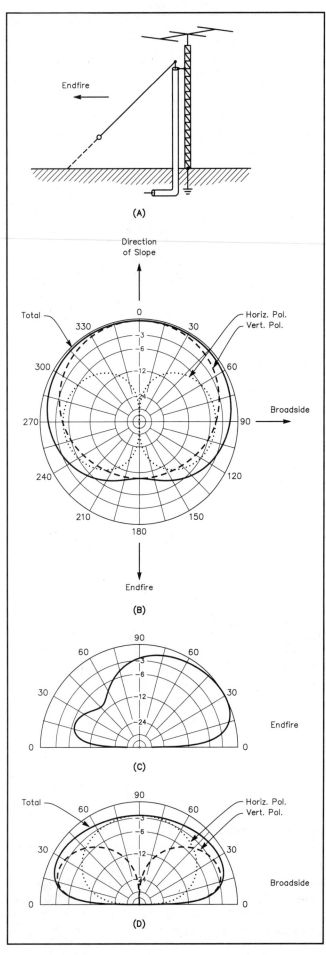

(A)

Direction of Slope

(B)

(C)

(D)

from the horizontal component of the slant wire. The antenna radiates a lot of high-angle signal (coming from the slant wire).

- Over poor ground the antenna has some front-to-back advantage in the direction of the slope, ranging from 10 to 15 dB at certain wave angles.
- Over good and excellent ground the F/B ratio is not more than a few dB.

In essence the half sloper is a top-loaded vertical, which is fed at a point along the tower where the combination of the tower impedance and the impedance presented by the sloping wire combine to a 50-ohm impedance (at least that's what we want). The sloping wire also acts as a sort of "radial" to which the "other" conductor of the feed line is connected (like radials on a vertical). In other words, the sloping wire is only a minor part of the antenna, a part that helps to create resonance as well as to match the feed line. Belrose (Ref 647) also recognized that the half sloper is effectively a top-loaded vertical. Fig 10-26 (B through D) shows the typical radiation patterns obtained with a half-sloper antenna.

While modeling the antenna, it was very critical to find a point on the tower and a sloper length and angle that give a good match to a 50-ohm line. The attachment point on the tower need not be at the top. It is not important how high it is, as you are not really interested in the radiation from the slant wire.

Changing the attachment point and the sloper length does not appreciably change the radiation pattern. This indicates that it is the tower (capacitively loaded with the Yagi) which does the bulk of the radiating. As the antenna mainly produces a vertically polarized wave, it requires a good ground system, at least as far as its performance as a low-angle radiator is concerned.

From my experience in spending a few nights modeling half slopers, I would highly recommend any prospective user to first model the antenna on MININEC. (ELNEC is just great for such a purpose, as it has the most user-friendly interface for multiple iterations.)

There is an interesting analysis by D. DeMaw (Ref 650). DeMaw correctly points out that the antenna requires a metal support, and that a tree or a wooden mast will not do. But he does not emphasize anywhere in his study that it is the metal support that is responsible for most of the desirable low-angle radiation. DeMaw, however, recognizes the necessity of a good ground system on the tower, which implicitly admits that the tower does the radiating. DeMaw also says, "The antenna is not resonant at the operating frequency," by which he means that the slant wire is not a quarter-wave long. This is again very confusing, as it seems to indicate that the slant wire is the

Fig 10-26—At A, a half-sloper mounted on an 18-m (59 ft) tower that supports a 3-element full-size 20-meter Yagi. See text for details. At B, the azimuth pattern for a 45-degree wave angle with vertically and horizontally polarized components, and at C and D, elevation patterns. The antenna shows a modest F/B ratio in the end-fire direction at a 45-degree wave angle.

antenna, which it is not. Describing the on-the-air results, DeMaw confirms what we have modeled: Due to its high-angle radiation, it outperforms the vertical for short- and medium-range contacts, while the vertical takes over at low angles for real DX contacts.

To summarize the performance of half slopers, it is worthwhile to note Belrose's comment, "If I had a single quarter-wave tower, I'd employ a full-wave delta loop, apex up, lower-corner fed, the best DX-type antenna I have modeled."

Of course, a delta loop still has a baseline of approximately 100 feet (on 80 meters), which is not the case with the half sloper. But the half sloper, like any vertical, requires radials in order to work well. It may look like the half sloper has a space advantage over many other low-band antennas, but this is only as true as for any vertical.

VERTICAL ARRAYS

■ 1. RADIATION PATTERNS
■ 2. ARRAY ELEMENTS
■ 3. DESIGNING AN ARRAY
  3.1. Modeling Arrays
  3.2. Getting the Right Current Magnitude and Phase
    3.2.1. The effects of mutual coupling.
    3.2.2. Calculating the drive impedances.
    3.2.3. Modeling the array.
  3.3. Designing a Feed System
    3.3.1 The wrong way.
    3.3.2. Christman method.
    3.3.3. Lewallen method.
    3.3.4. The modified Lewallen method.
    3.3.5. Collins method.
    3.3.6. Gehrke method.
    3.3.7. Choosing the best feed system.
    3.3.8. Tuning and measuring vertical arrays.
    3.3.9. Network component ratings.
■ 4. POPULAR ARRAYS
  4.1. The 90 Degree, ¼-wave Spacing Cardioid
    4.1.1. Feeding the array
  4.2. The 135 Degree, ⅛-wave Spacing Cardioid
    4.2.1. The modified Lewallen feed system
    4.2.2. Christman method
  4.3. Two-element in Phase with ¼-wave Spacing
    4.3.1. Feed system
  4.4. Three Elements in Phase, Half-wave Spacing, Binomial Current Distribution
    4.4.1. Current forcing feed system
  4.5. Two-Element Bidirectional End-Fire Array, ½-wave Spacing, Fed 180 Degrees out of Phase
    4.5.1. Current forcing feed system.
    4.5.2. Closer spacing.
  4.6. Three-element Quarter-wave Spaced Quadrature-fed End-fire Array
    4.6.1 The Lewallen feed system.
    4.6.2. The Collins feed system.
  4.7. Three Element Quarter-wave Spaced, End-fire Array, Non Quadrature Fed
    4.7.1. Modified Christman feed system.
    4.7.2. Current-forcing system.
  4.8. Three-element ⅛th-spaced, end-fire Array, Non Quadrature Fed

  4.9. Four-Square Array Arrays
    4.9.1. Quarter-wave-spaced square, quadrature fed.
      4.9.1.1. *The Lewallen feed method.*
      4.9.1.2. *The Collins feed method.*
    4.9.3. ⅛-wavelength-spaced square.
      4.9.3.1. *The Modified Lewallen method.*
  4.10. Other Square Arrays
    4.10.1. Two ¼ wave spaced cardioid arrays side by side, spaced wavelength, fed in phase.
    4.10.2. Two ⅛ wave spaced cardioid arrays side by side, spaced ¼ wavelength, fed in phase.
    4.10.3. Two ¼ wave spaced cardioid arrays side by side, spaced ¼ wavelength, fed in phase.
    4.10.4. Two ⅛ wave spaced cardioid arrays side by side, spaced ⅛ wavelength, fed in phase.
    4.10.5. Two ⅛ wave spaced cardioid arrays side by side, spaced ⅛ wavelength, fed in phase.
  4.11. Triangular Arrays
    4.11.1. The quadrature-fed triangular array.
      4.11.1.1. *First alternative.*
      4.11.1.2. *Second alternative.*
    4.11.2. Triangular array with improved phasing.
      4.11.2.1. *The first alternative.*
      4.11.2.2. *The second alternative.*
    4.11.3. Half-size triangular array.
      4.11.3.1. *The first alternative.*
      4.11.3.2. *The second alternative.*
  4.12. Conclusions

■ 5. ELEMENT CONSTRUCTION
  5.1. Mechanical Considerations
  5.2. Shunt versus Series Feeding
  5.3. A Four-Square with Wire Elements
  5.4. T-loaded Vertical Elements

■ 6. ARRAYS OF SLOPING VERTICALS
  6.1. The Square Array with Sloping ½-wave Dipoles
  6.2. The K8UR Sloping Dipole Square Array
  6.3. The 4-square Array with Sloping Quarter-wave Verticals

■ 7. CONCLUSIONS

VERTICAL 11 ARRAYS

If you want gain and directivity on one of the low bands and if you live in an area with good or excellent ground, an array made of vertical elements may be the answer, provided you have room for it.

If you are in the desert or live in a rocky area with poor electrical ground properties, you probably would do better looking at an array made of horizontally polarized elements or maybe a (shortened) Yagi or quad antenna if you want gain and efficiency.

Arrays made with vertical elements have the same requirements as single vertical antennas as far as ground quality is concerned. If you can take care of a good ground system for collecting element return currents (that is usually not a problem) and if you are fortunate to have good electrical ground in your area (that's harder if not impossible to control), then you are in the game for a well-performing vertical array. Before you decide to put one up, take the time to understand the mechanism of an array with all-fed elements.

Dipoles, monopoles and other antennas can be combined to form an array in order to obtain increased directivity in either the horizontal or the vertical plane (or both). Horizontal directivity is commonly sought on the HF bands, while at VHF, vertical directivity is often needed to concentrate RF energy close to the horizon (as with repeater antennas).

In this chapter I cover the subject of arrays made of elements which, by themselves, have an omnidirectional horizontal radiation pattern: vertical antennas.

■ 1. RADIATION PATTERNS

How the pattern is formed

Let us consider two verticals with spacing D and fed with a phase difference of a'. Fig 11-1 shows two vertical antennas (A and B). The paper represents the ground and both radiators are omnidirectional by definition. Rays a and a' from antenna A and B have a phase difference which depends on four factors:
1) Spacing.
2) The phase difference with which RF current is applied at the feed point of the antenna.
3) Angle of ray a and a' with respect to line AB.
4) The current magnitude in each element.

Consider the specific case where the spacing is ¼ wavelength and the phase difference is 90 degrees, as shown in Fig 11-1. Rays b and b' are clearly in phase (¼ wave due to spacing minus ¼ wave due to phase difference of 90 degrees). Similarly, d and d' are 180 degrees out of phase.

Rays a and a' will reinforce one another, but c and c' will

complement each other to a much lesser degree. The resulting radiation pattern is called a cardioid.

Directivity Over Perfect Ground

Fig 11-2 shows a range of radiation patterns obtained by different combinations of two monopoles over perfect ground and at zero wave angle. These directivity patterns are classics in every good antenna handbook. These are patterns for a theoretical zero wave angle.

Directivity Over Real Ground

Over real ground there is no radiation at zero wave angle.

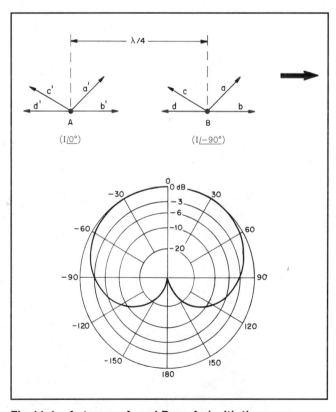

Fig 11-1—Antennas A and B are fed with the same current, but antenna A leads in phase by 90 degrees. Graphic analysis of a few rays shows that the array will radiate most power in the direction of rays B and B'where these rays, because of the physical separation and phase relationship between the elements, will show maximum reinforcement. The resultant radiation pattern is calculated at a 0-degree wave angle over ideal ground.

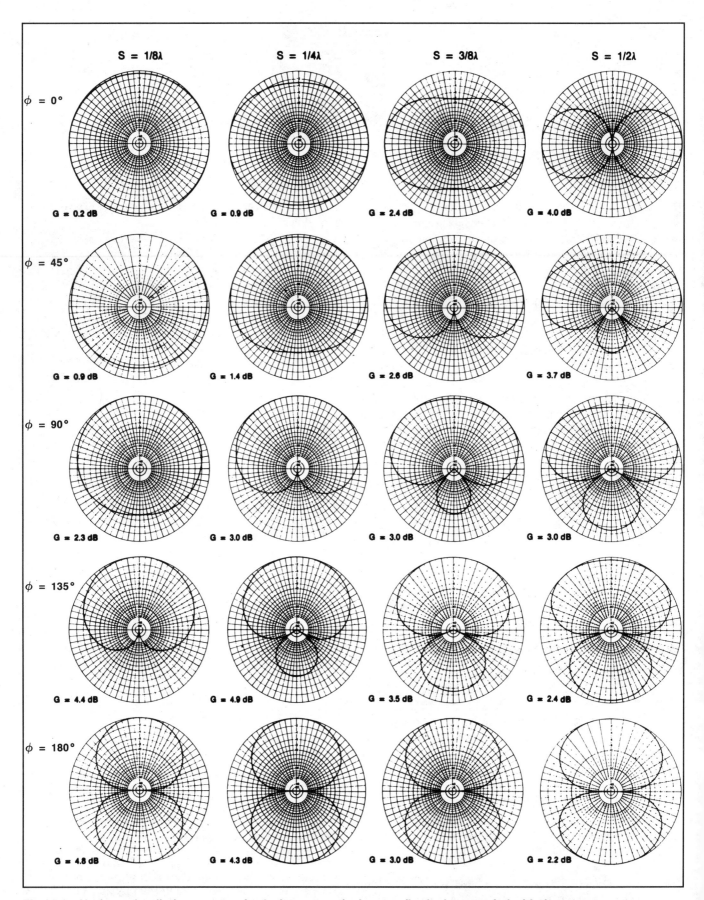

Fig 11-2—Horizontal radiation patterns for 2-element vertical arrays (both elements fed with the same current magnitude). The elements are in line with the vertical axis, and the top element is the one with the lagging phase angle. Patterns are for zero-degree wave angle over ideal ground. *(After The ARRL Antenna Book)*

All the effects that were described in detail in the chapter on verticals apply to arrays of verticals.

Direction of Firing

The rule is simple: An array always fires in the direction of the element with the lagging feed current.

■ 2. ARRAY ELEMENTS

In principle, the whole range of verticals described in the chapter on vertical antennas can be used as elements for a vertical array. Quarter-wave elements have gained a reputation of giving a reasonable match to a 50-ohm line, which is certainly true for single vertical antennas. In this chapter we will learn the reason why quarter-wave resonant verticals do not have a resistive 36-ohm feed-point impedance when operated in arrays (even assuming a perfect ground). Quarter-wave elements still remain a good choice as they have a reasonably high radiation resistance, which ensures good overall efficiency. On 160 meters, the elements could be top-loaded verticals as described in the chapter on verticals.

The design methodology for arrays given in par 3, as well as all the designs described in par 4, assume that all the array elements are physically identical elements, with a current distribution that is the same on each element. In practice this means that only elements with a length of *up to* ¼ wavelength should be used. The patterns given in par 4, do *not* apply if you use elements much longer than ¼ wave. They certainly do *not* apply for elements that are ½ or ⅝ wavelength long. If you want to use "long" elements, you will have to model the design using the particular element lengths (Ref. 959). This may be a problem if you want to use shunt-fed towers, carrying HF beams as elements for an array. With their top load, these towers are often much longer than ¼ wavelength.

■ 3. DESIGNING AN ARRAY

The radiation patterns as shown in Fig 11-2 give a good idea what can be obtained with different spacings and different current phase delays for a 2-element array. For arrays with more elements there are a number of popular classic designs. They are all covered in detail in this chapter.

A good array should meet the following specifications:
• High gain.
• Broad forward lobe (3 dB beamwidth).
• Good front-to-back ratio, also at high elevation angles.
• Ease of feeding.
• Ease of direction switching.

3.1. Modeling Arrays

MININEC is not directly suited for modeling arrays. Excitation of elements in MININEC is by voltage. In arrays we normally define *currents* for the RF sources. It is the current (magnitude and phase) in each element that determines the radiation pattern of the array. Therefore currents, rather than voltages, must be specified.

ELNEC, which is based on MININEC, has overcome this problem, and the user has the choice of defining the sources as voltage or current sources.

It is only if you want to do some modeling that includes the influence of a radial system plus the influence of a "poor" ground that the full-blown NEC program is required. Studies on elevated radial systems and on buried radials require NEC (NEC3 if buried radials are involved).

In this chapter we will compare arrays against a single vertical, *over an identical ground*. The influence of the radial system has been included in the form of an equivalent loss resistance in series with each element feed point.

3.2. Getting the Right Current Magnitude and Phase

There is a world of difference between designing an array on paper or with a computer modeling program and realizing it in real life. With single-element antennas (a single vertical, a dipole, etc) we do not have to bother about the feed current (magnitude and phase), as there is only one feed point anyway. With phased arrays things are vastly different.

First we will need to make up our mind which array to build. Once this is done, the problem will be how to achieve the right feed currents in all the elements (magnitude and angle).

When we analyze an array with a modeling program, we notice that the feed-point impedances of the elements change from the value for a single element. If the feed-point impedance of a single quarter-wave vertical is 36 ohms over perfect ground, it is always different from that value in an array. Why? Because of mutual coupling.

3.2.1. The effects of mutual coupling.

Few articles in Amateur Radio publications have addressed the problems associated with mutual coupling in designing a phased array and in making it work as it should. Gehrke, K2BT, wrote an outstanding series of articles on the design of phased arrays (Ref. 921-925, 927). These are highly recommended for anyone who is considering putting up phased arrays of verticals. Another excellent article by Christman, KB8I (Ref. 929), covers the same subject. The subject has been very well covered in the 15th and 16th editions of *The ARRL Antenna Book*, where R. Lewallen, W7EL, wrote a comprehensive contribution on arrays.

If we bring two resonant circuits into the vicinity of each other, mutual coupling will occur. This is the reason that antennas with parasitic elements work as they do. Horizontally polarized antennas with parasitically excited elements are widely used on the higher bands. On the low bands the proximity of the ground limits the amount of control the designer has on the current in each of the elements. Arrays of (vertical) antennas, where each element is fed, overcome this limitation, and in principle the designer has an unlimited control over all the design parameters. With so-called phased arrays, all elements are individually and physically excited by applying power to the elements via individual feed lines. Each feed line supplies current of the correct magnitude and phase.

There is one frequently overlooked major problem with arrays. As we have made up our minds to feed all elements, we too often assume (incorrectly) there is no mutual coupling or that it is so small that we can ignore it. Taking mutual coupling into account complicates life, as we now have two sources of applied power to the elements of the array: parasitic coupling plus direct feeding.

Self-Impedance

If a single quarter-wave vertical is erected, we know that the feed-point impedance will be $36 + j0$ ohms, assuming resonance, a perfect ground system, and a reasonable conductor diameter. In the context of our array we will call this the self-impedance of the element.

Coupled Impedance

If other elements are closely coupled to the original element, the impedance of the original element will change. Each of the other elements will couple energy into the original element and vice versa. The coupled impedance is the impedance of an element being influenced by one other element. Coupling from the coupled element results in a coupled impedance being totally different from the self-impedance in most cases.

Mutual Coupling

Mutual coupling is the phenomenon that relates to the interaction of closely spaced elements in an array, causing the coupled impedances of the elements to be different from the self-impedance.

Mutual Impedance

The mutual impedance is a term that defines unambiguously the effect of mutual coupling between a set of two antennas (elements).

Mutual impedance is an impedance that *cannot* be measured. It can *only* be calculated.

The calculated mutual impedances and driving impedances have been extensively covered by Gehrke, K2BT (Ref. 923).

Drive Impedance

In order to design a correct feed-system for an array, we must know the drive impedances of each of the elements, the elements being fed as required to produce the wanted radiation pattern (correct current magnitude and current angle).

3.2.2. Calculating the drive impedances.

You cannot measure mutual impedance. It must be calculated. Mutual impedances are calculated from measured self-impedances and drive impedances. Here is an example: We are constructing an array with three quarter-wave elements in a triangle, spaced ¼ wavelength apart. We erect the three elements and install the ground system. Then the following steps are carried out:

1) Open-circuit elements 2 and 3 (opening an element will effectively isolate it from the other elements in the case of quarter-wave elements; when using half-wave elements the elements must be grounded for maximum isolation, and open-circuited for maximum coupling).
2) Measure the self-impedance of element 1 (= Z11).
3) Ground element 2.

4) Measure the coupled impedance of element 1 with element 2 coupled (= Z1,2).
5) Open-circuit element 2.
6) Ground element 3.
7) Measure the coupled impedance of element 1 with element 3 coupled (= Z1,3).
8) Open-circuit element 3.
9) Open-circuit element 1.
10) Measure the self-impedance of element 2 (= Z22).
11) Ground element 3.
12) Measure the coupled impedance of element 2 with element 3 coupled (= Z2,3).
13) Open-circuit element 3.
14) Ground element 1.
15) Measure the coupled impedance of element 2 with element 1 coupled (= Z2,1).
16) Open-circuit element 1.
17) Open-circuit element 2.
18) Measure the self-impedance of element 3 (= Z33).
19) Ground element 2.
20) Measure the coupled impedance of element 3 with element 2 coupled (= Z3,2).
21) Open-circuit element 2.
22) Ground element 1.
23) Measure the coupled impedance of element 3 with element 1 coupled (= Z3,1).

This is the procedure for an array with three elements. The procedures for 2- and 4-element arrays can be derived from the above.

As you can see, measurement of coupling is done by pairs of elements. At step 15, we are measuring the effect of mutual coupling between elements 2 and 1, and it may be argued that this has already been done in step 4. It is useful, however, to make these measurements again in order to recheck the previous measurements and calculations. Calculated mutual couplings Z12 and Z21 (see below) using the Z1,2 and Z2,1 inputs should in theory be identical, and in practice should be within an ohm or so.

The self-impedances and the driving impedances of the different elements should match closely if the array is to be made switchable.

The mutual impedances can be calculated as follows:

$$Z12 = \pm\sqrt{Z22 \times (Z11 - Z1,2)}$$

$$Z21 = \pm\sqrt{Z11 \times (Z22 - Z2,1)}$$

$$Z13 = \pm\sqrt{Z33 \times (Z11 - Z1,3)}$$

$$Z31 = \pm\sqrt{Z11 \times (Z33 - Z3,1)}$$

$$Z23 = \pm\sqrt{Z33 \times (Z22 - Z2,3)}$$

$$Z32 = \pm\sqrt{Z22 \times (Z33 - Z3.2)}$$

It is obvious that if Z11 = Z22 and Z1,2 = Z2,1, then Z12 = Z21.

If the array is perfectly symmetrical (such as in a 2-element array or in a 3-element array with the elements in an equilateral triangle), all self-impedances will be identical

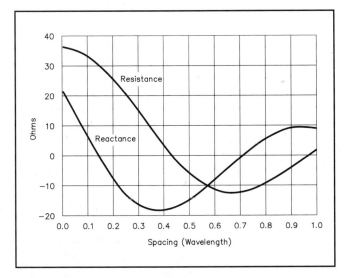

Fig 11-3—Mutual impedance for two quarter-wave elements. For shorter vertical elements (length between 0.1 and 0.25 wavelength), one can calculate the mutual impedance by multiplying the figures from the graph by the ratio $R_{rad}/36.6$ where R_{rad} = the radiation resistance of the short vertical.

($Z11 = Z22 = Z33$), and all driving impedances as well ($Z2,1 = Z1,2 = Z3,1 = Z1,3 = Z2,3 = Z3,2$). Consequently, all mutual impedances will be identical as well ($Z12 = Z21 = Z31 = Z13 = Z23 = Z32$). In practice, the values of the mutual impedances will vary slightly, even when good care is taken to obtain maximum symmetry.

Because all impedances are complex values (having real and imaginary components), the mathematics involved are difficult.

The MUTUAL IMPEDANCE AND DRIVING IMPEDANCE software module of the NEW LOW BAND SOFTWARE will do all the calculations in seconds. No need to bother with complex algebra. Just answer the questions on the screen.

Fig 11-3 shows the mutual impedance to be expected for quarter-wave elements at spacings from 0 to 1.0 wavelength. The resistance and reactance values vary with element separation as a damped sine wave, starting at zero separation with both signs positive. At about 0.10 to 0.15 wavelength spacing, the reactance sign changes from + to –. This is important to know in order to assign the correct sign to the reactive value (obtained via a square root).

Gehrke, K2BT emphasizes that the designer should actually measure the impedances and not take them from tables. Some methods of doing this are described in Ref. 923. The published tables show ballpark figures, enabling you to verify the square-root sign of your calculated results.

After calculating the mutual impedances, the drive impedances can be calculated, taking into account the drive current (amplitude and phase). The driving-point impedances are given by

$$Zn = \frac{I1}{In} \times Zn1 + \frac{I2}{In} \times Zn2 + \frac{I3}{In} \times Zn3 + \ldots + \frac{In}{In} \times Znn$$

where n is the total number of elements. The number of equations is n. The above formula is for the nth element. Note also that $Z12 = Z21$ and $Z13 = Z31$, etc.

The above-mentioned program module performs the rather complex driving-point impedance calculations for arrays with up to 4 elements. The required inputs are:

1) The number of elements.
2) The driving current and phase for each element.
3) The mutual impedances for all element pairs.

The outputs are the driving-point impedances Z1 through Zn.

Design Example

Let us take the example of an array consisting of two quarter-wave-long verticals, spaced a quarter wavelength apart and fed with equal magnitude currents, with the current in element 2 lagging the current in element 1 by 90 degrees. This is the most common end-fire configuration with a cardioid pattern.

Self-Impedance

The quarter-wave long elements of such an array are assumed to have a self-impedance of 36.4 ohms over a perfect ground. A nearly perfect ground system consists of at least 120 half-wave radials (see chapter on vertical antennas). For example, a system with only 60 radials may show a self-impedance on the order of 40 ohms.

Mutual Impedance

The mutual impedances were calculated with the above-mentioned computer program: $Z12 = Z21 = 20 - j15$ ohms. From the mutual impedance curves in Fig 11-3 it is clear that the minus sign is the correct sign for the reactive part of the impedance.

Drive Impedance

The same software module calculates the drive impedances (also called feed-point impedances) of the two elements.

$Z1 = 51 + j20$ ohms for the –90-degree element.
$Z2 = 21 - j20$ ohms for the 0-degree element

We have now calculated the impedance of each element of the array, the array being fed with the current (magnitude and phase) as set out. We have used impedances that we have measured; we are not working with theoretical impedances.

3.2.3. Modeling the array.

As MININEC does not allow you to specify the element excitation as a feed current (but only as a feed voltage), it is not directly suited to do array modeling. ELNEC, which is based on MININEC, provides the possibility of specifying feed currents and is therefore very well suited for modeling arrays. As the MININEC based programs do not take into account "real ground" for calculating near-field and feed-point impedances, to be accurate we must add some series resistance (the equivalent loss resistance for the radial system) in series with the antenna feed point. We can, eg, simulate the effect of a

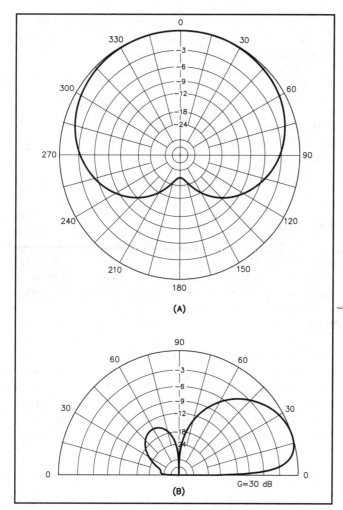

Fig 11-4—Vertical and horizontal radiation patterns for the 2-element cardioid array, spaced 90 degrees and fed with 90 degrees phase difference. The pattern was calculated for very good ground with a radial system consisting of 120 radials, each 0.4 wavelength long (the equivalent ground resistance is 2 ohms). The gain is 3.0 dB as compared to a single vertical over the same ground and radial system. The horizontal pattern at A is for an elevation angle of 19 degrees.

radial system consisting of 60 quarter-wave radials by inserting 4 ohms in series with the feed point of each antenna.

Modeling the cardioid antenna over a perfect ground system, ELNEC comes up with the following impedances:

Z1 = 50.9 + j18.4 ohms
Z2 = 19.2 − j18.4 ohms

These are very close to the values worked out with the NEW LOW BAND SOFTWARE. The vertical and the horizontal radiation patterns for the 2-element cardioid array are shown in Fig 11-4.

3.3. Designing a Feed System

The challenge now is to design a feed system that will supply the right current to each of the array elements. As we now know the current requirements as well as the drive-impedance data for each element of the array, we have all the required inputs to design a correct feed system.

Each element will need to be supplied power with its own feed line. In a driven array each element gets power or possibly delivers power. During calculations we will sometimes encounter a negative feed-point impedance which means the element is actually delivering power into the feed network. If the element impedance is zero, this means that the element can be shorted to ground. It then acts as a parasitic element.

Eventually all the feed lines will be connected to a common point, which will be the common feed point for the entire array. You can only connect feed lines in parallel if the voltages on the feed lines (at that point) are identical (in magnitude and phase)—the same as with ac power!

Designing a feed system consists of calculating the feed lines (impedance, length) as well as the component values of networks used in the feed system, so that the voltages at the input ends of the lines are identical. It is as simple as that.

The ARRL has published the original (1982) work by Lewallen, W7EL, in the latest editions of *The ARRL Antenna Book*. This material is a must for every potential array builder. However, there are other feed methods than the Lewallen method.

3.3.1. The wrong way.

In just about all cases, the drive impedance of each element will be different from the characteristic impedance of the feed line. This means that there will be standing waves on the line. This has the following consequences:

• The impedance, voltage and current will be different in each point of the feed line.
• The current and voltage phase shift is *not* proportional to the feed line length, except for a few special cases (eg, a half-wave-long feed line).

This means that if we feed these elements with 50-ohm coaxial cable, we cannot simply use lengths of feed line as delay lines by making the line length in degrees equal to the desired delay in degrees. In the past we have seen arrays where a 90-degree-long coax line was inserted in one of the feed lines to an element to create a 90-degree antenna current phase shift. Let us take the example of the 2-element cardioid array (as described above) and see what happens (see Fig 11-5).

We run two 90-degree-long coax cables to a common point. Using the COAX TRANSFORMER/SMITH CHART software module, we calculate the impedances at the end of those lines (I took RG-213 with 0.35 dB attenuation per 100 ft at 3.5 MHz). The array element feed impedances (including 2 ohms of equivalent ground loss resistance) are:

Z1 = 51 + j20 ohms

I1 = 1 $\angle - 90°$

E1 = 54.8 $\angle - 68.6°$

Z2 = 21 − j20 ohms

I2 = 1 $\angle 0°$

E2 = 29 $\angle - 43.6°$

At the end of the 90-degree-long RG-213 feed lines the impedances (and voltages) become:

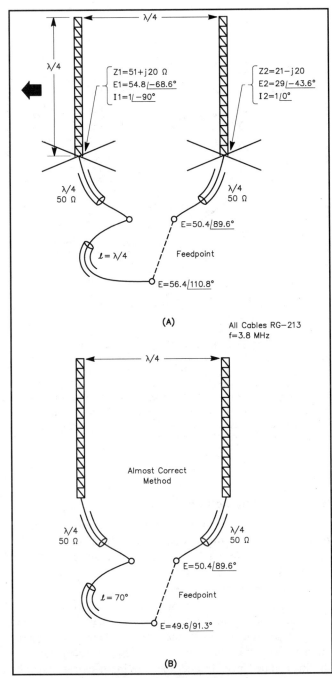

Fig 11-5—At A, the incorrect way of feeding a 2-element cardioid array (90-degree phase, 90-degree spacing). Note that the voltages at the input ends of the two feed lines are not identical. In B we see the same system with a 70-degree-long phasing line, which now produces almost correct voltages. The F/B ratio of existing installations will jump up by 10 or 15 dB, just by changing the line length from 90 to 73 degrees.

$Z1' = 42.81 - j16.18$ ohms

$E1' = 50.89 \angle 0.39°$

$I1' = 1.11 \angle 21.09°$

$Z2' = 63.1 + j56.94$ ohms

$E2' = 50.37 \angle 89.61°$

$I2' = 0.59 \angle 47.54°$

If we make the line to the lagging element 180 degrees long (plus the extra 90 degrees for obtaining an extra 90-degree phase shift), we end up with:

$Z1'' = 51.18 + j18.64$ ohms

$E1'' = 56.42 \angle 110.77°$

$I1'' = 1.04 \angle 90.76°$

We see already that E2' and E1'' are not identical. This means we cannot connect the lines in parallel at those points without upsetting the antenna current (magnitude and phase).

From the above voltages we see that the extra 90-degree line created an actual current phase delay of $90.76° - 21.09° = 68.67$ degrees, and not 90 degrees as required.

The software module IMPEDANCES, CURRENTS AND VOLTAGES ALONG FEED LINES is ideally suited for analyzing this phenomenon. Look at the values of voltage and current as you scan along the line, and remember we want the right current phase shift and we want the same voltage where we connect the feed lines in parallel.

If you have such a feed system, do not despair. Simply by shortening the phasing line from 90 to 70 degrees, you can obtain an almost perfect feed system. (See Fig 11-5.)

3.3.2. Christman Method.

In the Christman (KB8I) method (Ref. 929), we scan the feed lines to the different elements looking for points where the voltages are identical. If we find such points, we connect them together. It's really as simple as that. Whatever the length of the lines are, provided you have the right current magnitude and phase at the input ends of the lines, you can always connect two points with identical voltages in parallel. That's also where you feed the entire array.

Christman makes very clever use of the transformation characteristics of the feed lines. We know that on a feed line with SWR, voltage, current and impedance are different in every point of the line.

The question is now, "Are there points with identical voltage to be found on all of the feed lines?" and "Are the points located conveniently; in other words are the feed lines long enough to be joined?" This has to be examined case by case.

It must be said that we cannot apply the Christman method in all cases. I have encountered situations where identical voltage points along the feed lines could not be found.

The software module, IMPEDANCE, CURRENT AND VOLTAGE ALONG FEED LINES, which is part of the NEW LOW BAND SOFTWARE, can provide a printout of the voltages along the feed lines. The required inputs are:

• Feed-line impedance.
• Driving-point impedances (R and X).
• Current magnitude and phase.

Continuing with the above example of a 2-element configuration (90-degree spacing, 90-degree phase difference, equal currents, cardioid pattern), we find:

$E1 = (155 \text{ degrees from antenna element}) = 47.28 \angle 86.1°$

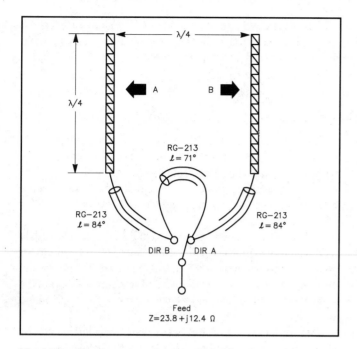

Fig 11-6—Feed system for the 2-element quarter-wave-spaced cardioid array, fed 90 degrees out of phase. Note that the two feed lines are 84 degrees long (not 90 degrees), and that the "90-degree phasing line" is actually 71 electrical degrees in length. The impedance at the connection point of the two lines is 23.8 + j12.4 ohms (representing an SWR of 2.3:1 in 50-ohm line), so some form of matching network is desirable.

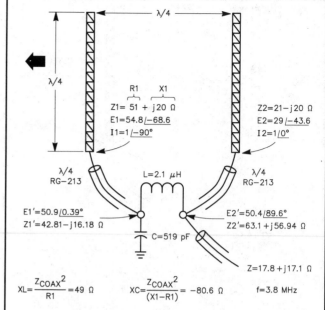

Fig 11-7—The Lewallen (W7EL) feed method for quadrature-fed arrays as applied to the 2-element cardioid (90-degree spacing, 90-degree phasing). Note the voltage magnitudes and phase angles at the input ends of the 90-degree-long feed lines. The 50 V comes from 50 ohms and 1 A antenna current. The L network provides a 90-degree phase shift without changing the voltage magnitude. See text for details.

$E2 = (84 \text{ degrees from antenna element}) = 47.28 \angle 85.9°$

Notice on the printout that the voltages at the 180-degree point on line 1 and at the 90-degree point on line 2 are not identical (see par 3.3.1), which means that *if* you connect the lines in parallel in those points, you will not have the proper current in the antennas.

All we need to do now is to connect the two feed lines together where the voltages are identical. If you want to make the array switchable, run two 84-degree-long feed lines to a switch box, and insert a 155 − 84 = 71-degree-long phasing line, which will give you the required 90-degree antenna-current phase shift. Fig 11-6 shows the Christman feed method.

Of course the impedance at the junction of the two feed lines is not 50 ohms. Using the COAX TRANSFORMER/SMITH CHART software module, we calculate the impedances at the input ends of the two lines we are connecting in parallel.

$Z1_{end} = 39 + j12$ ohms
$Z2_{end} = 50 + j52$ ohms

The software module PARALLEL IMPEDANCES calculates the parallel impedance as $23.8 + j12.4$ ohms. This is the feed-point impedance of the array. You can use an L network, or any other appropriate matching system to obtain a more convenient SWR on the 50-ohm feed line.

3.3.3. Lewallen Method.

Lewallen, W7EL, uses a method which takes advantage of the specific properties of quarter-wave feed lines (Lewallen calls it "current-forcing"). This method is covered in great detail by W7EL in recent editions of *The ARRL Antenna Book.*

A quarter-wave feed line has the following wonderful property, which is put at work with this particular feed method: The magnitude of the input current of a quarter-wavelength transmission line is equal to the output voltage divided by the characteristic impedance of the line, and it is independent of the load impedance. In addition, the input current lags the output voltage by 90 degrees and is also independent of the load impedance.

There are very slight deviations from this statement with real cables, as the above statement is 100% correct only if there are no losses in the cables. The Lewallen method is a feed method which can only be applied to antennas fed in *quadrature*, which means antennas where the elements are fed with phase differences which are a multiple of 90 degrees.

Fig 11-7 shows the application of the Lewallen method for our 2-element cardioid array. From par 3.3.1 we know the voltages at the end of the 90-degree-long "real" feed lines (quarter-wave RG-213 with 0.35 dB loss per 100 ft on 80 meters). Notice that even with the losses, the real values are very close to the theoretical values (50 V, 90 degrees and 0 degrees):

El' = 50.9 $\angle 0.39°$

Z1' = 42.81 − j16.18 ohms

E2' = 50.4 $\angle 89.6°$

Z2' = 63.1 + j56.94 ohms

If the feed line had no losses, El' would be 50 $\angle 0°$, and E2' would be 50 $\angle 90°$.

Remember, we said that in order to be able to connect the feed lines in parallel, the voltages need to be identical. The magnitudes are almost the same but there still is a 90-degree phase difference.

In a Lewallen feed system, the array feed point is always at the end of the quarter-wave feed line that goes to the element(s) with the leading current angle. A network must be installed between the end of the feed lines going to the element(s) with the lagging feed current. The L network of Fig 11-7 provides the required 90-degree voltage-angle transformation, without changing the voltage magnitude.

The elements of the L network can easily be calculated (this formula is valid only for 2-element arrays):

$$X_S = \frac{Z_{coax}^2}{R1}$$

$$X_P = \frac{Z_{coax}^2}{X1 - R1}$$

where

X_S = reactance of the series element of the L network
X_P = reactance of the parallel element of the L network
Z_{coax} = characteristic impedance of the quarter-wave feed lines
R1 = feed-point resistance of the element with the lagging feed current
X1 = feed-point reactance of the element with the lagging feed current

For calculation of the L network in an array with more elements, see par. 4.9.1.1.

For our 2-element cardioid array we calculate the component reactances as follows:

$$X_S = \frac{50^2}{51} = 49 \text{ ohms}$$

$$X_P = \frac{50^2}{20 - 51} = -80.6 \text{ ohms}$$

The values of the components can be calculated as follows:

If the reactance is positive, $L = \dfrac{X}{2\pi f}$

If the reactance is negative, $C = \dfrac{10^6}{2\pi fX}$

where

L = inductance, µH
C = capacitance, pF
f = frequency, MHz

In our case and for a design frequency of 3.8 MHz, the series element is a coil with an inductance of 2.1 µH; the shunt element is a capacitor with a capacitance of 519 pF.

Let's calculate the resulting feed impedance of the array. The impedance at the input end of the line running to the element with the lagging current is transformed by the L network. We can use the SHUNT/SERIES IMPEDANCE NETWORK to calculate the transformed impedance:

−j80.6 ohms in parallel with 42.81 − j16.18 ohms = 24.83 − j24.46 ohms.

This in series with +j49 ohms = 24.83 + j24.54 ohms.

Now we connect this impedance in parallel with 63.1 + j56.94 ohms. The result is 17.8 + j17.1 ohms.

The 2 EL AND 4 EL VERTICAL ARRAYS module of the NEW LOW BAND SOFTWARE is a tutorial and engineering program that takes you step by step through the design of a 2-element cardioid type phased array (and also the famous 4-element square array, which is described later). The results as displayed in that program will be slightly different from the results shown here, as the software uses ideal (lossless) feed lines. It is interesting, however, to compare the figures from this paragraph with the figures from the software program to assess the error caused by using lossless cables. Figs 11-8 and 11-9 show the screen print of two pages from the 2-element design case as covered by the tutorial program.

3.3.4. The Modified Lewallen Method.

The L network described by Lewallen achieves a 90-degree voltage phase shift without changing the voltage magnitude. This means that the approach is applicable only with quadrature-fed arrays. Let's take the case where we change our 2-element cardioid slightly from a 90-degree phase shift to a 110-degree phase shift. This increases the gain of the array by 0.6 dB!

Refer to Fig 11-10. The data for the two elements are now:

Z1 = 43.3 + j23.9 ohms

I1 = 1 $\angle -110°$

E1 = 49.46 $\angle -81.1°$

Z2 = 15.1 − j13.7 ohms

I2 = 1 $\angle 0°$

E2 = 20.39 $\angle -42.2°$

At the end of the 90-degree-long RG-213 feed lines the impedances (and voltage) become:

Z1' = 44.67 − j23.63 ohms

E1' = 50.8 $\angle -19.56°$

Z2' = 91.03 + j76.99 ohms

E2' = 50.37 $\angle 89.6°$

This time we need a network between the ends of the two cables that takes care of a phase shift of 89.6 − (−19.56) = 109.16 degrees.

To do this we can use a constant-impedance pi or T phase-

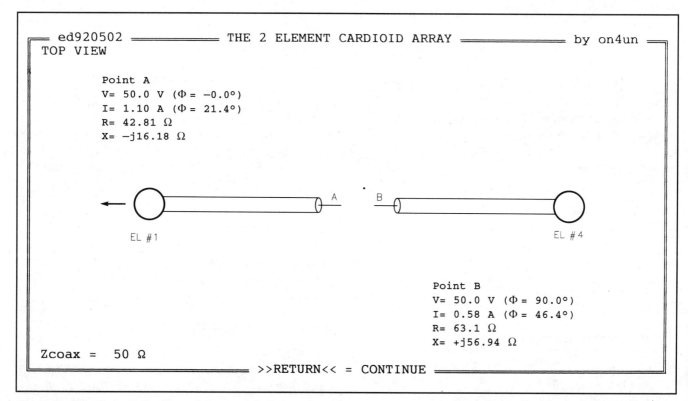

	EL # 1		EL # 2	
	R	X	R	X
SELF IMPEDANCE	36.0	0.0	36.0	0.0
MUTUAL Z TO EL # 1			20.0	-15.0
MUTUAL Z TO EL # 2	20.0	-15.0		
ANTENNA CURRENT	1		1	
PHASE (DEG)	-90		0	

```
                                        R        X
                                      -----    -----
            FEED IMPEDANCE EL #  1  ->  51.0     20.0
            FEED IMPEDANCE EL #  2  ->  21.0    -20.0
```

Here we have the feedpoint impedances of the 2 elements of our 2-element cardioid array. We will need those for futher calculations.

>RETURN< = CONTINUE ═══════ >B< BACK 1 PAGE ═══════ >G< GRAPH ═══ >X< EXIT

Fig 11-8—Screen print of a worksheet from the VERTICAL ARRAY TUTORIAL software program showing how the element drive impedances are calculated from the self-impedances, the mutual impedances and the antenna current. The program can be used in a tutorial mode (showing a classic design case) or as a calculator to calculate a specific case with data entered from the keyboard.

Fig 11-9—The Calculation/Tutorial program makes use of many graphic representations to clearly indicate where in the array we have certain impedances, voltages, currents, etc. Every design step is covered by a graphic representation.

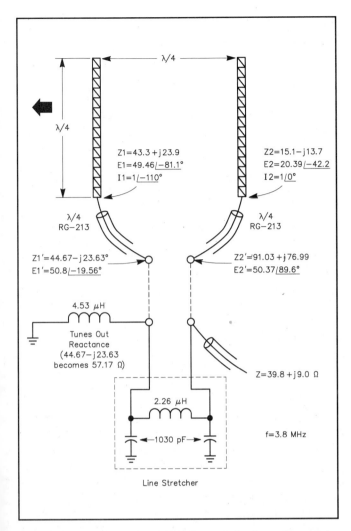

Z1=43.3+j23.9
E1=49.46∠−81.1°
I1=1∠−110°

Z2=15.1−j13.7
E2=20.39∠−42.2
I2=1∠0°

λ/4
RG−213

λ/4
RG−213

Z1'=44.67−j23.63°
E1'=50.8∠−19.56°

Z2'=91.03+j76.99
E2'=50.37∠89.6°

4.53 μH

Tunes Out
Reactance
(44.67−j23.63
becomes 57.17 Ω)

Z=39.8+j9.0 Ω

2.26 μH

1030 pF

f=3.8 MHz

Line Stretcher

Fig 11-10—The modified Lewallen method can be used for arrays that are not quadrature fed. The combination of a shunt element and a pi or T network makes it possible to insert a voltage phase shift of any angle. See text for details.

shift network. The pi and T networks are designed to provide the correct phase shift in a system impedance *that has no reactive part*. This means we will first have to add a *shunt* element to the end of the feed line going to the element with the lagging feed current, in order to make the impedance real. We cannot use a series element as that would change the voltage magnitude as well as the angle. We can use the SHUNT/SERIES IMPEDANCE NETWORK module to do that.

Connecting an inductor with a reactance of 108.1 ohms in parallel with the feed line to Z1 brings the impedance to 57.17 ohms. At 3.8 MHz the required inductance is 4.53 μH.

Next we use the LINE STRETCHER (pi or T) module to calculate the values of the phase-shift network. The output phase angle must be specified as −19.56 degrees, the input phase angle as 89.6 degrees, and the system impedance as 57.17 ohms. The resulting pi-network values are

$X_S = +j54$ ohms

$X_P = -j40.66$ ohms

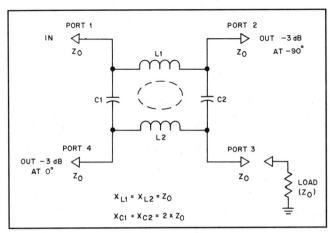

Fig 11-11—Hybrid coupler providing two −3-dB outputs with a phase difference of 90 degrees. L1 and L2 are closely coupled. See text for construction details.

For f = 3.8 MHz the values are

Series coil: 2.26 μH

Parallel capacitors: 1030 pF

The final feed system is shown in Fig 11-10. The impedance in the junction is the parallel equivalent for:

Z1" = 57.17 ohms

Z2' = 91.03 + j76.99 ohms

The software module PARALLEL IMPEDANCES calculates the parallel impedance as 39.8 + j9.0 ohms. This is the feed-point impedance of the array. You can use an L network, or any other appropriate matching system to obtain a more convenient SWR on the 50-ohm feed line.

Conclusion: The modified Lewallen method allows you to use the "current-forcing" method with arrays that are *not* quadrature-fed. The network that must provide the correct voltage phase shift is no longer a simple L network, however.

Remark: In the above example we have inserted the phase-adjusting network in the leg going to the element with the lagging current angle, while the array feed line is connected directly to the quarter-wave line going to the element with the leading current. The other alternative is equally valid, connecting the feed line directly to the quarter-wave line going to the element with the current lagging. Make sure you specify input and output phase angles correctly when using the PI or T LINE-STRETCHER software module. The choice, as well as the choice between pi- and T-network stretchers, should in practice be determined by practical aspects such as impedances and component values (too low impedance values result in too high currents; too high impedance values result in too high voltages).

3.3.5. Collins Method

The Collins feed system is similar to the Lewallen system in that it uses "current-forcing" quarter-wavelength feed lines to the individual elements. There is one exception, however. Instead of using an L network, Collins uses a quadrature hybrid coupler, shown in Fig 11-11.

The hybrid coupler divides the input power (at port no. 1) equally between port nos. 2 and 4, with theoretically no power output at port 3 if all four port impedances are the same. When the output impedances are not the same, power will be dissipated in the load resistor connected to port no. 4. In addition, the phase difference between the signal at port nos. 2 and 4 will be different by 90 degrees if the load impedance of these ports is not real or, if complex, they do not have an identical reactive part. We will examine whether or not this characteristic of the hybrid coupler is important as to its application as a feed system for a quadrature-fed array.

Hybrid Coupler Construction

The values of the hybrid coupler components are:

$X_{L1} = X_{L2} = 50$ ohms (system impedance)

$X_{C1} = X_{C2} = 2 \times 50 = 100$ ohms

For 3.8 MHz the component values are

$$L1 = L2 = \frac{X_L}{2\pi f} = \frac{50}{2\pi \times 3.8} = 2.09 \text{ }\mu H$$

$$C1 = C2 = \frac{10^6}{2\pi fX_C} = \frac{10^6}{2\pi \times 3.8 \times 100} = 419 \text{ pF}$$

When constructing the coupler, one should take into account the capacitance between the wires of the inductors, L1 and L2, which can be as high as 10% of the required total value for C1 and C2. The correct procedure is to first wind the tightly coupled coils L1 and L2, then measure the inter-winding capacitance and deduct that value from the theoretical value of C1 and C2 to determine the required capacitor value. For best coupling, the coils should be wound on powdered-iron toroidal cores. The T225-2 ($\mu = 10$) cores from Amidon are a good choice for power levels well in excess of 2 kW. The larger the core, the higher the power-handling capability. Consult Table 6-1 in Chapter 6 for core data. The T225-2 core has an A_L factor of 120. The required number of turns is calculated as

$$N = 100\sqrt{\frac{2.09}{120}} = 13.2 \text{ turns}$$

The coils should be wound with AWG 14 or AWG 16 multistrand Teflon-covered wire. The two coils can be wound with the turns of both coils wound adjacent to one another, or the two wires of the two coils can be twisted together at a rate of 5 to 7 turns per inch before winding them (equally spaced) onto the core.

At this point, measure the inductance of the coils (with an impedance bridge or an LC meter) and trim them as closely as possible to the required value of 2.09 µH for each coil. Moving the windings on the core can help you fine-tune the inductance of the coil. Now the inter-winding capacitance can be measured. This is the value that must be subtracted from the capacitor value calculated above (419 pF). A final check of the hybrid coupler can be made with a vector voltmeter or a dual-trace oscilloscope. By terminating ports 2, 3 and 4 with 50-ohm resistors, you can now fine-tune the hybrid for an exact 90-degree phase shift between ports 2 and 4. The output voltage amplitudes should be equal.

Performance of the Hybrid Coupler

I have tested the performance of a commercially made hybrid coupler (ComTek, Ref. par. 3.3.7). First the coupler was tested with the two load ports (port nos. 2 and 4) terminated in a 50-ohm load resistor. Under those conditions the power dissipated in the 50-ohm dummy resistor (port no. 3) was 21 dB down from the input power level. This means that the coupler has a directivity of 21 dB under ideal loading conditions (equivalent to 12 watts dissipated in the dummy load for a 1500-watt input). The results were identical for both 3.5 and 3.8 MHz. The input SWR under the same test conditions was approximately 1.1:1 (25-dB return loss).

I also checked the hybrid coupler for its ability to provide a 3-dB signal split with a 90-degree phase-angle difference. When the two hybrid ports were terminated in a 50-ohm load I measured a difference in voltage magnitude between the two output ports of 1.7 dB, with a phase-angle difference of 88 degrees at 3.8 MHz. At 3.5 MHz the phase-angle difference remained 88 degrees, but the difference in magnitude was down to 1.2 dB (theoretically the difference should be 0 dB and 90 degrees).

The commercially available hybrid coupler system from ComTek uses a toroidal-wound transmission line to achieve a 180-degree phase shift over a wide bandwidth. The phase transformer consists of a bifilar-wound conductor pair, where wire A is grounded on one end and wire B on the other end of the coil. The other two ends are the input and output connections, whereby the voltages are shifted 180 degrees in phase. This approach eliminates the long (half-wavelength) coax that is otherwise required for achieving the 180-degree phase shift, and it is broadbanded as well.

I have measured the performance of this "compressed" delay line. Using a 50-ohm load, the delay was 168 degrees, with an insertion loss of 0.8 dB. With a complex-impedance load the phase shift varied between 160 and 178 degrees. Measurements were done with a Hewlett-Packard vector voltmeter. The hybrid coupler was also evaluated using "real" loads in a four-square array configuration. See par. 5.3 for details.

After investigating the components of the ComTek hybrid-coupler system, I evaluated the performance of the coupler (without the delay-line), using impedances as found at the input ends of the quarter-wavelength feed lines in real arrays as load impedances for ports 2 and 4 of the coupler. Let us examine the facts and figures for our 2-element end-fire cardioid array.

The SWR on the quarter-wave feed lines to the two elements (in the cardioid-pattern configuration) is not 1:1. Therefore, the impedance at the ends of the quarter-wave feed lines will depend on the element impedances and the characteristic impedances of the feed lines. We want to choose the feed-line impedances such that a minimum amount of power is dissipated in the port 3 terminating resistor.

The impedances at the end of the 90-degree-long "real"

feed lines (quarter-wave RG-213 with 0.35 dB loss per 100 ft on 80 meters) are

$Z1' = 42.81 - j16.18$ ohms

$Z2' = 63.1 - j56.94$ ohms

These values are reasonably close to the 50-ohm design impedance of our commercial hybrid coupler. With 75-ohm feed lines the impedance would be

$Z1' = 95.11 - j35.88$ ohms

$Z2' = 141.05 - j125.4$ ohms

It is obvious that for our 2-element cardioid array, 50 ohms is the logical choice for the feed-line impedance. This can be different for other types of arrays. The basic 4-element four-square array, with ¼ wavelength spacing and quadrature-fed, is covered in detail in par 4.9.2.2. A special version of the four-square array is analyzed in detail in par. 5.3.

Array Performance

Although the voltage magnitudes and phase at the ends of the two quarter-wave feed lines are not exactly what is needed for a perfect quadrature feed, it turns out that the array only suffers slightly from the minor difference. The incorrect phase angle will likely deteriorate the F/B, but the gain will remain almost the same as with the ideal driving conditions (see also Fig 11-15).

Different Design Impedance

We can also design the hybrid coupler with an impedance that is different from the 50-ohm quarter-wave feed-line impedance in order to realize a lower SWR at ports 2 and 4 of the coupler. The load resistor at port 3 must of course have the same ohmic value as the hybrid design impedance. Alternatively we can use a standard 50-ohm dummy load with a small L network connected between the load and the output of the hybrid coupler.

With the aid of the software module SWR ITERATION, one can scan the SWR values at ports 2 and 4 for a range of design impedances. The results can be cross-checked by measuring the power in the terminating resistor and alternately connecting 50- and 75-ohm quarter-wave feed lines to the elements. A practical design case is illustrated in par 4.9.2.2.

By choosing the most appropriate feed-line impedance as well as the optimum hybrid-coupler design impedance, it is possible to reduce the power dissipated in the load resistor to 2-5 percent of the input power. Whether or not reducing the lost power to such a "low" degree is worth all the effort may be questionable, but covering the issue in detail will certainly help in better understanding the hybrid coupler and its operation as a feed system for a phased array with elements fed in quadrature.

3.3.6. Gehrke Method

Gehrke, K2BT, has developed a technique that is fairly standard in the broadcast world. The elements of the array are fed with randomly selected lengths of feed line, and the required feed currents at each element are obtained by the insertion of discrete component (lumped-constant) networks in the feed system. He makes use of L networks and constant-impedance T or pi delay networks. The detailed description of this procedure is given in Ref. 924.

The Gehrke method consists of selecting equal lengths (not necessarily 90-degree lengths) for the feed lines running from the elements to a common point where the array switching and matching are done. With this method, the length of the feed lines can be chosen by the designer to suit any physical requirements of the particular installation. The cables should be long enough to reach a common point, such as the middle of the triangle in the case of a triangle-shaped array.

As an example, we will work out a 2-element end-fire array with a cardioid pattern (fed with equal current magnitudes, but 90 degrees out of phase). All the calculations are done assuming we use RG-213 coax (0.35 dB loss/100 ft at 3.8 MHz). We'll use the software for "real" feed lines, which takes into account the effect of cable loss.

Next, the required impedances at the T junction must be determined. Continuing with the above example, the element feed-point impedances are:

$Z1 = 51 + j20$ ohms for the –90 degree element

$Z2 = 21 - j20$ ohms for the 0-degree element

As the current in both antennas is 1 A (arbitrarily chosen), the power levels are

$P1 = 1^2 \times 51 = 51$ W

$P2 = 1^2 \times 21 = 21$ W

$P_{tot} = 21 + 51 = 72$ W

If you want to work with real powers, voltages, and currents, divide the transmitter output power by P_{tot}, and replace the 1 A of current with the square root of the output power divided by the total power. Example: If $P_{out} = 1500$ W, then

$$I = \sqrt{\frac{1500}{72}} = 4.56 \text{ A}$$

Now you can read real voltages and real currents, which can be an advantage when determining components for the circuit.

At the T junction (assuming we want an SWR of 1:1 on the 50-ohm line to the shack), the voltage will be

$$E = \sqrt{RP} = \sqrt{50 \times 72} = 60 \text{ V}$$

Looking toward element 1, the impedance at the T junction must be

$$Z = \frac{E^2}{P} = \frac{60^2}{51} = 70.6 \text{ ohms}$$

For element 2, the impedance at the T point must be 171 ohms. A simple check can be made to verify that the resulting impedance will be 50 ohms:

$$\frac{1}{70.6} + \frac{1}{171} = \frac{1}{50}$$

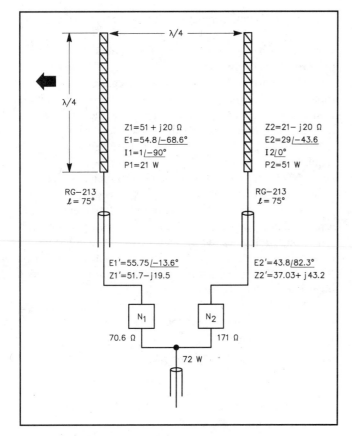

Fig 11-13—Schematic representation of the Gehrke approach to feeding the elements of an array. The networks N1 and N2 transform the complex impedances at the end of the feed lines to resistive values at the T junction and provide voltages at the junction that are identical in magnitude and phase. See text for details.

The impedance, current and voltage at the element feed points are (Ref. par 3.3.1)

$Z1 = 51 + j20$ ohms

$I1 = 1 \angle -90°$

$E1 = 54.8 \angle -68.6°$

$Z2 = 21 - j20$ ohms

$I2 = 1 \angle 0°$

$E2 = 29 \angle -43.6°$

E1 and E2 are the voltages (magnitude and phase) that must be present at the feed points of the elements in order to produce the pattern resulting from quarter-wave spacing, equal current magnitude, and a 90-degree phase delay. Fig 11-13 shows the impedance, current and voltage values, and where they are present in the array.

The values of I, E, and Z at the element feed points must now be transformed to the input ends of the coaxial feed lines. If we decide to make the direction of the array switchable, it is recommended that all feed lines be cut to the same electrical length, unless one element remains in the same position (such as the center element in a 3-element in-line array), because the direction-switching harness will be easier to construct. Other-

wise, there is no reason why the feed lines must be of equal length. Let's take two cables each 75 degrees long.

We calculate the impedance at the input end of the two coaxial cables using the software module COAX TRANS-FORMER/SMITH CHART. The result of the transformation via the 75 degree long 50-ohm lines is

$Z1' = 51.7 - j19.5$ ohms

$E1' = 55.75 \angle -13.6°$ volts

$I1' = 1.01 \angle 7.05°$ amperes

$Z2' = 37.03 + j43.2$ ohms

$E2' = 43.8 \angle 82.3°$ volts

$I2' = 0.77 \angle 32.88°$ amperes

These are the values of Z, E and I that must be present at the ends of the coaxial cables in order for the array to perform as it was designed to.

Next we have to calculate the lumped-constant networks. The networks must be designed to transform the impedances at the end of the cables to the resistive values (determined above as 70.6 and 171 ohms). This transformation can be done with a shunt-input L network, as the output impedance is lower than the input impedance. The only requirement for the network is the impedance transformation. L networks have a phase delay which is inherently coupled to the transformation ratio, which means that we have no separate control over the phase delay. The phase delays in current and voltage can be calculated using matrix algebra (Ref. 925). The software module L-NETWORK does the job in seconds. Each L-network design yields at least two solutions, where the input voltage magnitudes are the same, but the phase angles are different.

L Network for Z1 (Element with the Lagging Current)

Input data:

$Z_{out} = 70.6$ ohms
$Z1' = 51.7 - j19.5$ ohms
$E1' = 55.85 \angle -13.60°$ volts
$I1' = 1.01 \angle 7.05°$ amperes

Solution 1

$E1'' = 60.96 \angle 24.09°$ volts
$I1'' = 0.863 \angle -24.09°$ ampere
$X_S = -11.76$ ohms (the minus sign indicates capacitive reactance)
$X_P = 116.77$ ohms

Solution 2

$E1'' = 60.96 \angle 38.22°$ volts
$I1'' = 0.863 \angle 38.22°$ ampere
$X_S = 50.76$ ohms
$X_P = -116.77$ ohms (capacitive reactance)

L Network for Z2 (Element with the Leading Current)

Input data:

$Z_{out} = 171$ ohms

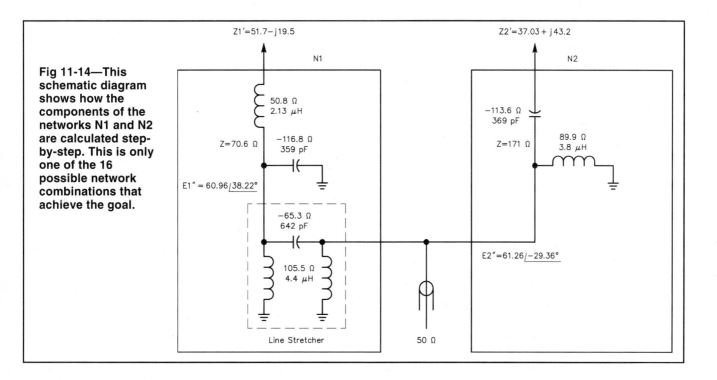

Fig 11-14—This schematic diagram shows how the components of the networks N1 and N2 are calculated step-by-step. This is only one of the 16 possible network combinations that achieve the goal.

$Z1' = 51.7 - j19.5$

$Z2' = 37.03 + j43.2$

N1

N2

50.8 Ω
2.13 µH

−113.6 Ω
369 pF

$Z = 70.6$ Ω

−116.8 Ω
359 pF

$Z = 171$ Ω

89.9 Ω
3.8 µH

$E1'' = 60.96 \underline{/38.22°}$

−65.3 Ω
642 pF

$E2'' = 61.26 \underline{/-29.36°}$

105.5 Ω
4.4 µH

Line Stretcher

50 Ω

$Z2' = 37.03 + j43.2$ ohms
$E2' = 43.8 \underline{/82.3°}$ volts
$I2' = 0.77 \underline{/32.88°}$ ampere

Solution 3

$E2'' = 61.26 \underline{/-29.36°}$ volts
$I2'' = 0.358 \underline{/-29.36°}$ ampere
$X_S = -113.63$ ohms
$X_P = 89.9$ ohms

Solution 4

$E2'' = 61.26 \underline{/95.17°}$ volts
$I2'' = 0.358 \underline{/95.17°}$ ampere
$X_S = 27.23$ ohms
$X_P = -89.9$ ohms

For each solution the voltage and current are in phase, as the impedance is a pure resistance. The networks can now be inserted in the feed lines to the elements. See Fig 11-14. First we must decide which L networks to use. Our choice will depend on the values of the components involved, as well as on the phase difference that will have to be compensated for with the line-stretcher network. Let's assume we have chosen solutions 2 and 3.

Looking at the voltage inputs to the above two networks, E1'' and E2'', we can see that the magnitudes are practically the same but the phase relationships are different: +38.22 degrees for element 1 and −29.36 degrees for element 2. In this case, an additional phase delay will have to be accomplished in a line stretcher in order to make up for the phase difference. This is done with a symmetrical pi or T network designed around an input (and output) impedance of 70.6 or 171 ohms and delivering the required phase shift.

This network can be designed using the software module LINE STRETCHER (pi or T). If you use the software make sure you specify input and output angles correctly. One possible solution is a pi network with the branch data that follows.

Let's put the stretcher in the 70.6-ohm branch: The output phase angle is 38.22 degrees, and the input phase angle −29.36 ohms. Make sure you specify input phase and output phase correctly: Looking from the input of the network toward the antenna loads you first have the input phase; the output phase is the phase toward the load.

The values of the pi network are

$X_S = -65.26$ ohms (642 pF at 3.8 MHz)

$X_P = 105.5$ ohms (4.4 µH at 3.8 MHz)

Ahead of the line stretcher, the voltages are identical in both amplitude and phase, and the input terminals of networks N1 and N2 can be connected in parallel to obtain the required feed-system impedance.

The input impedance of the array is $1/(1/171 + 1/70.6) = 50$ ohms. Remember, that's how we started the design procedure. Fig 11-14 shows the resulting feed configuration as calculated above.

There are a large number of solutions that can be designed. For each of the L networks we have two solutions, and we can connect the constant-impedance line stretcher in either the line going to element 1 or to element 2. All are valid solutions. For this 2-element cardioid array there are a total of 16 possible L-network line-stretcher combinations that will meet our design criteria.

3.3.7. Choosing the Best Feed System

Until Gehrke published his excellent series on vertical arrays, it was general practice to simply use feed lines as delay

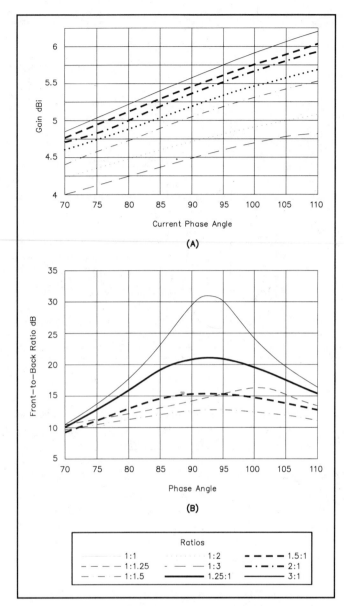

Fig 11-15—Calculated gain and the front-to-back ratio of a 2-element cardioid array versus current magnitudes and phase shifts. Calculations are for very good ground at the main wave angle. The array tolerates large variations as far as gain is concerned, but is very sensitive as far as front-to-back ratio is concerned.

lines, and to equate electrical line length to phase delay under all circumstances. We now know that there are better ways of accomplishing the same goal (Ref. par 3.3.1).

Fortunately, as Gehrke states, these vertical arrays are relatively easy to get working. Fig 11-15 shows the results of an analysis of the 2-element cardioid array with deviating feed currents. The feed-current magnitude ratio as well as the phase angle are quite forgiving as far as gain is concerned. As a matter of fact, a greater phase delay (eg, 100 versus 90 degrees) will increase the gain by about 0.3 dB. The picture is totally different as far as F/B ratio is concerned. To achieve an F/B of better than 20 dB, the current magnitude as well as the

phase angle need to be tightly controlled. But even with a "way off" feed system it looks like you always get between 8 and 12 dB of F/B ratio, which is indeed what we used to see from arrays that were incorrectly fed with coaxial phasing lines having the electrical length of the required phase shift.

Current-forcing methods (Lewallen, modified Lewallen and Collins) can be used if the current magnitudes are all the same or if the correct current magnitude can be provided by the correct choice of coaxial feed-line impedance.

Let's take an example. A 4-element array, where relative current magnitudes of 1, 1.5, 2 and 3 are required on the four elements, can be fed using coaxial feed lines of 75 ohms, 50 ohms, 37.5 ohms (two 75-ohm lines in parallel) and 25 ohms (two 50-ohm lines in parallel). At the end of each of the quarter-wave feed lines the voltage magnitude will be 75 V.

If the current angles are in a quadrature relationship, either the Lewallen or the Collins feed method can be applied. The big advantage of the Collins method is that you don't need to measure anything. The Collins system requires very few discrete components.

With the Collins system, essentially the same front-to-back ratio can be achieved in the range from 3.5 to 4.0 MHz, which makes this approach very attractive for those who want broadband performance. It does not make sense, however, to judge the operational bandwidth of the hybrid-coupler system by measuring the SWR curve at the input of the coupler. The coupler will show a *very* flat SWR curve (typically less than 1.3:1), even from 3.5 to 4 MHz. The reason is that, away from its design frequency, the impedances on the hybrid ports will be extremely reactive, resulting in the fact that *nearly all* power fed into the system will be dissipated in the dummy resistor. It is typical that an array tuned for element resonance at 3.8 MHz will dissipate 50 to 80% of its input power in the dummy load when operating at 3.5 MHz (the exact amount will depend on the Q factor of the elements). On receive, the same array will still exhibit excellent directivity on 3.5 MHz, but its gain will be down by 3 to 7 dB from the gain at 3.8 MHz (as we are wasting 50 to 80% of the received signal as well into the dummy resistor). It is clear that the only bandwidth-determining parameter is the power wasted in the load resistor.

Compared to the other current-forcing methods (Lewallen and modified Lewallen methods), the hybrid coupler has the disadvantage of wasting some of the transmitter power (and receive power as well, but that's probably much less relevant) in the dummy-load resistor. As long as the power is not more than 10%, the loss is really negligible from a practical point of view. The amount of wasted power can be reduced by the correct choice of the impedance of the quarter-wave feed lines, as well as of the hybrid-coupler design impedance (see par 3.3.5. and 4.9.2.2.).

Another disadvantage of the hybrid-coupler system is that the coupler does not produce the *exact* phase-quadrature phase shift unless some very specific load conditions exist (resistive loading or loading with identical reactive components on both ports). Most of the quadrature-fed arrays, however, are quite lenient, tolerating a certain degree of deviation from the perfect quadrature condition. The Collins-type coupler can only be used with an array that has quadrature-fed elements (current phase angles in multiples of 90 degrees).

The Christman method makes maximum use of the transformation characteristics of coaxial feed lines, thus minimizing the number of discrete components required in the feed network. This is an attractive solution, and should not scare off potential array builders. For a 2-element cardioid array this is certainly the way to go. Of course you need to go through the trouble of measuring the impedances.

The Christman method is very useful for 2-element arrays. With arrays of more elements, it is likely that identical voltages will only be found on two lines. For the third line, lumped-constant networks will have to be added. In such case the Lewallen or modified Lewallen method is preferred.

The Collins and Lewallen system of "current-forcing" have the advantage that they are not as sensitive to less-than-perfect symmetry in the array in the case of direction switching, as the other systems. This can be seen in the more constant front-to-back ratios in different directions with these systems.

For the Lewallen method, one only needs to know the impedance of the element with the lagging current. I don't know if this is an advantage. If you measure one element, you can just as well measure all. With the modified Lewallen method, nonquadrature-fed arrays can also be handled. Lewallen has published a number of L-network values for the 2-element cardioid and the 4-element square arrays, which a candidate builder can use for building the L network without doing any measuring. In that case (in any case) some performance measuring will have to be done to come to the right component values (see par 3.3.7.). The Lewallen method will not yield a good F/B over the entire 80-meter band, but it is entirely feasible to make two switchable L networks, one for 3.8 and one for 3.5 MHz.

The Gehrke design is rather impractical for amateur applications as it uses a large number of networks. The Gehrke approach is nevertheless given, as it helps in understanding how feed systems for arrays can be designed. The adjustment is very complex. Also, the system is narrow-banded. Typically, a Gehrke system designed for 3.8 MHz would show very little F/B ratio at 3.5 MHz, although the gain would remain essentially unchanged.

3.3.8. Tuning and measuring vertical arrays.

Impedance Measurement

Unless you want to use the Collins feed method (the hybrid coupler), you will have to measure impedances. Access to an accurate impedance bridge is essential. The bridge will be needed for measurement of element impedances and, in the case of a Gehrke-type feed system, measurement of the reactances of the components that make up the networks.

Commercially available noise bridges will almost certainly not give the required degree of accuracy, as rather small deviations in resistance and reactance must be accurately recorded. A genuine impedance bridge is more suitable, but with care, a well-constructed and carefully calibrated noise bridge may be used. Several excellent articles covering noise bridge design and construction were published: one written by Hubbs, W6BXI, Doting, W6NKU (Ref. 1607), Gehrke, K2BT

(Ref. 1610) and J. Grebenkemper, KI6WX (Ref. 1623); D. DeMaw, W1FB (Ref. 1620); and J. Belrose, VE2CV (Ref. 1621).

These articles are recommended reading material for anyone considering using a noise bridge in array design and measurement work. The software module RC/RL TRANSFORMATION part of the NEW LOW BAND SOFTWARE is very handy for transforming the value of the noise-bridge capacitor, connected in parallel with either the variable resistor or the unknown impedance, first to a parallel reactance value and then to an equivalent reactance value for a series LC circuit. This enables the immediate computation of the real and imaginary parts of the series impedance equivalent, expressed in "A + jB" form.

In order to obtain maximum directivity from an array, it is essential that the self-impedances of the elements be identical. Measurement of these impedances also requires a good impedance or noise bridge. Equalizing the resonant frequency can be done by changing the radiator lengths, while equalizing the self-impedance can be done by changing the number of radials used. If you cannot easily get equal impedances, you will have to suspect that one or more of the array elements are

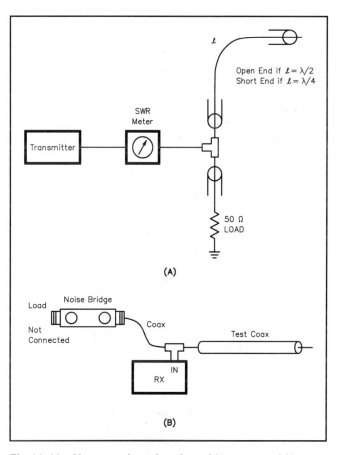

Fig 11-16—Very precise trimming of ¼-wave and ½-wave lines can be done by connecting the line under test in parallel with a 50-ohm dummy load, shown at A. Watch the SWR meter while the line length or the transmitter frequency is being changed. The alternative method at B uses a noise bridge and a receiver. See text for details.

coupling into another antenna or conducting structure. Take down all other antennas that are within ½ wavelength from the array to be erected. Do *not* change the length of one of the radiators to get the impedances equal!

Cutting Feed-Line Cable Lengths

Never go by the published velocity-factor figures, certainly not when you are dealing with foam coax. There is a very simple way of cutting coax cable to exact length as shown in Fig 11-16A. Connect your transmitter through a good SWR meter (a Bird 43 is a good choice) to a 50-ohm dummy load. Insert a coaxial T connector at the output of the SWR bridge.

If you need to cut a quarter-wave line (or odd multiple of quarter-waves), short the end of the coax. Make sure it is a good short, not a short with a lot of inductance. Insert the cable in the T connector. If the cable is a quarter-wave long, the cable end at the T connector will show as an infinite impedance and there will be no change at all in SWR (will remain 1:1). If you change the frequency of the transmitter you will see that on both sides of the resonant frequency of the line, the SWR will rise rather sharply. I have found this method very accurate, and the cable lengths can be trimmed very precisely to within a few kHz.

When adjusting half wavelengths, the far end of the cable should remain open-circuited. Odd lengths can also be adjusted this way after a little calculating. Assume you need a 72-degree long line at 3.65 MHz. This line will be 90 degrees long at $3.65 \times 90/72 = 4.56$ MHz. The cable can now be cut to a quarter wavelength on 4.56 MHz using the method described above.

If you have a noise bridge there is another simple method, whereby you use the noise bridge only as a wide-band noise source, without using the internal bridge. Instead you will connect the line to be trimmed across the output of the noise bridge, and trim the length until the noise level on the receiver will be reduced to zero. Switch off the receiver AGC to make the final adjustments (see Fig 11-16B).

Using a grid dip oscillator is not a very accurate way of trimming precise cable lengths. The pick-up loop will typically account for a 2 to 3 degree error when dipping a quarter-wave cable length.

Network Measurements

Constructing a Gehrke-type feed system requires quite a bit of network designing. Off-site measurement and adjustment of the networks is required also. To do this, first make dummy antennas that have the same impedance as the feed impedance of the array elements (such as $21 - j20$ ohms and $51 + j20$ ohms in the case of the 2-element end-fire array with cardioid pattern). The former is a series connection of a 21-ohm resistor and 2122 pF of capacitance (at 3.75 MHz); the latter is a series connection of a 51-ohm resistor with a 0.85-μH inductor. Inductors can be measured precisely by dipping the resonant circuit made by the coil and a standard-value capacitor. Alternatively, one may measure air-wound or toroidal coils using an impedance bridge or an LC meter. The various sub-units of the feed system can now be tested in the lab. Voltages can be measured using a high-quality oscillo-

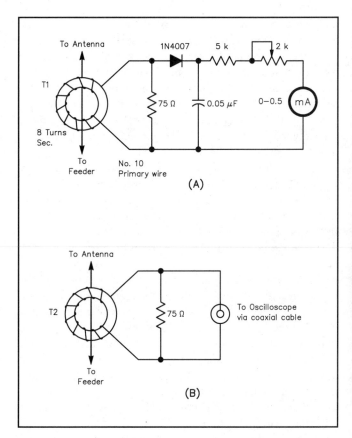

Fig 11-17—Current amplitude probe (at A) and phase probe (at B) for measuring the exact current at the feed point of each array element. See text for details.

T1, T2—Primary, single wire passing through center of core; secondary, 8 turns evenly spaced. Core is ½ diam ferrite, μ_i = 125 (Amidon FT-50-61 or equiv.).

scope. If a dual-trace scope is used, the phase difference between two points of interest can also be measured.

Suitable current amplitude and phase probes have been described by Gehrke (Ref. 927 and *The ARRL Antenna Book*). When measuring the impedances of the building blocks of a total feed system, make sure you know exactly what you are measuring. All impedances mentioned during the design were impedances looking from the generator toward the load. If a network is measured in the reverse direction (terminating the input of the network with a resistive impedance to measure the output impedance), you will measure the conjugate value. (A conjugate value has the opposite reactance sign; the conjugate of $A + jB$ is $A - jB$). All tuning and measurement procedures are adequately covered by Gehrke in Ref. 927. The correct coaxial cable lengths can be cut using the methods described in the chapter on feed lines and matching.

Antenna Feed Current Measurement

It is essential to be able to measure the feed current in order to assess the correct operation of the array. A good-quality RF ammeter is used for element-current magnitude measurements and a good dual-trace oscilloscope to measure the phase difference. The two inputs to the oscilloscope will

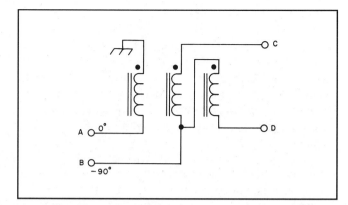

Fig 11-18—This quadrature transformer has a trifilar winding. Notice the phasing dots; the windings must be correctly phased. If voltages A and B are 90 degrees out of phase, the voltage from B to C will be 180 degrees out of phase.

have to be fed via identical lengths of coaxial cable. Fig 11-17 shows the schematic diagram of the RF current probes for current amplitude and phase-angle measurement. Details of the devices can be found in Ref. 927. D. M. Malozzi, N1DM, pointed out that it is important that the secondary of the toroidal transformer always sees its load resistor, as otherwise the voltage on the secondary can rise to extremely high values and destroy components and also the input of an oscilloscope if the probe is to be used with a scope. He also pointed out that it is best to connect two identical resistors at each end of the coax connecting the probe to the oscilloscope. Both resistors should have the impedance of the coax. Make sure the resistors are noninductive, and of adequate power rating. It is not necessary to do your measurement with high power (nor advisable from a safety point of view).

Quadrature-Fed Arrays

If you are designing an array with quadrature-fed elements, it is possible to check the element current magnitudes and phase relationships by using the simple piece of test equipment described below.

The heart of the circuit is a wide-band, single-ended, push-pull transformer. When fed as shown in Fig 11-18, the secondary (C-D) should be completely out of phase. To test this, you can rectify the RF and measure the sum of the two voltages. If you connect points A and B to the end of the quarter-wave feed lines (feeding the elements with a current phase difference of 90 degrees), the voltages at C and D will be 180 degrees out of phase if the voltages at A and B are 90 degrees out of phase. The transformer can be wound on a ferrite core, such as an Indiana General BBR-7731 (also used for feeding Beverage antennas; see Chapter 7, Special Receiving Antennas). The winding consists of four turns of AWG 20 to 26 enameled copper wire, trifilar wound. Make sure the phasing is as shown in Fig 11-18.

Where quarter-wave feed lines are used (current-forcing method), measuring identical voltage magnitudes at the input ends of those lines guarantees identical element feed current magnitudes (if all the feed lines have the same impedance).

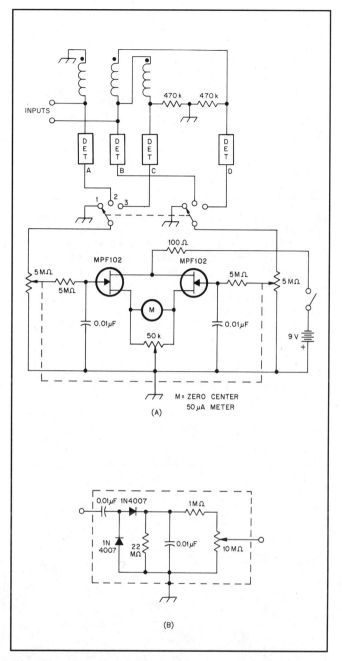

Fig 11-19—The simple quadrature tester consists of a transformer, four detector modules, a mode switch and a differential voltmeter. The diagram for the detector modules is shown at B. Note that the two 5-MΩ potentiometers of the tester are ganged. This is the sensitivity control.

Fig 11-19 shows the schematic diagram of this piece of equipment. It can be built in a small, well-shielded box. The circuit contains four voltage-doubling rectifier arrangements with separate sensitivity adjustment potentiometers. All modules should be adjusted for the same sensitivity with the output potentiometers.

The measuring circuit is a straightforward differential FET voltmeter that is fed with a small 9-V battery. The ganged potentiometers in the source circuit of the FETs can be used to

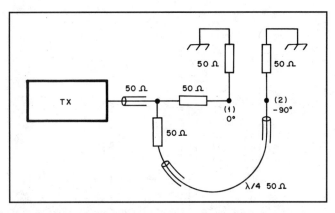

Fig 11-20—In this phase-calibration system for the quadrature tester, RF voltage from the transmitter is divided down with two 50-ohm series resistors (to ensure a 1:1 SWR), routed directly to a 50-ohm lead, and through a 90-degree-long 50-ohm line (RG-58) to the second 50-ohm load. For a frequency of 3.65 MHz, the cable has a nominal length of 44.49 feet (13.56 m). The cable length should be tuned using the method described in Chapter 6 on feed lines and matching.

adjust the overall circuit sensitivity. The three-position input switch has a balancing position (position 1) for adjustment of the 50-kΩ balance potentiometer. With the switch in position 2, the circuit measures the difference between the magnitudes of the voltages at the two inputs. Identical voltage inputs are indicated by a zero meter reading.

With the switch in position 3, the circuit checks for a 90-degree phase difference between the two inputs. In order to make a nonzero phase-shift reading more meaningful, the meter can be calibrated with the setup shown in Fig 11-20. The phase calibrator consists of a quarter-wavelength of 50-ohms delay line. At the frequency where the delay line is exactly ¼ wavelength long, the voltages at A and B will be equal in magnitude but 90 degrees out of phase. The meter can be calibrated by varying the transmit frequency by 5% down and noting the meter reading, then moving the transmit frequency 5% up and making sure that the meter reading is the same. The test circuit can be checked for symmetry by inverting the inputs. The meter should read the same value for the normal or inverted mode. Note that for actual testing in an array, the device must be installed at the ends of the quarter-wave feed lines to the elements (where the direction switching is done).

This device is a very handy tool for making fine adjustments in a Lewallen type of feed system. The meter could be mounted in the shack for convenience. If you are building a Collins-type feed system, you can use this device to check the performance of the hybrid coupler by terminating all three output ports of the coupler with resistors equal to the design impedance of the coupler and then connecting the quadrature checker between the ports that have a 90-degree phase shift between them. If the coupler is working properly, the meter should read zero.

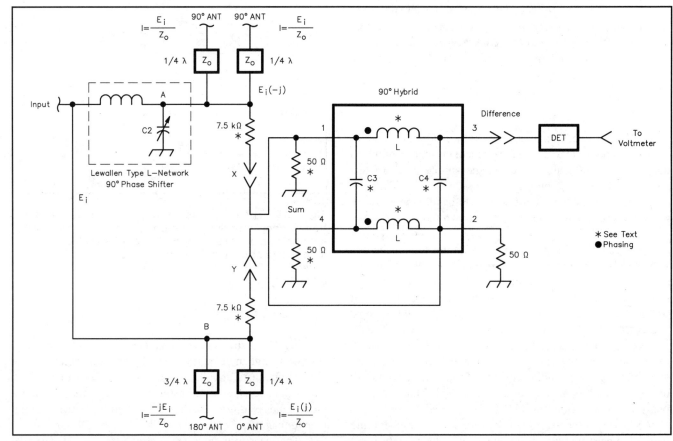

Fig 11-21—The W1MK phase measuring setup for quadrature-fed arrays. The unit employs a hybrid coupler as used in the Collins feed system for arrays. The unit can be left permanently in the circuit if the voltage dividing resistors are of adequate wattage. See text for details.

R. Lahlum, W1MK (Ref. 968) described a hybrid coupler (identical to the coupler used in the Collins feed system) for monitoring the exact 90-degree phase relationship in quadrature-fed arrays (see Fig 11-21). If high-wattage resistors are used (15-watt noninductive resistors are required for the 7.5-kΩ resistors!), the hybrid coupler can be left connected to the feed system at all times. The voltage from the HF detector at the output port of the coupler can be routed to the shack via a (long) shielded cable.

Both elements (C and L) of the L network for the Lewallen-type feed system can be made continuously variable by a little trick. If the networks require eg, a coil with a reactance of 50 ohms, make a coil with double the reactance (100 ohms or 4.2 μH at 3.8 MHz) and connect in series a variable capacitor with (at maximum capacitance) a reactance of –50 ohms or less. If you use –25 ohms (1675 pF at 3.8 MHz), the series connection of the two elements will now yield a continuously variable reactance (at 3.8 MHz) of 25 (or less) to 75 ohms. See Fig 11-22 for a diagram. If you motorize both capacitors and use the above-described monitoring system, you can now remotely tune the L networks for peak performance over the band.

Unwanted Mutual Coupling

If you happen to have large towers within ¼ wave of one of the elements of the array, it is possible that you will induce a lot of current into that tower by mutual coupling. The tower will act as a parasitic element, which will upset the radiation pattern of the array and also change the feed impedances of the elements and the array.

To eliminate the unwanted effect from the parasitic coupling proceed as follows:

- Decouple all the elements of the array with the exception of

the element closest to the suspect parasitic tower. For quarter-wave element decoupling, this means lifting the elements from ground (see par 3.2.2.).
- Measure the feed-point impedance of the vertical under investigation.
- If a suspect tower is heavily coupled to one of the elements of the array, a substantial current will flow in it. Probe the current by one of the methods described by D. DeMaw, W1FB (Ref. *W1FB's Antenna Notebook,* ARRL publication, 1987, p 121) and shown in Fig 11-23. If there is an appreciable current, you will have to "detune" the tower.
- Attach a shunt-fed wire at the top of the suspect tower (see Fig 9-60) and connect the bottom end to ground through a 1000-pF variable capacitor (a broadcast variable will do). Before closing the circuit, pass the vertical wire through the core of a current probe (see Fig 11-17).
- While applying power to the single vertical, tune the BC variable for minimum current in the "parasitic" tower. You

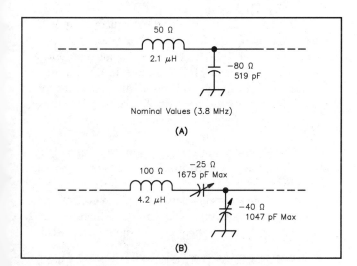

Fig 11-22—To make the Lewallen L network continuously adjustable, replace the coil with a coil of twice the required value and connect a capacitor in series. The net result will be a continuously variable reactance. With the values shown, the nominal +50-ohm reactance is adjustable from +75 to +25 ohms (and less). The two capacitors can be motor driven to make the phase-shift network remotely controllable.

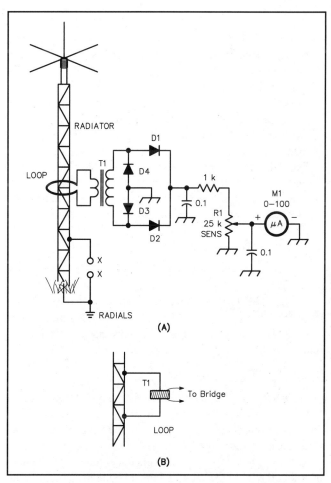

Fig 11-23—Current-sampling methods for use with vertical antennas, as described by DeMaw, W1FB. Method A requires a single-turn loop of insulated wire around the tower. The loop is connected to a broadband transformer, T1. A high-mu ferrite toroid, as used with Beverage receiving antennas (see Chapter 7 on special receiving antennas), can be used with a 2-turn primary and 2 to 10 turns secondary, depending on the power level used for testing.

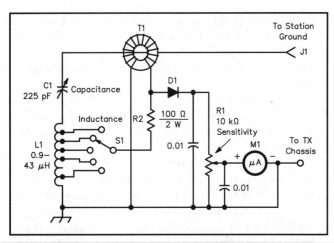

Fig 11-24—Schematic diagram of the MFJ-931 artificial RF ground. The unit includes a current probe (toroidal transformer), a detector, and a series tuning arrangement (L and C). When used to decouple a tower, L and C should be varied until *minimum* current is obtained. See text for details

may have to choose another attachment point on the tower to bring the current down to zero or a very small value. Note the value of the tuning capacitor.

• Measure the feed-point impedance of the vertical again. If you have properly detuned the parasitic tower, you will likely see a rise in impedance.

• Reconnect the whole array and fire in the direction of the "parasitic" tower.

• Check the current in the parasitic tower, and if necessary make final adjustments to minimize the current in the tower. You can use high power now in order to be able to tune the tower very sharply. In general the tuning will be quite broad, however.

• Replace the BC variable with a fixed capacitor.

You now have made the offending tower invisible for your array.

The MFJ-931 (artificial RF ground) is a useful instrument for detuning a tower. Fig 11-24 shows the schematic of the unit. The inductance/capacitance can be varied until minimum current flows in the circuit.

Performance Measurement

Measuring gain is something that is out of reach for all but a few of those lucky enough to have access to an antenna test range. Front-to-back ratio, however, can be measured fairly easily with the use of a second antenna mounted several wavelengths away from the antenna under test, or by the help of a neighbor ham (he must be located quite accurately in the back of the array in order to optimize F/B).

The directivity of most of the arrays described in this chapter is very high at low angles. Some designs show major back lobes at high angles (60 or even 90 degrees). Even the best array will show very little directivity at high angles, because it also radiates very little power at high angles in the forward direction. All this is to say that in practice you must evaluate the array with DX signals. Properly fed 4-square

arrays show an operational F/B of 25 to 35 dB in practice. In many instances it is like going from an S9 signal to "inaudible." On signals within 1500 km (900 miles) the directivity of the array will be mediocre at best.

3.3.9. Network component dimensioning.

When designing array feed networks using the computer modules from the NEW LOW BAND SOFTWARE, you can use absolute currents instead of relative currents.

The feed currents for the 2-element cardioid array (used so far as a design example) have so far been specified as $1 \angle 0°$ and $1 \angle 90°$. The feed-point impedances of the array are

Z1 = 51 + j20 ohms

Z2 = 21 − j20 ohms

With 1-A antenna current in each element, the total power taken by the array is 51 + 21 = 72 W. If the power is 1500 W, the true current in each of the elements will be

$$I = \sqrt{\frac{1500}{72}} = 4.56\,A$$

Using this current magnitude in the relevant computer program module (COAXIAL TRANSFORMER) will now show the user the real current and voltage information all through the network design phase. The components can be chosen according to the current and voltage information shown.

If there is any question as to the voltage rating of any of the feed lines that are used as transformers in our designs (all have an SWR greater than 1), the program FEED LINE VOLTAGE with the real current as an input can be used to calculate what the highest voltage is at any point on the line. We find that for the 2-element array with a cardioid pattern (fed according to the Christman method), the highest voltage on a feed line of any length to element 1 (which has a 1.48:1 SWR) is only 397 V with 3 kW applied. For feed line 2, the maximum voltage is 352 V. For the 4-square array with ¼ wavelength spacing, the feed-line-voltage values are 234 V, 253 V, 253 V and 391 V. This should not represent any problem with good-quality RG-213 cable. In a similar fashion the voltages across capacitors or currents through capacitors in the lumped-constant networks can be determined. When evaluating coils, use the following guidelines: For up to 5 μH, it is advisable to use air-wound coils. The best Q factors are achieved with coils having a length-to-diameter ratio of 1. For higher values, use powdered-iron toroidal cores if necessary. Information on this subject as well as on the subject of dimensioning capacitors in a network is given in Chapter 6 on feed lines and matching. The computer module COIL CALCULATION may be helpful in designing the coils.

■ 4. POPULAR ARRAYS

This section briefly describes the most popular arrays and a few feed systems. I will not systematically cover all the possible feed systems.

The gains quoted in the following paragraphs are for arrays made of quarter-wave verticals and are quoted over a single quarter-wavelength vertical over the same ground. All arrays are modeled over very good ground, with an extensive radial system that accounts for an equivalent series loss resistance of 2 ohms (for each element). The element feed-point impedances shown include this 2 ohms of loss resistance. If you want to calculate your feed system for different equivalent ground loss resistances, apply the following procedure:

- Take the values from the array data (see below). The resistive part includes 2 ohms of loss resistance. If you want the feed-point impedance with 10 ohms of loss resistance, just add 8 ohms to the resistive part of the feed-point impedance shown in the array data. The imaginary part of the impedance remains unchanged.
- Follow the feed-system design criteria as shown, but apply the new feed-point impedance values.

4.1. The 90-Degree, ¼-Wave-Spacing Cardioid

Array Data

Spacing: ¼ wavelength
Feed currents: I1 = 1 $\angle 0°$; I2 = 1 $\angle -90°$
Gain: 3.1 dB over a single vertical
3 dB beamwidth: 176 degrees
Mutual Impedance: Z(12) = Z(21) = approx. 15 + j20 ohms
Feed-point impedance (including 2 ohms ground loss):

Z (lagging phase element) = 51 + j20 ohms
Z (leading phase element) = 21 − j20 ohms

Radiation patterns are shown in Fig 11-4.

4.1.1. Feeding the array.

This is the array we have used extensively in par 3 to examine the different feed methods for arrays. If you can put up only two elements, this array, when made switchable, will cover two directions. In order to cover also the perpendicular direction, both elements can be fed in phase. Fig 11-25 shows the wiring of the array with the Lewallen feed method, including the switching harness. Positions 1 and 2 are for the two end-fire cardioid patterns.

In position 3, both elements are fed in phase, and an L network can be used to match the parallel-connected quarter-wave lines to the feed line. In this configuration, the array will have a bidirectional broadside pattern with a gain of 1 dB over a single vertical. The front-to-side ratio is only 3 dB. The feed impedance of two quarter-wave-spaced elements fed in phase is approximately 57 − j15 ohms, assuming an almost-perfect ground system with 2 ohms equivalent ground loss resistance. Notice that both elements have the same impedance, which is logical as they are fed in phase.

Assuming a feed impedance of 57 − j15 ohms and RG-213 coax with 0.35 dB loss per 100 ft at 3.8 MHz, the impedance at the end of the 90 degree feed lines (calculated with the COAXIAL TRANSFORMER software module) is

Z = 41.3 + j10.5 ohms

Paralleling the two feed lines yields an impedance of 20.65 + j5.25 ohms. This impedance can be matched to the feed-line impedance with an L network.

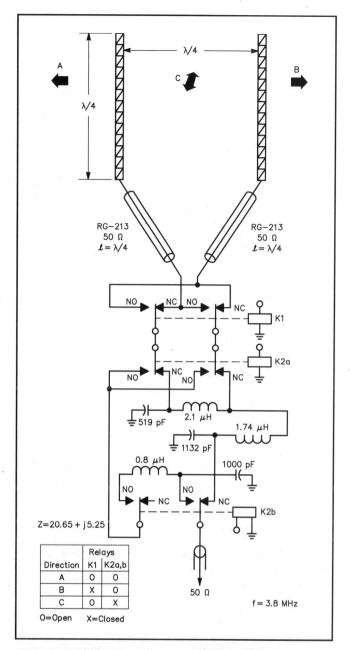

Fig 11-25—The 2-element vertical array (¼-wave spacing) can be fed in phase in order to cover the broadside directions. The matching networks to achieve a 1:1 SWR on a 50-ohm feed line are also shown.

4.2. The 135-Degree, ⅛-Wave-Spacing Cardioid

This array is known as the ZL-special or the HB9CV array.

Array Data

Spacing: ⅛ wavelength
Feed currents: I1 = 1 $\angle 0°$; I2 = 1 $\angle -135°$
Gain: 3.7 dB over a single vertical
3 dB beamwidth: 142 degrees

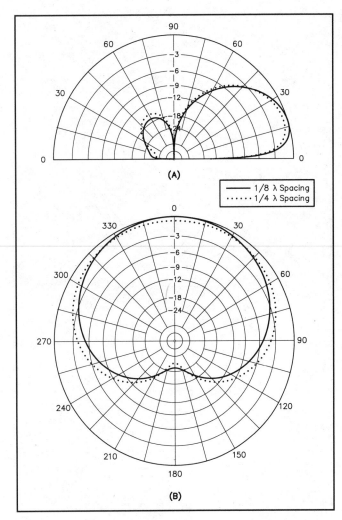

Fig 11-26—Radiation patterns for the 2-element cardioid array with ⅛-wave spacing when fed 135 degrees out of phase. The patterns of the ¼-wave spaced (90 degrees out of phase) array are superimposed for comparison. The gain is calculated over very good ground, using a radial system with an equivalent loss resistance of 2 ohms.

The feed-point impedance (including 2 ohms ground loss):

Z (leading phase element) = 13 − j21 ohms
Z (lagging phase element) = 18 + j23 ohms

Radiation patterns are shown in Fig 11-26. The horizontal pattern also shows the pattern for the ¼-wave spacing, 90 degrees out of phase, for comparison.

Because the elements are not fed in quadrature, the Collins and the Lewallen feed methods cannot be used. The modified Lewallen, the Christman and the Gehrke methods can be used, however.

4.2.1. The Modified Lewallen feed system.

Using the COAX TRANSFORMER program from the NEW LOW BAND SOFTWARE, we first calculate Z, I, and E at the ends of the four quarter-wave feed lines.
Input data:

Z1 = 13 − j21 ohms

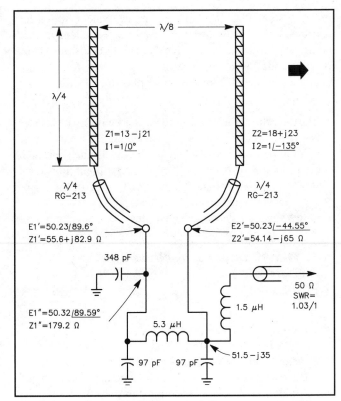

Fig 11-27—Modified Lewallen feed system for the 2-element cardioid array (⅛-wave spacing, 135 degrees out of phase). The modified Lewallen network uses a pi (or T) filter plus a shunt reactance (coil or capacitor) instead of an L network, but can handle any phase shift, whereas the Lewallen network handles only 90-degree phase shifts.

$I1 = 1 \angle 0°$

$Z2 = 18 + j23$ ohms

$I1 = 1 \angle -135°$

At the end of the quarter-wave feed lines we find

$Z1' = 55.6 + j82.9$ ohms

$E1' = 50.23 \angle 89.6°$ V

$Z2' = 54.14 - j65$ ohms

$E2' = 50.23 \angle -44.55°$ V

Let us feed the array at the end of the line to the element with the leading phase (we can choose either).

We must now add a shunt reactance to make the input impedance real (we will use a constant-impedance line stretcher to provide the additional phase shift).

The shunt impedance (calculated with the SHUNT IMPEDANCE NETWORK module) required to achieve a resistive impedance is −120.2 ohms (this is 348 pF at 3.8 MHz).

With the capacitor in parallel the values have become:

$Z2'' = 179.2$ ohms

$E2'' = 50.23 \angle -89.59°$ V

Now we calculate the constant-impedance pi line stretcher:

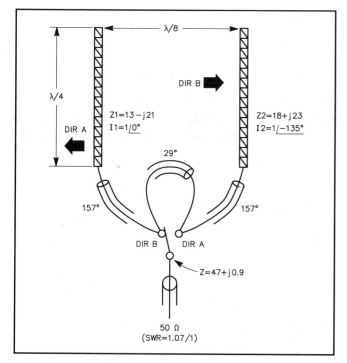

Fig 11-28—Christman feed method for the ⅛-wave-spaced cardioid pattern array. This system turns out to be very simple, and it yields an almost perfect 1:1 SWR on a 50-ohm feed line without the need for a matching network. The direction switching is done with an SPDT relay.

Output phase angle: –89.59 degree
Input phase angle: –44.55 degree

The pi-filter components are

X_S = 126.8 ohms (= 5.3 μH at 3.8 MHz)
X_P = –432.2 ohms (= 97 pF at 3.8 MHz)

Fig 11-27 shows the final layout of the array with all the feed-system components.

The impedance at the array feed point can be calculated by paralleling 179.2 ohms and 54.14 – j64.97 ohms. The result is 51.48 – j35.6 ohms. This impedance can be matched almost perfectly to a 50-ohm line by merely connecting a 1.5-μH inductor in series with the feed line.

4.2.2. Christman Method.

Fig 11-28 shows the Christman feed method for this array.
Input data:

Z1 = 13 – j21 ohms
I1 = 1 $\angle 0°$

Z2 = 18 + j23 ohms
I2 = 1 $\angle -135°$

Using the program FEED LINE VOLTAGE, one can scan both 50-ohm feed lines for points where the voltages are the same on both lines. Two such sets of points are found in this case.

- One is 157 degrees from element 1 (the element with the leading current) and 196 degrees from element 2. Note that the 135-degree current phase shift is accomplished with a feed-line-length difference of only 61 degrees.
- The second one is 38 degrees from element 1 and 158 degrees from element 2.

There's a clear choice here because the second set of points occurs at areas of high variation of feed-line voltage for small variations in distance, making these points a poor choice. Using the second set of points would also decrease the bandwidth of the array. The location of one point at only 38 degrees from the element would make it impossible to make the array switchable in direction. Neither of these problems are encountered with the first set of points. The second solution requires a fair amount of feed line, however.

The feed lines can now simply be parallel-connected at these points. The impedances can be calculated using the COAX TRANSFORMER software module:

Z1' = 24.9 – j47 ohms
E1' = 41 $\angle 108°$ V

Z2' = 28 + j38.4 ohms
E2' = 41 $\angle 108°$ V

The combined impedance can then be calculated with the T-JUNCTION module. The impedance for this array comes out to 47.2 + j0.9 ohms, which yields an SWR of 1.07:1 when connected to a 50-ohm cable, and will require no further matching.

4.3. Two Elements in Phase with ½-Wave Spacing

Array Data

Spacing: ½ wavelength
Feed currents: I1 = 1 $\angle 0°$; I2 = 1 $\angle 0°$
Gain: 3.8 dB over a single vertical
3 dB beamwidth: 62 degrees
Radiation: Bidirectional, broadside

Mutual impedance: Z(12) = Z(21) = approx. –9 – j13 ohms

The feed-point impedance (including 2 ohms ground loss resistance) is

Z1 = Z2 = 31 – j14 ohms

Fig 11-29 shows the radiation patterns over very good ground.

4.3.1. Feed system.

In principle the array can be fed with two feed lines of equal lengths.

Feeding via ¼-wave (or ¾-wave) feed lines, however, has the advantage of "forcing" equal currents in both elements, whatever the difference in element impedances might be. It is therefore advised to feed the array via two ¾-wave-long feed lines. Quarter-wave feed lines are too short (due to the velocity factor) to reach the center of the array.

The impedance at the end of the 270-degree-long RG-213 feed line (attenuation = 0.35 dB/100 ft at 3.8 MHz) is

Z = 65.84 + j26.37 ohms

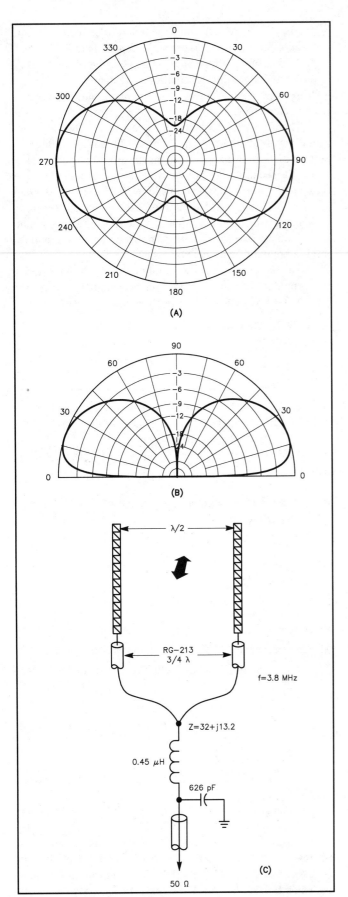

(A)

(B)

(C)

Fig 11-29—A, horizontal and B, vertical radiation patterns for an array made of two verticals spaced ½ wavelength apart and fed in phase. It is best to feed the elements via two ¾-wave-long feed lines, as shown at C.

The two feed lines in parallel result in an array impedance of

$Z_{array} = 32.0 + j13.2$ ohms

The feed system and an L network providing a 1:1 SWR to a 50-ohm feed line are shown in Fig 11-29.

4.4. Three Elements in Phase, Half-Wave Spacing, Binomial Current Distribution

Array Data

Number of elements: 3
Spacing: ½ wavelength
Feed currents: $I1 = 1 \angle 0°$, $I2 = 2 \angle 0°$, $I3 = 1 \angle 0°$
Gain: 5.2 dB over a single vertical
3-dB beamwidth: 46 degrees
Radiation: bidirectional, broadside

The feed-point impedances (including 2 ohms ground loss resistance) are

$Z1 = Z3 = 25.0 - j19.4$ ohms

$Z2 = 30.7 - j13.7$ ohms

Fig 11-30 shows the radiation patterns over very good ground.

4.4.1. Current-forcing feed system.

For reasons explained in par 3.3.7., it is always best to try to feed the elements with feed lines that are an odd multiple of quarter-wavelengths long. Three-quarter-wavelength-long feed lines to elements 1 and 3 will just reach the center of the array if they are made of solid PE coaxial cables (0.75-wavelength-long feed line × 0.66 velocity factor = 0.5 wavelength).

We will run ¾-wave-long feed lines to all elements. The feed line to the center element will require half the impedance of the cables to the outer elements to obtain the proper current magnitude. We use two 50-ohm feed lines in parallel (Z = 25 ohms). All calculations are done with RG-213 coax (0.35 dB/100 ft attenuation at 3.8 MHz).

The element impedances are

$Z1 = Z3 = 25.0 - j19.4$ ohms

$Z2 = 30.7 - j13.7$ ohms

The impedances and voltages at the end of the feed lines are calculated using the software module COAXIAL CABLE TRANSFORMER/SMITH CHART.

Elements 1 and 3 are fed via a 270-degree-long 50-ohm line.

$Z1' = Z3' = 63.1 + j42.6$ ohms
$E1' = E3' = 51.37 \angle -91.1°$

Element 2 is fed via a 270-degree-long 25-ohm line:

$Z2' = 17.41 + j7.3$ ohms
$E1' = 51.6 \angle -90.8°$

The voltages are essentially identical, so the feed lines can simply be connected in parallel. The array impedance is made up by the parallel connection of the impedances at the end of the three feed lines.

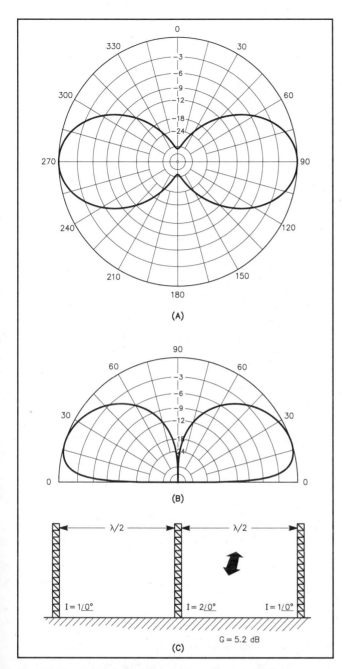

Fig 11-30—A, horizontal and B, vertical radiation pattern for the three-in-line array with ½-wave spacing. The element feed currents are in phase but the center element gets twice as much current as the outer ones (binomial current distribution). Notice the rather narrow lobe beamwidth in the azimuth pattern at A.

$Z_{array} = 11.3 + j5.6$ ohms

We can design an L network to match this impedance to the 50-ohm feed line. The layout with all the values is shown in Fig 11-31.

4.5. Two-Element Bidirectional End-Fire Array, ½-Wave Spacing, 180 Degrees Out of Phase

Array Data

Number of elements: 2

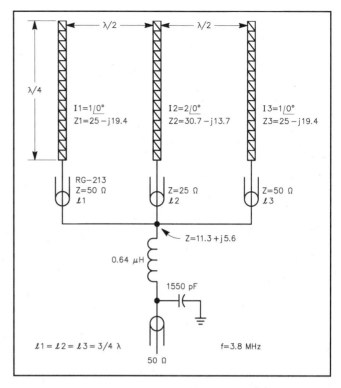

Fig 11-31—Feed system for the three verticals in line with binomial current distribution. The center element is fed via two parallel 50-ohm feed lines in order to obtain the double current. The current-forcing method ensures that variations in element self-impedances have a minimum impact on the performance of the array.

Spacing: ½ wavelength
Feed currents: $I1 = 1 \angle 0°$, $I2 = 1 \angle -180°$
Gain: 2.4 dB over a single vertical
3-dB beamwidth: 116 degrees
Radiation: Bidirectional, end-fire

Mutual impedance: $Z(12) = Z(21) =$ approx. $-9 - j13$ ohms

The feed-point impedance (including 2 ohms ground loss resistance): $Z1 = Z2 = 45.4 + j14$ ohms.

Fig 11-32 shows the radiation patterns over very good ground.

4.5.1. Current-forcing feed system.

We will run a 270-degree-long feed line to the element with the leading current, and a 450-degree-long feed line to the element with the lagging feed current. With the lines being odd multiples of quarter wavelengths long, we enhance the "current-forcing" principle (currents will be equal in magnitude even though element impedances may be slightly different). A 90-degree- and a 270-degree-long feed line are too short for the array, as the elements are spaced ½ wavelength. To preserve symmetry, the T junction where the lines to the elements join must be located at the center of the array. The element with the leading current is fed via a ¾-wave feed line, the lagging element via a ⁵⁄₄-wave.

The impedances at the end of the feed lines can be calculated with the COAX TRANSFORMER software module.

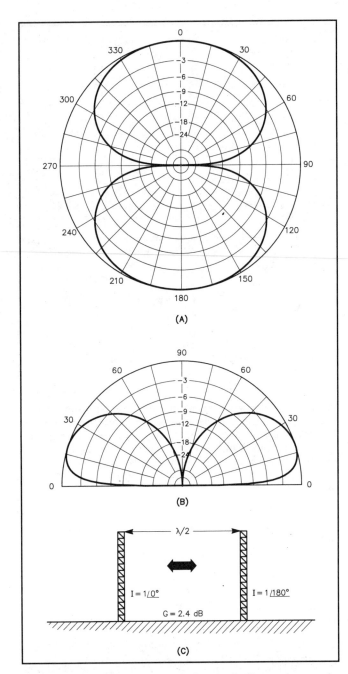

Fig 11-32—Radiation patterns for the half-wave spaced bidirectional end-fire array. The two elements are fed in phase opposition (180 degrees out of phase).

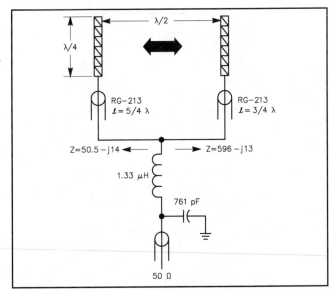

Fig 11-33—Current-forcing feed system for the 2-element bidirectional end-fire array. Three quarter-wave-long feed lines are used because ¼-wave-long feed lines would not reach to the center of the array.

Z1' = 50.5 – j14 ohms

Z2' = 59.6 – j13 ohms

The combined impedance can then be calculated with the T-JUNCTION module.

The impedance for this array comes out to 27.4 – j6.8 ohms. An L network can be designed for matching this impedance to a 50-ohm line. The feed system is shown in Fig 11-33.

4.5.2. Closer spacing.

An alternative where you can use a 90- and a 270-degree feed line is to use foam dielectric line (VF ≈ 80%) and move the two radiators closer together. As you reduce the spacing the gain increases, and reaches a maximum at 0.3-wavelength separation. At this spacing, feed lines with solid PE dielectric (eg, RG-213) will reach. We will analyze this configuration.

Array Data

Spacing: 0.3 wavelength

Feed currents: $I1 = 1 \angle 0°$; $I2 = 1 \angle -180°$

Gain: 3.1 dB over a single vertical

3-dB beamwidth: 98 degrees

Radiation: Bidirectional, end-fire

The feed-point impedance (including 2 ohms of ground loss resistance) is

Z1 = Z2 = 24.5 + j18.3 ohms

Fig 11-34 shows the radiation pattern.

The element with the leading current is fed via a ¼-wave feed line, the lagging element via a ¾-wave line. The impedances at the end of the feed lines can be calculated with the COAX TRANSFORMER software module:

Z1' = 65.7 – j46.8 ohms

Z2' = 65.8 – j42.7 ohms

The two impedances would have been identical if the two feed lines were lossless.

The combined impedance can then be calculated with the T-JUNCTION module. The impedance for this array comes out to 32.9 – j22.4 ohms. An L network can be designed for matching this impedance to a 50-ohm line (Fig 11-35).

4.6. Three-Element Quarter-Wave-Spaced Quadrature-Fed End-Fire Array

A very effective three-element end-fire array uses quarter-wave spacing and 90 degrees of phase shift between

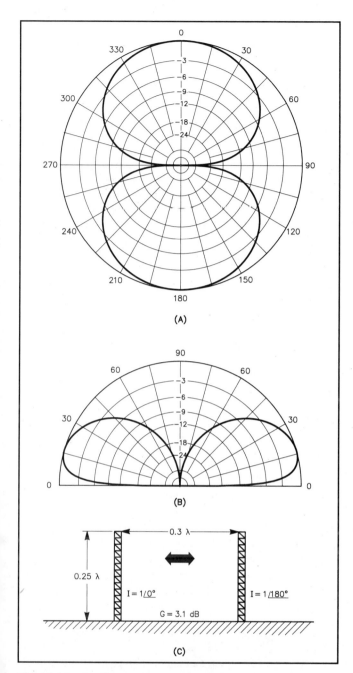

Fig 11-34—Radiation patterns for the 2-element end-fire out-of-phase array, but for reduced spacing (0.3 wavelength). The reduced spacing results in superior gain.

adjacent elements. The center element is supplied with twice as much current as the outer ones.

Array Data

Number of elements: 3
Spacing: 0.25 wavelength
Feed currents: $I1 = 1 \angle -90°$; $I2 = 2 \angle 0°$; $I3 = 1 \angle +90°$
Gain: 4.1 dB over a single vertical
3-dB beamwidth: 142 degrees
Radiation: Unidirectional, end-fire

Mutual impedances (approx. values):

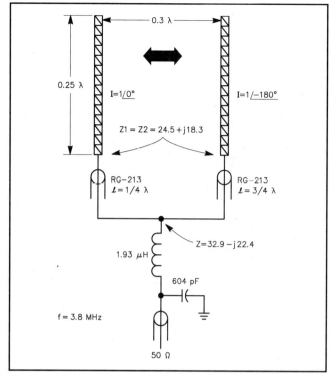

Fig 11-35—Current-forcing feed method for the 2-element out-of-phase end-fire array using reduced spacing (0.3 wavelength). The reduced spacing allows the use of ¼-wave-long feed lines.

$Z(12) = 15 - j15$ ohms

$Z(13) = -9 - j13$ ohms

$Z(23) = Z(12)$

The feed-point impedances (including 2 ohms ground loss resistance) are

$Z1 = 76.1 + j51$ ohms (–90 degrees)
$Z2 = 26.3 - j0.4$ ohms
$Z3 = 15 - j22.6$ ohms (+90 degrees)

Fig 11-36 shows the radiation patterns over very good ground.

As this antenna is quadrature-fed, it is obvious that the Lewallen or the Collins feed methods are the logical choices for the feed system.

4.6.1 The Lewallen feed system.

If we want to double the current in one of the elements of an array fed with the "current-forcing" method, all we need to do is to run a coaxial cable with half the impedance of the coax feeding the other elements. In other words, the feed line to the center element will consist of two parallel-connected feed lines.

Quarter-wave feed lines can only be used to feed the elements if the array is not to be made switchable. If the array is to be made switchable, ¾-wave-long feed lines will have to be used.

The impedance data at the elements are

$Z1 = 76.1 + j51$ ohms (–90 degrees)

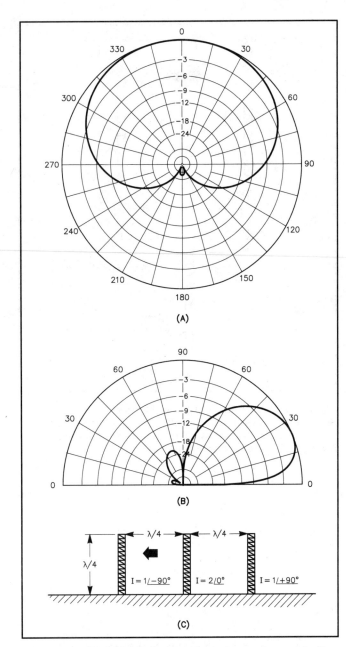

Fig 11-36—Radiation pattern of the three-element in-line array, with elements spaced ¼ wavelength and with quadrature phasing conditions. The center element gets twice as much current as the outer elements.

$Z2 = 26.3 - j0.4$ ohms

$Z3 = 15 - j22.6$ ohms (+90 degrees)

The impedances at the end of the feed lines were calculated using the COAX TRANSFORMER software module (all elements are fed with 50-ohm cables RG-213 with 0.35 dB/ 100 ft loss at 3.8 MHz):

Element 1 is fed via a 270-degree (¾-wave-long) 50-ohm cable:

$Z1' = 24.9 - j14.46$ ohms

$E1' = 54.06 \angle -171.21°$

Element 2 is fed via two parallel 50-ohm cables (equivalent feed-line impedance = 25 ohms):

$Z2' = 23.8 + j0.3$ ohms

$E2' = 51.4 \angle -90°$

The third element is fed via an extra 180-degree-long line; the total feed line is 450 degrees long:

$Z3' = 58.5 + j63.5$ ohms

$E3' = 52.5 \angle 177.8$

The end of the feed lines to elements 1 and 3 can be connected together: The resulting (parallel) impedance is calculated using the PARALLEL IMPEDANCE software module:

$Z_P = 25 - j5.9$ ohms.

The phases of E1' and E3' would both be 180 degrees (= –180 degrees), but the losses of the rather long feed lines (270 and 450 degrees) account for the slight differences.

The only thing left to do is to calculate the value of the Lewallen design L network to take care of the 90 degree voltage phase shift:

$$X_S = \frac{Z_{coax}^2}{R(2)} = \frac{50^2}{26.3} = 95.5 \text{ ohms or}$$

L (at 3.8 MHz) = 4 μH

$$X_P = \frac{Z_{coax}^2}{X(2) - R(2)} = \frac{50^2}{-0.4 - 26.3} = -93.6 \text{ ohms}$$

or: $C = 448$ pF

Let us calculate out the feed-point impedance for the entire array. The parallel connection of the feed lines to element 1 ($Z1' = 24.9 - j14.46$ ohms) and element 3 ($Z3' = 58.5 + j63.5$ ohms) is $Z(1,3) = 25 - j5.9$ ohms.

The impedance at the end of the feed line to the central element (element 3) is shunted by the capacitor with a reactance of –93.6 ohms. The impedance becomes (use the SHUNT IMPEDANCE NETWORK software module)

$Z2'' = 22.5 - j5.44$ ohms.

The coil reactance ($X_L = 95.5$ ohms) is in series with this impedance. The net result is: $Z2''' = 22.5 + j90.06$ ohms.

Now we connect this impedance in parallel with $Z(1,3)$.

$Z_{total} = 24.66 + j0.92$ ohms.

An L network or a quarter-wave transformer made by two parallel-connected quarter-wave long 75-ohm cables can be used to provide a 1:1 SWR to a 50-ohm feed line.

Fig 11-37 shows the feed system for the array with the direction-switching harness.

4.6.2. The Collins feed system.

We have calculated the impedances at the end of the feed lines (270 degrees, 270 degrees and 450 degrees long) in par 4.6.1.

The impedance at the parallel connection of the feed lines to elements 1 and 3 was calculated in par 4.6.1. as $Z(1,3) = 25 - j5.9$ ohms. The impedance at the end of the two parallel 50-ohm feed lines to element 2 is $Z2' = 23.8 + j0.3$ ohms.

Notice that both impedances result in a very low SWR in a 25-ohm system. The performance of the coupler will be very

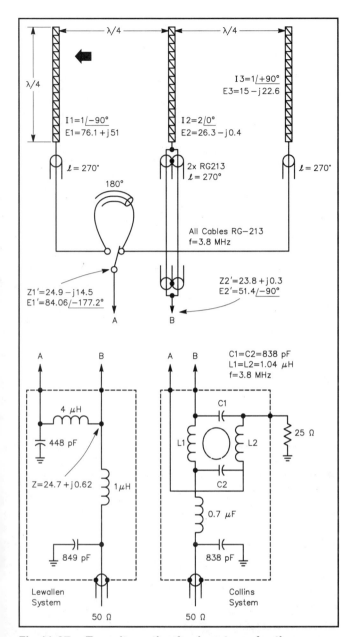

Fig 11-37— Two alternative feed systems for the 3-element in-line end-fire array. Both the Lewallen and the Collins feed systems are ideally suited for this array. Direction switching is extremely simple and requires only one SPDT relay.

good if we design the hybrid coupler with a nominal imped-ance of 25 ohms.

The values of the coupler components are

$$X_{L1} = X_{L2} = 250 \text{ ohms} (= \text{system impedance})$$

$$X_{C1} = X_{C2} = 25 \text{ ohms}$$

For 3.8 MHz, the component values are

$$L1 = L2 = \frac{X_L}{2\pi f} = \frac{25}{2\pi \times 3.8} = 1.04 \ \mu\text{H}$$

$$C1 = C2 = \frac{10^6}{2 \times 2\pi f X_C} = \frac{10^6}{4\pi \times 3.8 \times 25} = 838 \text{ pF}$$

Fig 11-37 shows the feed system for the array.

4.7. Three-Element Quarter-Wave-Spaced End-Fire Array, Nonquadrature Fed

A. Christman, KB8I, published a configuration of a 3-element in-line array ("Phased drive arrays for the low bands," *QST*, May 1992, p 49), with a nonquadrature feed-current distribution, which results in superior gain and front-to-back ratio as compared to the quadrature-fed array de-scribed in par 4.6.

Array Data

Number of elements: 3
Spacing: 0.25 wavelength
Feed currents: $I1 = 1 \angle -116°$; $I2 = 2 \angle 0°$; $I3 = 1 \angle 117°$
Gain: 5.2 dB over a single vertical
3-dB beamwidth: 114 degrees
Radiation: Unidirectional, end-fire
The feed-point impedances (including 2 ohms ground loss resistance) are

$$Z1 = 42.3 + j61.5 \text{ ohms} (-116 \text{ degrees})$$
$$Z2 = 28 + j6.3 \text{ ohms}$$
$$Z3 = 9.6 - j17 \text{ ohms} (+117 \text{ degrees})$$

Fig 11-38 shows the radiation patterns over very good ground.

As this is not a quadrature-fed array, this array can obviously not be fed using the Collins or the Lewallen meth-ods. We will calculate a modified Christman and a current-forcing system (modified Lewallen feed system).

4.7.1. Modified Christman feed system.

First we'll design a feed system using the modified Christman method (par 3.3.2). We use the software program VOLTAGE ALONG FEED LINES and see if we can find points on the three feed lines where the voltages are identical. Don't forget to specify cable losses per wavelength (not the usual dB per 100 ft!).

Such points can be found on the lines to element 1 and element 3, as follows.

Line 1, at 304.5 degrees from the load:

$$E1' = 29.8 \angle -132.4°$$

$$Z1' = 16.8 + j2.15 \text{ ohms}$$

Line 3, at 167 degrees from the load:

$$E2' = 29.9 \angle -131.8°$$

$$Z2' = 13.95 - j29.9 \text{ ohms}$$

Note from the listing that the length of line 1 is very critical!

For all practical purposes we can consider these values as identical. This means we can connect the end of those two 50-ohm feed lines together. I tried several feed line imped-ances (25, 50 and 75 ohms) but could not find a point on a feed line running to the central element that had the same voltage.

The solution is to use an L network (Ref. the Gehrke system, par 3.3.5). With the software module SERIES/SHUNT INPUT L-NETWORK ITERATION we can design an L

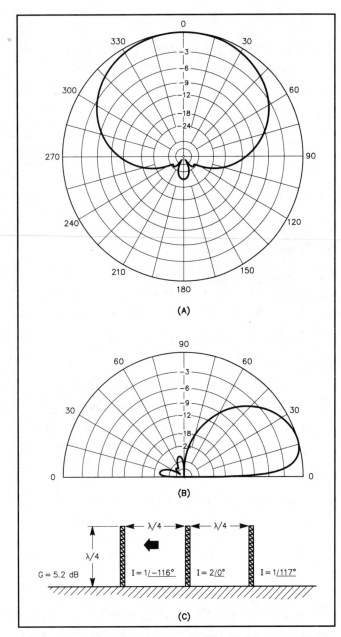

Fig 11-38—Radiation patterns for the 3-element in-line array using ¼-wave spacing and optimized current angles (*after Christman*). Notice the superior high-angle F/B performance as compared to the quadrature-fed array from Fig 11-36.

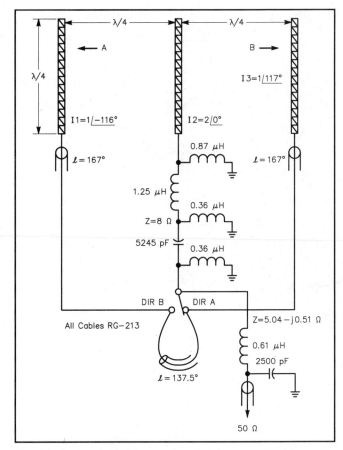

Fig 11-39—Modified Christman feed system for the three-in-line end-fire array (quarter-wave spacing) with optimized current phase angles. See text for details.

network that will transform the impedance at the base of the central element (Z2 = 28 + j6.3 ohms, E2 = 57.4 $\angle 12.68°$) so that the *voltage magnitude* at the input of the filter (the resistive impedance end) is 32.5 V. There are two solutions to the problem.

Solution 1

X_S = 29.9 ohms (1.25 µH at 3.8 MHz)

X_P = 20.8 ohms (0.87 µH at 3.8 MHz)

Z_{in} = 8 ohms

E_{in} = 29.9 $\angle -45.9°$ V

Solution 2

X_S = 13.1 ohms (0.55 µH at 3.8 MHz)

X_P = −15.8 ohms (2652 pF at 3.8 MHz)

Z_{in} = 8 ohms

E_{in} = 29.9 $\angle 71.2°$ V

Now that the voltage magnitude is correct we need to shift the phase to −132.5 degrees. Let us take solution 1.

We use a constant-impedance T or pi network to do the phase shifting. The software module LINE STRETCHER (PI OR T) does the calculations in seconds. Let us take a pi network. The solution is

Z_{filter}: 8 ohms

Voltage input phase angle: −132.5 degrees

Voltage output phase angle: −45.9 degrees

X_S = −8 ohms (5244 pF at 3.8 MHz)

Z_P = 8.5 ohms (0.36 µH at 3.8 MHz)

The final network is shown in Fig 11-39.

The input impedance of the array is given by the parallel connection of three impedances:

Z1 = 16.8 + j2.15 ohms

Z2 = 8 ohms

Z3 = 13.95 − j29.9 ohms

The parallel combination of these three impedances is Z_{array} = 5.0 − j0.51 ohms. This is a very low value. Very high currents will be circulating in the components of the network, so care must be taken in the construction. An L network seems to be the logical choice for matching this impedance to the feed line.

I'd like to comment on this solution. In order to be able to draw double the current in the central element (as compared to the current in the outer elements), the impedances involved are very low. This is because the impedances at the end of the two feed lines are already low (16.8 + j21.5 and 14 − j30 ohms) to start with. This results in components in the phasing system that have very low impedances. If you would like to construct this system, I would strongly advise to take extreme care when making the phasing network, as extremely high currents will circulate in the components with high power.

4.7.2. Current-forcing system.

We will run ¾-wave feed lines from the outer elements to our switch-box and a ¼-wave feed line of paralleled 50-ohm cables from the center element. This combination guarantees us "current-forcing." The magnitudes of the voltages at the end of the three lines will be identical (50 V). All we will then do is use constant-impedance line stretchers to obtain the proper phase angle.

The element feed-point impedances are:

Z1 = 42.3 + j61.5 ohms (−116 degrees)

Z2 = 28 + j6.3 ohms

Z3 = 9.9 − j17 ohms (+117 degree)

The impedances at the end of the feed lines are calculated with the software module COAXIAL TRANSFORMER/ SMITH CHART.

270-degree 50-ohm line to element 1:

Z1' = 21.9 − j26.5 ohms

E1' = 52.35 ∠157.5°

90-degree 25-ohm line to element 2:

Z2' = 21.3 − j4.7 ohms

E2' = 50.5 ∠90.12°

270-degree 50-ohm line to element 3:

Z3' = 72.5 + j95.3 ohms

E3' = 50.6 ∠−153°

We will keep the central element (no. 2) as the reference element and line up the phase angles of the voltages at the end of the feed lines to elements 1 and 3 with the phase angle at the end of the quarter-wave feed line to the center element. This will be done with constant-impedance line stretchers. First we must cancel the reactive component in the impedance by adding a shunt impedance, using the SHUNT/SERIES IMPEDANCE NETWORK module.

Line to element 1:

Impedance was Z1' = 21.9 − j26.5 ohms

Adding a shunt reactance of 44.6 ohms (1.9 μH coil at 3.8 MHz) tunes out the reactive part of the impedance. The impedance now is

Z1" = 54 ohms

Line to element 3:

Impedance was: Z1' = 72.5 + j95.3 ohms

Adding a shunt reactance of −150.5 ohms (278 pF at 3.8 MHz) tunes out the reactive part of the impedance. The impedance now is

Z1" = 198 ohms

Now we will design the pi-network line stretchers (T would also be possible) using the LINE STRETCHER (PI or T) software module:

Line stretcher to element 1:

Impedance: 54 ohms
Voltage input phase angle: 90.12 degrees
Voltage output phase angle: 157.5 degrees
X_S = −49.8 ohms (840 pF at 3.8 MHz)
X_P = 81 ohms (3.4 μH at 3.8 MHz)

Line stretcher to element 3:

Impedance: 198 ohms
Voltage input phase angle: 90.12 degrees
Voltage output phase angle: −153 degrees = +207 degrees
X_S = −177 ohms (237 pF at 3.8 MHz)
X_P = 121.6 ohms (5.1 μH at 3.8 MHz)

The output of the line stretchers and the line to element 2 can now be connected in parallel, as the voltages are identical. The impedance in that point is the parallel of:

Z1" = 54 ohms
Z2 = 21.3 − j4.7 ohms
Z3 = 198 ohms

The resulting impedance is the array feed-impedance (calculated with the PARALLEL IMPEDANCES module):

Z_{array} = 14.3 − j2.1 ohms

An appropriate L network will ensure a 1:1 SWR into a 50-ohm feed line. This feed system is shown in Fig 11-40. Comparing this solution with the solution described in par 4.7.2., it is obvious that this solution is far superior. Component values are more "normal" because "normal" impedances are involved. This feed system is obviously the better choice.

4.8. Three-Element ⅛-Wave-Spaced End-Fire Array, Nonquadrature Fed

Another design by A. Christman, KB8I, uses three ⅛-wavelength-spaced elements in line to obtain an excellent F/B behavior and a gain comparable to that of the ¼-wave-spaced array.

Array Data

Number of elements: 3
Spacing: 0.125 wavelength
Feed currents: I1 = 1 ∠−149°; I2 = 2 ∠0°; I3 = 1 ∠146°

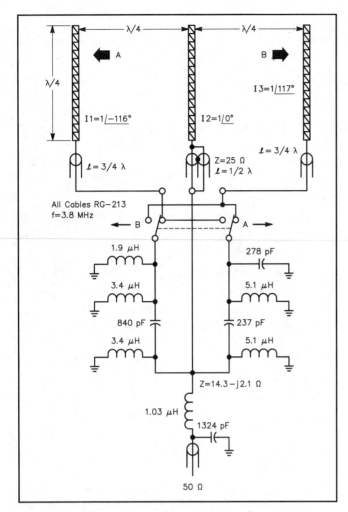

Fig 11-40—Current-forcing feed system for the three-in-line end-fire array (¼-wave spacing) with optimized feed current angles. The system requires a DPDT relay for direction switching but is nevertheless the logical choice as compared to the feed system from Fig 11-39. See text for details.

Gain: 4.1 dB over a single vertical
3-dB beamwidth: 94 degrees
Radiation: Unidirectional, end-fire

The feed-point impedances (including 2 ohms ground loss resistance) are

Z1 = 4.6 + j19 ohms (–149 degrees)
Z2 = 12 + j1.6 ohms
Z3 = –19 + j13.4 ohms (+146 degrees)

Fig 11-41 shows the radiation patterns over very good ground.

In view of the very low impedances involved with ⅛-wave spacing, I highly recommend using a "current-forcing" feed system, as the system is more lenient with changes in impedance of the individual elements than other systems. Note the negative impedance of the third element, which means that this element is actually returning current to the feed system.

Current-Forcing Feed System

We will run ¼-wavelength feed lines from the outer

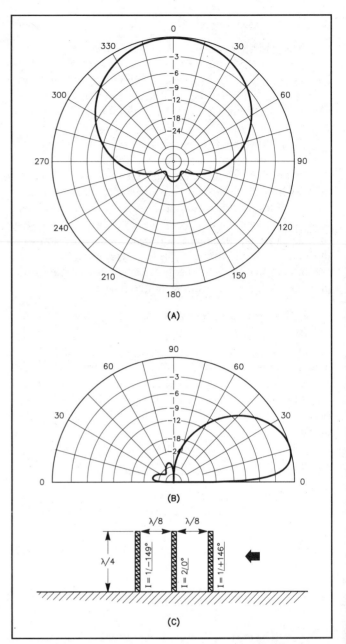

Fig 11-41—Radiation patterns for the three-in-line end-fire array with ⅛-wave element spacing and optimized feed current angle distribution (–149, 0 and +146 degrees).

elements to our switch-box and a ¼-wave feed line of parallel-connected 50-ohm cables from the center element. These combinations guarantee us "current-forcing." The magnitudes of the voltages at the end of the three lines will be identical (50 V). All we will then do, is use constant-impedance line stretchers to obtain the proper phase angle.

The element feed-point impedances are:

Z1 = 4.6 + j19 ohms (–149 degrees)
Z2 = 12 + j1.6 ohms
Z3 = –19 + j13.4 ohms (+146 degrees)

The impedances at the end of the feed lines are calculated

with the software module COAXIAL TRANSFORMER/ SMITH CHART.

90-degree 50-ohm line to element 1:

$Z1' = 35.7 - j121.5$ ohms

$E1' = 50.1 \angle -50.6°$ V

90-degree 25-ohm line to element 2:

$Z2' = 50.5 - j6.6$ ohms

$E2' = 50.2 \angle 90.03°$ V

90-degree 50-ohm line to element 3:

$Z3' = -88.3 - j65.8$ ohms

$E3' = 49.7 \angle -123.7°$ V

The methodology is described in par 4.7.2.

Line to element 1:

Impedance was $Z1' = 35.7 - j121.5$ ohms

Adding a shunt reactance of 132 ohms (5.53-μH coil at 3.8 MHz) tunes out the reactive part of the impedance. The impedance now is

$Z1'' = 449$ ohms

Line to element 3:

Impedance was $Z1' = -88.3 - j65.8$ ohms

Adding a shunt reactance of +184 ohms (7.7 μH at 3.8 MHz) tunes out the reactive part of the impedance. The impedance now is

$Z3'' = -137.1$ ohms

Now we will design the pi-network line stretchers using the LINE STRETCHERS software module.

Line stretcher to element 1:

Impedance: 449 ohms

Voltage input phase angle: 90.03 degrees

Voltage output phase angle: –50.6 degrees

$X_S = -285$ ohms (147 pF at 3.8 MHz)

$X_P = 161$ ohms (6.7 μH at 3.8 MHz)

Line stretcher to element 3:

Impedance: 198 ohms

Voltage input phase angle: 90.03 degrees

Voltage output phase angle: –123.7 degrees = +236.3 degrees

$X_S = 110$ ohms (4.6 μH at 3.8 MHz)

$X_P = -60$ ohms (698 pF at 3.8 MHz)

The output of the line stretchers and the line to element 2 can now be connected in parallel, as the voltages are identical. The impedance in that point is the parallel of

$Z1'' = 449$ ohms

$Z2 = 50.5 - j6.6$ ohms

$Z3'' = -137.1$ ohms

Again, the –137.1 ohms means that current will be

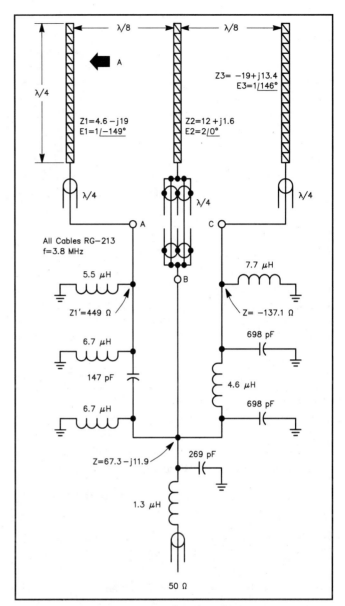

Fig 11-42—Current-forcing feed method for the ⅛-wave-spaced end-fire three-in-line array with optimized feed current angle distribution.

flowing from the antenna toward the junction of the three feed lines. The third element is supplying current to the other elements. The NEW LOW BAND SOFTWARE copes very well with negative impedances.

The resulting impedance is the array feed impedance (calculated with the PARALLEL IMPEDANCES module):

$Z_{array} = 67.33 - j11.9$ ohms

An appropriate L network will ensure a 1:1 SWR into a 50-ohm feed line. This feed system is shown in Fig 11-42.

4.9. Four-Square Arrays

In 1965 D. Atchley, W1CF (then W1HKK), described two arrays which were computer modeled, and later built and tested with good success (Ref. 930, 941). Although the theoretical benefits of the 4-square were well understood, it took a while before the correct feed methods were developed that could guarantee performance at par with the paperwork.

The 4-square can be switched in 4 quadrants. Atchley also developed a switching arrangement that made it possible to switch the array directivity in increments of 45 degrees. The second configuration consists of two side by side cardioid arrays. This antenna is discussed in detail in par 4.10.3.

The practical advantage of the extra directivity steps, however, does not seem to be worth the effort required to design the much more complicated feeding and switching system, as the forward lobe is so broad that switching in 45-degree steps makes very little difference. It is also important to keep in mind that the more complicated a system is, the more failure-prone it is.

4.9.1 Pattern switching for the 4-square arrays.

Fig 11-43 shows a direction-switching system that can be used with all the 4-square arrays, on condition that the two diagonal (central) elements are fed in phase. The "front" element (in the direction of firing) will of course be fed with the lagging feed angle, the back element with the leading feed angle.

While designing the feed systems of the individual arrays, I will simply show the "black box" containing the feed system. The box has four terminals:

1) 50-ohm input to transmitter.
2) Two outputs to the central element (phase angle zero).
3) One output to the front element (lagging phase angle).
4) One output to the back element (leading phase angle).

4.9.2. Quarter-wave-spaced square, quadrature-fed.

Array Data

Number of elements: 4
Placement of elements: In a square, spaced 0.25 wavelength per side

Elements 2 and 3 = a diagonal of the square
Feed currents:
$$I1=1\angle-90°;\ I2=1\angle0°;\ I3=1\angle0°;\ I4=1\angle90°$$
Gain: 5.5 dB over a single vertical
3-dB beamwidth: 96 degrees
Radiation: Unidirectional

The feed-point impedances (including 2 ohms ground loss resistance) are

$Z1 = 61.7 + j54.4$ ohms (−90 degrees)
$Z2 = Z3 = 41 − j19.3$ ohms
$Z4 = −0.4 − j15.4$ ohms (+90 degrees)

Fig 11-44 shows the radiation patterns over very good ground.

The four elements of the antenna are positioned in a square, with quarter-wave spacing between adjacent elements. All elements are fed with equal current. The two central elements are fed at 0 degrees (reference), the rear element is fed at 90 degrees, and the front element is fed at −90 degrees. The direction of maximum signal is along the diagonal from the rear to the front element (an array always radiates in the direction of the element with the lagging current).

Several feed methods can be developed. I have worked

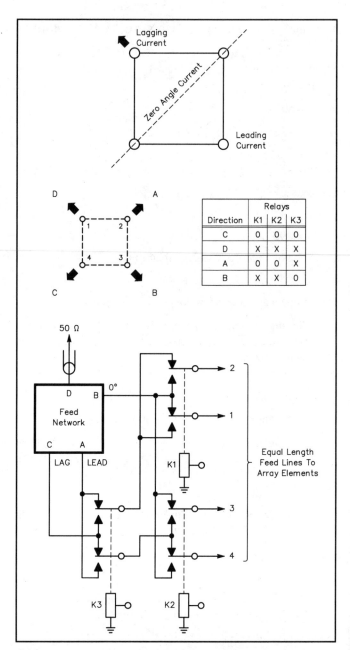

Fig 11-43—Universal direction-switching system that can be used with any of the 4-square arrays. The condition is that the two "central" elements be fed with the reference (zero-angle) current, the front element with the lagging current, and the back element with the leading current. From the switching network, four lines of equal length (¼ or ¾ wavelength long) go to the individual elements. The lengths and specifications (impedance, type) are different for every type of square array.

out 2 systems, the Lewallen method and the Collins method.

4.9.2.1. The Lewallen feed method.

The 2 EL AND 4 EL VERTICAL ARRAYS module of the NEW LOW BAND SOFTWARE is a tutorial and engineering program that takes you step by step through the design of the 4-element square array. The results as displayed from that program will be slightly different from the results

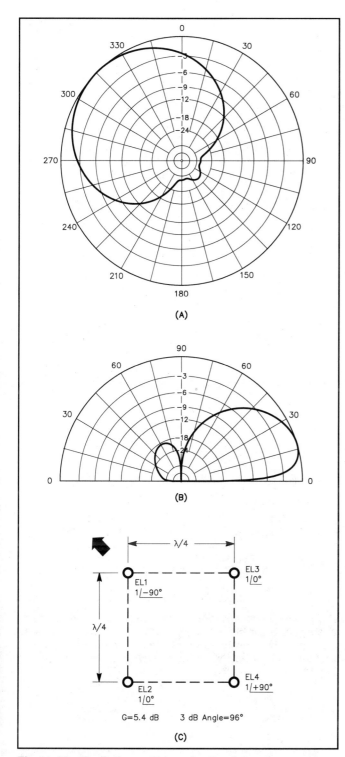

Fig 11-44—Radiation patterns for the 4-square array with ¼-wave element spacing.

shown here, as in that program ideal feed lines (no losses) are used. It is interesting, however, to compare the values from this paragraph with the values from the software program to assess the error caused by using lossless cables.

The impedances at the elements are:

$Z1 = 61.7 + j59.4$ ohms (–90 degrees)

$Z2 = Z3 = 41 – j19$ ohms

$Z4 = –0.4 – j15$ ohms (+90 degrees)

We cannot reach the center of the array with quarter-wave feed lines with a velocity factor of 0.66 (solid PE, eg, RG-213). Foam-type RG-8 will be required. For the calculations I used VF = 0.79 and attenuation = 0.3 dB/100 ft.

Using the software module COAX TRANSFORMER, voltages, currents and impedances at the end of the four lengths of coaxial cable can be calculated.

270 degrees from element 1:

$Z1' = 23.56 – j19.31$ ohms
$E1' = 53.43 \angle -176.62°$

90 degrees from element 2 and from element 3:

$Z2 = Z3 = 50.37 + j22.45$ ohms
or $R2 = 50.37$ and $X2 = 22.45$
$E2' = E3' = 50.73 \angle 89.62°$ V

90 degrees from element 4:

$Z4 = 6.24 + j166.44$ ohms
$E4' = 50.00 \angle 179.7°$

The feed lines to element 1 and element 4 can be connected in parallel (the voltages are practically identical). The resulting impedance is

$Z_{total}(1,4) = 29.26 – j16.92$ ohms

The elements of the Lewallen L network that provide the necessary 90-degree voltage phase shift can easily be calculated:

$$X_S = \frac{Z_{coax}^2}{2R(1)} = \frac{50^2}{2 \times 50.37} = 24.61 \text{ ohms}$$

$$X_P = \frac{Z_{coax}^2}{2[X(1) - R(1)]} = \frac{50^2}{2 \times (22.45 - 50.37)} = -44.8 \text{ ohms}$$

Series element (inductor): 1.03 μH at 3.8 MHz
Parallel element (capacitor): 395 pF

Note: If more than one element is fed via the L network (in this case the L network is supplying the extra 90-degree phase shift to the two central elements), the formulas for X_S and X_P are

$$X_S = \frac{Z_{coax}^2}{\Sigma(R)}$$

$$X_P = \frac{Z_{coax}^2}{\Sigma(X) - \Sigma(R)}$$

where

$\Sigma(R) =$ the sum of the feed-point resistances of all elements connected to the output side of the L network. In our case, $\Sigma(R) = 2 \times R2$

$\Sigma(X) =$ the sum of the feed-point reactances of all elements connected to the output side of the L network. Here, $\Sigma(X) = 2 \times X2$

Calculating the Total Feed Impedance of the Array

The feed lines from elements 2 and 3 are in parallel at the output of the L network. The total impedance is

$Z_{total}(2,3) = 25.18 + j11.23$ ohms

This impedance is first shunted by a capacitor with a reactance of –44.8 ohms. Using the SHUNT IMPEDANCE NETWORK module we calculate the resulting impedance:

$Z(2,3)' = 28.7 - j6.54$ ohms

In series with this impedance we have the reactance of the coil from the L network, 24.61 ohms. The net resulting impedance becomes

$Z(2,3)'' = 28.7 + j18.07$ ohms

The input impedance of the array is the parallel connection of

$Z(2,3)'' = 28.7 + j18.07$ ohms
$Z1' = 23.56 - j19.31$ ohms
$Z4 = -6.24 + j166.44$ ohms

The result is $20.1 + j0.5$ ohms.

The Lewallen feed method for this array is worked out in great detail in *The ARRL Antenna Book*, and L-network values are listed for a range of feed-line impedances and ground systems. The layout of the feed system is shown in Fig 11-45A.

4.9.2.2. *The Collins feed method.*

The feed-line configuration (length, type, etc) is identical to that for the Lewallen feed system. The impedance and voltage values at the end of the lines are calculated in par 4.9.2.1.

In the Collins feed system we replace the L network with the hybrid coupler. In order to optimize the performance of the coupler we must determine the system impedance which best matches the impedances at the end of the feed lines.

270 degrees from element 1:

$Z1' = 23.56 - j19.31$ ohms

$E1' = 53.43 \angle -176.62°$ V

90 degrees from element 2 and element 3:

$Z2 = Z3 = 50.37 + j22.45$ ohms

$E2' = E3' = 50.73 \angle 89.62°$ V

90 degrees from element 4:

$Z4 = 6.24 + j166.44$ ohms

$E4' = 50.00 \angle 179.7°$ V

Paralleling the two feed lines to elements 2 and 3 yields a total impedance of

$Z(2,3)' = 25.37 + j11.22$ ohms

Paralleling the lines to elements 1 and 4 yields

$Z(1,4)' = 29.26 - j16.92$ ohms

Running both impedances in the SWR ITERATION software program shows that the lowest SWR is obtained with a hybrid-coupler impedance of 32 ohms (SWR 1.7:1 and 1.6:1). The 32-ohm hybrid coupler can be constructed as described in Par 3.3.4, with

$X_{L1} = X_{L2} = 32$ ohms
$X_{C1} = X_{C2} = -62$ ohms

For a design frequency of 3.8 MHz, the component values are

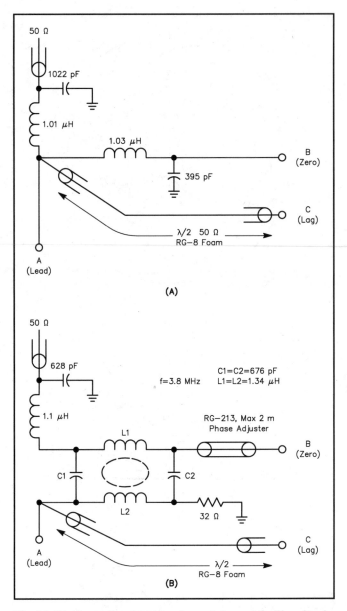

Fig 11-45—Lewallen feed system at A, and Collins feed system at B for the 4-square array with ¼-wave element spacing. The identification of the feed system units matches the direction switching system as shown in Fig 11-43.

$L = 1.34$ µH
$C = 676$ pF

The hybrid coupler can be fed with a 50-ohm feed line via an appropriate L network.

The front-to-back ratio can be fine-tuned for ultimate rejection by inserting a variable length of feed line between port 2 and the paralleled feed lines to the –90-degree elements. This line should be between 1 and 9 electrical degrees long (1 to 6 feet on 80 meters).

Collins measured the power in the terminating resistor of the hybrid coupler for a 4-square array that was designed for 3.8 MHz. Table 11-1 shows the power in the terminating resistor over a frequency range from 3.5 to 4 MHz. If you want to use the array over such a wide frequency range you will

Table 11-1

Power Reflected Into Dummy Resistor at Port 4 of Collins Hybrid Coupler

Frequency (MHz)	Power Reflected into Load (dB)
3.5	−7.2
3.6	−10.0
3.7	−12.2
3.8	−18.0
3.9	−13.5
4.0	−10.5

Table 11-2

Measured Element Feed Current with Hybrid Coupler

Frequency (MHz)	Back Element Current (amps)	Angle (deg)	Side Elements Current (amps)	Angle (deg)	Front Element Current (amps)	Angle (deg)
3.5	7.7	0	7.5	83	7.8	173
3.8	7.9	0	8.5	90	7.9	180
4.0	6.3	0	8.2	90	6.5	185

have to provide a terminating resistor that can take approximately 200 W if you run 1500 W into the array. Collins also measured the feed-current magnitude and phase over this wide frequency range. The results are shown in Table 11-2. If we calculate the directivity patterns using the current data from that table, we note a constant gain (within less than 0.1 dB from 3.5 to 4 MHz), and an F/B ratio of more than 22.5 dB from 3.5 to 3.8 MHz. On 4 MHz the F/B ratio has dropped to 16 dB.

The layout of the feed system is shown in Fig 11-45.

4.9.3. ⅛-wavelength-spaced square.

Array Data

Number of elements: 4

Placement of elements: In a square, spacing 0.125 wavelength per side

Elements 2 and 3 = 1 diagonal of the square

Feed currents:

$I1 = 1 \angle -135°$; $I2 = 1 \angle 0°$; $I3 = 1 \angle 0°$; $I4 = 1 \angle 135°$

Gain: 4.7 dB over a single vertical

3-dB beamwidth: 90 degrees

Radiation: Unidirectional

The feed-point impedances (including 2 ohms ground loss resistance) are

Z1 = −10.4 + j21.3 ohms
Z2 = Z3 = 20.2 − j7.6 ohms
Z3 = −21.1 − j12.4 ohms

Fig 11-46 shows the radiation patterns over very good ground.

Note that, especially with close-spaced designs, driving-point impedances with a negative resistance part can be found. This means that the parasitic coupling supplies too much current (power) to this element, and that the element is then supplying this power back into the feed network.

The operating bandwidth over which this array shows a usable front-to-back ratio is expected to be rather narrow, which is not a great handicap on 160 meters.

4.9.3.1. *The Modified Lewallen method.*

As the ⅛-wavelength-spaced square array does not use quadrature feed angles, the Lewallen feed method using a single L network cannot be used. We will use the modified method having a shunt network plus a line stretcher, as explained in detail in Par 3.3.4.

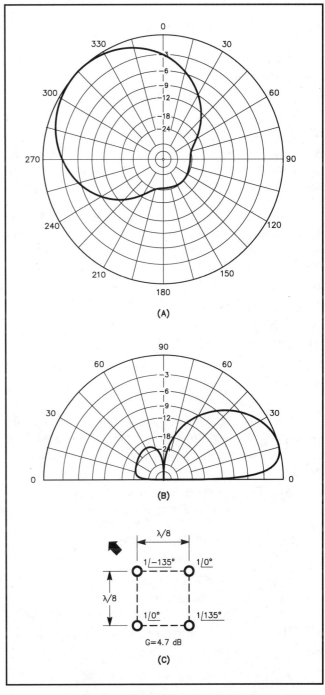

Fig 11-46—Radiation patterns for the 4-square array with ⅛-wave element spacing.

We chose the two center elements as the elements to be fed directly with quarter-wave feed lines. This is the logical choice, as these are the only two elements that take power from the feed line; the other two supply power to the feed system by virtue of mutual coupling.

The networks between A and B and between A and C are designed as follows.

The impedances at the elements are

$Z1 = -10.4 + j21.3$ ohms (-135 degrees)
$Z2 = Z3 = 20.2 - j7.6$ ohms
$Z3 = -21.1 - j12.4$ ohms (135 degrees)

At the end of the 90-degree feed lines the impedances and voltages are:

$Z1' = -42.91 - j97.73$ ohms
$E1' = 49.83 \angle -44.58°$ V
$Z2' = Z3' = 105.86 + j37.89$ ohms
$E2' = E3 = 50.36 \angle 89.95°$ V
$Z4' = -88.92 + j55.01$ ohms
$E4' = 49.64 \angle -135.25°$ V

Because we used "current-forcing" line lengths (90 degrees), we see the same voltage magnitude at the end of all four feed lines (except for slight differences due to line losses).

We must now design a network to be inserted in the feed line to element 1 and another one for insertion at the end of line 3 to equalize the voltage phase angles. The network will consist of a shunt reactance (coil or capacitor) and a constant-impedance line stretcher.

Line to element 1:

$Z1' = -42.91 - j97.73$ ohms
$E1' = 49.83 \angle -44.58°$ V

Adding a shunt impedance of 117 ohms (4.9 μH at 3.8 MHz) tunes out the imaginary part of the impedance. The new impedance is:

$Z1'' = -265$ ohms

The minus sign indicates that we are still dealing with power being delivered from the element into the network.

The pi-network line stretcher is:

Impedance: -265 ohms
Output voltage phase angle: -44.5 degrees
Input voltage phase angle: 89.85 degrees
$X_P = 111$ ohms (4.67 μH at 3.8 MHz)
$X_S = -189$ ohms (221 pF at 3.8 MHz)

Line to element 2:

$Z4' = -88.92 + j55.01$ ohms
$E4'' = 49.64 \angle -135.25°$ V

Adding a shunt impedance of -199 ohms (211 pF at 3.8 MHz) tunes out the imaginary part of the impedance. The new impedance is:

$Z4'' = -123$ ohms

The pi-network line stretcher is:

Impedance: -123 ohms

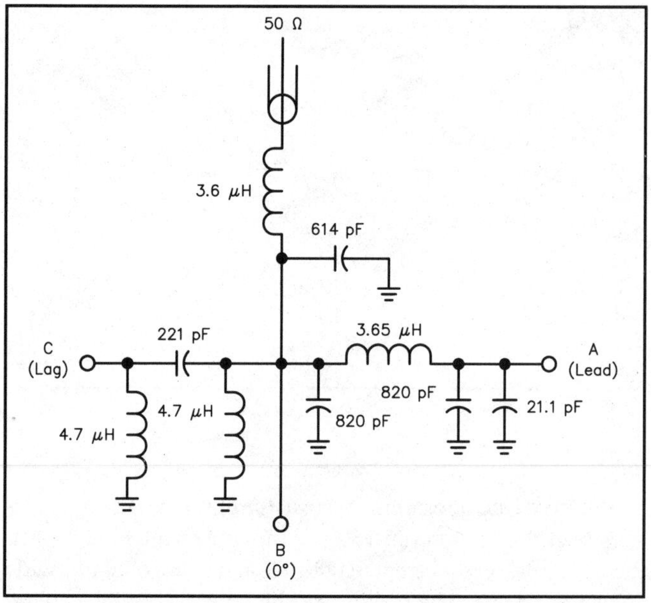

Fig 11-47—Current-forcing feed system for the 4-square array with ⅛-wavelength spacing. The identification of the feed system units matches the direction-switching system shown in Fig 11-43.

Output voltage phase angle: $-135.22 = 224.78$ degrees
Input voltage phase angle: 89.85 degrees
$X_P = -51.1$ ohms (820 pF at 3.8 MHz)
$X_S = 87$ ohms (3.65 μH at 3.8 MHz)

The impedance at the T junction of the three branches is given by the parallel connection of:

$Z1'' = -265$ ohms
$Z2' = Z3' = 105.86 + j37.89$ ohms
$Z4'' = -123$ ohms
$Z_{array} = 82.6 + j97.35$ ohms

The layout of the modified Lewallen feed method is shown in Fig 11-47.

4.9.4. Optimized 4-square array.

J. Breakall, WA3FET, optimized the quarter-wave-spaced 4-square array to obtain a better F/B ratio. From Fig 11-44 we learn that the original 4-square exhibits a very major high-angle backlobe (-18 dB only). Changing the current magnitudes and angles of the front and the back elements changes the size and the shape of the back lobe. Full optimization is a compromise between optimization in the elevation and the azimuth planes. With Breakall's optimization, the gain of the array went up by 0.7 dB. He came up with the following design.

Array Data

Two ¼-wave-spaced cardioids
Feed currents:
  $I1 = 0.969 \angle -107°$; $I2 = 1 \angle 0°$; $I3 = 1 \angle 0°$; $I4 = 1.11 \angle 111°$
Gain: 6.2 dB over a single vertical
3-dB beamwidth (at main wave angel): 84 degrees
The feed-point impedances (including 2 ohms ground loss resistance) are

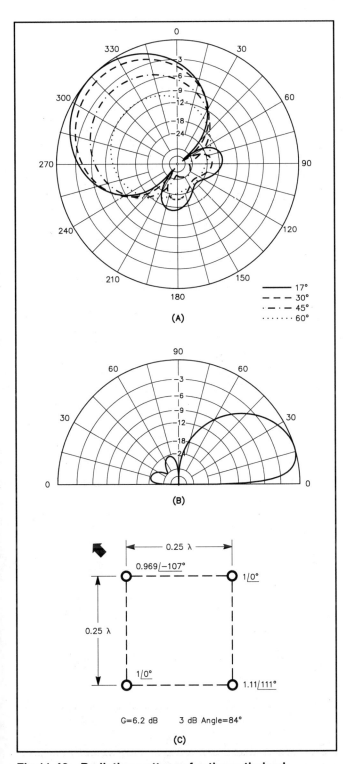

Fig 11-48—Radiation patterns for the optimized 4-square array. The horizontal patterns at A are for a 17-degree wave angle (main wave angle), 30, 45 and 60 degrees. The array was optimized in both the horizontal and the vertical planes in order to get the minimal total three-dimensional back lobe.

Z1 = 37.5 + j57.7 ohms
Z2 = Z3 = 30.8 – j7.0 ohms
Z4 = 60 – j3.4 ohms
Fig 11-48 shows the radiation patterns over very good ground.

While this optimized design shows what can be achieved by tweaking a design, it has a number of disadvantages:

- The elements are not quadrature fed; this means that the Lewallen feed system cannot be used.
- Because of the odd values of feed current, the current-forcing method with the modified Lewallen feed method is also out of the question.

I developed a modified Christman-type feed system. A Gehrke system would have been possible as well, although the network would have contained more components.

I first ran the VOLTAGES ALONG FEED LINES software module to see if there were points of identical voltage. I used 75-ohm feed lines (0.35 dB loss/100 ft at 3.8 MHz). The following points were selected:

At 119 degrees on the line to element 1:

> Z1' = 25.9 – j23 ohms
> E1'' = 41.8 $\angle 9.5°$ V

At 164 degrees on the lines to elements 2 and 3:

> Z2' = Z3' = 36.5 – j24.5 ohms
> E2' = E3' = 41.8 $\angle 138.7°$

At 212 degrees on the line to element 4:

> Z4' = 11.24 + j41.52 ohms
> E4'' = 41.8 $\angle 9.5°$

The feed lines to elements 1 and 4 can be connected in parallel as the voltages are identical. The voltage magnitude at the input ends of the feed lines to elements 2 and 3 are identical. The phase angle needs adjusting, which can be done with a constant-impedance line stretcher (pi network).

The parallel impedance of the lines to elements 2 and 3 is

Z(2,3)' = 18.25 – j12.25 ohms

Using the SHUNT IMPEDANCE module we calculate the shunt impedance that will tune the reactive component in this impedance: 39.5 ohms. A 1.7 µH coil (3.8 MHz) turns the above impedance into

Z(2,3)''' = 26.49 ohms

Now we design the pi-network line stretcher around a 26.49-ohm characteristic impedance:

Output voltage phase angle: 138.7 degrees
Input voltage phase angle: 9.5 degrees
X_S = –20.5 ohms (2040 pF at 3.8 MHz)
X_P = 12.6 ohms (0.53 µH at 3.8 MHz)

The input impedance of the array is the parallel of three impedances:

> Z1' = 25.9 – j23 ohms
> Z2,3''' = 26.49 ohms
> Z4' = 11.24 + j41.52 ohms

The resulting impedance is: 15.25 + j0.76 ohms

The feed system for this array is shown in Fig 11-49. There are, of course, other possible combinations for a feed system.

This design has the disadvantage of not using a "current-forcing" feed system, which means that the directivity, while theoretically better, will be more sensitive to variations in changes of element feed-point impedances when the array is switched around.

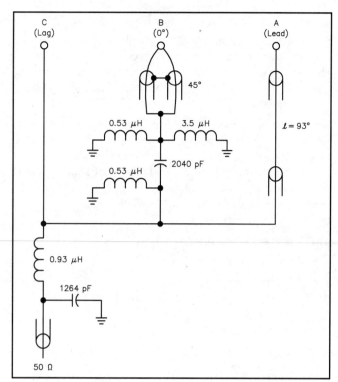

Fig 11-49—Modified Christman feed system for the optimized 4-square array of Fig 11-48. The identification of the feed system units matches the direction-switching system shown in Fig 11-43. This design is for 3.8 MHz. All coax is 75-ohm RG-11; the four feed lines are 119 electrical degrees in length.

4.10. Other 4-Element Rectangular Arrays

I have analyzed a few more 4-element arrays. All of the following arrays are made up of two groups of 2-element cardioid arrays with different X and Y spacings and feed current phase angles.

Although the Gehrke, Christman and Collins feed methods may be valid alternatives, I have only calculated the (modified) Lewallen method for the following arrays. Where the array is quadrature fed, the Lewallen L network can be replaced by a hybrid coupler. For details see Par 3.3.4.

The schematics of the feed systems for these arrays do not include a direction-switching system, but the system in all cases is extremely simple; only a single DPDT relay is required.

4.10.1. Two ¼-wave-spaced cardioid arrays side by side, spaced ½ wavelength, fed in phase.

The basic group is a 2-element cardioid array, 90-degree spacing, 90-degree phase shift (see par 4.1.). The groups are spaced ½ wavelength apart, placed side by side, and fed in phase. This array is also mentioned by W7EL in *The ARRL Antenna Book*.

Array Data

Two ¼-wave-spaced cardioids, spaced ½ wavelength apart
Feed currents:

$I1 = 1 \angle -90°$; $I2 = 1 \angle 0°$; $I3 = 1 \angle -90°$; $I4 = 1 \angle 0°$

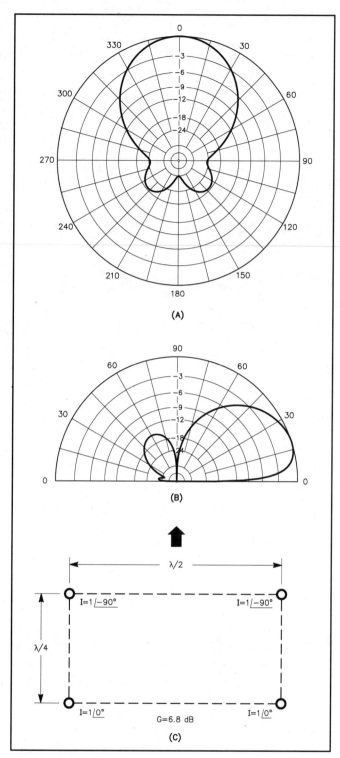

Fig 11-50—Radiation patterns for a rectangular array made of two 2-element cardioid arrays (90-degree spacing, 90-degree phase shift), spaced ½ wavelength.

Gain: 6.8 dB over a single vertical
3-dB beamwidth: 62 degrees
The feed-point impedances (including 2 ohms ground loss resistance) are
$Z1 = Z3 = 54.6 - j5.1$ ohms
$Z2 = Z4 = 5.5 - j21.2$ ohms
Fig 11-50 shows the radiation patterns over very good ground.

Note the high gain, and also note the relative narrow beamwidth (which of course always go together!).

The element feed impedances are

$Z1 = Z3 = 54.6 - j5.1$ ohms
$Z2 = Z4 = 5.5 - j21.2$ ohms

At the end of the quarter-wave feed lines (RG-213 with 0.35 dB/100 ft loss at 3.8 MHz) the data become

$Z1' = Z3' = 45.55 + j4.11$ ohms
$E1' = E3' = 50.95 \angle -0.1°$
$Z2' = Z4' = 33.59 + j108.58$ ohms
$E2' = E4' = 50.1 \angle -89.58°$

Designing the 90-degree voltage-phase-shift L network (Ref. par 3.3.3)

$$X_S = \frac{2500}{54.6} = 45.8 \text{ ohms (1.9 µH at 3.8 MHz)}$$

$$X_P = \frac{2500}{-5.1 - 54.6} = -42 \text{ ohms (998 pF at 3.8 MHz)}$$

The parallel or shunt impedance (–42 ohms) converts the impedance of $Z1' = Z3'$ (calculated with the SHUNT IMPEDANCE MODULE) to

$Z1'' = 22.94 - j23.24$ ohms

The series reactance (45.8 ohms) converts the impedance to

$Z1''' = 22.94 + j22.56$ ohms. This is the feed impedance for one of the groups.

To connect the two groups there are several possibilities. As the spacing between the two groups is 0.5 wavelength, the cable to the center must be 0.25 wavelength (physical), or in case of a velocity factor of 0.66,

$$L_{min} = \frac{0.25}{0.66} = 0.38 \text{ wavelength (137 electrical degrees).}$$

We connect two 137-degree-long (50-ohm) cables. The impedances at the end of the cables are:

$Z = 20.64 - j10.84$ ohms

The two lines in parallel will give the array impedance

$Z_{array} = 10.32 - j5.42$ ohms

Other alternatives are left to the reader's imagination. The layout for this feed system is shown in Fig 11-51 A.

Alternative Feed System

Lewallen described another method where he runs four ¾-wave-long 50-ohm feed lines to the center of the array:

The data at the end of the ¾-wave long lines are:

$Z1' = Z3' = 45.84 + j3.86$ ohms
$E1' = E3' = 52.89 \angle 179.71°$ V
$Z2' = Z4' = 42.7 + j103.1$ ohms
$E2' = E4' = 50.36 \angle -91.24°$ V

Designing the L network (Ref. par 4.9.1.1)

$$X_S = \frac{2500}{2 \times 54.6} = 22.9 \text{ ohms (0.95 µH at 3.8 MHz)}$$

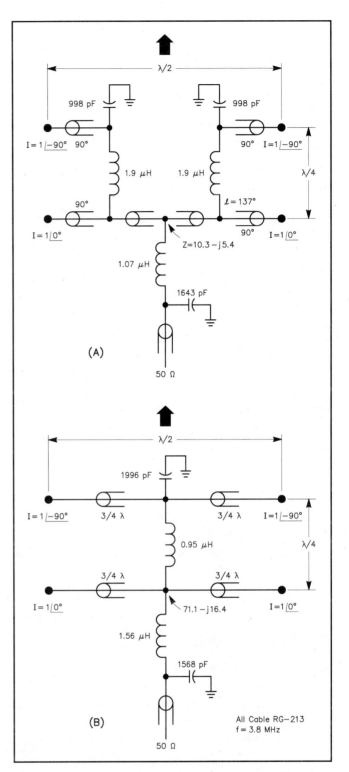

Fig 11-51—Alternative feed systems for the rectangular array shown in Fig 11-50.

$$X_P = \frac{2500}{2(-5.1 - 54.6)} = -21 \text{ ohms (1996 pF at 3.8 MHz)}$$

As calculated with the SHUNT IMPEDANCE MODULE, the shunt impedance (–21 ohms) converts the impedance of $Z1'/2$ ($= Z3'/2$) to

$Z1'' = 11.1 - j16.4$ ohms

The series reactance (22.9 ohms) converts the impedance to

$Z1''' = 11.1 + j6.5$ ohms.

This is the feed impedance of the array. The layout of this feed system is shown in Fig 11-51 B.

4.10.2. Two ⅛-wave-spaced cardioid arrays side by side, spaced ½ wavelength, fed in phase.

Array Data

Two ⅛-wave-spaced cardioids, spaced ½ wavelength apart
Feed currents:

$I1 = 1 \angle -135°$; $I2 = 1 \angle 0°$; $I3 = 1 \angle -135°$; $I4 = 1 \angle 0°$
Gain: 7.0 dB over a single vertical
3-dB beamwidth: 58 degrees

The feed-point impedances (including 2 ohms ground loss resistance) are

$Z1 = Z3 = 24.9 + j12.5$ ohms
$Z2 = Z4 = 3.1 - j19.2$ ohms

Fig 11-52 shows the radiation patterns over very good ground.

The feed system is a modified Lewallen feed system as the feed angles are not in quadrature. Because the two cardioids are ½-wave spaced, we need ¾-wave-long feed lines to reach the center of the array.

At the end of the 270-degree-long feed lines the impedances and voltages are

$Z1' = Z3' = 77.76 - j34.20$ ohms
$E1' = E3' = 51.36 \angle 135.72°$ V

$Z2' = Z4' = 37.9 + j119.42$ ohms
$E2' = E4' = 50.24 \angle -91.13°$ V

Because we used current-forcing line lengths (90 degrees), we see the same voltage magnitude at the end of all four feed lines (except for slight differences due to line losses).

We will feed the array at the junction of the feed lines going to elements 1 and 3 (in principle we could have chosen the junction of lines 2 and 4 instead). The impedance at the junction of the feed lines 1 and 3 is

$Z(1,3)' = 38.83 - j17.10$ ohms

We must now design a network to be inserted in the joined feed lines to elements 2 and 4 to equalize the voltage phase angles. The network will consist of a shunt reactance (coil or capacitor) and a constant-impedance line stretcher.

The two feed lines connected in parallel give

$Z(2,4) = 18.95 + j59.71$ ohms
$E(2,4) = 50.24 \angle -91.13°$

We will connect a shunt impedance to cancel the reactive part of the impedance (calculated using the SHUNT REACTANCE software module):

A shunt capacitance of –65.7 ohms (637 pF at 3.8 MHz) tunes out the imaginary part of the impedance. The new impedance is

$Z(2,4)' = 207.1$ ohms

The pi-network line stretcher is

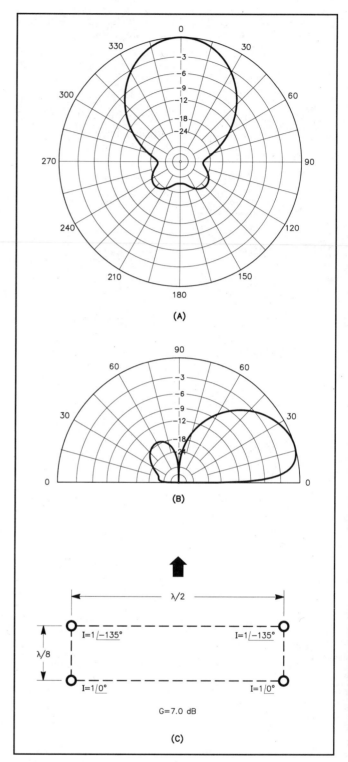

Fig 11-52—Radiation patterns for a rectangular array made of two 2-element cardioid arrays (⅛-wave spacing, 135-degree phase shift), spaced ½ wavelength.

Impedance: 207.1 ohms
Output voltage phase angle: –91.13 = +268.87 degrees
Input voltage phase angle: 135.72 degrees
$X_P = 90$ ohms (3.76 µH at 3.8 MHz)
$X_S = -151$ ohms (277 pF at 3.8 MHz)

The impedance at the T junction of the two branches is

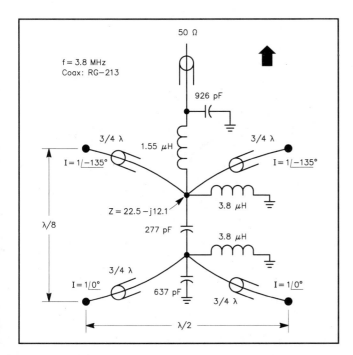

Fig 11-53—Modified Lewallen feed system for the rectangular array described in Fig 11-52.

given by the parallel connection of

$Z(2,4)' = 207.1$ ohms
$Z(1,3)' = 38.83 - j17.10$ ohms
$Z_{array} = 22.54 - j12.07$ ohms

The layout of the modified Lewallen feed method is shown in Fig 11-53.

4.10.3. Two ¼-wave-spaced cardioid arrays side by side, spaced ¼ wavelength, fed in phase.

This is the same physical layout as the famous quarter-wave-spaced four-square. In par 4.9. I referred to the possibility of making a square array that could be switched in eight directions. This is the array that would fill in the "other" four directions.

Array Data

Two ¼-wave-spaced cardioids, spaced ¼ wavelength
Feed currents:
    $I1 = 1 \angle -90°$; $I2 = 1 \angle 0°$; $I3 = 1 \angle -90°$; $I4 = 1 \angle 0°$
Gain: 4.3 dB over a single vertical
3-dB beamwidth: 122 degrees

The feed-point impedances (including 2 ohms ground loss resistance) are

$Z1 = Z3 = 88.2 + j7.2$ ohms
$Z2 = Z4 = 18.7 - j37.7$ ohms

Fig 11-54 shows the radiation patterns over very good ground.

To reach the center of the array with ¼-wave feed lines we must use coax with cellular PE insulation. I assumed a VF of 0.79 (RG-8 foam type), with 0.30 dB loss per 100 ft at 3.8 MHz (see also par 4.9.1.1.)

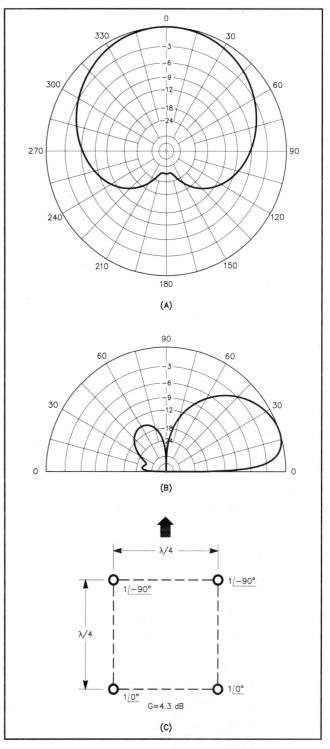

Fig 11-54—Radiation patterns for a rectangular array made of two 2-element cardioid arrays (¼-wave spacing, 90 degrees out of phase), spaced ¼ wavelength.

The data at the end of the ¼ wave long lines are

$Z1' = Z3' = 28.76 - j2.25$ ohms
$E1' = E3' = 51.56 \angle -44.86°$ V

$Z2' = Z4' = 43.41 + j60.16$ ohms
$E2' = E4' = 50.34 \angle 89.44°$ V

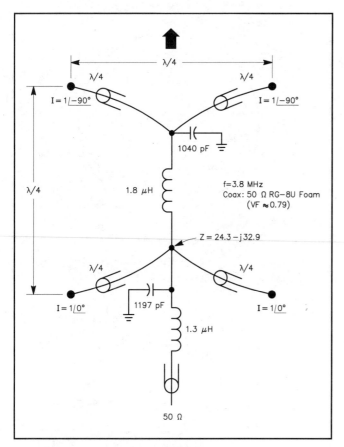

Fig 11-55—Lewallen-type feed system for the rectangular array shown in Fig 11-54.

Designing the L network (Ref. par. 4.9.1.1),

$$X_S = \frac{2500}{2 \times 28.76} = 43.5 \text{ ohms (1.8 μH at 3.8 MHz)}$$

$$X_P = \frac{2500}{2(-2.25 - 28.76)} = -40.3 \text{ ohms (1040 pF at 3.8 MHz)}$$

The shunt impedance (−40.3 ohms) converts the impedance of Z1'/2 (= Z3'/2)

Z1" = 24.29 − j10.62 ohms

as calculated with the SHUNT IMPEDANCE module. The series reactance (43.5 ohms) converts the impedance to

Z1''' = 24.29 + j32.88 ohms

This is the feed impedance of the array. The layout of this feed system is shown in Fig 11-55.

4.10.4. Two ⅛-wave-spaced cardioid arrays side by side, spaced ¼ wavelength, fed in phase.

Array Data

Two ⅛-wave-spaced cardioids, spaced ¼ wavelength
Feed currents:
   I1=1 $\angle -135°$; I2=1 $\angle 0°$; I3=1 $\angle -135°$; I4=1 $\angle 0°$
Gain: 4.9 dB over a single vertical
3-dB beamwidth: 100 degrees

The feed-point impedances (including 2 ohms ground loss resistance) are

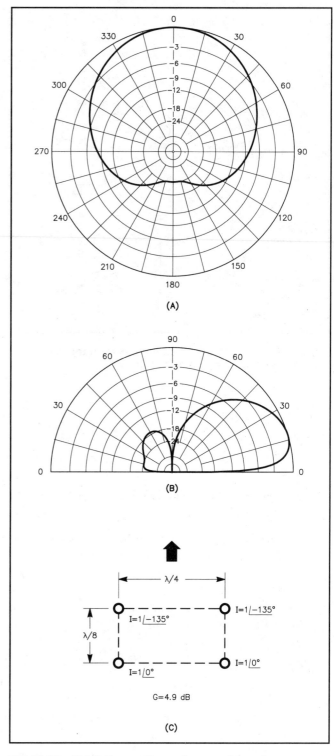

(A)

(B)

G=4.9 dB

(C)

Fig 11-56—Radiation patterns for a rectangular array made of two 2-element cardioid arrays (⅛-wave spacing, 135 degrees out of phase), spaced ¼ wavelength.

Z1 = Z3 = 38.2 + j28.5 ohms
Z2 = Z4 = 6.8 − j33.6 ohms

Fig 11-56 shows the radiation patterns over very good ground.

The feed system is a modified Lewallen feed system (the feed angles are not in quadrature). Feed lines that are 90 degrees long will reach the center of the array. At the end of the

90-degree feed lines the impedances and voltages are

Z1' = Z3' = 42.62 + j28.50 ohms
E1' = E4' = 50.57 $\angle -44.45°$ V

Z2' = Z4' = 17.0 + j70.71 ohms
E2' = E4' = 50.13 $\angle 89.34°$ V

We will feed the array at the junction of the feed lines going to elements 1 and 3 (in principle we could have chosen the junction of lines to elements 2 and 4 instead).

The impedance at the junction of the feed lines 1 and 3 is

Z(1,3)' = 21.31 – j14.25 ohms

We must now design a network to be inserted in the joined feed lines to elements 2 and 4 to equalize the voltage phase angles. The network will consist of a shunt reactance (coil or capacitor) and a constant-impedance line stretcher.

The two feed lines connected together give

Z(2,4) = 8.55 + j30.35 ohms
E(2,4) = 50.13 $\angle 89.34°$ V

We will connect a shunt impedance to cancel the reactive part of the impedance (calculated using the SHUNT IMPEDANCE software module):

A shunt inductance of –32.8 ohms (1279 pF at 3.8 MHz) tunes out the imaginary part of the impedance. The new impedance is

Z(2,4)' = 116.28 ohms

The pi-network line stretcher is

Impedance: 116.28 ohms
Output voltage phase angle: –44.45 degrees
Input voltage phase angle: 89.34 degrees
X_P = –49.6 ohms (844 pF at 3.8 MHz)
X_S = 83.9 ohms (3.5 µH at 3.8 MHz)

The impedance at the T junction of the two branches is given by the parallel connection of

Z(2,4)' = 116.28 ohms
Z(1,3)' = 21.31 – j14.25 ohms
Z_{array} = 19.05 – j10.07 ohms

The layout of the modified Lewallen feed method is shown in Fig 11-57.

4.10.5. Two ⅛-wave-spaced cardioid arrays side by side, spaced ⅛ wavelength, fed in phase.

Array Data

Two ⅛-wave-spaced cardioids, spaced ⅛ wavelength
Feed currents:
   I1=1 $\angle -135°$; I2=1 $\angle 0°$; I3=1 $\angle -135°$; I4=1 $\angle 0°$
Gain: 4.2 dB over a single vertical
3-dB beamwidth: 128 degrees

The feed-point impedances (including 2 ohms ground loss resistance) are

Z1 = Z3 = 39.8 + j43.8 ohms
Z2 = Z4 = 14.8 – j36.8 ohms

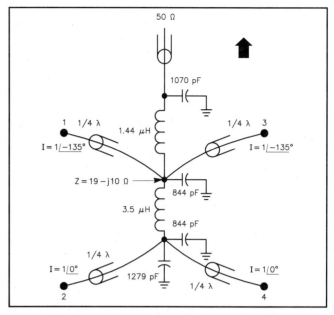

Fig 11-57—Feed system according to the modified Lewallen system for the array shown in Fig 11-56.

Fig 11-58 shows the radiation patterns over very good ground.

The feed system is again a modified Lewallen feed system (the feed angles are not in quadrature). At the end of the 90-degree feed lines the impedances and voltages are

Z1' = Z3' = 29.31 – j30.65 ohms
E1' = E3' = 50.7 $\angle -44.15°$ V

Z2' = Z4' = 25.33 + j57.5 ohms
E2' = E4' = 50.27 $\angle 89.28°$ V

We will feed the array at the junction of the feed lines going to elements 1 and 3. The impedance at the junction of the feed lines 1 and 3 is

Z(1,3)' = 14.65 – j15.32 ohms

We must now design a network to be inserted in the joined feed lines to elements 2 and 4 to equalize the voltage phase angles. The network will consist of a shunt reactance (coil or capacitor) and a constant-impedance line stretcher.

The two feed lines connected together give

Z(2,4) = 12.66 + j28.75 ohms
E(2,4) = 50.27 $\angle 89.28°$ V

We will connect a shunt impedance to cancel the reactive part of the impedance (calculated using the SHUNT IMPEDANCE software module). A shunt inductance of –34.3 ohms (1220 pF at 3.8 MHz) tunes out the imaginary part of the impedance. The new impedance is

Z(2,4)' = 78 ohms

The pi-network line stretcher is

Impedance: 78 ohms
Output voltage phase angle: –44.15 degrees
Input voltage phase angle: 89.28 degrees
X_P = –33.6 ohms (1247 pF at 3.8 MHz)

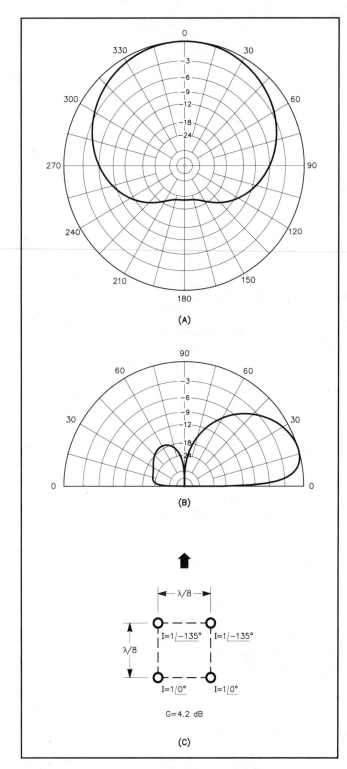

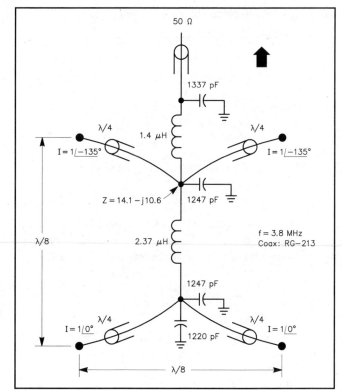

Fig 11-59—Modified Lewallen-type feed system for the square array shown in Fig 11-58.

The layout of the modified Lewallen feed method is shown in Fig 11-59.

4.11. Triangular Arrays

A last group of antennas consists of the triangular arrays. The gain is comparable to the gain of the 4-square arrays, and they also have a broad forward-lobe beamwidth. I have analyzed three different equilateral triangle arrays. All three can be fed in two different ways:

- Beaming off the top of the triangle. The top corner is fed with a current of lagging phase angle. The two elements at the bottom of the triangle are fed with the leading current.
- Beaming off the bottom of the triangle. Both bottom-corner elements are fed by the current with the lagging phase angle. The top vertical is fed with the leading phase angle.
- In both cases the "solitary" top element is fed with twice the current magnitude when compared to the two elements at the corners of the bottom base line of the triangle.

Being a triangle, each array can be switched in three directions. The "alternative" feed method adds another three directions, which means that with a rather complex switching system a triangular array can be made switchable in 6 directions. The alternative array has the same gain (within 0.1 dB) and an almost identical radiation pattern.

If both alternatives are to be used in an array that can be switched in six directions, separate phasing networks will be required. I will leave it to your imagination as an array designer to develop your switching harness. The problem is that you will have to run two RG-213 cables to each of the element feed points, because there always will be either one of the elements

Fig 11-58—Radiation patterns for a square array made of two 2-element cardioid arrays (⅛-wave spacing, 135 degrees out of phase), spaced ⅛ wavelength.

$X_S = 56.6$ ohms (2.37 µH at 3.8 MHz)

The impedance at the T junction of the two branches is given by the parallel connection of

$Z(2,4)' = 78$ ohms
$Z(1,3)' = 14.65 - j15.32$ ohms
$Z_{array} = 14.08 - j10.57$ ohms

that will require a feed current of "double magnitude," and hence the need for a 25-ohm feed line. When there is only one cable required (50 ohms), you will have to short the quarter-wave feed line to ground. At the antenna element the short will look like an open.

As each of the directivity patterns has a 3-dB beamwidth of approximately 146 degrees, it is questionable if the added complexity is worth the effort.

I will describe three different triangle arrays. The difference is in the element spacing and current phase angles.

4.11.1. The Quadrature-fed triangular array.

Atchley, W1CF, described a 3-element array where the verticals are positioned in an equilateral triangle with sides measuring 0.29 wavelength (Ref. 939 and 941). The original version of the array used equal current magnitude in all elements. Later, Gehrke, K2BT, improved the array by feeding the two back elements with half the current of the front element. This improved the zero-wave-angle front-to-back ratio to almost infinity, with a back rejection of 20 dB or better at the main wave angle over approximately 60 degrees.

4.11.1.1. *First alternative.*

One element is fed with twice the current magnitude as the other two, and is leading the other two by 90 degrees. Radiation is always off the element with the lagging current. Thus, it radiates broadside to the line connecting the two elements with the lagging current.

Array Data

Side triangle: 0.29 wavelength
Feed currents: $I1 = 2 \angle 0°$; $I2 = 1 \angle -90°$; $I3 = 1 \angle -90°$
Gain: 3.9 dB over a single vertical
3-dB beamwidth: 140 degrees

The feed-point impedances (including 2 ohms ground loss resistance) are

$Z1 = 18.6 - j12.7$ ohms
$Z2 = Z3 = 84.6 + j9.7$ ohms

Fig 11-60C shows the array configuration. The radiation patterns over very good ground are shown at A and B of Fig 11-60.

Feeding the Array

Besides using the Collins-type hybrid coupler, we can also use the Lewallen-type feed system (see par 3.3.3 for details). Quarter-wave-long feed lines will easily reach the center of the array. Calculations were done assuming RG-213 cable with 0.35 dB attenuation/100 ft at 3.8 MHz.

The data at the end of the ¼-wave-long 25-ohm line ($2 \times$ RG-213 in parallel) are

$Z1' = 23.03 + j15.40$ ohms
$E1'' = 50.32 \angle 89.75°$ V

At the end of the 50-ohm lines to elements 2 and 3 we find

$Z2' = Z3' = 29.73 - j3.28$ ohms
$E2' = E3' = 51.46 \angle 0.19°$ V

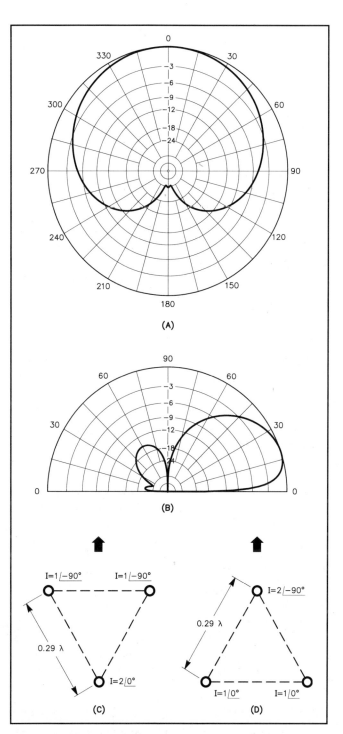

Fig 11-60—Radiation patterns for a triangular array with an element spacing of 0.29 wavelength (quadrature fed). The alternative feed method at D produces almost identical gain and radiation patterns.

The parallel impedance of these two lines is

$Z(2,3)' = 14.86 - j1.64$ ohms

Designing the L network (Ref. par 4.9.1.1):

$$X_S = \frac{2500}{2 \times 23.03} = 54.3 \text{ ohms (2.3 H at 3.8 MHz)}$$

$$X_P = \frac{2500}{2(15.4 - 23.03)} = -163.8 \text{ ohms (255 pF at 3.8 MHz)}$$

The shunt impedance (−163.8 ohms) converts the impedance of $Z(2,3)'$ (calculated with the SHUNT IMPEDANCE MODULE) to

$Z(2,3)'' = 14.45 − j2.92$ ohms

The series reactance (54.3 ohms) converts the impedance to $Z1''' = 14.45 + j53.4$ ohms. This is the feed impedance of the array.

The layout of this feed system is shown in Fig 11-61.

4.11.1.2. Second alternative.

In this configuration the radiation is off one of the "tips" of the triangle. The element at this tip is fed with twice the current magnitude when compared to the other ones, and with a current lagging the other elements by 90 degrees. This configuration in combination with the configuration described in par 4.10.1.1. makes it possible to make a triangular array that covers six directions. The impedances are different and the Lewallen L networks will be different.

Array Data

Side triangle: 0.29 wavelength
Feed currents: $I1 = 2 \angle -90°$; $I2 = 1 \angle 0°$; $I3 = 1 \angle 0°$
Gain: 3.8 dB over a single vertical
3-dB beamwidth: 145 degrees

The feed-point impedances (including 2 ohms ground loss resistance) are

$Z1 = 54.2 − j13.5$ ohms
$Z2 = Z3 = 14.4 − j43.9$ ohms

Fig 11-60D shows the array configuration. The radiation pattern is for all practical purposes identical to the pattern generated with the array described in par 4.10.1.1.

Feeding the Array

Here too, the Collins-type hybrid coupler will be the easy approach, especially if we want to make the array switchable in six directions.

I shall describe the Lewallen-type feed system (see par 3.3.3 for details). The data at the end of the ¼-wave-long 25-ohm line to element 1 are

$Z1' = 11.3 + j2.68$ ohms
$E1' = 50.93 \angle -0.26°$ V

At the ends of the two ¼-wave 50-ohm lines to elements 2 and 3:

$Z2' = Z3' = 18.52 + j50.79$ ohms
$E2' = E3' = 50.26 \angle 89.14°$

Designing the L network (Ref. par 4.9.1.1):

$$X_S = \frac{2500}{11.3} = 221 \text{ ohms (9.3 μH at 3.8 MHz)}$$

$$X_P = \frac{2500}{2.68 − 11.3} = −290 \text{ ohms (144 pF at 3.8 MHz)}$$

The shunt impedance (−290 ohms) converts the impedance of $Z1'$ (calculated with the SHUNT IMPEDANCE MODULE) to

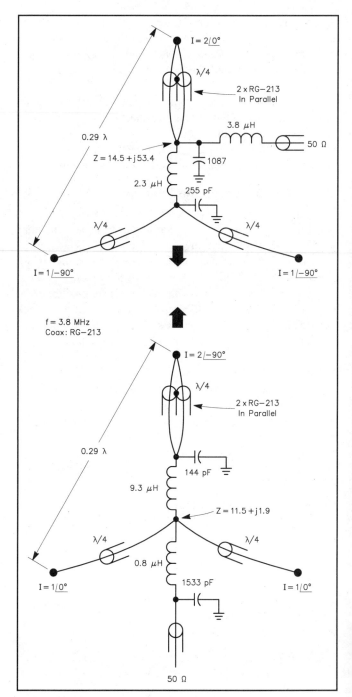

Fig 11-61—Lewallen-type feed systems for the triangular array described in Fig 11-60. The phase-shift L networks, as well as the array impedances, are different in the two different "firing positions."

$Z1'' = 11.46 + j1.85$ ohms

The series reactance (221 ohms) converts the impedance to

$Z1''' = 11.46 + j222.85$ ohms. This is the feed impedance of the array.

The layout of this feed system is shown in Fig 11-61.

4.11.2. Triangular array with improved phasing.

This array was optimized to reduce the high angle backlobe. Instead there is a large backlobe at a 15-degree wave angle. I think it is more important to have a good high-angle front-to-back. It may even be advantageous to hear the DX (low angle) off the back a little better. At the same time the gain has increased by 0.6 dB, which is not negligible.

4.11.2.1. *The first alternative.*

Array Data

Side triangle: 0.29 wavelength
Feed currents: $I1 = 2 \angle 0°$; $I2 = 1 \angle -115°$; $I3 = 1 \angle -115°$
Gain: 4.5 dB over a single vertical
3-dB beamwidth: 120 degrees

The feed-point impedances (including 2 ohms ground loss resistance) are

$Z1 = 14.9 - j4.3$ ohms
$Z2 = Z3 = 70.6 + j21.5$ ohms

Fig 11-62 shows the radiation patterns over very good ground and the array configuration at C.

This is not a quadrature-fed array, so the modified Lewallen-type feed system is indicated (see par 3.3.4 for details). At the end of the 90-degree 25-ohm feed line (two parallel RG-213 cables) to element 1, the impedance and voltage are:

$Z1 = 38.47 + j10.88$ ohms
$E1 = 50.26 \angle 89.92°$ V

At the end of the 90-degree-long 50-ohm feed lines to elements 2 and 3 we find:

$Z2' = Z3' = 32.93 - j9.65$ ohms
$E2' = E3' = 51.22 \angle -24.59°$ V

We must now design a network to be inserted in the joined feed lines to elements 2 and 3 to equalize the voltage phase angles. The network will consist of a shunt reactance (coil or capacitor) and a constant-impedance line stretcher.

The two feed lines connected together give

$Z(2,3) = 16.46 + j4.82$ ohms
$E(2,3) = 51.22 \angle -24.59°$ V

We will connect a shunt impedance to cancel the reactive part of the impedance (calculated using the SHUNT IMPED-ANCE software module):

A shunt inductance of –61 ohms (686 pF at 3.8 MHz) tunes out the imaginary part of the impedance. The new impedance is

$Z(2,4)' = 17.8$ ohms

The pi-network line stretcher is
Impedance: 17.8 ohms
Output voltage phase angle: –24.59 degrees
Input voltage phase angle: 89.92 degrees
$X_P = -11.4$ ohms (3658 pF at 3.8 MHz)
$X_S = 16.2$ ohms (0.68 µH at 3.8 MHz)

The impedance at the T junction of the two branches is given by the parallel connection of

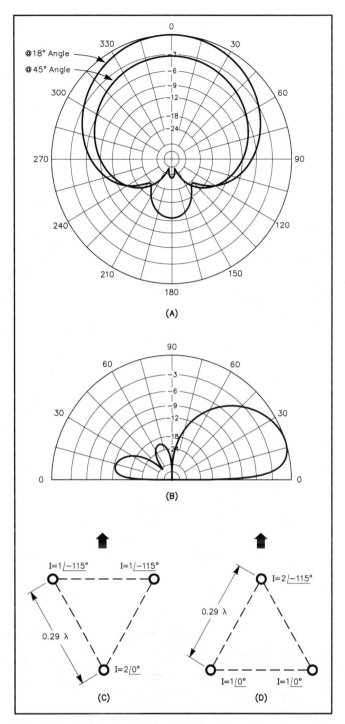

(A)

(B)

(C)

(D)

Fig 11-62—Radiation patterns for a triangular array with an element spacing of 0.29 wavelength and improved phase angle (115 degrees). The alternative feed method at D produces almost identical gain and radiation patterns.

$Z(2,4)' = 17.8$ ohms
$Z(1,3)' = 38.47 + j10.88$ ohms
$Z_{array} = 12.37 - j1.05$ ohms

The layout of the modified Lewallen feed method is shown in Fig 11-63. There are many other possible alternative networks, all using this same network methodology (see par 3.3.4.).

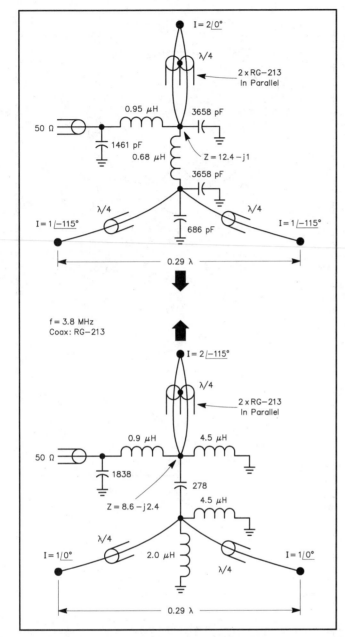

Fig 11-63—Lewallen-type feed systems for the triangular array described in Fig 11-62. The phase-shift L networks, as well as the array impedances, are different in the two different "firing positions."

4.11.2.2. *The second alternative.*

Array Data

Side triangle: 0.29 wavelength
Feed currents: $I1 = 2 \angle -115°$; $I2 = 1 \angle 0°$; $I3 = 1 \angle 0°$
Gain: 4.4 dB over a single vertical
3-dB beamwidth: 124 degrees

The feed-point impedances (including 2-ohm ground loss resistance) are:

$Z1 = 64.9 + j19.7$ ohms
$Z2 = Z3 = 6.5 - j26.5$ ohms

Fig 11-62D shows the array configuration. The radiation

pattern is for all practical purposes identical to the pattern generated with the array described in 4.10.2.1.

This is not a quadrature-fed array, so the modified Lewallen-type feed system is indicated (see par 3.3.4 for details). At the end of the 90-degree 25-ohm feed line (two parallel RG-213 cables) to element 1, the impedance and voltage are

$Z1 = 9.01 - j2.66$ ohms
$E1 = 51.12 \angle -24.62°$ V

At the end of the 90-degree-long 50-ohm feed lines to elements 2 and 3 we find

$Z2' = Z3' = 25.18 - j87.56$ ohms
$E2' = E3' = 50.12 \angle 89.48°$ V

We must now design a network to be inserted in the joined feed lines to elements 2 and 3 to equalize the voltage phase angles. The network will consist of a shunt reactance (coil or capacitor) and a constant-impedance line stretcher.

The two feed lines connected together give

$Z(2,3) = 12.59 - j43.78$ ohms

We will connect a shunt impedance to cancel the reactive part of the impedance (calculated using the SHUNT IMPED-ANCE software module):

A shunt inductance of 47.4 ohms (2.0 µH at 3.8 MHz) tunes out the imaginary part of the impedance. The new impedance is

$Z(2,3)' = 164.8$ ohms

The pi-network line stretcher is

Impedance: 164.8 ohms
Output voltage phase angle: 89.48 degrees
Input voltage phase angle: −24.62 degrees
$X_P = 106.8$ ohms (4.5 µH at 3.8 MHz)
$X_S = -150$ ohms (278 pF at 3.8 MHz)

The impedance at the T junction of the two branches is given by the parallel connection of

$Z(2,3)' = 164.8$ ohms
$Z(1)' = 9.01 - j2.66$ ohms
$Z_{array} = 8.58 - j2.39$ ohms

The layout of this modified Lewallen feed method is shown in Fig 11-63. There are many other alternative networks possible, all using this same network methodology (see par. 3.3.4.).

4.11.3. Half-size triangular array.

The phase angles are adjusted for a well-balanced front-to-back ratio. Above a wave angle of 30 degrees the F/B is better than 20 dB. This looks like an attractive array for 160 meters. This array trades in only 0.2 dB of gain as compared to the array with twice the dimensions.

4.11.3.1. *The first alternative.*

Array Data

Side triangle: 0.145 wavelength

Feed currents: $I1 = 2 \angle 0°$; $I2 = 1 \angle -145°$; $I3 = 1 \angle -145°$
Gain: 4.3 dB over a single vertical
3-dB beamwidth: 122 degrees

The feed-point impedances (including 2 ohms ground loss resistance) are

$Z1 = 9.1 - j13$ ohms
$Z2 = Z3 = 26.6 + j35.9$ ohms

Fig 11-64 shows the array layout and radiation patterns over very good ground.

This is not a quadrature-fed array, so the modified-Lewallen-type feed systems is indicated (see par. 3.3.4 for details).

At the end of the 90-degree 25-ohm feed line (two parallel RG-213 cables) to element 1 the impedance and voltage are

$Z1 = 22.98 + j31.76$ ohms
$E1 = 50.16 \angle -89.74°$ V

At the end of the 90-degree-long 50-ohm feed lines to elements 2 and 3 we find

$Z2' = Z3' = 34.46 - j43.93$ ohms
$E2' = E3' = 50.47 \angle -54.3°$

We must now design a network to be inserted in the joined feed lines to elements 2 and 3 to equalize the voltage phase angles. The network will consist of a shunt reactance (coil or capacitor) and a constant-impedance line stretcher.

The two feed lines connected together give

$Z(2,3) = 17.23 - j21.96$ ohms

We will connect a shunt impedance to cancel the reactive part of the impedance (calculated using the SHUNT IMPEDANCE software module):

A shunt inductance of 35.5 ohms (1.5 µH at 3.8 MHz) tunes out the imaginary part of the impedance. The new impedance is

$Z(2,3)' = 45.22$ ohms

The pi-network line stretcher is

Impedance: 45.22 ohms
Output voltage phase angle: –54.3 degrees
Input voltage phase angle: 89.74 degrees
$X_P = -14.7$ ohms (2854 pF at 3.8 MHz)
$X_S = 26.6$ ohms (1.1 µH at 3.8 MHz)

The impedance at the T junction of the two branches is given by the parallel connection of

$Z(2,3)' = 45.22$ ohms
$Z(1)' = 22.98 + j31.76$ ohms
$Z_{array} = 20.37 + j11.3$ ohms

The layout of this modified Lewallen feed method is shown in Fig 11-65. There are many other alternative networks possible, all using this same network methodology (see par. 3.3.4.).

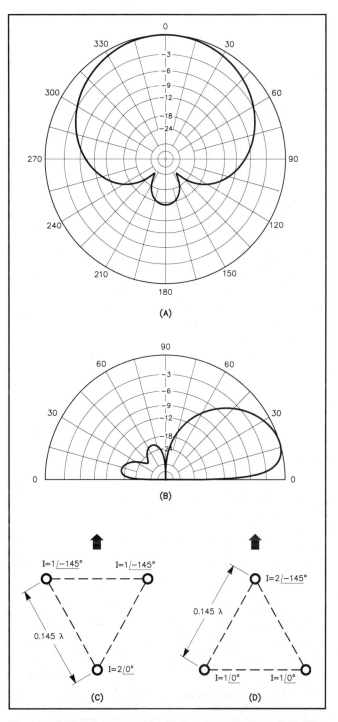

Fig 11-64—Radiation patterns for a triangular array with an element spacing of 0.145 wavelength (elements fed 145 degrees out of phase). The alternative feed method at D produces almost identical gain and radiation patterns.

4.11.3.2. *The second alternative.*

Array Data

Side triangle: 0.145 wavelength
Feed currents: $I1 = 2 \angle -145°$; $I2 = 1 \angle 0°$; $I3 = 1 \angle 0°$
Gain: 4.2 dB over a single vertical
3-dB beamwidth: 124 degrees

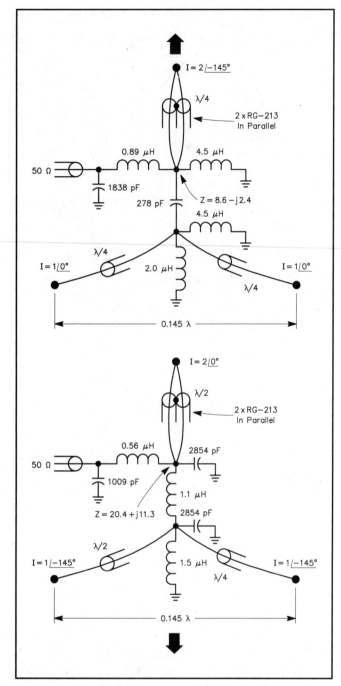

Fig 11-65—Lewallen-type feed systems for the triangular array described in Fig 11-64. The phase-shift L networks as well as the array impedances are different in the two different "firing positions."

The feed-point impedances (including 2 ohms ground loss resistance) are

Z1 = 17.2 + j20.3 ohms
Z2 = Z3 = 10.3 − j31.5 ohms

Fig 11-64D shows the array configuration. The radiation pattern is for all practical purpose identical to the pattern generated with the array described in 4.10.3.1. This is not a quadrature-fed array, so the modified Lewallen type of feed system is indicated (see par 3.3.4 for details). At the end of the

90-degree 25-ohm feed line (two parallel RG-213 cables) to element 1, the impedance and voltage are

Z1 = 15.43 − j17.73 ohms
E1 = 50.30 $\angle -54.60°$ V

At the end of the 90-degree-long 50-ohm feed lines to elements 2 and 3 we find

Z2' = Z3' = 25.84 + j70.49 ohms
E2' = E3' = 50.19 $\angle 89.38°$ V

We must now design a network to be inserted in the joined feed lines to elements 2 and 3 to equalize the voltage phase angles. The network will consist of a shunt reactance (coil or capacitor) and a constant-impedance line stretcher. The two feed lines connected together give

Z(2,3) = 12.92 + j35.24 ohms

At the end of the two parallel feed lines to element 1 we have

Z1 = 15.43 − j17.73 ohms

We will connect a shunt impedance to cancel the reactive part of the impedance (calculated using the SHUNT IMPED-ANCE software module):

A shunt inductance of 31.2 ohms (1.3 μH at 3.8 MHz) tunes out the imaginary part of the impedance. The new impedance is

Z(2,3)' = 35.8 ohms

The pi-network line stretcher is

Impedance: 35.8 ohms
Output voltage phase angle: 89.38 degrees
Input voltage phase angle: −54.6 degrees
X_P = 11.6 ohms (0.49 μH at 3.8 MHz)
X_S = −21.1 ohms (1989 pF at 3.8 MHz)

The impedance at the T junction of the two branches is given by the parallel connection of

Z(2,3)' = 35.8 ohms
Z(2,3) = 12.92 + j35.24 ohms
Z_{array} = 18.53 + j12.49 ohms

The layout of this modified Lewallen feed method is shown in Fig 11-65. There are many other alternative networks possible all using this same network methodology (see par. 3.3.4.).

■ 5. ELEMENT CONSTRUCTION

5.1. Mechanical Considerations

Self-supporting quarter-wave elements are easy to construct on 40 meters. On 80 meters it becomes more of a challenge, but self-supporting elements are feasible even with tubular elements when using the correct materials and element taper. Lattice-type constructions are more commonly used, with tapering-diameter aluminum tubing at the top. On top band most vertical radiators will be guyed towers. As it is advisable to series feed the elements of an array, the elements must be insulated from ground, which poses extra mechanical constraint on the construction.

I used the ELEMENT STRESS ANALYSIS module of the YAGI DESIGN software (see chapter on software) to develop self-supporting elements for 40 and 80 meters that withstand high wind loads. As the element is vertical, there is no loading of the element by its own weight, which means that the same element in a vertical position will sustain a higher wind load than in a horizontal position. When using the ELEMENT STRESS ANALYSIS module, one can create this condition by entering a near-zero specific weight for the material used.

It will, however, be much easier if you plan to have at least one level where the vertical can be guyed. This will typically lower the material cost for constructing a wind-survival vertical by a factor of 3 or more. Finally, the element construction that is best for your project will be dictated to a large extent by material availability.

Needless to say, guying materials need to be electrically transparent guy wires (Kevlar, Phyllistran, Nylon, Dralon, etc) or metallic guy wires broken up into small nonresonant lengths by egg-type insulators. Refer to *The ARRL Antenna Book* (Chapter 22), which covers this aspect in great detail.

All the array data in this chapter are for quarter-wave full-size elements. It is not necessary, however, to use full-size elements. Top-loaded elements which are physically ⅔ full-size length can be used without much compromising. If guyed elements (eg, aluminum tubing) are used, the set of top guy wires can be used to load the element (see chapter on vertical antennas). If the array must cover 3.8 MHz as well as 3.5 MHz, a small inductance can be inserted at the base of each vertical (make sure the loading coils are identical!) to establish resonance for all elements at 3.5 MHz.

5.2. Shunt Versus Series Feeding

Shunt feeding the elements of an all-fed array is to be avoided in just about all cases. The matching system (gamma match, omega match, slant-wire match, etc) introduces addi-

tional phase shifts that are difficult to control. Such phase shifts will mess up the correct feed current in the antenna elements.

Only with arrays where all the feed impedances are identical could shunt feeding be applied successfully. The feed impedances of all elements of an array will be identical only when all the elements are fed in phase (or 180 degrees out of phase). Shunt feeding may be considered for such arrays if the vertical elements as well as the matching systems are identical (including the values of any capacitors or inductors used in the matching system).

If you feel tempted to use your tower loaded with HF antennas as an element of an array, be aware that you might be trying to achieve the impossible:

• The loaded tower may be electrically "quite" long, which could very well be a hindrance to achieve the required directivity (see par. 2.).
• You will be forced to use shunt feeding, which is just about uncontrollable, especially if all elements are not strictly identical (which will hardly ever be the case with "loaded" towers).

Loaded towers are just great for single verticals, but are more than a hassle in arrays.

5.3. A Four-Square with Wire Elements
5.3.1. The concept.

An 80-meter 4-square takes a lot of room to put up. I have installed a somewhat special version of the four-square around my full-size quarter-wave 160-meter vertical. From the top of the vertical I run four 6-mm (¼ in.) nylon ropes in 90-degree increments, to distant supports (poles). These nylon ropes serve as support cables from which I suspend the four verticals. A single radial is directed away from the center of the square (where the 160-m vertical is located). See Fig 11-66.

In my particular case with the support being high enough, I managed full-size vertical elements, with the feed-point and the radial 5 m (17 ft) above ground. In this setup the single radial serves three purposes:

1) It provides the necessary low-impedance connection for the feed line outer shield.
2) It helps to establish the resonance of the antenna (which is *not* the case with multiple radials or buried radials, where the resonance is only determined by the length of the vertical member).
3) It provides some high-angle radiation. We can debate whether or not this is wanted, but in my particular case I wanted a fair amount of high-angle radiation as well, in order to be able to use the array successfully in contests, where shorter range contacts are also needed.

While modeling the array, I found that the quality of the ground under the array was important as to its gain as well as front-to-back ratio at low angles. In my particular case, there are some 250 radials (20 to 60 m or 66 to 200 ft long) under the array, basically serving as the radial system for the 160-meter vertical that supports the array. With the extensive radial system, the array exhibits a low-angle F/B of 20 to 25 dB, and

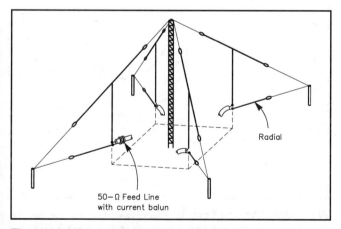

Radial

50–Ω Feed Line
with current balun

Fig 11-66—If enough space is available, one can run four cables (insulated material) from the top of the support tower to four supports mounted in a square. These cables then support the verticals and their loading structures, if any. Sloping top-loading wires as shown exhibit no horizontal radiation component, provided the length is the same on both sides of the vertical.

still a very reasonable amount of directivity at relatively high angles (20 dB F/B at 60 degrees).

The gain of this array at low angles is very comparable (only 0.4 dB less) to the gain of a 4-square over a system using a perfect ground system. The slight drop is due to the power radiated at higher angles. The gain is 5.1 dB over a single element, which is very substantial.

Fig 11-68 shows the horizontal and vertical radiation patterns for the array as well as a single element over identical good ground (very good ground with 250 radials). Both the single vertical as well as the 4 elements of the four-square use a single elevated radial.

The bottom ends of the four vertical wires are supported by steel masts that are located on the corners of a square measuring 20 m (66 ft), with the 160-meter vertical (39 m or 128 ft) right in the center of the square. The masts can be folded over for easy access to the element feed point. The vertical elements are 19.5 m (64 ft) long. Together with a radial of 18.7 m (61.35 ft), the elements are resonant at 3.75 MHz. The individual elements of the array were measured to have a feed-point resistance of 40 ohms at resonance (3.75 MHz). The impedance was measured over a frequency range going from 2 to 5 MHz using an HP network analyzer with a Smith Chart display. Mutual coupling to other antennas and surrounding structures shows up on the Smith Chart as a kink or a dip in the impedance chart of one or more elements at a specific frequency. It is important that the impedance curves be as near alike as possible over the frequency range of interest, if the impedance variations when switching antenna directions are to be kept at a minimum. Par. 3.3.8.6. deals with the problem of eliminating unwanted mutual coupling.

5.3.2. Loading the Elements for CW Operation

In order to make the antenna cover the CW end of the band as well, I use a stub, inserted in the radial at the feed point, to shift the resonance of the elements to 3.5 MHz. A small box

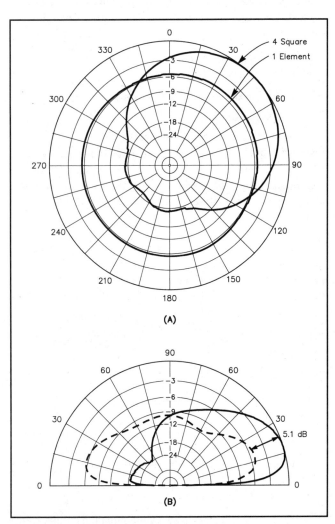

Fig 11-68—Horizontal and vertical radiation patterns of the 4-square array with one elevated radial. Also shown is the pattern of a single vertical element. Both are modeled with a single radial (per element), but over an extensive buried radial system, 5 m (17 ft) below the radial over very good ground. The buried radials are installed like spokes from the center of the square.

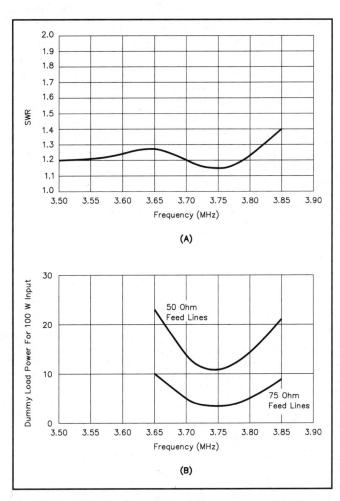

Fig 11-69—SWR and dissipated power curves for the 4-square array tuned for operation in the 3.7-3.8 MHz portion of the 80-meter band. Note that the dissipated power is much lower with 75-ohm feed line than with 50-ohm line. The SWR curves for both the 50- and the 75-ohm systems are identical. The curve remains very flat anywhere in the band, but it is clear that the power dissipated in the load resistor is what determines a meaningful bandwidth criterion for this antenna.

50 OHM FEED LINES						
			EL #1	EL #2	EL #3	EL #4
VOLTAGE	THEORETICAL		50 ∠0 deg	50 ∠90 deg	50 ∠90 deg	50 ∠180 deg
	MEASURED		41 ∠−13 deg	50 ∠90 deg	50 ∠90 deg	44.2 ∠186 deg
CURRENT	THEORETICAL		1 ∠−90 deg	1 ∠0 deg	1 ∠0 deg	1 ∠+90 deg
	CALCULATED		0.82 ∠−103 deg	1 ∠0 deg	1 ∠0 deg	0.88 ∠96 deg
GAIN	THEORETICAL		8.13 dBi			
	CALCULATED		8.07 dBi			
F / B	THEORETICAL		19 - 25 dB			
	CALCULATED		17 - 25 dBi			

Fig 11-70—Voltages at the ends of the quarter-wavelength feed lines of the 4-square array with one elevated radial. With the current-forcing method employed (see par. 3.3.3.), the relative element feed-current requirement (equal magnitude, quadrature phase relationship) is reflected in voltages of equal magnitude (where $E = Z_k \times I$ or $E = 50$ V for a 50-ohm line) at the ends of the quarter-wave feed lines. The table shows the deviation from the theoretical values. From these voltage values the feed currents have been calculated. The resulting gain and F/B performance data as modeled using ELNEC are also listed in the table. The resulting radiation patterns are shown in Fig 11-71.

is mounted on top of each mast. All connections (to the vertical element, radial, and feed lines) are made inside this box. The box also contains a relay that can switch the stub in and out of the circuit. The stub is supported by stand-off insulators along the metal support mast.

The calculated reactance of the stub is 130 ohms. Using 3-mm-OD (AWG 9) copper wire with a spacing of 20 cm (8 in.), the length of the stub turned out to be 2.25 m (7.4 ft) long to lower the resonant frequency to 3.505 MHz. The same stub, when shortened to 75 cm (2.5 ft) resonates the element at 3.65 MHz. A nice feature is that the resonant frequency can be changed anywhere between 3.5 and 3.75 MHz by using a movable shorting bar across the stub. This way, one can create different operating windows on 80-meters. A relay can be used to switch the 3.65-MHz shorting bar in and out of the circuit, making the window selection remotely controlled.

5.3.3. The Quarter-Wave Feed Lines.

Each element is fed via an electrical quarter wavelength of coaxial feed line with a current balun (50 stacked ferrite beads on a short length of small-diameter Teflon coax) at the feed point. The short length of coax together with the ferrite beads is covered by a heat-shrink (Raychem ATUM) tube to provide protection from the weather. The feed lines were cut to be a quarter wavelength at 3.75 MHz. If a perfect 90-degree phase shift is desired at 3.5 MHz, the feed lines can be lengthened by a 1-m (3.3 ft) long piece of coax (VF = 0.66 %).

5.3.4. Wasted Power

With 50-ohm feed lines, the combined feed line impedances that load the ports of our 50-ohm hybrid coupler are quite low ($22 + j19$ ohms and $23 + j17$ ohms), which results in up to 11% of the power being dissipated in the load resistor. With 75-ohm feed lines, these impedances are much higher

($51 + j37$ ohms and $48 + j43$ ohms), which results in much less power being dissipated in the load resistor (4%). As already explained in par 3.3.7, the main parameter that determines the operational bandwidth of an array fed with a hybrid-coupler is the amount of power being dissipated in the load resistor.

Fig 11-69 shows both the dissipated power as well as the array input SWR for the array tuned to the high end of the band (3.7-3.8 MHz), for both the 50-ohm and the 75-ohm feed-line impedance case.

5.3.5. Gain and Directivity

Par 3.3.8. explains that the feed current in the elements can be assessed by measuring the voltage at the end of the quarter-wave feed lines going to the elements. I used a vector voltmeter to measure the voltages. The results of the measurements using 50-ohm feed lines are listed in Fig 11-70. As expected, the voltage magnitudes and phase angles were not exactly as in the theoretical model (perfect quadrature). The voltage magnitude varied as much as 1.7 dB (41 V versus 50 V), while the phase angle was up to 13 degrees off from the theoretical value for the 50-ohm feed-line case. The table in Fig 11-70 lists all the data and also shows the transposed current values at the base of the verticals. In a pleasant surprise, even the relatively important deviations of the 50-ohm impedance case influenced the directivity pattern and gain only very marginally.

At the time of writing the array has not yet been evaluated using 75-ohm feed lines, but I assessed the results using a lab setup where I terminated the hybrid-coupler ports with impedances as they will be when using 75-ohm feed lines. The results show that the 75- and 50-ohm systems are very similar in all respects, except when it comes to the amount of power dissipated in the dummy load. With the 75-ohm feed lines, much less power is dissipated in the dummy resistor. A change from

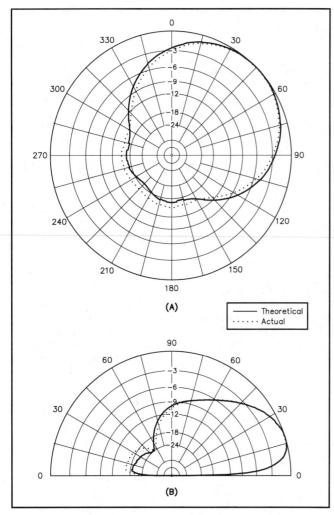

Fig 11-71—Vertical and horizontal radiation patterns (at a 20-degree wave angle) for the theoretical (ideal) currents and the actual currents at each element of the 4-square array (see Fig 11-70). Note that although there are some significant current deviations (phase angle and magnitude) from the theoretical values, the array suffers only very slightly from these differences. These patterns were calculated with ELNEC.

Fig 11-72—Cabinet located at the base of the 160-meter vertical, housing the hybrid coupler and direction-switching circuitry for the 4-square array. All components are mounted on a 20 × 20 cm (8 × 8 in.) printed-circuit board that is located behind the aluminum panel with the six type N connectors. The cabinet also contains the dummy-load resistor and a relay for switching the feed line between the 160-meter vertical and the 80-meter 4-square array.

11 to 4% represents a relative gain of 0.33 dB, which is respectable.

Fig 11-71 shows the superimposed vertical radiation patterns of the array with both the theoretical current values as well as the measured values (50-ohm case).

5.3.6. Construction

The 50-ohm hybrid coupler (with 180-degree phase shift) and the hybrid-coupler load resistor (Heath Cantenna) are located in a cabinet mounted at the base of the 160-meter vertical, which is in the center of the 4-square array. The cabinet also contains the relay which switches the feed line between the 160-meter vertical and the 80-meter four-square array (Fig 11-72). Fig 11-73 shows one of the element supporting masts with the connection box at the top. Notice the 3.5 MHz stub running along the pole.

In order to *know* at all times how much power is being

dissipated in the dummy load, I added a small RF detector to the dummy-load resistor and feed the dc voltage into the shack, where the relative power is displayed on a small moving-coil instrument that is mounted on the homemade direction-switching box. The box also contains the switch to select the subbands. In addition, a level-detector circuit is included, using an LM339 voltage comparator, which turns on a red LED if the dissipated power goes above a preset value. Fig 11-74 shows the schematic of the system and Fig 11-75 shows the actual switch-box.

5.3.7. Alternative Feed System

The logical alternative to prevent power from being wasted is to use the W7EL feed system. The drawback of the W7EL system is that the SWR and directivity bandwidth of the array are much narrower than with the hybrid-coupler system. It is possible, however, to obtain a perfect quadrature feed at

Fig 11-73—A 10 × 10 × 3 cm (4 × 4 × 1.2 in.) plastic box is mounted on top of the 5 m (17 ft) support pole for the elevated verticals. Inside the box, the vertical wire and the single radial are connected to the feed line, which is equipped with a stack of 50 ferrite cores to remove any RF from flowing on the outside of the feed line. The box also houses the relay that switches the stub in and out of the circuit to lower the operating frequency to 3.5 MHz. The stub can be seen running along the steel mast.

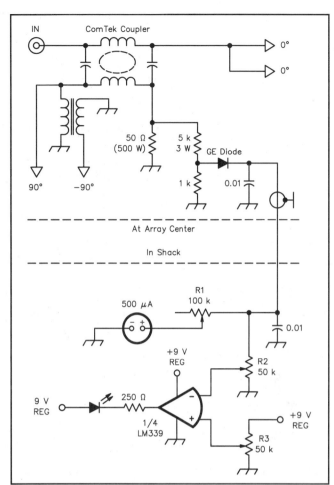

Fig 11-74—Schematic diagram of the RF detector and voltage comparator used to monitor the RF into the hybrid terminating resistor. The LED will switch on if the voltage coming from the detector is higher than the preset voltage supplied by the potentiometer R3. R1 adjusts the sensitivity of the indicator, and R2 the alarm level.

Fig 11-75—Array direction switch box, including the dummy-load relative RF power indicator and alarm circuit as shown in Fig 11-74.

the design frequency, which, by the nature of the hybrid coupler, is impossible with an array presenting complex loads to the coupler. From an operating and performance point of view, the advantage of a "perfect" quadrature feed is quite unimportant as the deviations result in unnoticeably small variations in gain and F/B as compared to the theoretical "perfect" model.

5.3.8. Array Performance

Assessing the array performance by measuring its SWR is totally meaningless (see par. 3.3.7). With a hybrid coupler, this array shows an SWR of less than 1.3:1 over the entire 80-meter band, wherever the resonance of the elements is.

Based on a sound wasted-power bandwidth criterion, the bandwidth of this array is 100 kHz. Fig 11-69 shows the wasted-power curve for the 4-square array with a single elevated radial. The steepness of the dissipated-power curve is

determined by the Q factor of the array elements. In the case of this particular 4-square, the elements being made of wire, the Q is high and the bandwidth narrow. Also the fact that I use a single radial instead of a comprehensive (buried) radial system adds to the sharpness of the curve. While changing the frequency away from the design frequency, the single radial (just like the vertical element) will introduce reactance into the feed-point impedance, which would not be the case with a buried radial system.

Practically speaking, this array is *by far* the best antenna I have ever had on 80 meters. On-the-air tests continuously indicate that the signal strength on DX is ranging with the best signals from the continent. As far as directivity is concerned, it is clear that the array has a nice wide forward lobe, and that the relative loss half-way between two adjacent forward lobes is hardly noticeable (typically 2 dB). Long-haul DX very often reports, "You are S9 on the front and not copyable off the back." Even on European signals there is always a good deal of directivity with this array (typically 15 dB).

Array Data

Feed currents:

$$I1 = 1 \angle{-90°}; I2 = 1 \angle{0°}; I3 = 1 \angle{0°}; I4 = 1 \angle{90°}$$

Gain: 5.1 dB over a single vertical with a single radial
3-dB beamwidth: 95 degrees
Design frequency: 3.75 MHz
Length of verticals: 19.5 m (64 ft)
Length radials: 18.7 m (67.3 ft)

The calculated feed-point impedances are

Z1 = 59 + j51 ohms
Z2 = Z3 = 37 − j3 ohms
Z4 = 10.7 − j5.8 ohms

5.4. T-loaded Vertical Elements

If the central tower is not high enough to support full-size quarter-wave verticals from the sloping support wires, these verticals can be top loaded by a sloping top-wire. The top-loading wires can be part of the support system, as shown in Fig 11-66. The vertical elements are loaded with sloping top-wires in order to show resonance at 3.8 MHz. The sloping support wires have the property of not producing any horizontally polarized signal, provided the lengths on both sides of the vertical are the same.

As long as the vertical wire is not shorter than ⅔ of full size (approximately 15 meters or 50 ft), the loaded verticals will produce the same results as the full-size verticals, with only some reduction in bandwidth.

■ 6. ARRAYS OF SLOPING VERTICALS

In the chapter on dipoles, I describe the vertical half-wave dipole as well as the sloping half-wave dipole and its evolution into a quarter-wave vertical with one radial.

Sloping verticals are well suited for making a 4-square array from using a single, tall tower as a support.

6.1. The Square Array With Sloping ½-Wave Dipoles

The 4-square array made of four slopers (sloping at 30 degrees with respect to the support) requires a 36-m (118 ft) tower.

Array Data

Feed currents:

$$I1 = 1 \angle{-90°}; I2 = 1 \angle{0°}; I3 = 1 \angle{0°}; I4 = 1 \angle{90°}$$

Gain: 4.3 dB over a single sloping vertical
3-dB beamwidth: 108 degrees
Design frequency: 3.65 MHz
Length dipole: 40 m (131.2 ft)

The feed-point impedances calculated with a grounded 36-m support tower are

Z1 = 205 + j172 ohms
Z2 = Z3 = 89 − j51 ohms
Z4 = 28 + j13 ohms

Fig 11-76 shows the radiation patterns. For comparison, the vertical pattern of a single element is included.

The array shows a fair amount of high angle radiation, which is due to the horizontal radiation component originated by the sloping wires. The array can be fed with a Collins-type network, designed for a nominal impedance of 75 ohms. The elements should be fed with 75-ohm quarter-wave-long feed lines to the hybrid network.

6.2. The K8UR Sloping Dipoles Square Array

D. C. Mitchell, K8UR, described his 4-element sloping array (Ref. "The K8UR Low-Band Vertical Array," *CQ*, Dec '89, p 42). He uses half-wave slopers where the bottom half is sloped back toward the tower. This eliminates all the high-angle radiation, as the horizontal component is now canceled due to the folding of the elements.

Array Data

Feed currents:

$$I1 = 1 \angle{-90°}; I2 = 1 \angle{0°}; I3 = 1 \angle{0°}; I4 = 1 \angle{90°}$$

Gain: 4.0 dB over a single identical sloping vertical
3-dB beamwidth: 123 degrees
Design frequency: 3.65 MHz
Length of sloping verticals 2 × 21.2 m (2 × 69.55 ft)

The feed-point impedances calculated with a grounded 36-m support tower are

Z1 = 66 + j136 ohms
Z2 = Z3 = 90 − j2.5 ohms
Z4 = −17 − j41 ohms

Fig 11-77 shows the radiation patterns. For comparison, the vertical pattern of a single element is included in B.

Because the elements are folded back toward the tower, the elements are very tightly coupled to the tower. There seems to be no influence on the radiation pattern. The feed-point impedance is much lower with the tower than without, however, which indicates heavy mutual coupling.

Mitchell uses the Collins-type feed-system. In his design of the network, he has replaced the 180-degree phasing line with a hybrid-type network, taking care of the required 180-degree phase shift.

6.3. The 4-Square Array With Sloping Quarter-Wave Verticals

Another variant I developed does not require such a high tower. I modeled the 4-square array using the sloping quarter-

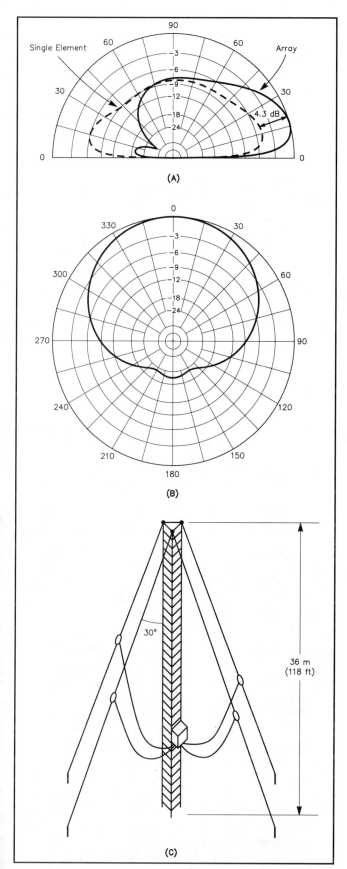

Fig 11-76—Configuration and radiation patterns of a
4-square array made of four half-wave sloping verticals.
For 80 meters a 36-m (118 ft) support is required. The
antenna was modeled over very good ground. Note the
high-angle radiation component. The vertical pattern for
a single sloper is included for comparison.

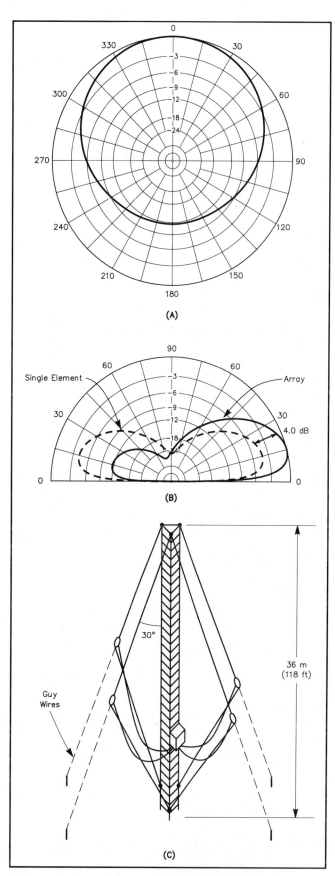

Fig 11-77—Configuration and radiation patterns of the 4-
element K8UR array. The high-angle radiation
component has been completely eliminated by folding
the bottom half of the elements back to the tower. The
vertical radiation pattern for a single element is shown
for comparison.

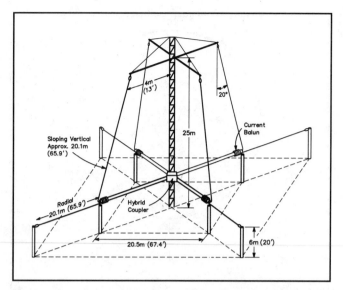

Fig 11-78—Four-square array made of four quarter-wave sloping verticals with a single sloping radial. The slope angle was kept at 20 degrees in order to minimize the horizontal radiation component. This requires two 8-m (26 ft) cross-arms to be mounted on the supporting tower.

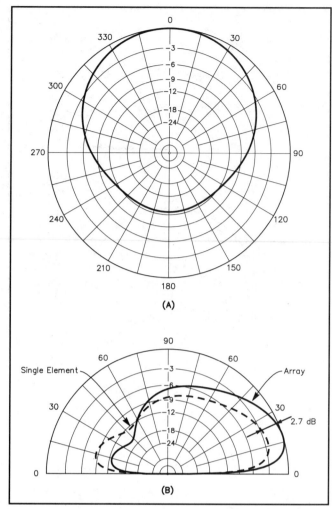

Fig 11-79—Radiation patterns for the 4-square array made of sloping quarter-wave verticals with a single radial, as shown in Fig 11-78. The vertical radiation pattern of a single sloping element is added for comparison. Modeling is done over very good ground, and includes the tower supporting the array.

wave vertical with a single radial, as described in the chapter on dipoles (par. 6.3.).

Because I had put up my full-size 133-ft vertical for 160 meters, I was looking for something better than a single vertical on 80, something I could support from the tall tower without too much coupling from the 160-meter antenna into the 80-meter one and vice versa. Fig 11-78 shows the array that evolved. At 25 m (82 ft) height, two 8-m (26 ft) cross-arms are mounted in the tower. Each cross-arm tip (4 m or 13 ft from the tower) will support the top of the sloping vertical. The feed point of the vertical is 6 m (20 ft) above ground, and the four feed points are the corners of a square measuring 21.1 m or 69.2 ft (¼ wavelength). Each sloping vertical has a single sloping radial with the end connected to a stake 6 m (20 ft) above ground.

Array Data

Feed currents:
$I1 = 1 \angle -90°$; $I2 = 1 \angle 0°$; $I3 = 1 \angle 0°$; $I4 = 1 \angle 90°$
Gain: 2.7 dB over a single sloping vertical
3-dB beamwidth: 112 degrees
Design frequency: 3.65 MHz
Length sloping verticals and radials: 20.1 m (65.9 ft)

The feed-point impedances are

Z1 = 57 + j76 ohms
Z2 = Z3 = 53.6 – j12 ohms
Z4 = 10.2 – j22 ohms

Fig 11-79 shows the radiation patterns.

Although the array has only 2.7 dB of gain over a single identical element, the gain over isotropic is 7.0 dBi. This is 0.2 dB better than the K8UR array, only 0.05 dB less than the

half-wave sloper array described in par 6.1, and 0.7 dB down from the 4-square array using fully vertical members and a single elevated radial (see par 5.3). All these values are for operation over very good ground.

The array could easily be further optimized to exhibit a better F/B ratio by adjusting the feed-current phase angles and magnitudes. This would, however, make the feed system much more complicated.

The array was modeled including the 39-m grounded vertical that supports the array. The coupling of the array on the 160-meter band was also analyzed and found to be negligible (no impedance change). This was done with the feed lines both open and short circuited.

Using 2 mm OD (AWG no. 12) wire and a slope angle of 20 degrees, the sloping wire length is 20.12 m to produce resonance at 3.79 MHz over a perfect mirror. The single elevated radial (at 6 m or 20 ft) which produces a resonant element on the same frequency, is 21.0 m.

If space is available, the single radial can be replaced by

two radials (in line). This will decrease the high-angle radiation, which is mainly coming from the single sloping radial (see par 6.3. in the chapter on dipoles). If two radials (or 4, or 8) are used, install them two-by-two in a straight line. This will effectively cancel all radiation from each pair of radials.

■ 7. CONCLUSION

Now that we have powerful modeling programs available (eg, ELNEC), I would like to encourage everyone to try to develop an array that fits his or her own requirements. The latest modeling program ANTENNA OPTIMIZER (AO), by Beezley, is a valuable tool as well.

As far as array gain is concerned, always compare the array gain against an antenna made by a single element, modeled over the same ground. This will tell you exactly how much you will gain by going from a single vertical to an array. All other comparisons are pretty much meaningless. Make sure you use the same ground quality specifications in all circumstances. If you want to model the antenna for designing your own feed system, don't forget to include the equivalent loss resistance for the less than perfect ground radial system.

Modeling an antenna is one thing; building it and making it work as it says on paper (or the computer screen) is another thing. If you have to compromise a little in order to be able to use a much easier-to-make feed-system (eg, quadrature fed versus the exotic phase angles or current magnitude), I would advise the compromise, unless you have the required measuring setup.

Finally, measure. If you use a quadrature-fed array, there are some very simple tools available that will tell you exactly how well the array has been fed, and how well it will work. If you choose an array with more exotic current angles, try to get hold of a quality oscilloscope or a vector voltmeter. I guarantee, the results will be well worth the effort.

OTHER ARRAYS

- **1. Two-Element Array, Spaced ⅛ Wave, Fed 180 Degrees out of Phase**

- **2. Unidirectional 2-Element Horizontal Array**

- **3. Two-Element Parasitic Array**

- **4. Two-Element Delta Loop Array**

    4.1. Two-element delta loop with sloping elements

- **5. Three-Element Dipole Array with All-Fed Elements**

- **6. Three-Element Parasitic Dipole Array**

- **7. Delta Loops in Phase (Collinear)**

- **8. The ZL Special**

- **9. Bobtail Curtain**

- **10. Half-Square Antenna**

OTHER 12 ARRAYS

I have dedicated a whole chapter to vertical arrays, and another to Yagi and quad arrays. There are, of course, other types of arrays that are more than interesting to look at for the low bands. Even at relatively low heights (0.3 wavelength), arrays made of horizontal elements (dipoles) can be quite attractive. Their intrinsic radiation angle is certainly higher than for an array made of vertical elements, but unless the electrical quality of the ground is good to excellent, the horizontal array may actually outperform the vertical array even at low angles.

The vertical radiation angle (wave angle) of arrays made with vertical elements (typical ¼-wavelength long elements) depends only on the quality of the ground in the Fresnel zone. Radiation angles range typically from 15 to 25 degrees.

The wave angle for antennas with horizontally polarized elements basically depends on the height of the antenna above ground. For low antennas (with resulting high wave angles), the quality of the ground right under the antenna (near field) will also play a role in determining the wave angle (see Chapter 8 on dipoles). But as DXers, we are not interested in antennas producing wave angles that radiate almost at zenith.

Over good ground a dipole at ¼ wavelength height radiates its maximum energy at the zenith. Over average ground, the angle is 72 degrees. The only way to drastically lower the radiation angle with an antenna at such low height is to add another element.

If we install a second dipole at close spacing (eg, ⅛ wavelength), and at the same height (¼ wave), and feed this second dipole 180 degrees out of phase with respect to the first dipole, we achieve two things:
• Approximately 2.5 dB of gain in a bidirectional pattern.
• A lowering of the wave angle from 72 degrees to 37 degrees!

At the zenith angle the radiation is a perfect null, whatever the quality of the ground is. This is because, at the zenith, the reflected wave from element no. 1 (reflected from the ground right under the antenna) will cancel the direct wave from element no. 2. The same accounts for the reflected wave from element no. 1 and the direct 90-degree wave from element no. 2. All the power that is subtracted from the high angles is now concentrated at lower angles. Of course there also is a narrowing of the horizontal forward lobe. Example: A half-wave 80-m dipole at 25 m (80 ft) has a −3-dB forward-lobe beamwidth of 124 degrees at a wave angle of 45 degrees. The 2-element version, described above, has a −3-dB angle of 95 degrees at the same 45-degree wave angle. The impedance of the two dipoles has dropped very significantly to approximately 8 ohms.

Fig 12-1 shows the vertical radiation angle (wave angle)

for three types of antennas over average ground: a horizontal dipole, two half-waves fed 180 degrees out of phase (spaced ⅛ wavelength), and a 2-element Yagi. From this graph you can see that the only way to achieve a reasonably low radiation angle from a horizontally polarized antenna at low height (typically ⅓ wavelength or less) is to add a second element. The 180-degree-out-of-phase element lowers the radiation angle at lower antenna heights (below 0.35 wavelength) significantly more than a Yagi or a 2-element all-fed array. It also has the distinct advantage to suppress *all* the high-angle radiation, which is not the case with the other types of arrays (Yagi or all-fed arrays).

■ 1. TWO-ELEMENT ARRAY SPACED ⅛ WAVE, FED 180 DEGREES OUT OF PHASE

The vertical and the horizontal radiation patterns of the 2-element array are shown in Fig 12-2. As the antenna elements are fed with a 180-degree phase difference, the feeding is simple. The impedances at both elements are identical. Fig 12-3 gives the feed-point impedance of the elements as a function of the spacing between the elements and the height. Within the shown limits, spacing has no influence on the gain or the directivity pattern. Very close spacings give very low impedances, which makes feeding more complicated

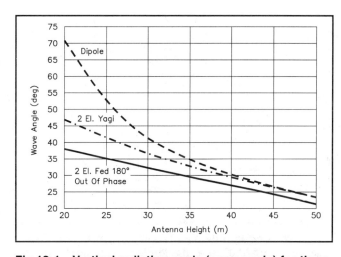

Fig 12-1—Vertical radiation angle (wave angle) for three types of antennas over average ground: a half-wave dipole, a 2-element parasitic array (Yagi) and two close-spaced half-wave dipoles fed 180 degrees out of phase. Note the remarkable superiority of the last antenna at low heights. The graph is applicable for 80 meters.

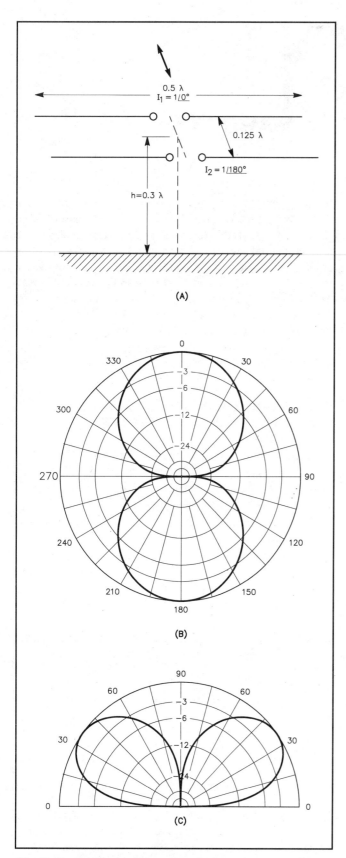

(A)

(B)

(C)

Fig 12-2—Configuration and radiation patterns of two close-spaced half-wave dipoles fed 180 degrees out of phase, at a height of 0.3 wavelength above average ground. The azimuth pattern at B is taken for a wave angle of 36 degrees. Note in the elevation pattern at C that all radiation at the zenith angle is effectively canceled (see text for details).

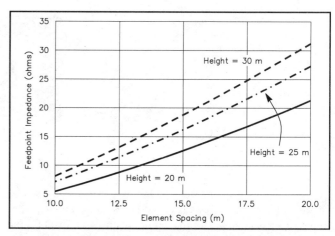

Fig 12-3—Feed-point impedance of the 2-element close-spaced array with elements fed 180 degrees out of phase, as a function of spacing between the elements and height above ground. The design frequency is 3.75 MHz.

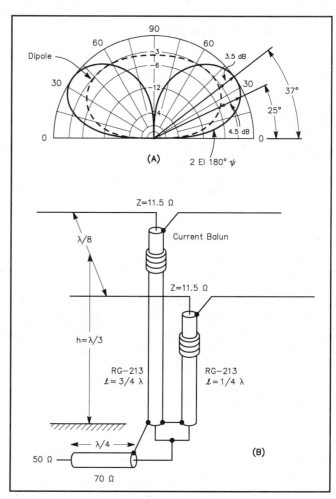

Fig 12-4—At A, vertical radiation pattern of the 2-element close-spaced array as compared to a single dipole at the same height of 0.3 wavelength (25 m or 80 ft for 3.8 MHz). The feed method for a spacing of ⅛ wavelength is shown at B. The feed-point impedance is approximately 100 ohms at the junction of the ¼- and the ¾-wavelength 50-ohm feed lines. A quarter-wave long 70-ohm feed line can be used to provide a perfect match to a 50-ohm feed line.

and increases losses in the system. A minimum spacing of 0.15 wavelength is recommended.

Compared to a single dipole at the same height, this antenna has a gain of 3.5 dB at its main wave angle of 37 degrees, and of 4.5 dB at a wave angle of 25 degrees (see Fig 12-4).

Feeding the array is done by running a ¼-wave feed line to one element, and a ¾-wave feed line to the other element. The feed point at the junction of the two feed lines is approximately 100 ohms for an element spacing of 0.125 wavelength. A quarter-wave long 75-ohm cable will provide a perfect match to a 50-ohm feed line.

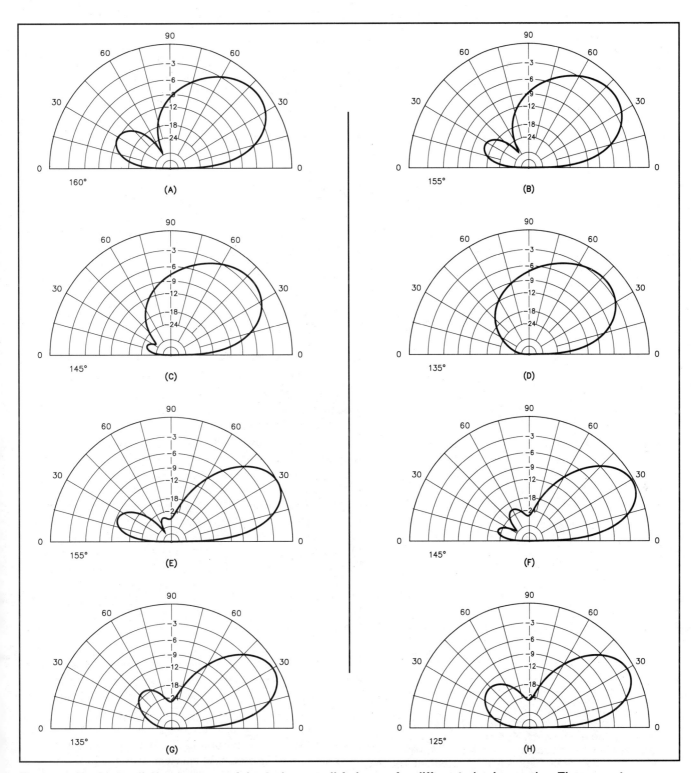

Fig 12-5—Vertical radiation patterns of the 2-element all-fed array for different phasing angles. The current magnitude is the same for both elements. All patterns are plotted to the same scale. Patterns are shown for antenna heights of ¼ wavelength (at A through D) and ½ wavelength (at E through H).

A—160° phase difference.	C and F—145° phase difference.	H—125° phase difference.
B and E—155° phase difference.	D and G—135° phase difference.	

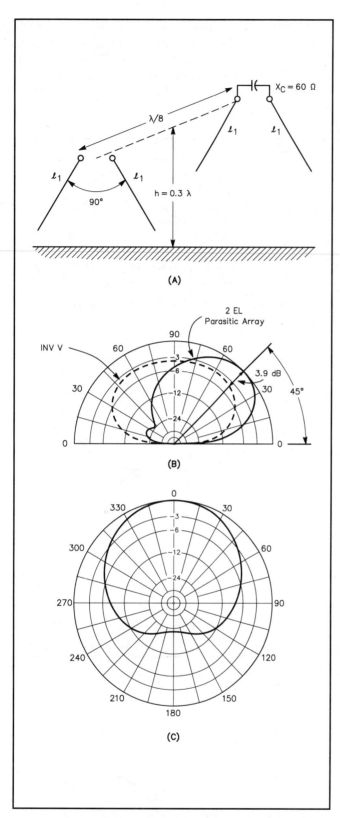

(A)

(B)

(C)

Fig 12-6—Configuration and calculated radiation patterns for the 2-element parasitic array using inverted-V-dipole elements. The array is installed with an apex angle of 90 degrees, at a height of 0.3 wavelength (25 m or 80 ft for 3.8 MHz). Element spacing is ⅛ wavelength. The vertical pattern of a single inverted-V dipole is included at B for comparison. At C the azimuth pattern is shown for a wave angle of 45 degrees. The gain at the main wave angle (45 degrees) is 3.9 dB over the single inverted-V dipole.

■ 2. UNIDIRECTIONAL 2-ELEMENT HORIZONTAL ARRAY

Starting from the above array, we can now alter the phase of the feed current to change the bidirectional horizontal pattern into a unidirectional pattern.

The required phase to obtain beneficial gain and especially front-to-back ratio varies with height above ground. At ½ wavelength and higher, a phase difference of 135 degrees produces a good result. At lower heights, a larger phase difference (155 degrees) helps to lower the main wave angle. This is logical, as the closer we go to the 180-degree phase difference, the more the effect of the phase radiation cancellation at high angles comes into effect (see above).

Fig 12-5 shows the vertical radiation patterns obtained with different phase angles for a 2-element array at ¼ and at ½ wavelength heights. Note that as we increase the phase angle, the high-angle radiation decreases, but the low angle F/B worsens. The higher phase angle also yields a little better gain. For both antenna heights (25 and 40 m or 0.3 and 0.4 wavelength), a phase angle of 145 degrees seems a good compromise.

Feeding these arrays is not simple, as the feed-current phase angles are not in quadrature (phase angle differences in steps of 90 degrees). For a discussion of feed methods see Chapter 11 on vertical arrays. Current forcing using a modified Lewallen feed system seems to be the best choice.

The question that comes to mind is, "Can we obtain similar gain and directivity with a parasitic array?" Let's see.

■ 3. TWO-ELEMENT PARASITIC ARRAY

Our modeling tools teach us that we can indeed obtain exactly the same results with a parasitic array. A 2-element director-type array produces the same gain and a front-to-back ratio that is even slightly superior.

As a practical 2-element parasitic-type wire array, I have developed a Yagi with two inverted-V-dipole elements. Fig 12-6 shows the configuration as well as the radiation patterns obtained at a height of 25 m (0.3 wavelength). In order to make the array easily switchable, both wire elements are made equally long (39.94 m or 131.03 ft for a design frequency of 3.8 MHz). The inverted-V-dipole apex angle is 90 degrees. A 25-meter (80 ft) high support (mast, tower) is required. At that height we need to install a 10-m (33 ft) long horizontal support (boom), from the end of which we can hang the inverted-V dipoles. The gain is 3.9 dB versus an inverted-V dipole at the same height, measured at the main wave angle of 45 degrees.

A loading capacitor with a reactance of $-j60$ ohms produces the right current phase in the director. The radiation resistance of the array is 24 ohms. In order to make the array easily switchable, we run two feed lines of equal length to the elements.

From here on there are two possibilities:

• We use a length of coax feed line to provide the required reactance of $-j65$ ohms at the element.

• We use a variable capacitor at the end of a ½-wave feed line. The theoretical value of the capacitor is

$$\frac{10^6}{2\pi \times 3.8 \times 65} = 644 \text{ pF}$$

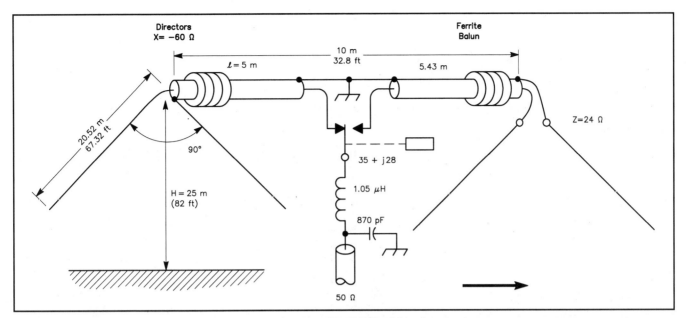

Fig 12-7—Feeding arrangement for the 2-element parasitic array shown in Figure 12-6. Two lengths of RG-213 run to a switch box in the center of the array. The coax feeding the director is left open at the end, producing a reactance of $-j65$ ohms (equivalent of 644 pF at 3.8 MHz) at the element feed point. The radiation resistance of the 2-element array is 29 ohms. An L network can be provided to obtain a perfect match to the 50-ohm feed line. A current type balun (stack of ferrite beads) *must* be provided at both element feed points.

Now we calculate the length of the feed line. The reactance at the end of an open feed line is given by:

$$X = -Z_C \times \tan(90 - L)$$

where

Z_C = characteristic impedance of the line
L = length of the line, degrees

This can be rewritten as

$$L = 90 - \arctan \frac{X}{Z_C}$$

In our case we need X = -60 ohms. Thus,

$$L = 90 - \arctan \frac{60}{50} = 39.8 \text{ degrees}$$

The physical length of this line is given by

$$L_{meters} = \frac{833 \times VF \times \ell}{1000 \times f_q}$$

where

VF = velocity factor (0.66 for RG-213)
F_q = design frequency
ℓ = length, degrees

$$L_{meters} = \frac{833 \times 0.66 \times 39.8}{1000 \times 3.8} = 5.76 \text{ m (18.9 ft)}$$

Fig 12-7 shows the feed and switching arrangements according to the two above mentioned systems.

■ 4. TWO-ELEMENT DELTA LOOP ARRAY

Using the same support as described above (a 10 m or 33 ft long boom at 25 m or 80 ft), we can also design a 2-element delta loop configuration. If the ground conductivity is excellent, and if we can install radials, the 2-element delta loop array should provide a lower angle of radiation and comparable gain as compared to the 2-element inverted-V-dipole array as described in par 3.

4.1. Two-Element Delta Loop with Sloping Elements

As the low-impedance feed point of the vertically polarized delta loop is quite a distance from the apex, and as most of the radiation comes from the high current areas of the antenna, we can consider using delta loop elements that are sloping away from the tower. We could not do this with the inverted-V 2-element array, as the high-current points are right at the apex.

In our example I have provided a boom of 6 m length (20 ft) at the top of our support (25 m). From the tips of the boom we slope the two triangles so that the base lines are now 8 m away from the support and approximately 2.5 m over the ground.

Fig 12-8 shows the radiation pattern obtained with the array when the loops are fed with equal current magnitude and with a phase difference of 120 degrees. Note the tremendous F/B at low angles (more than 45 dB!). Gain over a single element loop is 3.5 dB. The wave angle is 18 degrees over a very good ground. One of the problems is, of course, the feed system for an array that is not fed in quadrature.

Fig 12-9 shows the radiation patterns for the 2-element array with a parasitic reflector. The gain is the same as for the all-fed array and 3.4 dB over a single delta loop element. The parasitic array shows better discrimination at high angles, but less at low angles, as compared to the all-fed array (see Fig 12-8).

As with the 2-element dipole array, my personal prefer-

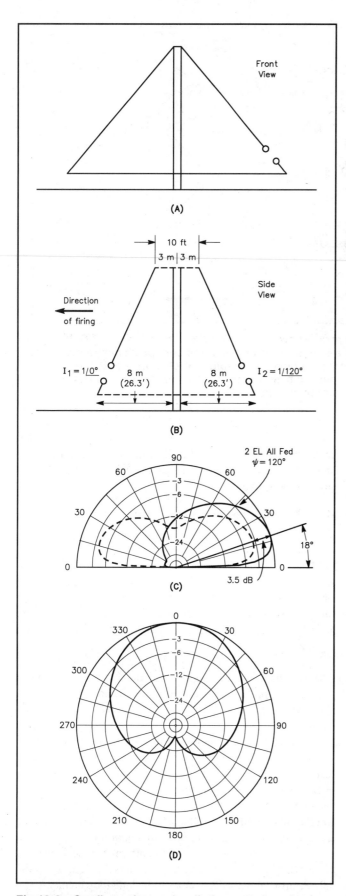

Fig 12-8—Configuration and radiation patterns of a 2-element delta-loop array, using sloping elements. The elements are fed with equal-magnitude current and with a phase difference of 120 degrees. The horizontal pattern at D is taken for a wave angle of 18 degrees.

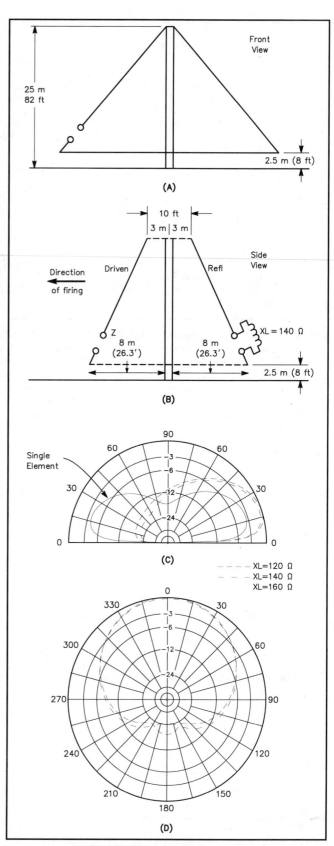

Fig 12-9—Radiation patterns for the 2-element delta loop array having the same physical dimensions as the all-fed array of Figure 12-8, but with one element tuned as a reflector. In practice both triangles are made equally long, and the required loading inductance is inserted to achieve the required phase angle. Patterns shown are for different values of loading coils (X_C = 120, 140 and 160 ohms). The feed-point impedance of the array will vary between 80 and 150 ohms, depending on the ground quality.

ence goes to the parasitic array, as the all-fed array is not fed in quadrature, which means that the feed arrangement is all but simple (it requires a modified Lewallen feed system). The obvious feed method for the 2-element parasitic array uses two equal-length feed lines to a common point midway between the two loops. A small support can house the switching and matching hardware.

As with the 2-element inverted-V array, we use two loops of identical length, and use a length of shorted feed line to provide the required inductive loading with the reflector element. The length of the feed line required to achieve the required 140-ohm inductive reactance is calculated as follows:

$$X_L = Z_C \times \tan \ell$$

where

X_L = required inductance
Z_C = cable impedance
ℓ = cable length

This can be rewritten as

$$\ell = \arctan \frac{X_L}{Z_C}$$

or

$$\ell = \arctan \frac{140}{75} = 61.8 \text{ degrees}$$

The physical length is given by

$$L_{meters} = \frac{833 \times VF \times \ell}{1000 \times f_q}$$

where

L_{meters} = length, meters
ℓ = length in degrees
VF = velocity factor of the cable
F_q = design frequency, MHz

We use foam-type RG-11 (VF = 0.81), because solid PE-type coax (VF = 0.66) will be too short to reach the switch box.

$$L_{meters} = \frac{833 \times 0.81 \times 61.8}{1000 \times 3.8} = 10.98 \text{ m (36 ft)}$$

Fig 12-10 shows the feed line and the switching arrangement for the array. Note that the cable going to the reflector must be short-circuited. The two coaxial feed lines must be equipped with current-type baluns (a stack of ferrite beads).

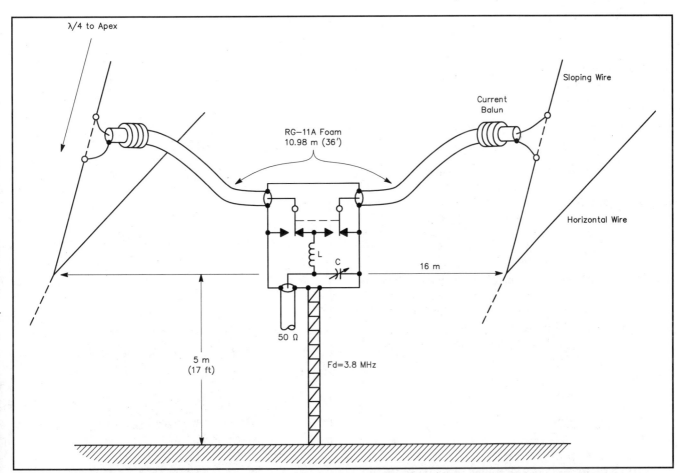

Fig 12-10—Feeding and direction-switching arrangement for the 2-element parasitic delta loop array as shown in Figure 12-9. The length of the 75-ohm feed lines going from the feed points to the switch box is 61.8 degrees. For 3.8 MHz, and using foam-type coax (VF = 0.81), this equals 10.98 m (36 ft). The spacing between the elements at the height of the feed points is approximately 15 m (50 ft). The switch box is mounted on a support approximately 5 m (17 ft) above the ground, half way between the elements. Note that the feed line to the reflector needs to be short-circuited. A simple L network provides a perfect match for a 50-ohm feed line.

The impedance of the array varies between 75 and 150 ohms, depending on the ground quality. If necessary, the impedance can easily be matched to the 50-ohm feed line using a small L network. This array can be made switchable from the SSB end of the band to the CW end by applying the capacitive loading technique as described in Chapter 10 on large loops.

■ 5. THREE-ELEMENT DIPOLE ARRAY WITH ALL-FED ELEMENTS

A 3-element phased array made of half-wave dipoles can be dimensioned to achieve a very good gain together with an outstanding F/B ratio. Three elements on a ¼-wavelength "boom" (⅛-wave spacing between elements) can yield nearly 6 dB of gain at the major radiation angle of 38 degrees over a single dipole at the same height (over average ground). A. Christman, KB8I, described a 3-element dipole array with outstanding directional and gain properties. (Ref 963.) I have modeled a 3-element inverted-V-dipole array using the same phase angles. The inverted-V elements have an apex angle of 90 degrees, and the apex at 25 m (80 ft) above ground. The radiation patterns are shown in Fig 12-11.

The elements are fed with the following currents:

$I1 = 1 \angle -149° \text{ A}$

$I2 = 2 \angle 0° \text{ A}$

$I3 = 1 \angle 146° \text{ A}$

With the antenna at 25 m above ground and elements that are 39.72 m long (130.31 ft (F_{design} = 3.8 MHz)), the element feed-point impedances are

$Z1 = -36 + j24.5 \text{ ohms}$

$Z2 = 12.3 + j25 \text{ ohms}$

$Z3 = 7.6 - j12.2 \text{ ohms}$

If you are confused with the minus sign in front of the *real* part of the impedance, it just means that in this array, element no. 1 is actually *delivering* power into the feed system, rather than taking power from it. This is a very common situation with driven arrays, especially where "close" spacing is used. See also the chapter on Vertical Arrays.

A possible feed method consists of running three ¼-wave lines to a common point. Current forcing is employed: We use 50-ohm feed lines to the outer elements, and two parallel 50-ohm lines to the central element. The method is described in detail in Chapter 11 on vertical arrays.

Assuming RG-213 cable with 0.3 dB loss per 100 ft, the voltages at the end of these lines are

$E1 = 49.74 \angle -58.79° \text{ V}$

$E2 = 50.13 \angle 90.42° \text{ V}$

$E3 = 50.06 \angle -124.1° \text{ V}$

Fig 12-11—Configuration and radiation patterns for two types of 3-element inverted-V-dipole arrays with the apex at 0.3 wavelength. At both C and D, one pattern is for the all-fed array and the other for an array with a parasitic reflector and director. The all-fed array outperforms the Yagi-type array by approximately 1 dB in gain as well as 10 dB in F/B ratio.

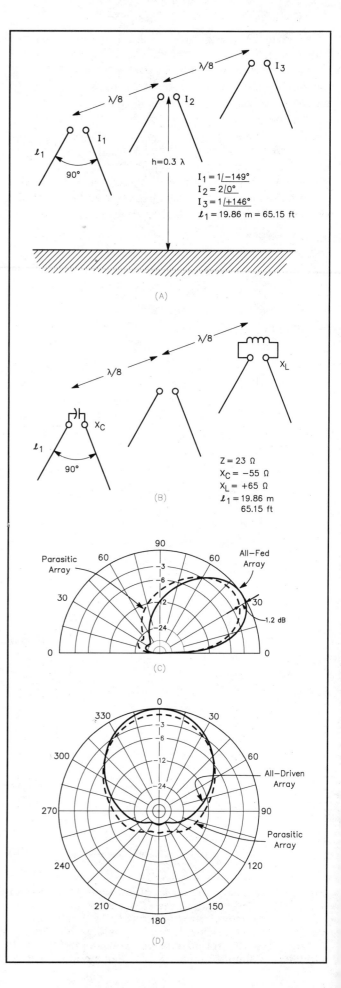

The impedances at the end of the three feed lines are:

Z1' = –47.14 – j 32.8 ohm

Z2' = 10.2 –j 20 ohm

Z3' = 94.2 + j 143.6 ohm

We will now calculate the shunt elements which we must connect across the feed lines to the outer elements to turn them into resistive impedance. This can be calculated using the SHUNT IMPEDANCE module of the NEW LOW BAND SOFTWARE.

For the line to element no. 1:

Z_{sh1} = +100.4 ohms
Component value (f = 3.8 MHz) = 4.2 µH
The new impedance becomes
Z1" = –69.9 ohms (still delivering power!)

For the line to element no. 2:
Z_{sh2} = –205.4 ohms
Component value (f = 3.8 MHz) = 205 pF
The new impedance becomes
Z2" = 313 ohms

Now we calculate the constant-impedance line stretchers that will provide the required voltage phase shift so the input of the line stretchers can be connected in parallel with the end of the feed line to the center element. The LINE STRETCHER module of the NEW LOW BAND SOFTWARE calculates either a T or a pi network to do the job.

Pi-network line stretcher to element no. 1:
Z_C = –69.9 ohms
Input voltage phase = 90.42 degrees
Output voltage phase = –58.79 degrees
$Z_{parallel}$ = 19.2 ohms
Z_{series} = –35.8 ohms
Parallel element: 0.81 µH
Series element: 1171 pF

Pi-network line stretcher to element no. 2:
Z_C = 313 ohms
Input voltage phase = 90.42 degrees
Output voltage phase = –124.1 degrees = +235.9 degrees
$Z_{parallel}$ = 97.2 ohms
Z_{series} = –177 ohms
Parallel element: 4.1 µH
Series element: 236 pF

At the junction of the three lines we have a parallel impedance which is the combination of

Z1" = –69.9 ohms

Z2' = 10.2 – j20 ohms

Z3" = 313 ohms

The parallel equivalent is calculated using the PARALLEL IMPEDANCE module of the NEW LOW BAND SOFTWARE.

Z_{total} = 5.5 – j23.9 ohms

Fig 12-12 shows the feed network for the array.

It is much easier to model such a wonderful array and to calculate a matching network than to build and align the matching system. Slight deviations from the calculated im-

pedance values mean that the network component values will be different as well. There is no method of measuring the driven impedances of the elements. All you can do in the way of measuring is use an HF vector voltmeter and measure the voltages at the end of the three feed lines. The voltage magnitudes should be identical, and the phase as indicated above (E1, E2 and E3). If they are not, the values of the networks can be tweaked in order to obtain the required phase angles. Good luck!

The question arises whether it is possible to design a 3-element array with similar performance characteristics that does not require such a complicated feed system! In other words, how about an array with parasitic elements?

■ 6. THREE-ELEMENT PARASITIC DIPOLE ARRAY

I attempted to do as well as A. Christman with his odd phase angles, but could not really come close. I fell short 1.2 dB in gain (that's a lot!). The gain at a wave angle of 43 degrees, over a single inverted-V dipole at the same height is 4.5 dB. The F/B ratio is just over 20 dB, as compared to just over 30 dB with the all-driven array. At the same antenna height (0.3 wavelength), the radiation angle of the 3-element parasitic was also slightly higher (43 degrees) than for the 3-element all-fed array (38 degrees), modeled over the same (average) ground.

Fig 12-11 shows the superimposed patterns for the all-driven and the parasitic 3-element array (for 80 meters at 25 m or 80 ft height). Note that the 3-element all-fed has a better rejection at high angles. This is because the currents in the outer elements have a greater phase shift (versus the driven element) than in the parasitic array. These phase shifts are

Reflector:
All-driven array: –149 degrees
Parasitic array: –147 degrees
Director:
All-driven array: +147 degrees
Parasitic array: +105 degrees

This demonstrates again that, with an all-driven array, we have much better control over all the parameters that determine the radiation pattern of the array.

Like the 2-element array described in par 3, the 3-element array is also made using three elements identical in length. The required element reactances for the director and reflector are obtained by inserting the required inductance or capacitance in the center of the element. In practice we bring a feed line to the outer elements as well. The feed lines are used as stubs, which represent the required loading to turn the elements into a reflector or director.

The question is, which is the most appropriate type of feed line for the job, and what should be its impedance. Table 12-1 shows the stub lengths obtained with various types of feed lines. The length of the open-ended stub serving to produce a negative reactance (for use as a director stub) is given by

$$\ell° = 90 - \arctan \frac{X_C}{Z_C}$$

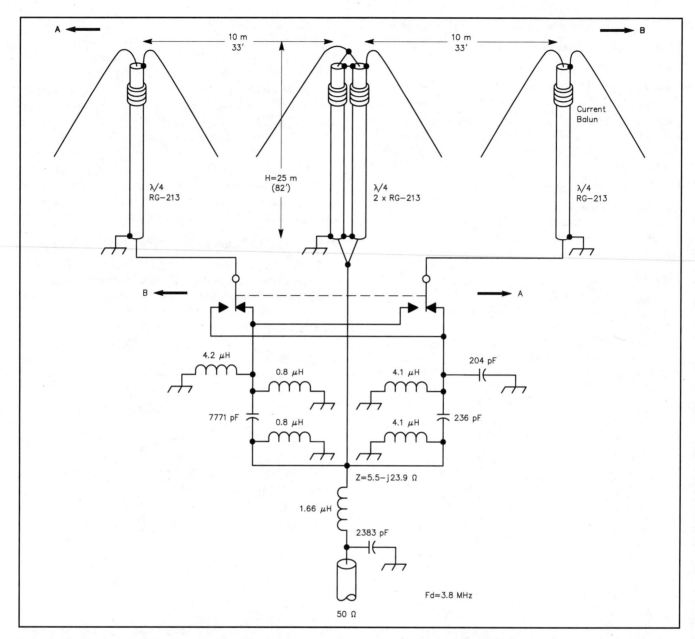

Fig 12-12—Current-forcing feed method for the 3-element inverted-V-dipole array. As the center element is fed with twice the current magnitude, compared to the outer elements, it must be fed with a coaxial feed line of half the impedance. Two RG-213 feed lines are used in parallel. The three feed lines are routed to a switch box in the tower which houses the required network components. See text for details.

For the short-circuited stub serving to produce a positive reactance (for the reflector), the formula is

$$\ell° = \arctan \frac{X_L}{Z_C}$$

- From Table 12-1 we learn the 450-ohm stub requires a very long length to produce the required negative reactance for the director (17.28 m or over 56.7 ft).
- When made from 50- or 75-ohm coax, we obtain attractive short lengths. The disadvantage is that you need to put a current balun at the end of the stubs to keep any current from flowing on the outside of the coax shield.
- A third solution is to use a 100-ohm shielded balanced line, made of two 50-ohm coax cables. The lengths are still very

attractive, and you no longer require the current balun.
- A final solution is to use the 450-ohm transmission line for the reflector (1.71 m long or 5.6 ft) and to load the line with an extra capacitor to turn it into a capacitor. I assumed a velocity factor of 0.95% for the transmission line. You must check this in all cases (see Chapter 11 on vertical arrays). The capacitive reactance produced by an open-circuited line of 1.71 m (5.6 ft) length at 3.8 MHz is

$$X_L = 450 \tan (90° - 8.22°) = +j3115 \text{ ohms}$$

This represents a capacitance value of only

$$\frac{10^6}{2\pi \times 3.8 \times 3115} = 13.4 \text{ pF}$$

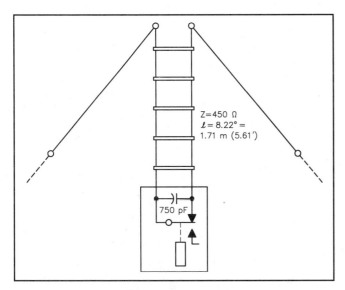

Fig 12-13—The 3-element parasitic type inverted-V dipole array is made with elements that have exactly the same length. The required element loading is obtained by inserting the required capacitance or inductance in the center of these elements. This is obtained by using stubs, as shown here. With a 450-ohm transmission line we require only a short 1.71-m (5.6 ft) long piece of short-circuited line to make a stub for the reflector. For the director we connect a 750-pF capacitor across the end of the line. This can be switched with a single-pole relay, as explained in the text.

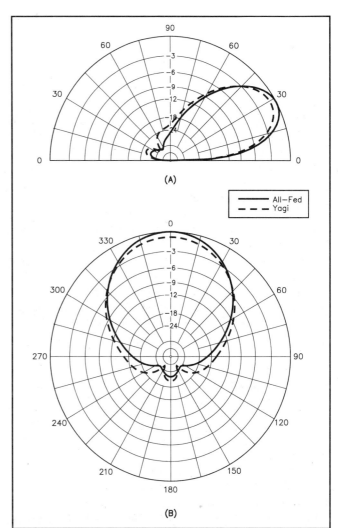

Fig 12-14—Radiation patterns of the 3-element inverted-V type array at a height of ½ wavelength. Note that the all-fed array still outperforms the Yagi-type array, but with a smaller margin than at a height of 0.3 wavelength (Fig 12-11). In order to produce an optimum radiation pattern, the values of the loading impedances were different than those for a height of 0.3 wavelength. See text for details.

12-1

Table 12-1

Required Line Length for the Loading Stubs of the Parasitic Version of the 3-Element Array of Fig 12-11

ZC, Ohms,	VF	Length, Degrees	Length, Meters	Length Feet
Director				
50	0.66	42.3	6.12	20.08
75	0.66	53.75	7.77	25.49
100	0.95	83.03	8.85	29.04
450	0.95	83.03	17.28	56.7
Reflector				
50	0.66	52.53	7.58	24.87
75	0.66	40.91	5.91	13.39
100	0.66	33.02	4.77	15.65
450	0.95	8.22	1.71	5.61

Other data:
Design frequency = 3.8 MHz, wavelength = 78.89 m
Director X_C = −55 ohms
Reflector X_L = +65 ohms

The required capacitive reactance was $-j55$ ohms, which represents a capacitance value of

$$\frac{10^6}{2\pi \times 3.8 \times 95} = 762 \text{ pF}$$

This means we need to connect a capacitor with a value of $762 - 13.4 = 750$ pF across the end of the open stub. This last solution seems to be the most flexible one. A parallel connection of two transmitting-type ceramic capacitors, 500 pF and 250 pF, will do the job perfectly. If you want even more flexibility you can use a 500-pF motor-driven variable in parallel with a 500-pF fixed capacitor. This will allow you to tune the array for best F/B.

The practical arrangement is shown in Fig 12-13. From each outer element we run a 1.71-m (5.6 ft) long piece of 450-ohm line to a small box which is mounted on the boom. The box can also be mounted right at the center of the inverted-V element, whereby the 1.71-m transmission line is shaped in a large 1-turn loop. The box houses a small relay which either shorts the stub (reflector) or opens, leaving the 750-pF capacitor across the line.

Is the "inferiority" of the parasitic array due to the low height? In order to find out I modeled the same antennas at

½ wavelength height. Fig 12-14 shows the vertical and the horizontal radiation patterns for the all-driven and parasitic array-versions of the 3-element inverted-V array at this height. Note that the all-driven array still has 0.9 dB better gain than the parasitic array. The F/B is still a little better as well, although the difference is less pronounced than at lower height. The optimum pattern was obtained when loading the director with a –50-ohm impedance and the reflector with a +30-ohm impedance. The gain of the all-fed array is 5.7 dB versus a dipole at the same height (at 28 degrees wave angle). For the 3-element parasitic array, the gain is 4.8 dB versus the dipole at its main wave angle of 29 degrees.

In looking at the vertical radiation pattern it is remarkable again that the all-driven array excels in F/B performance at high angles. Notice the "bulge" that is responsible for 5 to 10 dB less F/B in the 35-50 degree wave-angle region.

It must be said that I did not try to further optimize the parasitic array by shifting the relative position of the elements. By doing this, further improvement could no doubt be made. This, of course, would make it impossible to switch directions, as the array would no longer be symmetrical.

Conclusion

All-fed arrays made of horizontal dipoles or inverted-V dipoles always outperform the parasitic-type equivalents in gain as well as F/B performance. As they are not fed in quadrature, it is elaborate or even "difficult" to feed them correctly.

The parasitic-type arrays lend themselves very well for remote tuning of the parasitic elements. Short stubs (open-ended to make a capacitor, or short-circuited to make an inductor) make ideal tuning systems for the parasitic elements. Switching from director to reflector can easily be done with a single-pole relay and a capacitor at the end of a short open-wire stub.

The same 3-element array made of fully horizontal (flat top) dipoles exhibits 1.0 dB more gain than the inverted-V version at the same apex height.

■ 7. DELTA LOOPS IN PHASE (COLLINEAR)

Two delta loops can be erected in the same plane and fed with in-phase currents to provide gain and directivity. In the first configuration that we analyzed for operation on 3.8 MHz, we made the two delta loops touch with the tips. The array can be fed as shown in Fig 12-15. For the dimensions shown, the feed-point impedance is 35 ohms. The gain is a mere 1.3 dB over a single loop.

Separating the loops a little farther increases the gain and front-to-side ratio. With the tips separated by 10 meters. the gain has increased to 3.0 dB over a single loop, while the front-to-side ratio is now over 20 dB. Both loops show an impedance of approximately 165 ohms. They should be fed via two quarter-wave 70-ohm feed lines to a common point. The impedance at that point will be approximately 35 ohms. The radiation patterns and the configuration are shown in Fig 12-16.

This may be an interesting array if you happen to have two towers with the right separation and pointing in the right

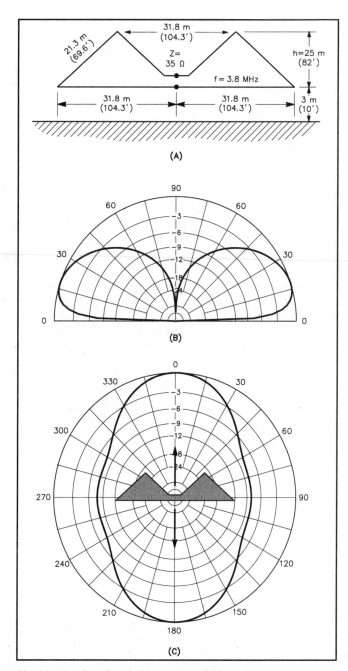

Fig 12-15—Configuration and radiation patterns of a 2-element collinear array made of two delta loops. The array is fed in the bottom corners where the two loops touch, shown at A, and exhibits a gain of 1.3 dB over a single loop. The horizontal pattern at C is for a wave angle of 18 degrees.

direction. As with all vertically polarized delta loops, the ground quality is very important as to the efficiency and the low angle radiation of the array (see Chapter 10 on large loops).

■ 8. THE ZL SPECIAL

The ZL Special, sometimes called the HB9CV, is a 2-element dipole array with the elements fed 135 degrees out of phase. This configuration is described in par 2.

These well-known configurations make use of a specific

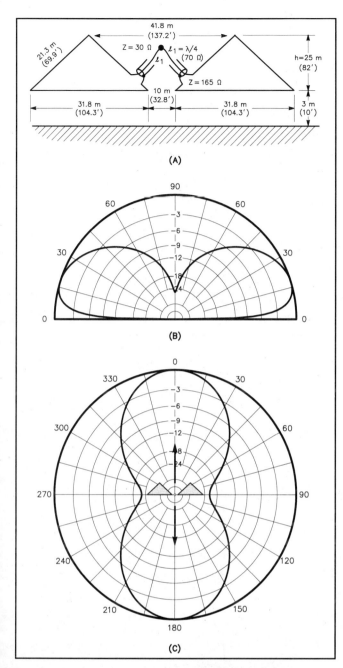

Fig 12-16—Configuration of the 2-element collinear delta loop array with 10-m spacing between the tips of the delta. This array has a gain of 3.0 dB over a single delta loop. The loops are fed ¼ wave from the apex on the sloping wire in the center of the array (see text for details). The pattern at C is taken for a wave angle of 18 degrees.

feeding method. The feed points of the two elements are connected via an open-wire feed line which is crossed. The crossing introduces a 180-degree phase shift. The length of the line, with a spacing of ⅛ wavelength between the elements, introduces an additional phase shift of approximately 45 degrees. The net result is 180 + 45 = 225 degrees phase shift, lagging. This is equivalent to 360 − 225 = 135 degrees leading.

Different dimensions for this array have been printed in various publications. Correct dimensions for optimum performance will depend on the material used for the elements and the phasing lines. Jordan, WA6TKT, who designed the ZL Special entirely with 300-ohm twin-lead (Ref. 908), recommends that the director (driven element) be $447.3/f_{MHz}$ and the reflector be $475.7/f_{MHz}$, with an element spacing of approximately 0.12 wavelength.

Using air-spaced phasing line with a velocity factor of 0.97, the phasing-line length is $119.3/f_{MHz}$. This configuration of the ZL Special with practical dimensions for a design frequency of 3.8 MHz is given in Fig 12-17, along with radiation patterns. As it is rather unlikely that this antenna will be made rotatable on the low bands, I recommend the use of open-wire feeders to an antenna tuner. Alternatively, a coaxial feed line can be used via a balun.

■ 9. BOBTAIL CURTAIN

The bobtail curtain consists of three top-fed quarter-wave verticals, spaced ½ wavelength apart and fed via a horizontal wire section. Through this feeding arrangement, the current magnitude in the outer verticals is half of the current in the center vertical. The current distribution in the top wire is such that all radiation from this horizontal section is effectively canceled. The configuration as well as the radiation patterns are shown in Fig 12-18.

The gain of this array over a single vertical is 4.4 dB. The −3 dB forward-lobe beamwidth is only 54 degrees, which is quite narrow. This is because the radiation is bidirectional. K. Svensson, SM4CAN, who published an interesting little booklet on the bobtail array, recommends the following formulas for calculating the lengths of the elements of the array.

Vertical radiators: $\ell = 68.63/f$

Horizontal wire: $\ell = 143.82/f$

where

  f = design frequency
  ℓ = length, meters
  To convert to feet, multiply the values found by 3.281.

The antenna feed-point impedance is high (several thousand ohm). The array can be fed as shown in Fig 12-19. This is the same feed arrangement as for the voltage-fed T antenna, described in Chapter 9 on vertical antennas. In order to make the bobtail antenna cover both the CW as well as the phone end of the band, it is sufficient to retune the parallel resonant circuit. This can be done by switching a little extra capacitor in parallel with the tuned circuit of the lower frequency, using a high-voltage relay.

The bottom ends of the three verticals are *VERY HOT* with RF. You must take special precautions so that people and animals cannot touch the vertical conductors.

Do not be misled into thinking that the bobtail array does not require a good ground system because it is a voltage-fed antenna. As for all vertically polarized antennas, it is the electrical quality of the reflecting ground that will determine the efficiency and the low-angle radiation of the array. Read all about it in par 3.3 of Chapter 9.

■ 10. HALF-SQUARE ANTENNA

The half-square antenna was first described by Vester, K3BC (Ref. 1125). As its name implies, the half-square is half

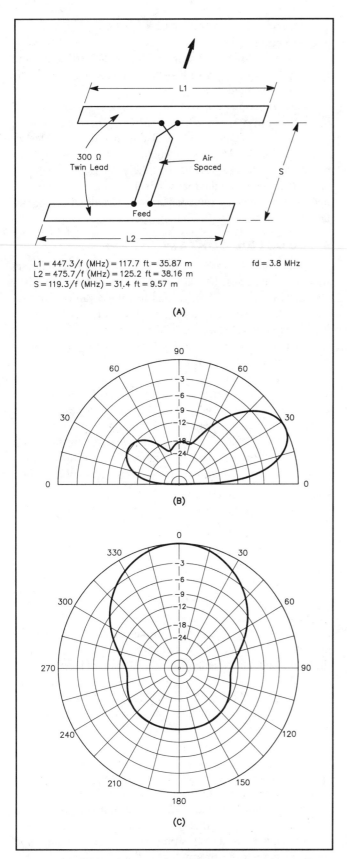

L1 = 447.3/f (MHz) = 117.7 ft = 35.87 m
L2 = 475.7/f (MHz) = 125.2 ft = 38.16 m
S = 119.3/f (MHz) = 31.4 ft = 9.57 m

fd = 3.8 MHz

(A)

(B)

(C)

Fig 12-17—The ZL Special (or HB9CV) antenna is a popular design that gives good gain and F/B for close spacing. Radiation patterns were calculated with ELNEC for the dimensions shown at A, for a height of ½ wavelength above average ground. The horizontal pattern at C is taken for a wave angle of 27 degrees.

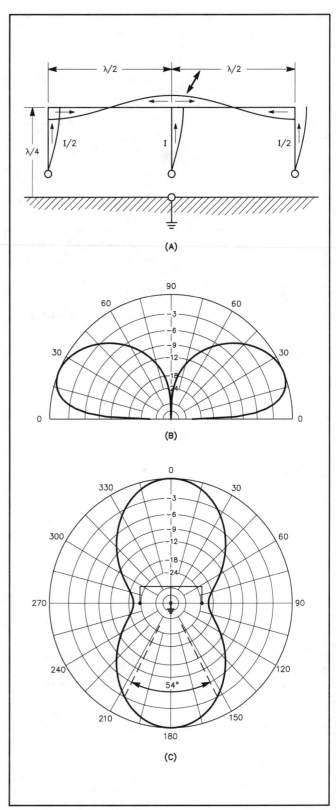

(A)

(B)

(C)

Fig 12-18—Configuration and radiation patterns for the bobtail curtain. This antenna exhibits a gain of 4.4 dB over a single vertical element. The current distribution, shown at A, reveals how the three vertical elements contribute to the low-angle broadside bidirectional radiation of the array. The horizontal section acts as a phasing and feed line and has no influence on the broadside radiation of the array. The horizontal pattern at C is taken for a wave angle of 22 degrees.

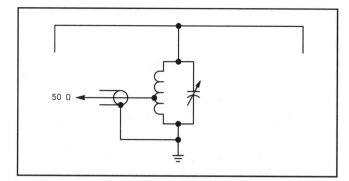

Fig 12-19—The bobtail curtain is fed at a high-impedance point. The antenna can best be fed via a parallel-tuned circuit, where the coax is tapped a few turns from the cold end of the coil. The array can be made to operate over a very large bandwidth by simply retuning the tuned circuit.

of a bi-square antenna (on its side), with the ground making up the other half of the antenna (see Chapter 10 on large loop antennas). It can also be seen as a bobtail with part of the antenna missing.

Fig 12-20 shows the antenna configuration and the radiation patterns. The feed-point impedance is very high (several thousand ohm), and the antenna is fed like the bobtail. The gain is somewhat less than 3.4 dB over a single quarter-wave vertical. The forward-lobe beamwidth is 68 degrees, and the pattern is essentially bidirectional. There is some asymmetry in the pattern which is caused by the asymmetry of the design: The current flowing in the two verticals is not identical. As far as the required ground system is concerned, the same remarks apply as for the bobtail antenna.

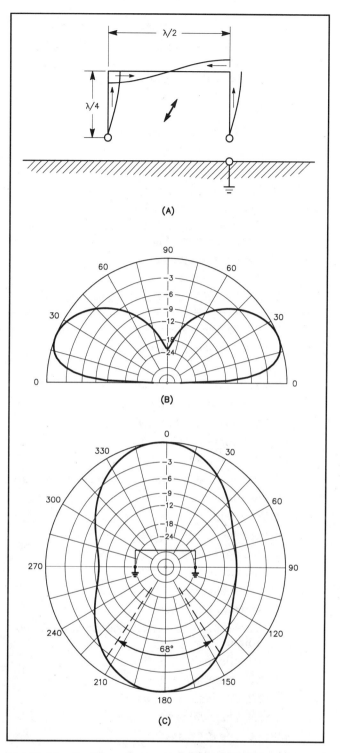

Fig 12-20—Configuration and radiation patterns of the half-square array, with a gain of 3.4 dB over a single vertical. The antenna pattern has a somewhat asymmetrical radiation pattern because the currents in the two vertical conductors are not identical. The azimuth pattern at C is for a wave angle of 22 degrees.

YAGIS AND QUADS FOR THE LOW BANDS

■ **1. ARRAYS WITH PARASITIC ELEMENTS**

■ **2. QUADS VERSUS YAGIS**

■ **3. YAGIS**

3.1. Modeling Yagi Antennas

3.2. Mechanical Design

  3.2.1. Terms and definitions

3.3. Computer-Designed 40-Meter Yagi

  3.3.1. Selecting an electrical design

  3.3.2. Principles of mechanical load and strength calculations for Yagi antennas

  3.3.3. Element strength calculation

    3.3.3.1. *Element sag*

    3.3.3.2. *Alternative element designs using US materials*

    3.3.3.3. *The driven element and the director*

    3.3.3.4. *Final-element tweaking*

  3.3.4. Boom Design.

    3.3.4.1. *Pointing the Yagi in the wind*

    3.3.4.2. *Weight balancing*

    3.3.4.3. *Yagi torque balancing*

    3.3.4.4. *Boom moments*

    3.3.4.5. *Boom sag*

  3.3.5. Element-to-boom and boom-to-mast clamps

  3.3.6. Materials

  3.3.7. Telescopic fits

  3.3.8. Material ratings and design conditions

  3.3.9. Element finishing

  3.3.10. Ice loading

  3.3.11. Material fatigue

  3.3.12. Matching the Yagi

  3.3.13. Tower, mast, mast bearings, drive shaft and rotator

    3.3.13.1. *The tower*

    3.3.13.2. *The rotating mast*

    3.3.13.3. *The mast bearings*

    3.3.13.4. *The rotator*

    3.3.13.5. *The drive shaft*

  3.3.14. Raising the antenna

  3.3.15. Conclusion

3.4. A 3-element Full-size 80-meter yagi

  3.4.1. Antenna height

  3.4.2. Electrical design

  3.4.3. Parasitic parallel capacitance with split elements

  3.4.4. Modeling the Yagi including the parasitic parallel capacitance

  3.4.5. The loading elements

  3.4.6. Remote tuning for optimum F/B

  3.4.7. Feeding the Yagi

  3.4.8. The mechanical design: the elements

  3.4.9. Building the Yagi

  3.4.10. The boom

  3.4.11. The OH6RM full-size 80-meter Yagi

  3.4.12. Conclusion

3.5. Commercial Low-Band Yagi Antennas

  3.5.1. The 80-meter KLM Yagis

    3.5.1.1. *Three-element 80-meter Yagi*

    3.5.1.2. *Two-element 80-meter Yagi*

    3.5.1.3. *Rotary 80-meter dipole*

  3.5.2. The 80-meter Creative Design Yagis

  3.5.3. The 40-meter Cushcraft Yagi

  3.5.4. KLM 40-meter Yagis

    3.5.4.1. *Four-element Yagi*

    3.5.4.2. *Three-element Yagi*

    3.5.4.3. *Two-element Yagi*

    3.5.4.4. *Rotatable dipole*

  3.5.5. The Hy-Gain 402-BA Yagi.

  3.5.6. The Hy-Gain Discoverer 7-2 2-element 40-meter Yagi

  3.5.7. The Hy-Gain Discoverer 7-3 3-element 40-meter Yagi

3.6. Wire Yagis

3.7. Vertical Yagis

3.8. Yagi Matching Systems

  3.8.1. The gamma match

    3.8.1.1. *Designing the gamma match with the YAGI DESIGN software*

  3.8.2.The omega match

    3.8.2.1. *Designing the omega match with the YAGI DESIGN software*

    3.8.2.2. *Tuning the omega/gamma match system*

  3.8.3. The hairpin match

    3.8.3.1. *Design guidelines for a hairpin system*

    3.8.3.2. *Element loading and a hairpin*

    3.8.3.3. *Hairpin match design with parasitic element-to-boom capacitance*

    3.8.3.4. *Designing the hairpin match with the Yagi design software*

    3.8.3.5. *Using a parallel capacitor to fine-tune a hairpin matching system*

  3.8.4. Selecting a Yagi matching system

■ **4. QUADS**

4.1. Modeling Quad Antennas

4.2. Two-element Full-Size 80-Meter Quad with a Parasitic Reflector

4.3. Two-element Reduced-Size Quad

4.4. Three-element 80-Meter Quad

4.5. Quad or Yagi?

YAGIS AND QUADS **13** FOR THE LOW BANDS

On the higher HF bands, almost all dedicated DXers use some type of rotatable directional antenna. Directional antennas produce gain to be better heard. They also show directivity, which is a help when listening. Yagi and cubical-quad antennas are certainly the most popular antennas on those bands.

On the low bands, rotatable directive antennas are huge. Forty-meter Yagis and quads, even full-size, exist in reasonable numbers these days. On 80 meters there are a few full-size Yagis and quads, while reduced-size Yagis and quads are a little more common. On 160 meters, rotatable Yagis still belong to dreamland.

I had the chance to operate a 3-element full-size quad as well as a 3-element full-size Yagi on 80 meters, and I must admit that it is only when you have played with such monsters that you appreciate what you are missing without them. The same is even more true on 40, where full-size Yagis and quads appear in ever-growing numbers on the band. Until the day I had my own full-size 40-meter Yagi, I always considered 40 as my "worst" band. Now that I have the full-size Yagi, I think it has become my "best" band.

Much of the work presented in this chapter is the result of a number of major antenna projects that were realized with the help of R. Vermet, ON6WU, who has been a most assiduous supporter and advocate in all my antenna work.

I also had the pleasure of developing a somewhat novel design for a full-size 3-element 80-meter Yagi for H. Lumpe, DJ6JC. At the time of printing, the 3-element Yagi is being built by DJ6JC in Germany. The design methodology and some of the exclusive mechanical features of this Yagi are described in detail in this chapter.

Until recently, little had been published in amateur literature covering the mechanical design of Yagis. In addition, some of the information published is incorrect. I hope to help clarify this situation somewhat.

■ 1. ARRAYS WITH PARASITIC ELEMENTS

In the chapter on vertical arrays I discuss groups of antennas (arrays) where each antenna element was fed via an individual feed line. During the analysis of these arrays we noticed that elements sometimes exhibit a negative impedance, which means that these elements do not draw power from the feed line, but actually deliver power into the feed system.

In such a case mutual coupling has already supplied enough (or too much) current into the element. Negative feed-point impedances are typical with close-spaced arrays where the coupling is more intensive than with wide-spaced arrays.

Parasitic arrays are arrays where only one element is fed, and where the other elements obtain their feed current only by mutual coupling with the various elements of the array. In order to obtain a desired radiation pattern and gain, feed current magnitudes and phases need to be carefully adjusted. This is done by changing the relative positions of the elements and by changing the lengths of the elements. The exact length of the "driven" element (the fed element) will not influence the pattern nor the gain of the array; it will only influence its feed-point impedance.

Unlike with driven arrays, you cannot obtain any specific feed-current magnitude and angle. In driven arrays you "force" the antenna currents, which means you add (or subtract) feed current to the element current already obtained by mutual coupling. You can make a driven array with three elements in line where all elements have an identical feed current. You cannot make a parasitic array where the three elements have the same current (phase and magnitude).

Arrays with parasitic elements are limited as to the current distribution in the elements. The best-known configuration is the configuration used with Yagi (Yagi/Uda) and cubical quad antennas.

In a 3-element Yagi or quad the two parasitic elements are adjusted (in length and position) to provide the required current with the lagging phase angle for the director, and with the required leading phase angle for the reflector.

■ 2. QUADS VERSUS YAGIS

It is not the intention to get into the debate of quads versus Yagis. Before I tackle both in more depth, let me clarify a few points and kill a few myths:

- For a given height above ground, the quad does *not* produce a markedly lower radiation angle than the Yagi. The vertical radiation angle of a horizontally polarized antenna in the first place depends on the height of the antenna above ground.
- For a given boom length, a quad will produce slightly more gain than a Yagi. This is logical as the aperture (capture area) is larger. The principle is simple: Everything being optimized, the antenna with the largest capture area has the highest gain, or can show the highest directivity.
- Yagis as a rule are easier to build and maintain. Being two-dimensional, the problems involved with low-band antennas are simplified one order of magnitude. Problems of wire breaking are nonexistent with Yagis. Large Yagis are also easier to handle and to install on a tower than large quads.
- There are other factors that will determine the eventual

choice between a Yagi or a quad, eg, material availability, maximum turning radius (the quad takes less rotating space!), and of course, personal preference.

■ 3. YAGIS

There have been a number of good publications on Yagi antennas. Until about 10 years ago, before we all knew about the effect of tapered elements, the W6SAI Yagi book was in many circles considered the Yagi bible. I built my first Yagi based on information from Orr's work.

It was Dr. J. Lawson, W2PV (SK), who wrote a very good series on Yagis back in the early 1980s. Later the ARRL published his work in the excellent book, *Yagi Antenna Design* (Ref. 957). In his work, Lawson explains how he scientifically designed a winning contest station, based on high-level engineering work.

Lawson was the first in amateur circles to bring up and study the effect of tapered elements. He came up with a tapering algorithm, which is still widely referred to as the "W2PV algorithm." It calculates the exact electrical length of an element as a function of the length of the individual (in diameter) tapered sections.

3.1. Modeling Yagi Antennas

The most widely used antenna modeling program is MININEC, which was developed by the US navy at NOSC in San Diego by J. C. Logan and J. W. Rockway. MININEC was released to the public in the early '80s, whereby finally every serious antenna builder was presented with a tool to model performing antennas. The W2PV taper algorithm together with MININEC have opened the eyes of many. I remember how I found out that my 5-element 20-meter Yagi peaked in both gain and front-to-back ratio around 14.45 MHz!

Since then progress has been spectacular. We now have very sophisticated modeling tools available, most of them based on the method of moments.

ELNEC is a very user-friendly version of MININEC, made available by R. Lewallen, W7EL, at a very attractive price. Other MININEC-based optimizing programs are around, eg, a version by Gordon, K4VX.

MN, by B. Beezley (K6STI) is another MININEC-code based modeling program that has become quite popular. Beezley also produces YAGI OPTIMIZER (YO), which is a Yagi (only) modeling program. YO models a Yagi on three frequencies and displays the results in graphical form, as well as in figures on the screen while modeling. YO is very fast but at a trade-off in accuracy, especially when so-called "marginal" designs are involved. The latest addition to the family of Beezley's software packages is AO (Antenna Optimizer).

If you consider modeling your own Yagi for the low bands, stick to the following guidelines:

1) Make sure you know exactly what you want before you start: maximum boom length, maximum gain, maximum directivity, low Q (large SWR bandwidth) etc.

2) First model the antenna in free space.

3) Always model the antenna on a range of frequencies (eg, 7.0, 7.1 and 7.2 MHz), so you can immediately assess the bandwidth characteristics (SWR, gain, F/B) of the design. You

can use one of the faster modeling programs (eg, YO) for your initial modeling, but make sure you always verify the design using a full-blown version of MININEC (eg, ELNEC, MN or AO).

4) Make sure the feed-point impedance is reasonable (it can be anything between 18 and 30 ohms).

5) When the array is optimized and meets your requirements in free space, you must repeat the exercise over real ground at the actual antenna height. If the antenna is stacked with other antennas, include the other antennas in the model as well.

6) If you consider making a Yagi with loaded elements, first model the full-size equivalent. When applying the loading devices, don't forget to include the resistance losses (especially for loading coils!) and possible parasitic capacitances or inductances.

3.2. Mechanical Design

Making a perfect electrical design of a low-band Yagi is easy nowadays with all the magnificent modeling software available. The real challenge comes when you have to turn your model into a mechanical design. When building a mechanically sound 40-meter Yagi, there is no room for guesswork. Don't ever take anything for granted when you are building a 40-meter Yagi. If you want your beam to survive the winds and/or ice loading you expect, you *must* go through a fair bit of calculating (making sure).

Physical Design of Yagi Antennas, by D. Leeson, W6QHS, published by the ARRL (Ref. 964) covers all the aspects of mechanical Yagi design. The book covers the theoretical aspects in detail. Leeson uses the "variable area" principle to assess the influence of wind on the Yagi. This principle is incorrect, however, as is argued in par 3.3.2. The book does not give any design examples of practical full-size 40- or for 80-meter Yagis. The only low-band antenna covered is the Cushcraft 40-2CD, a shortened 2-element 40-meter Yagi.

The mathematics involved in calculating all the structural aspects of a low-band Yagi element are complex. It is a subject which is ideally suited for computer assistance. Together with my friend R. Vermet, ON6WU, I have written a comprehensive computer program, YAGI DESIGN, which was released in early 1988 and updated a few times since. In addition to the "traditional" electrical aspects, YAGI DESIGN tackles the mechanical design aspects. This is especially of interest to the prospective builder of 40- and 80-meter Yagi antennas. While Yagis for the higher HF bands can be built "by feel," 40- and 80-meter Yagis require much closer attention if you want these antennas to stay up.

The different modules of the YAGI DESIGN software are reviewed in the chapter on low-band software.

This book is not a textbook on mechanical engineering, but a few definitions are needed in order to better understand some of the formulas I use in this chapter.

3.2.1. Terms and definitions.

Stress

Stress is the force applied to a material per unit of cross-sectional area. Bending stress is the stress applied to a structure by a bending moment. Shearing stress is the stress applied to a structure by a shearing moment. The stress is expressed in units of force divided by units of area (usually expressed in kg/mm² or lb/in.²).

Breaking Stress

The breaking stress is the stress at which the material breaks.

Yield Stress

Yield stress is the stress where a material suddenly becomes plastic (nonreversible deformation). The yield-stress to breaking-stress ratio differs from material to material. For aluminum the yield stress is usually close to the breaking stress. For most steel materials the yield stress is approximately 70% of the breaking stress. Never confuse breaking stress with yield stress, unless you want something to happen that you will never forget.

Elastic Deformation

Elastic deformation of a material is deformation that will revert to the original shape after removal of the external force causing the deformation.

Compression or Elongation Strain

Compression strain is the percentage change of dimension under the influence of a force applied to it. Being a ratio, strain is an abstract figure.

Shear Strain

Shear strain is the deformation of a material divided by the couple arm. It is a ratio and thus an abstract figure.

Shear Angle

This is the material displacement divided by the couple arm. As the angles involved are small, the ratio is a direct expression of the shear angle expressed in radians. To obtain degrees, multiply by $\dfrac{180}{\pi}$.

Elasticity Modulus

Elasticity modulus is the ratio stress/strain as applied to compression or elongation strain. This is a constant for every material. It determines how much a material will deform under a certain load. The elasticity modulus is the material constant that plays a role in determining the sag of a Yagi element. The elasticity modulus is expressed in units of force divided by the square of units of dimension (unit of area).

Rigidity Modulus

Rigidity modulus is the ratio shear-stress/strain as applied to shear strain. The rigidity modulus is the material constant that will determine how much a shaft (or tube) will twist under the influence of a torque moment (eg, the drive shaft between the antenna mast and the rotator). The rigidity modulus is expressed in units of force divided by units of area.

Bending Section Modulus

Each material structure (tube, shaft, plate T-profile,

I-profile, etc) will resist a bending moment differently. The section modulus is determined by the shape as well as the cross-section of the structure. The section modulus determines how well a particular shape will resist a bending moment. The section modulus is proper to a shape and not to a material.

The bending section modulus for a tube is given by

$$S = \pi \times \frac{OD^4 - ID^4}{32 \times OD}$$

where

    OD = outer diameter of tube
    ID = inner diameter of tube

The bending section modulus is expressed in units of length to the third power.

Shear Section Modulus

Different shapes will also respond differently to shear stresses. The shear stress modulus determines how well a given shape will stand stress deformation. For a hollow tube the shear section modulus is given by

$$S = \pi \times \frac{OD^4 - ID^4}{16 \times OD}$$

where

    OD = outer diameter of tube
    ID = inner diameter of tube

The bending section modulus is expressed in units of length to the third power.

3.3. Computer-Designed 40-Meter Yagi

Let us go through the design of a 3-element full-size 40-meter Yagi. This is not meant to be a step-by-step description of a building project, but I will try to cover all the critical aspects of designing a sound and lasting 40-meter Yagi. The Yagi described also happens to be the Yagi I have been using successfully over the past several years on 40 meters (it has brought several new European records in major contests on 40 meters).

The design criteria for the Yagi are
- Low Q, good bandwidth, F/B optimized.
- Survival at wind speeds up to 140 km/h (87 mi./h) with the elements broadside to the wind.
- Maximum ice load 10 mm (0.4 inch) at 60 km/h (37 mi/h) wind.
- Lifetime greater than 20 years.
- Boom length 10.7 m (35 ft) maximum

3.3.1. Selecting an electrical design.

Design no. 10 from the database of the YAGI DESIGN software program meets all the above specifications. Fig 13-1 shows a copy of the screen with all the data (performance and generic dimensional data) for the chosen design.

While another design with up to 0.5 dB more gain could have been selected, the no. 10 design was selected because of its excellent F/B pattern and wide bandwidth (SWR, gain and F/B ratio).

The Yagi was to be mounted 5 m (16 ft) above the 20-m Yagi (design no. 68 from the database), at 30 m above ground.

```
     DESIGN #   10    ELEMENTS: 3        NAME: FREDA              BOOM: 0.249   WVL

                    ———— Performance data ————
    FREQ.   GAIN    F/B     RESIST    REACT.    SWR    FOM
    -1.5%    7.4    20.5     28.8     -12.6     1.5    9.0         ┌──────────────────┐
    -1.0%    7.4    23.4     29.1      -9.0     1.3    9.4         │  ANT. Q =    14  │
    -0.5%    7.4    23.9     28.8      -5.3     1.1    9.7         │                  │
     0.0%    7.5    24.4     28.0      -1.4     1.0    9.9         │  SWR BW >    3 % │
    +0.5%    7.5    25.4     26.8       2.8     1.2    9.9         │                  │
    +1.0%    7.6    22.8     25.2       7.5     1.4    9.5         │  F/B BW >    3 % │
    +1.5%    7.7    19.2     23.4      12.5     1.8    8.9         └──────────────────┘

    ———— Dimensions in wavelengths ————        ———— Physical Boomlength ————
    ELEMENT        LENGTH      POSITION         28 Mhz ->   2.63 m.  OR    8.6 ft
    REFLECTOR     0.510217    -.105595          24 Mhz ->   2.99 m.  OR    9.8 ft
    DRIV. EL.     0.483032    0.000000          21 Mhz ->   3.52 m.  OR   11.5 ft
    DIR #  1      0.452359    0.143370          18 Mhz ->   4.12 m.  OR   13.5 ft
    DIR #  2      0.000000    0.000000          14 Mhz ->   5.27 m.  OR   17.3 ft
    DIR #  3      0.000000    0.000000          10 Mhz ->   7.37 m.  OR   24.2 ft
    DIR #  4      0.000000    0.000000           7 Mhz ->  10.51 m.  OR   34.5 ft

    El. lengths are for el. diam of .0010527 wavelengths (7/8 inch on 14.2 MHz).
        S = SELECT THIS DESIGN        C = CONTINUE        H = HELP        X = EXIT
```

```
    DESIGN # 10            NAME: FREDA                           ELEMENTS =   3
    FREQ. =    7.10 MHz    WAVEL.: 42.22535  m.     BOOM: 10.51 m or  34.49 ft
    DRIVEN ELEMENT REACTANCE =   -1.4 ohm.

        ELEMENT/POSITION        CENTIMETERS    INCHES      WAVELENGTHS
        POSITION REFLECTOR         -445.9      -175.6      -0.105595
        LENGTH REFLECTOR           2149.1       846.1       0.508953
        POSITION DRIV. ELEM.          0.0         0.0       0.000000
        LENGTH DRIV. ELEM.         2046.9       805.9       0.484767
        POSITION DIR # 1            605.4       238.4       0.143370
        LENGTH DIR # 1             1930.2       759.9       0.457122

        THESE LENGTHS ARE FOR A CONSTANT DIAMETER OF 7/8 INCH OR 2.2225 CM.
    X=EXIT    S=SAVE    F=FREQ.CHANGE    O=OTHER DESIGN    C=CHANGE DR. EL    H=HELP
```

Fig 13-1—Dimensional and performance data for the 3-element Yagi design no. 10 from the YAGI DESIGN software program database, for building a 40-meter full-size Yagi. The element lengths are expressed in terms of wavelength, for a fixed element diameter.

The combination of both antennas was modeled once more over real ground at the final height using MN, to see if there would be an important change in pattern and gain due to the presence of the second antenna. The YAGI DESIGN software includes a software module (UTILITIES) that allows you to specify a stack of antennas from the database) and automatically creates a test input file for MN. The performance figures (gain, F/B) and directivity pattern of the 40-meter Yagi changed very little at the 5-m stacking distance.

3.3.2. Principles of mechanical load and strength calculations for Yagi antennas.

D. Weber, K5IU, recently brought to our attention (Ref. 958) that the "variable-area" method, commonly employed by most Yagi manufacturers, and used by many authors in their publications as well as software, has *no* basis in science, nor is there any experimental evidence of the method.

The variable-area method assumes that the direction of the force created by the wind on an element is always in line with the wind direction, and that the magnitude is proportional to the area of the element as projected onto a plane perpendicular to the wind direction (proportional to the sine of the wind angle). This is the principle used by Leeson in his book, *Physical Design of Yagi Antennas*.

The scientifically correct method of analyzing the wind-force behavior, called the "cross-flow" principle, says that the direction of the force due to the wind is *always* perpendicular to the plane in which the element is situated, and that its magnitude is proportional to the square of the sine of the wind angle.

Fig 13-2 shows both principles. It is easy to understand that the cross-flow principle is the correct one. The experiment described by D. Weber, K5IU, can be carried out by anyone, and should convince anyone who has doubts:

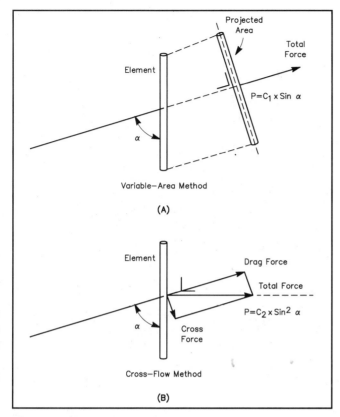

Fig 13-2—Most amateur literature uses the "variable area" method shown at A for calculating the effect of wind on an element. The principle says that the direction of the force created by the wind on an element is *always* in line with the direction of the wind, which is clearly incorrect. If this were correct, no plane would ever fly! The "cross-flow" principle, illustrated at B, states that the direction of the force is *always* perpendicular to the element, and is the resultant of two components, the drag force and the cross force (which is the lifting force in the case of an airplane wing). See text for details.

"Take a 1-m (3 ft) long piece of aluminum tubing (approximately 25 mm or 1 inch in diameter) for a car ride. One person drives, while another sits in the passenger seat. The passenger holds the tube in his hand, and puts his arm out the window positioning the tube vertically. The tube is now perpendicular to the wind stream (wind angle = zero). It is easy to observe a force (drag force) which is *in line* with the wind (and at the same time perpendicular to the axis of the tube). The passenger now rotates the tube approximately 45 degrees, top end forward. The person holding the tube will now clearly feel a force which pushes the tube [backwards] (drag force), but at the same time tries to [lift] (cross force) the tube. The resulting force of these two components (the drag and cross force) is a force which is *always* perpendicular to the direction of the tube. If the tube is inclined with the bottom end forward, the force will try to push the tube downwards."

This means that the direction of the force developed by the wind on an object exposed to the wind is not necessarily the same as the wind direction. There are some specific conditions where the two directions are the same, such as the case where the (flat) object is broadside to the wind direction. If you put

a plate (1 m² or 11 ft²) on top of a tower, and have the wind hit the plate at a 45-degree angle, it will be clear that the "push" developed by the wind hitting the plate will *not* be developed in the direction of the wind, but in the direction perpendicular to the plane of the flat plate. If you have any "feeling" for mechanics and physics, this should be fairly evident.

To remove any doubt from your mind, D. Weber states that Alexandre Eiffel, builder of the Paris Eiffel tower, used the cross-flow principle for calculating his tower. And it still stands there after more than 100 years.

Now comes a surprise: Take a Yagi, with the wind hitting the elements at a given wind angle (forget about the boom at this time). The direction of the force caused by the wind hitting the element at whatever wind angle, will *always* be *perpendicular* to the element. This means that the force will be in line with the boom. The force will not create any bending moment in the boom; it will merely be a compression or elongation force in the boom.

This force in the boom should not be of any concern, as the boom will certainly be strong enough to cope with the bending moments caused by the broadside (to the boom) winds. These bending moments in the boom (at the mast attachment plate) are caused only by the force created by the wind *on the boom only* (by the same "cross-flow" principle) or any other "components" which have an exposed wind area in line with the boom.

If the mast-to-boom plate is located in the center of the boom, the wind areas on both sides of the mast are identical, and the bending moments in the boom, on both sides of the mast (at the boom-to-mast plate) will be identical. This means there is no *mast torque*. If the areas are unequal, mast torque will result. This mast torque puts extra strain on the rotator, and should be avoided. Torque balancing can be done by adding a *boom dummy*, which is a (small) plate placed near the end of the shorter boom half, and which serves to reestablish the balance in bending moments between the left and the right side of the boom.

As the Yagi *elements* do *not* contribute to the boom moments, and therefore not to the mast torque, it makes no sense to create "dummy elements" to try to achieve a torque-balanced Yagi.

The MECHANICAL YAGI BALANCE module of the YAGI DESIGN software addresses all the issues as explained above, and uses the cross-flow principle to obtain scientifically correct results. It uses latest data from the latest EIA/TIA-222-E specification, which is somewhat different from the older EIA standard RS-222-C.

3.3.3. Element strength calculation.

While it is standard procedure to correct the boom sag by using support cables, element sag must be controlled to a maximum degree by using the properly designed tapered sections for making the element. Guyed elements are normally only used with 80-meter Yagis, although full-size 80-meter self-supporting elements with negligible sag have been designed and demonstrated (see par 3.4.9.). Unguyed 40-meter full-size tubular elements (24 m or 79 ft for a reflector) can be built to withstand very high wind speeds, as

```
    8586                        ELEMENT STRESS ANALYSIS                    on4un/on6wu
    SEC#    OD(in)   WT(in)    L(in)   RM(in.lbs) LMt(lbs.in) LMv(lbs.in) CONDIT.
    1       2.500    0.125    144.00   18463.8     19389.3     3207.7     FAIL
    2       2.000    0.083     66.00    8051.7      6416.7      935.0     SAFE
    3       1.250    0.110     42.00    3617.3      3382.5      458.9     SAFE
    4       1.000    0.110     36.00    2164.2      2124.5      269.0     SAFE
    5       1.000    0.058     45.00    1337.8      1331.6      161.4     SAFE
    6       0.625    0.110     18.00     691.0       651.7       74.9     SAFE
    7       0.625    0.058     40.00     469.9       464.7       52.0     SAFE
    8       0.500    0.058     65.00     280.1       171.5       18.9     SAFE
    Velocity=   85.0 Mph                            Wind press.=   17.3 lb/sqft
    Material= 6061-T6         Tens. str. = 35000 psi   Ice thickn.= 0 inch
    Rope     = YES            Ele. weight=   45.2 lbs   El.windload= 200.6 lbs
    Pr. area= 1389 sq.in      Half el.lgt= 456.0 inch   El. sag    =  56.4 inch

    If you intend to do a full physical design of a yagi, run each of the yagi
    elements and make a screen dump of the results. You will need the weight data
    as inputs to the BALANCE program.
       1=SPEED   2=GUSTFAC   3=MATER   4=ICE   5=DIM   6=NRUN   7=SECT   H=HELP   X=EXIT


    8586                        ELEMENT STRESS ANALYSIS                    on4un/on6wu
    SEC#    OD(in)   WT(in)    L(in)   RM(in.lbs) LMt(lbs.in) LMv(lbs.in) CONDIT.
    1       2.500    0.125    104.00   18463.8     14842.1     2384.1     SAFE
    2       2.000    0.083     66.00    8051.7      6416.7      935.0     SAFE
    3       1.250    0.110     42.00    3617.3      3382.5      458.9     SAFE
    4       1.000    0.110     36.00    2164.2      2124.5      269.0     SAFE
    5       1.000    0.058     45.00    1337.8      1331.6      161.4     SAFE
    6       0.625    0.110     18.00     691.0       651.7       74.9     SAFE
    7       0.625    0.058     40.00     469.9       464.7       52.0     SAFE
    8       0.500    0.058     65.00     280.1       171.5       18.9     SAFE
    Velocity=   85.0 Mph                            Wind press.=   17.3 lb/sqft
    Material= 6061-T6         Tens. str. = 35000 psi   Ice thickn.= 0 inch
    Rope     = YES            Ele. weight=   37.8 lbs   El.windload= 171.7 lbs
    Pr. area= 1189 sq.in      Half el.lgt= 416.0 inch   El. sag    =  41.6 inch

    If you intend to do a full physical design of a yagi, run each of the yagi
    elements and make a screen dump of the results. You will need the weight data
    as inputs to the BALANCE program.
       1=SPEED   2=GUSTFAC   3=MATER   4=ICE   5=DIM   6=NRUN   7=SECT   H=HELP   X=EXIT
```

Fig 13-3—Design table for the reflector of a 40-meter Yagi. The total reflector length is 912 inches (23.16 m), which should be long enough for a reflector. With the YAGI DESIGN software you can work either in the English system (inches, ft, lb), or the metric system (m, cm, mm, kg). For each of the element sections the OD, ID, the maximum allowable moment, and the actual moment in the vertical and horizontal planes are displayed, together with the safety status in the last column. Any of the input data can be changed via the prompt line. See text for details.

well as a substantial degree of ice loading.

D. Weber, K5IU (Ref. 966) wrote an excellent article concerning the structural behavior of Yagi elements. The mathematics involved are quite tedious, and a very good subject for a computer program. Leeson (Ref. 964) addresses the issue in detail in his book, and he has made a spreadsheet type of program available for calculating elements. As the element strength analysis is always done with the wind blowing broadside to the elements, the issue of "variable area" or "cross-flow principle" does not have to be taken into consideration at this point.

The ELEMENT STRENGTH module of the YAGI DESIGN software is a dedicated software program that allows the user to calculate the structural behavior of Yagi elements with up to nine tapering elements. The ELEMENT STRENGTH module operates in the English measurement system as well as in the metric system (as do all other modules of the integrated YAGI DESIGN software). It is based on the latest data from

the latest EIA/TIA-222-E specification. A drag factor of 1.2 is used for the element calculations (as opposed to 0.66 in the older RS-222-C standard).

Fig 13-3 shows a screen printout of the ELEMENT STRENGTH module of the YAGI DESIGN software. From the prompt line, each of the inputs can be easily changed whereby the impact on the performance is immediately displayed as in a spreadsheet. Input data that can be changed are section dimensions (length, diameter and wall thickness), wind speed, ice loading, material properties, etc.

The interactive designing of elements enables the user to achieve element sections that are equally loaded (ratio of actual bending moment to allowable bending moment). Many of the published designs show one section which is loaded to the limit, while other sections still exhibit a large safety margin. Such unbalanced designs are always inefficient as to weight, wind area (and load), as well as cost.

Each change (number of sections, section length, section

```
7547                      ELEMENT STRESS ANALYSIS              on4un/on6wu
SEC.#   OD(mm)    WT(mm)    L(cm)    RM(kgm)   LMt(kgm)  LMv(kgm)  CONDITION
 1      60.000    5.000     200.0    241.49    199.51    37.26       SAFE
 2      50.000    5.000     285.0    159.36    108.81    17.19       SAFE
 3      35.000    2.000      84.0     35.61     34.49     3.69       SAFE
 4      30.000    2.000     100.0     25.41     22.85     2.30       SAFE
 5      25.000    1.500     176.0     13.51     12.71     1.19       SAFE
 6      15.000    1.000      82.0      3.18      2.77     0.23       SAFE
 7      12.000    1.000     113.2      1.93      0.89     0.07       SAFE
Velocity= 140.0 Kph                          Wind press.=  88.7 kg/m²
Material= OTHER          Tens. str. = 22.0 kg/mm²  Ice thickn.= 0 mm
Rope     = YES           Ele. weight=  25.1 kg   El.windload=  83.4 kg
Pr. area=  7836 cm²      Half el.lgt=1040.2 cm   El. sag    =  83.6 cm



7547                      ELEMENT STRESS ANALYSIS              on4un/on6wu
SEC.#   OD(mm)    WT(mm)    L(cm)    RM(kgm)   LMt(kgm)  LMv(kgm)  CONDITION
 1      60.000    4.000     300.0    203.28    256.02    48.88       FAIL
 2      50.000    5.000     285.0    159.36    108.81    17.19       SAFE
 3      35.000    2.000      84.0     35.61     34.49     3.69       SAFE
 4      30.000    2.000     100.0     25.41     22.85     2.30       SAFE
 5      25.000    1.500     176.0     13.51     12.71     1.19       SAFE
 6      15.000    1.000      82.0      3.18      2.77     0.23       SAFE
 7      12.000    1.000     113.2      1.93      0.89     0.07       SAFE
Velocity= 140.0 Kph                          Wind press.=  88.7 kg/m²
Material= OTHER          Tens. str. = 22.0 kg/mm²  Ice thickn.= 0 mm
Rope     = YES           Ele. weight=  27.2 kg   El.windload=  96.2 kg
Pr. area=  9036 cm²      Half el.lgt=1140.2 cm   El. sag    = 132.4 cm



        Element half length = 1140.2 cm (ref file: FREDA9.ANT)
  If you intend to do a full physical design of a yagi, run each of the yagi
  elements and make a screen dump of the results. You will need the weight data
  as inputs to the BALANCE program.
   1=SPEED   2=GUSTFAC   3=MATER   4=ICE   5=DIM   6=NRUN   7=SECT   H=HELP   X=EXIT
```

Fig 13-4—Design of a 40-meter reflector (23 m length) using metric-dimension aluminum available in Europe. The element is first modeled being 1 m short (top table). Then the center section is lengthened by 1 meter, which is the length of the steel insert. At full length we see that the aluminum tube fails marginally (259 kg-m versus 241 kg-m). This is of no concern, as the steel insert will strengthen the tube considerably in the center of the element. The moment at the tip of the steel insert is 201 kg-m, which is well below the allowable moment of 241 kg-m.

diameter, wind speed, aluminum quality, ice load, etc) is immediately reflected in a change of the moment value at the interface of each taper section, as well as at the center of the element. When a safe limit is exceeded, the unsafe value will blink. The screen also shows the weight of the element, the wind area, and the wind load for the specified wind speed.

It is obvious that the design in the first place will be dictated by the material available. Material quality, availability and economical lengths are discussed in par 3.3.6. Table 13-2 there shows a range of aluminum tubing material commonly available in Europe.

A 40-m Yagi reflector is approximately 23 m (75½ ft) long. This is twice the length of a 20-meter element. Designing a good 40-meter element can be done by starting from a sound 20-meter element, which is then "lengthened" by more tapered sections toward the boom, calculating the bending stresses at each section drop.

When designing a Yagi element one must make sure that the actual bending moments (LM_t) at all the critical points match the maximum allowable bending moments (RM) as closely as possible. LM_v is the bending moment in the vertical plane, created by the weight of the element. This is the moment that creates the sag of the element. LM_t is the sum of LM_v and the moment created by the wind (in the horizontal plane). Adding those together may seem to create some safety, although it can be argued that turbulent wind may in actual fact blow vertically in a downward direction.

Fig 13-4 shows the design of the reflector element using material of metric dimensions available in Europe. The design was done for a maximum average wind speed of 140 km/h (87 mi/h), using F22 quality (Al Mg Si 0.5%) material. This material has a yield strength of 22 kg/mm² (31,225 lb/in.²). For material specifications see par 3.3.6.

All calculations have been done in a *static* condition.

Fig 13-5—Three-element 40-meter Yagi at ON4UN. The Yagi is mounted 5 m (16 ft) above a 5-element 20-meter Yagi with a 15-m (49 ft) boom, at a height of 30 m (100 ft). Note the very limited degree of element sag, which is proof of a good physical design.

Dynamic wind conditions can be significantly different, however. The highest bending moment is at the center of the element. Inserting a 2 m (6 ft) long steel tube (5- or 7-mm wall) in the center of the center-element will not only provide additional strength but also further reduce the sag.

Whether 140 km/h (87 mi/h) will be sufficient in your particular case depends on the following factors:
• The rating of the wind zone where the antenna is to be used.

The latest EIA/TIA-222-E standard lists the recommended wind speed per county in the US.
• Whether modifiers or safety factors are recommended (see EIA/TIA-222-E standard).
• Whether you will expose the element to the wind, or put the boom into the wind (see par 3.3.4.1).
• Whether you have your Yagi on a crank-up tower, so that you can nest it at protected heights during high wind storms.

Fig 13-5 shows the 3-element full-size 40-meter Yagi (16 ft above a 5-element 20-m Yagi), with a similar taper design. Note the very limited sag on the elements. The telescopic fits are discussed in par 3.3.8. Figs 13-6 and 13-7 show the section layout of the 40-meter reflector element as calculated for both metric and US (inch) materials.

3.3.3.1. *Element sag.*

Although element sag is not a primary design parameter, I have included the mathematics to calculate the sag of the element in the ELEMENT STRENGTH module of the YAGI DESIGN software. While designing, it is interesting to watch the total element sag. Minimal element sag is an excellent indicator of a good mechanical design.

A well-known manufacturer of Yagis sells a full-size 40-meter Yagi that exhibits an excessive sag of well over 200 cm. That is proof of rather poor engineering. Too much sag means there is somewhere along the element too much weight that does not contribute to the strength of the element. The sag of each of the sections of an element depends on:
• The section's own weight.
• The moment created by the section(s) beyond the section being investigated (toward the tip).
• The length of the section.

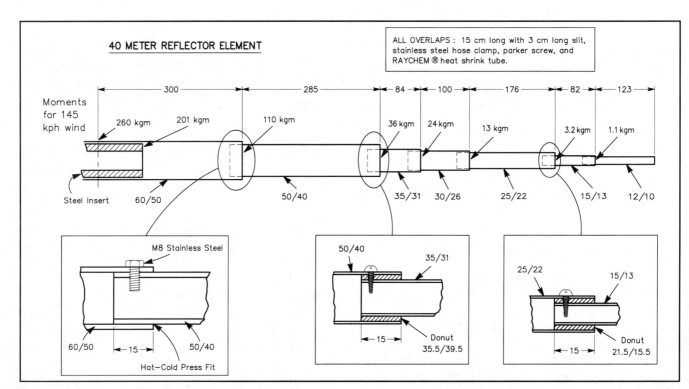

Fig 13-6—Mechanical layout of a 40-meter full-size reflector element using metric materials, as shown in the design sheet of Fig 13-4.

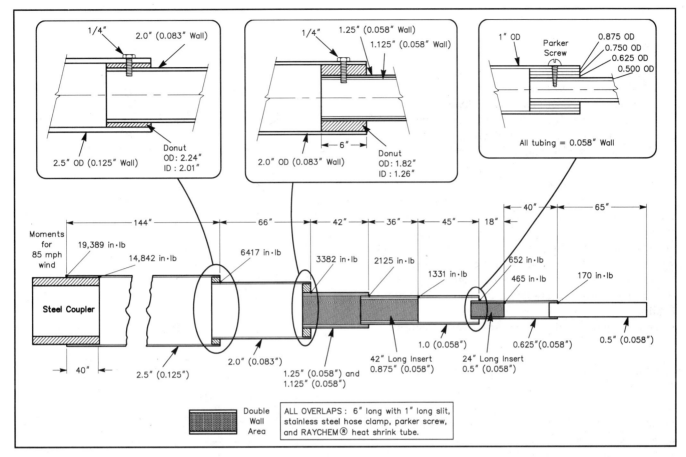

Fig 13-7—Layout of the 40-meter reflector element using US materials (inch dimensions). The element was calculated in Fig 13-3.

• The diameter of the section.
• The wall thickness of the section.
• The elasticity modulus of the material used.

The total sag of the element is the sum of the sag of each section.

The elasticity modulus is a measure of how much a material can be deformed (bent, stretched) without inducing permanent deformation. The elasticity modulus for all aluminum alloys is 700,000 kg/cm^2 (9,935,000 lb/in.^{2}). This means that an element with a stronger alloy will exhibit the same sag as an element made with an alloy of lesser strength.

The 40-meter reflector, as designed above, has a calculated sag of 129.5 cm (51 inches), not taking into account the influence of the steel insert (coupler). The steel coupler reduces the sag to approximately 91 cm (35.8 inches). These are impressive figures for a 40-meter Yagi. With everything scaled down properly, the sag is comparable to that of most commercial 20-meter Yagis. After mounting the element, the total element sag turned out to be exactly as calculated by the software.

3.3.3.2. *Alternative element designs using US materials.*

The US design is made by starting from standard tubing lengths of 144 inches. Tables 13-3 and 13-4 (appearing later in this chapter) show a list of some of the standard dimensions commonly available in the US. The availability of aluminum

tubes and pipes is discussed in par 3.3.6.

For the two larger diameter tubes, I used aluminum pipe. The remaining sections are from the standard tubing series with 0.058-inch wall thickness. From the design table we see that for some sections I used a wall thickness of 0.11 inch, which means that we are using a tight-fit section of ⅛-inch less diameter as an internal reinforcement.

The design table shows that the center sections would (marginally) fail at the 90-mi/h design wind speed. In reality this will not be a problem, as this design requires an internal coupler to join the two 144-inch center sections. This steel coupler must be strong enough to take the entire bending moment.

The section modulus of a tube is given by

$$S = \pi \times \frac{OD^4 - ID^4}{32 \times OD} \qquad \text{(Eq 13-1)}$$

where

    S = section modulus
    OD = tube outer diameter
    ID = tube inner diameter

The maximum moment a tube can take is given by

$$M_{max} = YS \times S$$

where

    YS = yield strength of the material
    S = section modulus as calculated above

or

$$M_{max} = YS \times \pi \times \frac{OD^4 - ID^4}{32 \times OD} \qquad \text{(Eq 13-2)}$$

The yield strength varies to a very large degree (Ref. 964 p 7-3). For different steel alloys it can vary from 21 kg/mm² (29,800 lb/in.²) to 50 kg/mm² (71,000 lb/in.²).

A 2-inch OD steel insert (with aluminum shimming material) made of high tensile steel with a YS = 55,000 lb/in.² would require a wall thickness of 0.15 inch to cope with the maximum moment of 19.622 in.-lb at the center of the 40-meter reflector element.

Note that the element sag (42.1 inches with 2×40-inch-long steel coupler) is very similar to the sag obtained with the metric design example. It is obvious that for an optimized Yagi element (and for a given survival wind speed), the element sag will always be the same, whatever the exact taper scheme may be. In other words, a good 40-meter Yagi reflector element, designed to withstand a 140 km/h (87 mi/h) wind should not exhibit a sag of more than approximately 40 inches (100 cm) when constructed totally of tubular elements. More sag than that proves it is a poor design.

3.3.3.3. *The driven element and the director.*

Once we have designed the longest element, we can design the shorter ones with no pain. We should consider taking the "left over" lengths from the reflector for use in the director (economical design). The lengths of the different sections for the 3-element Yagi no. 10 from the YAGI DESIGN database, according to the metric and US systems, are shown in Table 13-1. Typically, if the reflector is good for 144 km/h (90 mi/h), the director and the driven element will withstand 160 to 170 km/h (100 to 105 mi/h).

3.3.3.4. *Final element tweaking.*

Once the mechanical design of the element has been finalized, the exact length of the element tips will have to be calculated using the ELEMENT TAPER module of the software.

3.3.4. Boom design.

Now that we have a sound element for the 40-meter Yagi, we must pay the necessary attention to the boom. When the wind blows at right angle onto the boom, a maximum pressure is developed by the wind on the boom area. At the same time, the loading on the Yagi elements will be minimum.

There is *no* intermediate angle at which the loading on the boom is higher than at a 90-degree wind angle (when the wind blows broadside onto the boom).

3.3.4.1. *Pointing the Yagi in the wind.*

We all know the often heard question, "Should I point the elements toward the wind, or should I point the boom toward the wind?" The answer is simple.

If the area of the boom is smaller than the area of all the elements, then put the boom perpendicular to the wind. And vice versa. Let me illustrate this with some figures for the 40-meter Yagi. Calculations are done for a 140 km/h

13-1

Table 13-1

Element Design Data for the 3-Element 40-Meter Yagi Reflector, Driven Element and Director

Section	OD/Wall	Dir.	Dr. El.	Refl.
1	60/5	300	300	300
2	50/5	285	285	285
3	35/2	60	85	84
4	30/2	60	112	100
5	25/1.5	135	135	176
6	15/1	60	80	82
7	12/1	111	80	113
Total length (cm)		1011	1077	1150

Section	OD/Wall	Dir.	Dr. El.	Refl.
1	2.375/0.154	144	144	144
2	1.00/0.109	55	66	66
3	1.25/0.11	34	42	50
4	1.00/0.11	30	30	30
5	1.00/0.058	30	38	42
6	0.625/0.11	18	15	21
7	0.625/0.058	28	30	34
8	0.50/0.058	60	63	65
Total length (inches)		399	428	452

Note: This design assumes a boom diameter of 75 mm (3 inches) and U-type clamps to mount the element to the boom (L = 300 mm, W = 150 mm, H = 70 mm). This design is only meant as an example. Availability of materials will be the first restriction when designing a Yagi element.

(87 mi/h) wind, with the boom-to-mast plate in the center of the boom.

Zero Degree Wind Angle (wind blowing broadside onto the elements)
- Boom moment in the horizontal plane: Zero.
- Thrust on tower/mast 323 kg (712 lb).
- Maximum bending moment in the elements.
   90-Degree Wind Angle (wind blowing broadside onto the boom)
- Boom moment 114 kg-m (9,874 in.-lb)
- Thrust on tower/mast: 87 kg (191 lb)
- Minimum bending moment in the elements

The above figures are calculated in the MECHANICAL YAGI BALANCE module of the YAGI DESIGN software.

In this case it is obvious that we should at all times try to put the boom perpendicular to the wind during a high wind storm. For calculating and designing the rotating mast and tower, it is recommended, however, to take into account the worst case wind pressure of 323 kg (712 lb).

Relying on the exact direction of the Yagi as a function of wind direction to reduce safety design margins is a dangerous practice which should not be encouraged. This does not mean that in case of high winds one could not take advantage of the "best" wind angle to relieve load on the Yagi (or parts thereof), mast or tower, but what is gained by doing so should only be considered as extra safety margin only.

Remark: With long-boom Yagis on higher frequencies, eg, a 6-element 10-meter Yagi, it is likely that putting the

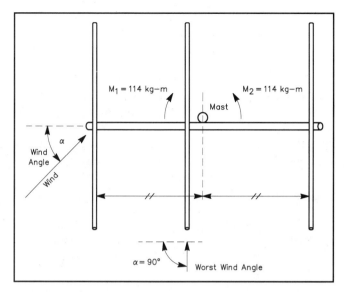

Fig 13-8—Boom moments in the horizontal plane as a result of the wind blowing onto the boom and the elements. The forces produced by the wind on the Yagi *elements* do not contribute to the boom moment; they only create a compression force in the boom (see text). The highest boom moments occur when the wind blows at a 90 degree angle (broadside to the boom).

elements perpendicular to the wind will be the logical choice.

3.3.4.2. *Weight balancing.*

In Fig 13-8, I have assumed that the mast is at the physical center of the boom. As the driven element is offset toward the reflector, the Yagi will not be weight balanced. A good

physical design must result in a perfect weight balance, as it is extremely difficult to handle an unbalanced 40-meter monster on a tower when trying to mount it on the rotating mast. The obvious solution is to shift the mast attachment point in such a way that a perfect balance is achieved.

The MECHANICAL YAGI BALANCE module of the software will weight-balance the Yagi. Fig 13-9 shows the screen print of the worksheet showing the weight-balanced Yagi. The software automatically calculates the area of the required boom dummy plate (see par 3.3.4.2), to reestablish torque balance. Components taken into account for calculating the weight balance are:

• The Yagi elements.
• The boom.
• The boom coupler (if any).
• The boom dummy (see par 3.3.4.3).
• The match box (box containing gamma/omega matching components).

Fig 13-10 shows the layout which produces perfect weight balance. In our example I have assumed no match box.

3.3.4.3. *Yagi torque balancing.*

The cause of mast torque has been explained in par 3.3.2. If the bending moment in the boom on one side of the mast is not the same as the bending moment at the other side of the mast, we have a resultant mast torque. One moment is trying to rotate the mast clockwise, while the other tries to rotate the mast counterclockwise. If the two moments are unequal in magnitude, there is a resulting "differential" moment, which we call *mast torque*.

In other words, the wind blowing on one side of the boom

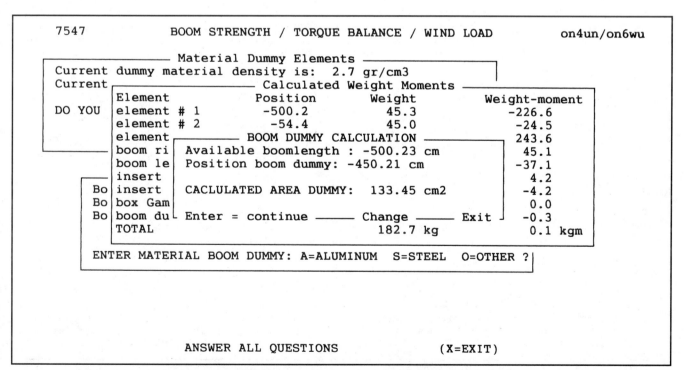

Fig 13-9—Screen print of the WEIGHT BALANCE screen from the YAGI MECHANICAL BALANCE software module. The mast attachment point has been moved 25 cm (10 inches) toward the reflector to restore weight balance. The program automatically calculates the boom dummy, which serves to restore the balance in boom moments in order to achieve a zero mast torque.

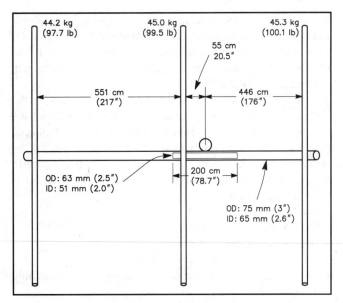

Fig 13-10—Weight-balanced layout of the 3-element 40-meter Yagi, showing the internal boom coupler. The net weight, without a match box (containing the gamma or omega matching capacitors) and without the boom-to-mast plate is 183 kg (403 lb).

is trying to rotate the mast in one direction, while the same wind blowing on the other side of the mast onto the boom is pushing the Yagi to rotate it in the opposite direction. Only when the boom areas on both sides of the mast are identical will the Yagi be perfectly torque balanced. The wind area of the elements and their placement on the boom do *not* play any

role in the mast torque, as the direction of the force developed by the wind on an element is always perpendicular to the element itself, which means in line with the boom. As such, element wind area cannot create a boom moment, but merely loads the boom with compression or elongation.

It is the mast torque which makes an antenna "windmill" in high winds. A good mechanical design must be torque-free at all wind angles.

During our "weight-balancing" exercise we shifted the mast attachment point somewhat to reestablish weight balance. This has caused the boom moments on both sides of the mast to become different. In order to reestablish balance, a small *boom dummy plate* will be mounted near the end of the shorter boom half. Fig 13-9 shows the size of the dummy as calculated by the software: A small plate of 133 cm² (20 in.²) should be mounted 50 cm (20 in.) from the reflector to achieve full torque-balance.

3.3.4.4. *Boom moments.*

Fig 13-11 shows the listing of the boom moments after torque-balancing. Note that a zero mast torque is obtained for all wind angles. The boom bending moments have increased slightly from 114 kg-m for the "non-weight-balanced Yagi" to 120 kg-m after weight balancing and adding the boom dummy. This is a negligible price to pay for having a weight-balanced Yagi.

Fig 13-12 shows all the data related to the boom design. The material stresses are shown for the coupler, as well as for the boom. The boom stress is only meaningful if the boom is not split in the center. With a split boom it is the coupler that takes the entire stress.

```
    7547              BOOM STRENGTH / TORQUE BALANCE / WIND LOAD              on4un/on6wu
    - 1 -     - 2 -      - 3 -      - 4 -     - 5 -       - 6 -       - 7 -       - 8 -
    0 deg     0 Kg     302 Kg     302 Kg    0.0 deg     0 Kgm       0 Kgm       0 Kgm
       5      -25        299        300      0.1            1          -1         -0
      10      -48        289        293      0.5            4          -4          0
      15      -67        274        282      1.2            8          -8          0
      20      -81        254        267      2.2           14         -14          0
      25      -91        232        249      3.7           21         -21         -0
      30      -94        208        228      5.6           30         -30         -0
      35      -92        183        205      8.2           39         -39         -0
      40      -86        160        181     11.7           49         -49          0
      45      -75        138        158     16.5           60         -60         -0
      50      -62        120        135     22.8           70         -70          0
      55      -47        106        116     31.1           80         -80          0
      60      -32         96        101     41.5           90         -90          0
      65      -18         89         91     53.6           98         -98          0
      70       -6         86         86     65.8          106        -106          0
      75        2         86         86     76.3          112        -112         -0
      80        6         87         87     84.0          116        -116          0
      85        5         89         89     88.5          119        -119         -0
      90        0         89         89     90.0          120        -120          0
 —— Wind Speed: 140 kph ————————————————————————————————————
   1 : Wind angle    2 : cross force      3 : drag force       4 : total force
   5 : load angle    6 : boom momt left   7 : boom momt right  8 : mast torque
 ———— H = HELP ——————————— W = Change Wind Speed ————————— ENTER = MENU ————
```

Fig 13-11—Screen print from the YAGI MECHANICAL BALANCE software. Column 4 lists the wind load of the antenna. Column 5 represents the load angle. The load angle is usually not the same as the wind angle (see text). Column 6 and 7 list the boom moments at the mast attachment point, and column 8 gives the resultant mast torque. The mast torque is zero if the boom moments are the same on both sides of the mast.

```
  7547          BOOM STRENGTH / TORQUE BALANCE / WIND LOAD       on4un/on6wu
         ┌──── BOOM DIMENSIONAL DATA ────┐  ┌──── BOOM STRENGTH DATA ────┐
            Boomlength: 1051 cm              Boom stress left:    6.6 kg/mm2
         1. Boom OD:   75.00 mm              Boom stress right:   6.6 kg/mm2
         2. Boom Wall:  5.000 mm             Stress INSERT left:  8.5 kg/mm2
            Boom length LEFT   500 cm        Stress INSERT right: 8.5 kg/mm2
            Boom length RIGHT:  551 cm
            Area boom LEFT =   3752 cm2       6. Wind speed =   140  Kph
            Area boom RIGHT =  4133 cm2      └────────────────────────────┘
         3. Boom Insert length:  200 cm     ┌──── MATCH BOX DATA ────┐
         4. Boom Insert OD:  63   mm         7.   AREA ALONG BOOM:      0 cm2
         5. Boom Insert wall:  6  mm         8.   AREA ALONG ELEMENTS:    0  cm2
            Spec. gravity insert:  7.87 kg/dm3  9. POSITION ON BOOM:      0 cm
                                              0.  WEIGHT:  0.0 Kg

         ┌──────────────────────────────────────────────────────────────┐
          BOOM STRESS: stress in the boom AT the mast attach point. If the yagi is
          torque balanced the LEFT and the RIGHT values are equal.
          STRESS INSERT: the stress of a boom insert or boom coupler with dimensions
          as specified, taking into account ONLY the coupler.
         └──────────────────────────────────────────────────────────────┘

         ┌──────────────────────────────────────────────────────────────┐
                       Enter the number of the item to be changed
            H = HELP                                          ENTER = MENU
         ─────────────── Antenna File: FREDA9.ANT ───────────────
```

Fig 13-12—The boom moment of 120 kg-m (see Fig 13-13) results in a material stress of 8.5 kg/mm² (12,065 lb/in.²) for a boom coupler of 63 mm (2.5 inches) OD, with a wall of 6 mm (¼ inch). If no boom coupler were used, the 75-mm (3-inch) OD boom, with a 5-mm wall (0.2 in.) would endure a stress of 6.6 kg/mm² (9,368 lb/in.²). In the final design of the 40-meter Yagi a steel boom coupler is used. This means that the entire moment is taken by the coupler. As explained in the text, the boom stress in the vertical plane due to weight loading is three times higher than the stress in the horizontal plane due to wind loading!

Note that even for a 140-km/h (87 mi/h) wind, the stresses shown are quite low. But as we will likely put the boom "in the wind" in high wind storms (Ref. 3.3.4.1.), it is advisable to build in a lot of safety. Also, as mentioned before, the 140-km/h does not include any safety factors or modifiers, as may be prescribed in the standard EIA/TIA-222-C.

It is proof of *poor* engineering to design a boom which needs support guys in order to render it strong enough to withstand the forces from the wind and the bending moments caused by it. If guy wires are employed to provide the required strength, guying will have to be done in both the horizontal as well as the vertical plane. Guy wires can be used to eliminate boom sag. This will only be done for cosmetic rather than strength reasons.

3.3.4.5. *Boom sag.*

The boom as now designed will withstand 140 km/h (87 mi/h) winds, with a good safety factor. The same boom however, without any wind loading, will have to endure a fair bending moment in the vertical plane, caused by the weight of the elements and the boom itself.

Fig 13-13 shows the forces and dimensions that create these bending moments. The weight moments were obtained earlier when calculating the Yagi weight balance. See Fig 13-11).

Weight moments to the "left" of the mast:
Element no. 1: –226.6 kg-m (–19,627 in.-lb)
Element no. 2: –24.5 kg-m (–2,122 in.-lb)
Boom left: –37.1 kg-m (–3,213 in.-lb)
Boom insert left: –4.2 kg-m (–364 in.-lb)

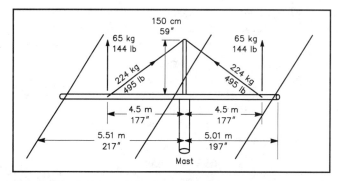

Fig 13-13—Layout of the boom supporting cables with the forces and tensions involved. The boom support cables are not installed to provide additional strength to the boom; they merely support the boom in order to compensate for the sag from weight loading of the boom.

Boom dummy: –0.3 kg-m (–26 in.-lb)
Total: –292.7 kg-m (–25,352 in.-lb)
Weight moments to the "right" of the mast:
Element no. 3: 243.6 kg-m (21,099 in.-lb)
Boom right: 45.2 kg-m (3,915 in.-lb)
Boom insert right: 4.2 kg-m (365 in.-lb)
Total: 293 kg-m (25,435 in.-lb)

The weight moment to the left of the mast is the same as to the right of the mast as the Yagi is weight-balanced.

Here comes another surprise: The boom is loaded almost *three times* as much by weight loading in the vertical plane

(293 kg-m or 25,378 in.-lb) than it is by wind loading at 140 km/h (87 mi/h) in the horizontal plane (120 kg-m or 10,394 in.-lb).

The maximum allowable bending moment for the boom steel insert with a diameter of 63 mm (2.5 inches) and 6 mm (0.24 inch) wall is 619 kg-m (53,614 in.-lb) as calculated with Eq 13-2 for a material yield strength of 20 kg/mm^2 (28,400 lb/in.^{2}). This steel coupler has a safety factor of *two* as far as the loading in the vertical plane (weight-loading) is concerned. Boom stress by weight will often be the condition that will specify the size of the boom with large low-band Yagis using heavy elements.

The boom, using the above calculated coupler, does not require any guying for additional strength. However, the high weight-loading of the very long elements sitting at the end of the boom halves will cause a very substantial sag in the boom. In the case of the 40-meter beam the sag amounts to nearly 65 cm (26 inches), which is really excessive from a cosmetic point of view. A sag of 10 cm (4 inches) is due to the boom's own weight and 55 cm (22 inches) is due to the weight of the elements at the tips of the boom.

It is proof of good engineering to eliminate the sag by supporting the boom using slant support cables. The two boom halves are supported by two sets of two parallel guy wires attached on the boom at a point 4.5 m (15 ft) from the mast attachment point. The guy wires are supported from a 1.4 m (4.6 ft) high support mast made of a 35 mm (1.4 inch) OD stainless steel tube, which is welded to the boom-to-mast plate. See Fig 13-13.

The weight to be supported is given by the moment (calculated before) divided by the distance of the cable attachment point to the boom center (or mast attachment point).

Vertical force = 293 kg-m/4.5 m = 65 kg (143 lb)

Assuming the two boom halves are hinged at the mast, each support cable must support the total weight as shown above, divided by the sine of the angle the support cable makes with the boom.

$$\text{Force in the cable} = \frac{65 \text{ kg}}{\sin 17°} = \frac{65}{0.29} = 223 \text{ kg (491 lb)}$$

Remark: Leeson (Ref. 964) covers the aspects of guyed booms in his publication. In the above case we are *not* guying the boom to give it additional strength, we do it only to eliminate the boom sag. Guying a boom is not a simple problem of moments, but a problem of a compressed column, where the slenderness of the boom and the compression force caused by the guy wire (usually in 3 directions) come into the picture. In our case these forces are so low that we can simplify the model as done above. In the above case we assume that the boom has enough lateral strength (which we had calculated). For solving the wire-support problem we assume that the boom is a "nonattached" cantilever. The fact that the boom is attached introduces an additional safety factor.

If a single steel cable is used, a 6 mm (0.24 inch) OD cable is required to safely support this weight. I use *two* cables of 4 mm (0.16 inch) OD Kevlar (also known as Phyllistran in the US). I use this because it was available at no cost, and it does

Fig 13-14—Detail of the tension-equalizing system used at the top of the support mast, where the two boom-support guy-wires are attached. The triangular-shaped plate can rotate freely around the 10 mm (0.4 inch) bolt, which serves to equalize the tension in the two guy-wires. See text for details.

not need to be broken up by egg insulators (Kevlar is a fully dielectric material which has the same breaking strength as steel and the same elongation). I recommend not using turnbuckles, as they may prove to be the weak link in the system. In addition, stainless-steel turnbuckles are very expensive. If two parallel cables are used, a tension equalizer must be used to ensure perfect equal stress in both cables. In the case of two support cables without equalization, one of the cables is likely to take most of the load.

Let me go into detail why I use two parallel support guys. Fig 13-14 shows the top of the support mast, on which two triangular-shaped stainless-steel plates are mounted. These plates can pivot around their attachment point, which consists of a 1 cm (0.4 in.) diameter stainless-steel bolt. The two guy wires are connected with the correct hardware (very important—consult the supplier of the cable!) at the base of these triangular pivoting plates. The pivoting plates now serve a double purpose:
• To equalize the tension in the two guy wires.
• To serve as a visual indicator of the status of the guy wires.

If something goes wrong with one of the support wires, the triangular plate will pivot around its attachment point. At the same time the remaining support (if properly designed) will still support the boom, although with a greatly reduced safety factor.

In order to install the support cables and adjust the system for zero or minimum boom sag without the use of turnbuckles, place the beam on two strong supports near the end of the boom so as to induce some inverse sag in the boom. Lift the center of the boom to control the amount of inverse sag. Now adjust the position of the boom attachment hardware to obtain the required support behavior.

Make sure you properly terminate the cables with thimbles and all. The load involved is not small, and improper terminations will not last long. This is especially true when Kevlar cable is used.

3.3.5. Element-to-boom and boom-to-mast clamps.

With an element weighing well over 40 kg (90 lb), attaching such a mass at the end of a 5 m (16½ ft) arm needs

Fig 13-15—The element-to-boom mounting system as used on the 40-meter Yagi.

Fig 13-16—The omega matching system and plastic "drainpipe" box containing the two variable capacitors. Note also the boom-to-mast mounting plate, made of 1 cm (0.4 in.) thick stainless steel. The boom is attached to the plate with eight U bolts and double saddles.

to be done with great care. The forces involved when we rotate the Yagi (start and stop) and when the beam swings in storm winds are impressive.

After an initial failure, I designed an element-to-boom mounting system that consists of three stainless-steel U-channel profiles (50 cm or 20 inches long) welded together. The element is mounted inside the central channel profile using four U bolts with ½-inch wide aluminum saddles. Four double saddle systems are used to mount the unit onto the boom (see Fig 13-15). U bolts must be used together with saddles. You must use saddles on both sides. The bearing strength of U bolts is far too low to provide a durable attachment under extreme wind loads without saddles on both sides. Never use U bolts made of threaded stainless-steel rods directly on the boom; if they can move but a hair, they become like perfect files which will machine a nice groove in the boom in no time.

At the center of the boom I have mounted a 60 cm (24 inch) wide 1 cm (0.4 inch) thick stainless-steel plate to which the 1.5 m (5 ft) long support mast for the boom guying is welded. The boom is bolted to the plate using eight U bolts with saddles matching the 75 mm (3 inch) OD boom

Table 13-2

Dimensions and Weight of Aluminum Tubing in F22 Quality

OD mm	Wall mm	Weight g/m
10	1	76
12	1	93
13	1	103
14	1	110
16	1	127
19	1.5	227
20	1.5	235
22	2	339
22	1.5	261
25	2.5	477
25	2	398
25	1.5	298
28	1.5	336
30	3	687
30	2	484
32	1.5	387
35	2	564
36	1.5	438
40	5	1495
40	2	644
40	1.5	489
44	2	541
48	1.5	603
50	5	1923
50	2	820
52	1.5	654
57	2	940
60	5	2350
60	3	1460
62	2	1040
70	5	2757
70	3	1718
80	5	3181
80	4	2579
84	2	1385
90	5	3605
100	5	4029
100	2	1676
110	5	4485

(Fig 13-16). On the tower, this plate is bolted to an identical plate (welded to the rotating mast) using just four 18-mm (0.7 inch) OD stainless-steel bolts. Fig 13-15 shows the boom-to-mast plate of the 40-meter Yagi.

3.3.6. Materials.

In the metric world (mainly Europe), aluminum tubes are usually available in 6-meter (20 ft) sections. Table 13-2 lists dimensions and weights of a range of readily available tubes. Aluminum tubing in F22 quality (Al Mg Si 0.5%) is readily available in Belgium in 6-meter lengths. The yield strength is 22 kg/mm^2 (31,250 lb/in.^{2}). It is currently sold in Belgium at retail outlets at approximately $7 per kg.

Tables 13-3 and 13-4 show a range of material dimensions that are available in the US. *The ARRL Antenna Book*

Table 13-3

List of Currently Available Aluminum Tubing in the US

OD in.	Wall in.	Weight lb/ft
0.25	0.058	0.04
0.375	0.058	0.07
0.5	0.058	0.10
0.625	0.058	0.12
0.750	0.058	0.15
0.875	0.058	0.18
1.0	0.058	0.20
1.125	0.058	0.23
1.25	0.058	0.26
1.375	0.058	0.28
1.5	0.058	0.31
1.5	0.065	0.34
1.5	0.083	0.43
1.625	0.058	0.34
1.75	0.058	0.36
1.75	0.083	0.51
2.0	0.065	0.45
2.0	0.083	0.59
2.5	0.0	0.
2.5	0.0	0.
2.5	0.083	0.74
2.5	0.083	1.10
3.0	0.065	11.33

(16th ed., p 20-7) also lists a wide range of aluminum tubing sizes. Make sure you know which alloy you are buying. The most common aluminum specifications in the US are

6061-T6: Yield strength = 24.7 kg/mm² (35,000 lb/in.²)
6063-T6: Yield strength = 17.6 kg/mm² (25,000 lb/in.²)
6063-T832: Yield strength = 24.7 kg/mm² (35,000 lb/in.²)
6063-T835: Yield strength = 28.2 kg/mm² (40,000 lb/in.²)

Economical Lengths

When designing the Yagi elements, a maximum effort should be made to use full fractions of the 6-meter tubing lengths, in order to maximize the effective use of the material purchased. A proper section overlap is 15 cm (6 inches). The effective net lengths of fractions of a 600-cm tube are 285, 185, 135, 85 and 60 cm.

In the US, aluminum is available in 12-ft lengths. The effective economical cuts (excluding the 6-inch overlap) are 66, 42, 30, 22.8 inches, etc.

3.3.7. Telescopic fits.

Good-fit telescopic joints are made as follows: With a metal saw, make two slits of approximately 30 mm (1.2 inch) length into the tip of the larger section. To avoid corrosion, use plenty of Penetrox (available from Burndy) when assembling the sections. A stainless-steel hose clamp will tighten the outer element closely onto the inner one (with the shimming material in between if necessary). A stainless-steel Parker screw will lock the sections lengthwise. For large diameters and heavy-wall sections, a stainless-steel 6- or 8-mm bolt (¼ or ⁵⁄₁₆ inch) is preferred in a pre-threaded hole.

Table 13-4

List of Currently Available Aluminum Pipe in the US

OD in.	Wall in.
1.05	0.113
1.05	0.154
1.315	0.133
1.315	0.179
1.66	0.065
1.66	0.109
1.66	0.140
1.66	0.191
1.90	0.065
1.90	0.109
1.90	0.145
1.90	0.2
2.375	0.065
2.375	0.109
2.375	0.154
2.375	0.218
2.875	0.203
2.875	0.276

Metric tube sections do not provide a snug telescoping fit as do the US series with a 0.125-in.-diameter step and 0.058-in. wall thickness. At best there is a 1-mm difference between the OD of the smaller tube and the ID of the larger tube. A fairly good fit can be obtained, however, by using a piece of 0.3-mm-thick aluminum shimming material. US tubes with 0.125-inch diameter increase and 0.058-inch wall provide a very good fit. The slit, hose clamp, Parker screw and heat-shrink tube make this a reliable joint as well.

Sometimes sections must be used where the OD of the smaller section is the same as the ID of the larger section. In order to achieve a fit, make a slit approximately 5 cm (2 inches) in length in the smaller tube. Remove all burrs and then drive the smaller tube inside the larger to a depth of 3 times the slit length (eg, 15 cm or 6 inches). Do this after heating up the outer tube (use a flame torch) and cooling down the inner tube (use ice-water). The heated-up outer section will expand, while the cooled-down inner section will shrink. Use a good-sized plastic hammer and enough force to drive the inner tube quickly inside the larger tube before the temperature-expansion effect disappears. A solid unbreakable press fit can be obtained. A good Parker screw or stainless-steel bolt (with pre-threaded hole) is all that's needed to secure the taper connection.

Under certain circumstances a very significant drop in element diameter is required. In this case a so-called donut is required. The donut is a 15 cm (6 inch) long piece of aluminum tubing that is machined to exhibit the right OD and ID to fill up the gap between the tubes to be fit. Often the donut can be made from short lengths of heavy-wall aluminum tubing.

I always cover each taper-joint area with a piece of heat shrinkable tube that is coated with a hot-melt on the inside (Raychem). This makes a perfect protection for the element joint and keeps the element perfectly watertight.

3.3.8. Material ratings and design conditions.

All the above calculations are done in a static environment, assuming a wind blowing horizontally at a constant speed. Dynamic modeling is very complex and falls out of the scope of this book. If all the rules, the design methodology and the calculating methods as outlined above and as used in the mechanical design modules of the YAGI DESIGN software are closely followed, a Yagi will result that will withstand the forces of wind, even in a "normal" dynamic environment, as has been proved in practice.

The 40-meter Yagi was designed to be able to withstand wind speeds of 140 km/h (87 mi/h), according to the EIA/TIA-222-E standard. The 140-km/h wind does *not* include any safety factors or other modifiers.

The most important contribution of all the above calculations is that the stresses in all critical points of the Yagi are kept at a similar level when loading. In other words, the mechanical design should be well balanced as the system will only be as strong as the weakest element in the system.

Make sure you know exactly the rating of the materials you are using. The yield stress for various types of steel and especially stainless steel can vary with a factor of 3! Do not go by assumptions. Make sure.

3.3.9. Element finishing.

As a final touch I always paint my Yagi beams with three layers of transparent metal varnish. It keeps the aluminum nice and shiny for a long time.

3.3.10. Ice loading.

Ice loading greatly reduces the wind survival speed. Fortunately, heavy ice loading is not often accompanied by very high winds, with an exception for the most harsh environments (near the poles).

Although we are almost never subject to ice loading here in Northern Belgium, it is interesting to evaluate what the performance of the Yagi would be under ice loading conditions.

Table 13-5 shows the maximum wind survival speed and element sag as a function of radial ice thickness. As the ice thickness increases, the sections that will first break are the tips. The reflector of our metric-design element will take up to 16 mm of radial ice before breaking. At that time the sag of the tips of the reflector element will have increased from 100 cm (40 inches) without ice to approximately 500 cm (200 inches) with the ice load. If the Yagi must be built with heavy ice loading in mind, you will have to start from heavier tubing at the tips. The ELEMENT STRENGTH module will help you design an element meeting your requirements in only a few minutes.

3.3.11. Material fatigue.

It has often been observed that especially light elements (thin wall, low wind-survival designs) will oscillate (flutter) under mild wind conditions. Element tips can oscillate with an amplitude of well over 10 cm (4 inches). Under such conditions a mechanical failure will be induced after a certain time. This failure mechanism is referred to as material fatigue.

Table 13-5

Ice Loading Performance of the 40-Meter Beam

Radial Ice		Max Wind Speed		Sag	
mm	inch	kph	mph	cm	inch
2.5	0.1	116	72	132	52
5.0	0.2	96	60	183	72
7.5	0.3	79	49	242	95
10	0.4	64	40	310	122
12.5	0.5	47	29	386	152
15	0.6	25	15	435	171
16	0.63	0	0	Break	

Note: As designed, the Yagi element will break with a 16-mm (0.63 inch) radial ice thickness at zero wind load, or at lower values of ice loading when combined with wind. The design was *not* optimized to resist ice loading. Optimized designs will use elements that are overall thicker, especially the tip elements.

Element vibrations can be prevented by designing elements consisting of strong heavy-wall sections. Avoid tip sections that are too light. Tip sections of a diameter of less than approximately 15 mm are not recommended, although difficult to avoid with a large 40-meter Yagi. Through the entire length of the element I run an 8-mm (0.3 inch) nylon rope which lies loosely in the element. This rope will dampen any self-oscillation that might start in the element.

At both ends, the rope is fastened at the element tips by injecting a good dose of silicone rubber into the tip of the element and onto the end of the rope. The tip is then covered with a heat-shrinkable plastic cable-head cover with internal hot-melt. At both ends of the element you must drill a small hole (3 mm or ⅛ in.) at the underside of the element about 5 cm (2 in.) from the tip of the element to allow the draining of any condensation water that may accumulate inside the element.

Make sure the cord lays loosely inside the element. The method is very effective, and not a single case of fatigue element failure has occurred when the guidelines as explained were followed. A simple test consists of trying to hand-excite the elements into a vibration mode. Without internal rope this can usually be done quite easily. You can get really frustrated in trying to get in an oscillation mode when the rope is present. Try for yourself!

3.3.12. Matching the Yagi.

The only thing left to do is design a system that will match the antenna impedance (28 ohms) to the feed-line impedance (50 ohms). The choice of the omega match is obvious:
• No need for a split element (mechanical complications).
• No need to adjust the length of a gamma rod.
• Fully adjustable from the center of the antenna.

The two capacitors are mounted in a housing made of a 50 cm (20 inch) long piece of plastic drainpipe (15 cm or 6 inch OD), which is mounted below the boom near the driven element (Fig 13-16). This is a very flexible way of constructing boxes for housing gamma and omega capacitors. The drain-pipes exist in a range of diameters, and the length can be adjusted by cutting off the required length. End caps are available that make professional-looking and perfectly water-tight units.

The design of the omega match is described in detail in par 3.2.2. The SWR was measured using a professional network analyzer. The 1.5:1 SWR bandwidth turned out to be 210 kHz.

3.3.13. Tower, mast, mast bearings, drive shaft and rotator.

If you want a long-lasting low-band Yagi system, the necessary attention should be paid to:

• The tower.
• The rotating mast.
• The mast bearings.
• The rotator.
• The drive shaft.

3.3.13.1. *The tower.*

Your tower supplier or manufacturer will want to know the wind area of your antenna. Or maybe you have a tower that's good for 2 m^2 (22 ft^2) of top load. Will it be okay for the 40-meter antenna?

Specifying the wind area of a Yagi is an issue of great confusion. Wind thrust (force) is generated by the wind hitting a surface exposed to that wind. The thrust is the product of the dynamic wind pressure multiplied by the exposed area, and with a so-called drag coefficient, which is related to the *shape* of the body exposed to the wind. The "resistance" to wind of a flat-shaped body (panel) is obviously different (higher!) than the resistance of a ball-shaped or tubular-shaped body.

This means that if we specify or calculate the wind area of a Yagi, we must always specify if this is the equivalent wind area for a flat plate (which really should be the standard) or if the area is simply meant as the sum of the projected areas of all the elements (or the boom, whichever has the largest projected area; see par 3.3.4.1.). In the former case we must use a drag coefficient of 2.0 (according to the latest EIA/TIA-222-E standard) to calculate the wind load, while for an assembly of (long and slender) tubes a coefficient of 1.2 is applicable.

This means that for a Yagi which consists only of tubular elements (Yagi elements and boom), the flat-plate wind area will be 66.6% lower (2.0/1.2) than the round-element wind area.

The 40-meter Yagi, excluding the boom-to-mast plate, the rotating mast and any match box, has a flat-plate equivalent wind area of 1.65 m^2 (17.8 ft^2. As the projected area of the 3 elements is 2.5 times larger than the projected area of the boom, the addition of the boom-to-mast plate and the match box will not change the wind load, which for this Yagi is only determined by the area of the elements.

The round-element equivalent wind area for the Yagi is 2.74 m^2 (29.5 ft^2).

The wind thrust generated by this Yagi at a wind speed of 140 km/h (87 mi/h) is 302 kg (665 lb), as shown in Fig 13-11. This figure is for 140 km/h (87 mi/h), without any safety margins or modifiers. Consult the EIA/TIA-222-E standard or your local building authorities to obtain the correct figure to be used in your specific case.

Let me make clear again that the thrust of 302 kg (665 lb) is only generated with the element broadside to the wind. If you put the boom in the wind, the loading on the tower will be limited to 90 kg (199 lb). See par 3.3.4.1. However, I would not advise using a tower that will take less than 300 kg (660 lb) of top load. Consider the margin between the boom in the wind and the elements in the wind as a safety margin.

3.3.13.2. The rotating mast.

Leeson (Ref. 964) covered the issue of masts very well. Again, what you use will probably be dictated in the first place by what you can find. In any case, make sure you calculate the mast. My 3-element 40-meter beam sits on top of a 17-ft-long stainless-steel mast, measuring 10 cm (4 inches) in diameter with a wall thickness of 10 mm (0.4 in.). This mast is good for a wind load of 579 kg (1,275 lb) at the top. I calculated the maximum wind load as 302 kg or 664 lb (see Fig 13-11). At the end of a 5 m (16½ ft) cantilever the bending moment caused by the beam is 1,510 kg-m (130,800 in.-lb). Knowing the yield strength of the tube we use, we can calculate the minimum required dimensions for our mast using Eq 13-2.

$$M_{max} = YS \times \pi \times \frac{10^4 - 8^4}{32 \times 10} = YS \times 58$$

where YS = yield strength

The stainless-steel tube I use has a yield strength of 50 kg/mm^2 or 5,000 kg/cm^2.

$$M_{max} = 5,000 \times 58 = 290,000 \text{ kg-cm} = 2,900 \text{ kg-m}$$

It appears that we have a safety factor of 75% versus the moment created by the Yagi (1,510 kg-m). I have not included the wind load of the mast, but the safety margin is more than enough to cover the bending moment caused by the mast itself.

The calculation in the English system is as follows.

$$M_{max} = YS \times \pi \times \frac{4^4 - 3.2^4}{32 \times 4} = YS \times 3.71$$

where YS = yield strength in lb/in.^{2}

The stainless-steel tube has a yield strength of 70,000 lb/in.^{2}.

$$M_{max} = 70,000 \times 3.71 = 259,700 \text{ in.-lb}$$

In my installation I have welded plates on the mast at the heights where the beam needs to be mounted. These plates are exact replicas of the stainless-steel plates mounted on the booms of the Yagis (the boom-to-mast coupling plates). When mounting the Yagi on the mast, you do not have to fool around with U bolts; the two plates are bolted together at the four corners with 18-mm-OD (0.7 inch) stainless-steel bolts. Between the two plates a number of stairs have been welded in order to provide a convenient working situation when installing the antennas.

3.3.13.3. *The mast bearings.*

The mast bearings are equally important parts of the antenna setup. Each tower with a rotating mast should use two types of bearings:

• The thrust bearing; it should take axial (weight) as well as radial load.

Fig 13-17—Thrust bearing for the 100-mm (4 in.) OD mast inside the top section of the 80-ft tower at ON4UN.

• The second bearing should only take radial load.

The thrust bearing should be capable of safely bearing the weight of the mast and all the antennas. The thrust-bearing assembly must be waterproof and have provisions for lubricating the bearing periodically. Fig 13-17 shows the thrust collar being welded on the stainless-steel mast inside the top tower section. Notice the stainless-steel housing of the thrust bearing. The bearing is a 120 mm ID, FAG model FAG30224A (T4FB120 according to DIN ISO 355). In my tower the thrust bearing is 2 meters (6½ ft) below the top of the tower.

The second (radial) bearing is mounted right at the top of the tower and consists of a simple 10 cm (4 in.) long nylon bushing with approximately 1 mm (0.04 in.) clearance with the mast OD.

The thrust bearing can also be at the top with the radial bearing at the lower point. This does not make any difference. The choice is dictated by practical construction aspects.

The mast and antenna weight should never be carried by the rotator. In my towers I have the rotator sitting at ground level, with a long drive shaft in the center of the self-supporting tower. The drive shaft is supported by a thrust bearing near the top of the tower. The fact that the heavy drive shaft "hangs" in the center of the tower adds to the stability of the tower. Replacing the rotator can be easily done. The coupling between the rotator and the drive shaft is done with a cardan axle.

3.3.13.4. The rotator.

I would not dare to suggest using one of the commercially available rotators with antennas of this size. Use a prop-pitch or a large industrial-type worm-gear reduction with the appropriate reduction ratio and motor.

3.3.13.5. The drive shaft.

The drive shaft is the tube connecting the rotating mast with the rotator. The drive shaft must meet the following specifications.

• It must have enough spring effect to act as a torque absorber when starting and stopping the motor. This effect can be witnessed when you start the rotator and the antenna starts moving but a second later. This action relieves a lot of stress from the rotator. Leeson (Ref. 964) uses an automotive transmission damper as a torque spring.

• The drive shaft should not have too much spring effect so as to keep the antenna in the right direction in high winds. Also, if there is too much spring effect, the excessive swinging of the antenna could damage the antenna. The acceleration and the forces induced at the element-to-boom mounting hardware at the tips of the boom may induce failure at the element-to-boom mounting system.

The torque moment will deform (twist) the drive shaft (hollow tube). The angle over which the shaft is twisted is directly proportional to the length of the shaft. In practice, we should not allow for more than ±30 degrees of rotation under the worst torque moment.

In an ideal world the Yagi is torque balanced, which means that even under high wind load there is no mast torque. In practice nothing is less true: Wind turbulence is the reason that the large wind capture area of the Yagi always creates a large amount of momentary torque moment during wind storms.

When rotation is initiated, the inertia of the Yagi induces twist in the drive shaft. This is witnessed by the fact that the antenna starts rotating some time after the rotator has been switched on. The same is true after stopping the rotator, when the antenna overshoots a certain degree before coming back to its stop position.

In practice you will have to make a judicious choice between the length of the drive shaft and the size of the shaft. Using a long drive shaft and the rotator at ground level has the following advantages (in a noncrank-up, self-supporting tower):

• No torque induced on the tower above the point where the rotator isolated.

• Motor at ground level facilitates maintenance and supervision.

The disadvantage is that you will need a sizable shaft to keep the swinging under control.

Calculating the Drive Shaft

Refer to par 3.2.1 for some of the definitions used. It is difficult, if not impossible to calculate the torque moment caused by turbulent winds. I have estimated the momentary maximum torque moment to be 3 *times* as high as the *torque* moment *on one side of the boom*, as calculated before for a wind speed of 140 km/h. This is 360 kg-m. Taking this figure as a maximum momentary shaft torque, caused by highly turbulent winds, means that we consider that the wind momentarily causes the antenna to rotate in only one direction, and that we disregard the forces trying to rotate the antenna in the opposite direction. In addition I added a 200% safety factor. I use this figure as the maximum momentary torque moment to calculate the requirements for the drive shaft. I have not found any better approach yet, and it is my practical experience that, using this approach, a fair approximation is obtained of what can happen under worst circumstances with peak winds in a highly turbulent environment.

• T = 360,000 kg-mm (31,200 in.-lb)

• The section shear modulus is

$$Z = \pi \times \frac{D^4 - d^4}{16 \times D}$$

Assume the following:
D = 8 cm (3.15 in.)
d = 6.5 cm (2.56 in.)
Z = 56.7 cm^3 = 56,700 mm^3 (3.46 in.^{3})

• The shear stress is given by
ST = T/Z
where
Z = modulus of section under shear stress
T = applied torque moment
ST = 36,000 kg-cm/56.7 cm^3 = 635 kg/cm^2 = 6.35 kg/mm^2

In US units:
ST = 31,252 in.-lb/3.46 in^3 = 9,032 lb/in.^{2}

This is a very low figure, meaning the tube will certainly not break under the torque moment of 36,000 kg-cm (31,252 in.-lb).

Fig 13-18 (left)—The 40-meter 3-element full-size Yagi is lowered on top of the rotating mast at a height of 30 m (100 ft) with the use of a 48-m (160 ft) hydraulic crane.

Fig 13-19 (below)—Vertical radiation patterns of a 3-element Yagi for various heights (see below). It is clear that the 0.5-wavelength height at A is by far the most suitable height for general DX-work on 80 meters. The high-angle secondary lobes and the narrow first lobe plus the minimum (dip) between the first and the second lobe make higher heights a bad choice for 80 meters, where the bulk of DX signals come in at wave angles between 25 and 50 degrees. The patterns are calculated for flat ground with good ground conductivity.

A—0.5 λ height   C—0.8 λ height
B—0.6 λ height   D—1.0 λ height

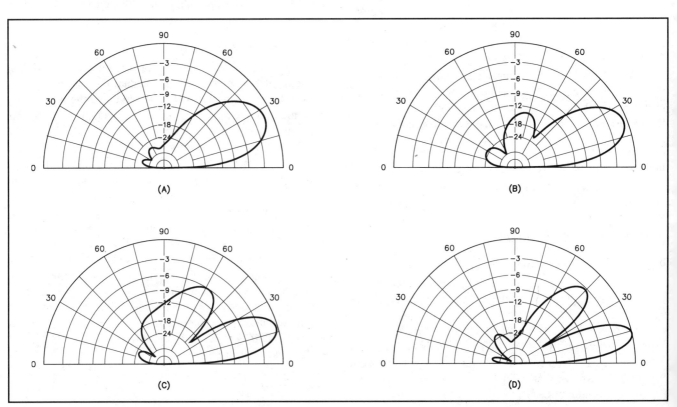

- The twist angle of the shaft is, of course, directly proportional to the shaft length. In my case the rotator is 21 m below the lower bearing, which makes the shaft 21 m long. The critical part of the whole setup is the shaft-twist angle under maximum mast torque.

The shaft-twist angle (TW) is given by

$$TW = \frac{T \times L}{J \times G}$$

where

T = applied torque (360,000 kg-mm = 31,252 in.-lb)
L = length of shaft (21,000 mm = 827 in.)
G = rigidity modulus of the material = 8,000 kg/mm^2 (11,380,620 lb/in.^{2})
J = section modulus × radius of tube = 56,700 mm^3 × 40 mm = 2,268,000 mm^4 = 5.4489 in.^{4}

$$TW = 360,000 \text{ kg-mm} \times \frac{21,000 \text{ mm}}{2,268,000 \text{ mm}^4 \times 8,000 \text{ kg}/\text{mm}^2}$$

= 0.44 radians = 25 degrees

or

$$TW = 31,252 \text{ in.-lb} \times \frac{827 \text{ in.}}{5.4489 \text{ in.}^4 \times 11,380,620 \text{ lb}/\text{in.}^2}$$

= 0.44 radians = 25 degrees

This means that our anticipated 360 kg-m (31,252 in.-lb) torque moment, applied to a 21 m (827 inch) long drive shaft, with OD = 80 mm (3.15 in.), ID = 65 mm (2.56 in.) and a rigidity modulus of 8,000 kg/mm^2 (11,380,620 lb/in.^{2}), will produce a twist angle of 25 degrees. This is an acceptable figure. The twist should in all cases be kept below 30 degrees, in order to keep the antenna from excessively swinging back and forth in high winds.

It is clear that the same result could be obtained with a much lighter tube, provided it was a much shorter length.

3.3.14. Raising the antenna.

A 3-element full-size 40-meter Yagi, built according to the guidelines outlined in the previous paragraphs, is a "monster." Including the massive boom-to-mast plate, it weighs nearly 250 kg (550 lb) and is huge.

A few years ago I met a man who has his own crane company. He has a whole fleet of hydraulic cranes that come in very handy for mounting large antennas on their tower. Fig 13-18 shows the crane arm extended to a full 48 m (160 ft), maneuvering the 40-meter Yagi on top of the 30 m (100 ft) self-supporting tower.

With the type of boom-to-mast plates shown in Fig 13-16, it takes but a few minutes to insert the four large bolts in the holes at the four corners of the plates and get the Yagi firmly mounted on the mast.

3.3.15. Conclusion.

Long-lasting full-size low-band Yagis are certainly not the result of much improvisation. They are the result of a serious design effort, which is 90% a mechanical engineering effort. Software is now available that will help design mechanically sound, large low-band Yagis. This makes it

possible to build a reliable antenna system that will outperform anything that is commercially available by a large margin. It also brings the joy of home-building back into our hobby, the joy and pride of having a no-compromise piece of equipment.

3.4. A 3-Element Full-size 80-Meter Yagi

One of the disadvantages of a rotatable Yagi is the fact that "switching directions" takes a while. Very large and heavy Yagi antennas should not be rotated at speeds of more than 0.5 to 1 r/min maximum. In order to overcome this problem, it is possible to design a Yagi where, by means of relays, the director is instantly transformed into a reflector, and vice

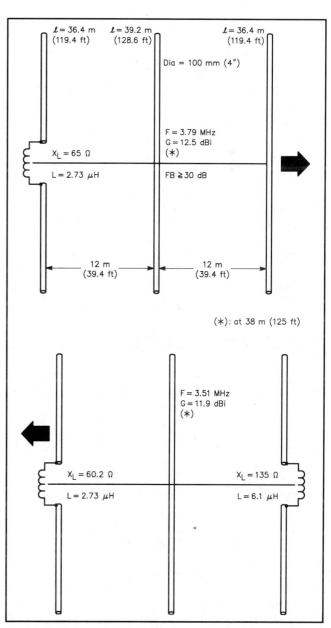

Fig 13-20—Design of equally spaced 3-element 80-meter Yagi. The element lengths shown are for a constant element diameter (100 mm or 4 inches). The loading coils make this an excellent Yagi for 3.5 as well as 3.8 MHz. Note that the same coil (2.73 μH) is used as a loading element for the reflector on 3.8 MHz and for the director on 3.5 MHz.

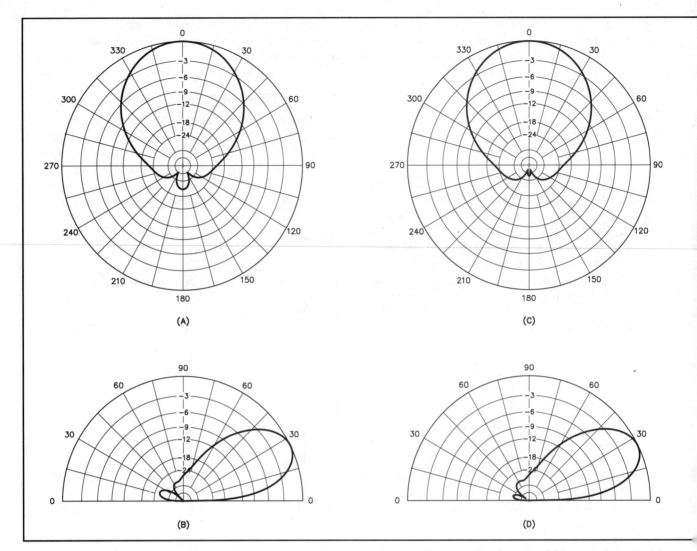

Fig 13-21—Horizontal and vertical radiation patterns for the 3-element 80-meter Yagi on the SSB end of the band. These patterns are for the Yagi design frequency of 3.79 MHz. All azimuth patterns are for a wave angle of 27 degrees.

A and B—3.8 MHz   E and F—3.775 MHz
C and D—3.79 MHz   G and H—3.75 MHz

versa. This means that at 1 r/min it would never take more than 15 seconds to get the antenna in any direction. On average, it would take 7.5 seconds.

Also, due to its high relative bandwidth (8.2% as compared to 2.4% for the 20-meter band), it is impossible to design a Yagi that will exhibit good gain, good F/B and an acceptable SWR at the high end (3.8 MHz) as well as the low end (3.5 MHz) of the band, without resorting to our bag of special tricks.

3.4.1. Antenna height.

Fig 13-19 shows the radiation patterns for a "standard" 3-element Yagi at heights ranging from ½ to 1 wavelength. Above ½ wavelength, an annoying high angle lobe appears, and a lot of RF is wasted at that angle. At a ½ wavelength height (Fig 13-19A), the radiation angle is approximately 25 to 30 degrees (depending on the ground quality), with a reasonable broad lobe (29 degrees at –3 dB). This is an ideal angle for most serious DX work on that band. If you put your Yagi at 1 wavelength (78 m or 250 ft), the main lobe is as low as 14 degrees (I know that's way too low for almost all DX on 80 meters). The lobe will be quite narrow (only 14 degrees, at –3 dB) and you have a null at 30 degrees, which happens to be the angle where you will have a lot of DX coming in. The second lobe is at 45 degrees, which in turn is already too high for serious DX work. I know very high antennas are like a status symbol, but this time (again), too high is no good! It is true that at 1 wavelength height the Yagi exhibits 1.0 dB more gain than at 0.5 wavelength, but what's the point of concentrating more energy at the wrong elevation angle?

The 3-element full-size Yagi described here has been developed to be installed at a height of 38 m (125 ft) over flat ground with good conductivity properties.

3.4.2. Electrical design.

The Yagi has been developed to be physically "fully

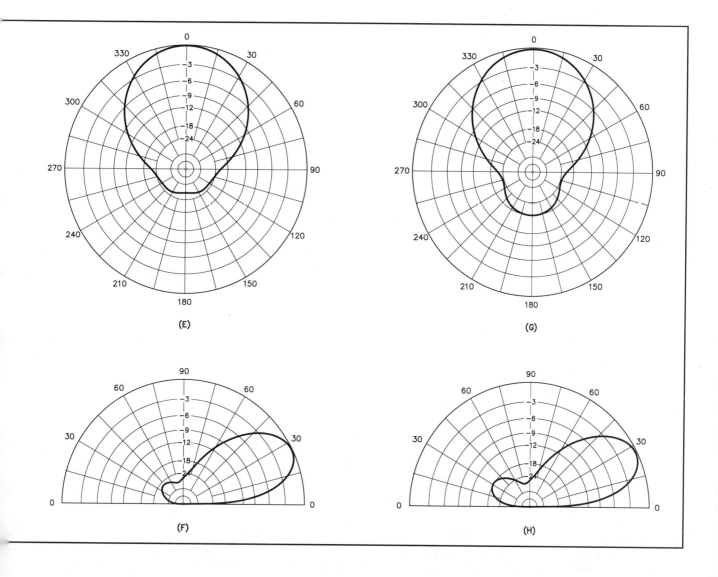

(E)

(F)

(G)

(H)

symmetrical." This means that the driven element is right at the center of the boom, with two parasitic elements of equal physical length (the director length at the highest operating frequency). The reflector is then loaded in the center (by an inductance) in order to lower its resonant frequency. This means that both parasitic elements need to be split (at the boom). By a set of relays it is possible to either short the split (turn the element into a director) or insert the required inductance (turn it into a reflector). I also set out to design a Yagi which should be switchable from the SSB to the CW portion of 80 meters without any compromise in performance (gain, F/B).

The constant-element-diameter design is shown in Fig 13-20. I used a constant diameter of 100 mm (4 inches) which (later) turned out to be the equivalent diameter of the tapering diameter element of our mechanical design (see par 3.4.8.). Using this element diameter and inserting a coil with $X_L = 65$ ohms in the reflector turns this into a Yagi with a very good gain and F/B ratio. Note that, with a smaller element diameter, the Q factor of the element would be higher, which in turn means that one would require more inductance to tune the element to the same frequency. For a constant diameter of 22.225 mm (⅞ inch), the required reactance would be 85 ohms.

To make the same Yagi work on 3.5 MHz, all that is required is a coil in the director element, and a second (larger) coil in the reflector. It turns out that on 80 meters, an element length that makes a perfect reflector for 3.8 MHz, is a perfect director on 3.5 MHz. In other words, the same coil that is used for loading the reflector on 3.8 MHz can be used as a loading coil for the director on 3.5 MHz.

In our example, the coil that has a reactance of 65 ohms on 3.79 MHz (2.73 µH) has a reactance of $65 \times 3.51/3.79 =$ 60.2 ohms on 3.51 MHz. Together with a loading coil having a reactance of $+j135$ ohms at 3.51 MHz (6.1 µH), this value results in a very good 3-element Yagi for the CW end of the 80-meter band. If the antenna is erected at a height of ½ wavelength, the F/B ratio is between 25 and 30 dB at any wave angle between 0 and 90 degrees, at both design frequencies (3.79 and 3.51 MHz).

The initial design was modeled with ELNEC. Modeling and optimizing of the Yagi for best gain and F/B was done over real (good) ground at a height of ½ wavelength. This is the ideal height for such an antenna. Under these conditions the gain is calculated as 12.5 dBi at 3.79 MHz and 11.9 dBi at 3.51 MHz. The horizontal and vertical radiation patterns for the 3-element Yagi are shown in Figs 13-21 and 13-22.

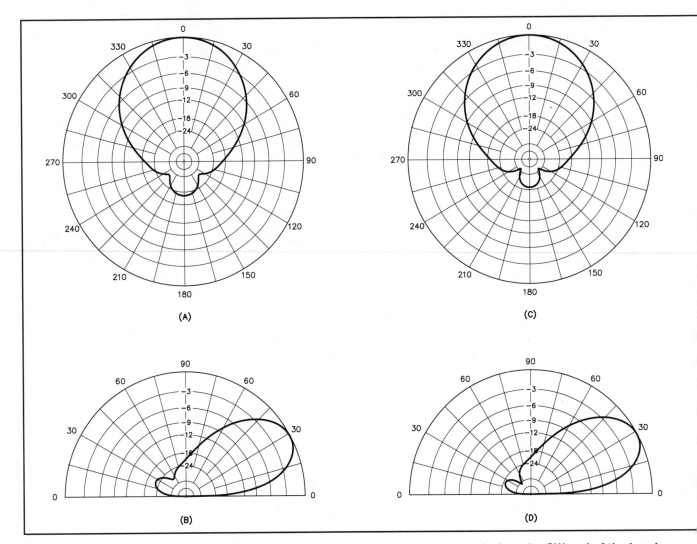

Fig 13-22—Horizontal and vertical radiation patterns for the 3-element 80-meter Yagi on the CW end of the band. These patterns are for the Yagi design frequency of 3.51 MHz. All azimuth patterns are for a wave angle of 28 degrees.

A and B—3.5 MHz   E and F—3.53 MHz
C and D—3.51 MHz   G and H—3.55 MHz

3.4.3. Parasitic parallel capacitance with split elements.

Split elements cannot be realized without introducing some parallel capacitance between the inside end of the half-element and the boom, or between the two element halves (in case you have no boom or have a dielectric boom). The ends of the insulated elements have a certain capacitance with the boom because of the mechanical construction of the insulating material and all the mounting hardware. If we were to use the loading coils as modeled above, without taking into account the "parasitic" capacitance, the loading effects could be way off.

The parasitic capacitance is the value of the series connection of the capacitances of each half element versus the boom. In other words, the values shown in Fig 13-23 are half the values as measured on one of the element legs. It is essential that this capacitance be measured. This can easily be done before the Yagi is raised. However, you cannot measure

it on a finished element, because the self-capacitance (from one side to the other and also to ground) of the full element itself would upset the results.

I made a mockup of the center insulator consisting of the boom and the mounting hardware, but no element. Then I measured the capacitance at the Yagi operating frequency. The capacitance can range from just a few pF, if special care has been taken to reduce it, to several hundred pF.

The mechanical design shown in Fig 13-24 turned out to have an extremely low parasitic capacitance of only 32 pF between the ends of the split elements (64 pF between each element half and the boom).

3.4.4. Modeling the Yagi including the parasitic parallel capacitance.

Now that we know we have 32 pF across the split elements where the loading lines (hairpins) will be connected, we must model the Yagi using a parallel tuned circuit as a

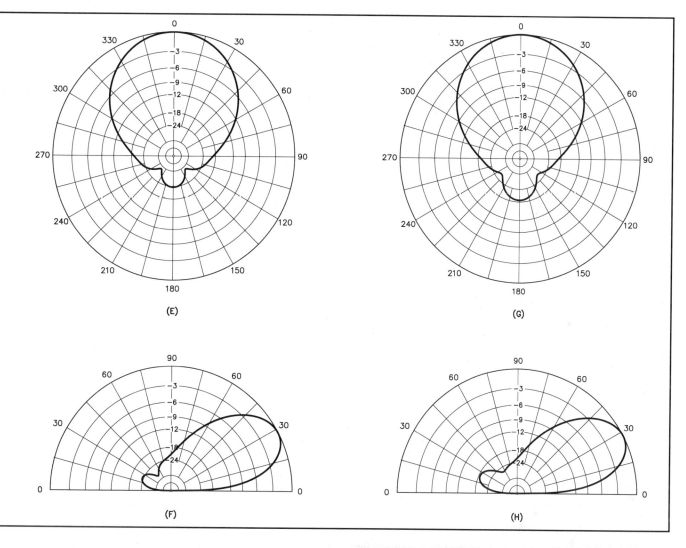

(E)

(G)

(F)

(H)

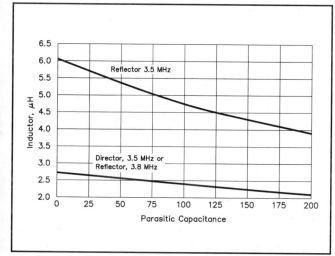

Fig 13-23—Value of the tuning coil for the 80-meter Yagi as a function of parallel capacitance. Center-insulated elements always suffer from parasitic parallel capacitance. This means that in fact the loading coils are part of the parallel circuits. The values must be adjusted in order to obtain the desired reactance. This chart shows the required reactance (in µH) as a function of the total parasitic capacitance (capacitance per half element ÷ 2), for the two loading coils. See text for details.

Fig 13-24—Detail of the mounting of the parasitic element on the boom. The boom is made of a steel lattice-tower type of construction (solid bars, no tubes!). The mounting and insulation method has been developed by DJ6JC, and ensures extremely low parasitic capacitance as well as simplicity in mounting and top mechanical strength. In this picture the boom is straight up (vertical). In this setup the boom supports the hairpin loading elements during the element resonant-frequency measuring session. DJ4PT (owner of the 3-element full-size 80-m quad described later) is in the foreground, with DJ6JC looking on in the background.

loading element, instead of just an inductor. The parallel capacitor of the tuned circuit is 32 pF. We must find the required inductance to achieve the desired loading as modeled before in our simplified model without parallel capacitance.

The following design methodology was used.
- The Yagi was first modeled and optimized without taking into account the parasitic capacitance.
- When the model was optimized, the resonant frequency of the director and the reflector was determined. This can easily be done as follows.

1) Delete all elements from the model, except the element whose resonant frequency we want to know.

2) Keep the loading device (if any), and excite the center of the element. The loading device can be simply in series with the excitation.

3) Change the resonant frequency until you find a feed-point impedance where the reactive part is zero (this is the definition of resonance). In our Yagi the director for the SSB design (f_{design} = 3.79 MHz) is resonant at 4.005 MHz; the reflector is resonant at 3.745 MHz. The CW design (f_{design} = 3.51 MHz) has a director that is resonant at 3.745 MHz, and a reflector that is resonant at 3.465 MHz.

- Now the loading inductors are replaced in the modeling program by a parallel tuned circuit ($C_{parallel}$ = 32 pF), and the inductance values are found that produce the same resonant frequencies as found in our simplified (no parallel capacitance) model.

The 3.745-MHz element turns out to require a loading inductance of 2.6 μH (in parallel with the 32 pF of parallel capacitance). This is $+j62$ ohms at 3.79 MHz, or 57.3 ohms at 3.51 MHz. Compare these values with the values of 65 ohms and 60.2 ohms (L = 2.73 μH) as required when there is no parasitic parallel capacitance.

The 3.465-MHz CW-band reflector requires a loading coil of 5.6 μH (in parallel with 32 pF). This represents a reactance of $+j123$ ohms at 3.51 MHz. Without the parallel capacitance the required loading inductance was 6.1 μH.

Fig 13-23 shows the adapted values of inductive reactance as a function of the parasitic capacitance. This chart is only valid for the Yagi with a given Q factor. In our design case, this is for a Yagi with an equivalent constant element diameter of 100 mm (4 inches). A Yagi with smaller diameter elements will require more loading inductance and vice versa. A similar chart can easily be constructed for any element Q factor by modeling the combinations using, eg, ELNEC.

3.4.5. The loading elements.

The loading coils can preferably be made in a hairpin configuration. I used a transmission line made of 8 mm (0.3 inch) OD aluminum rods, spaced 10 cm (4 inches), which gives a feed-line impedance of 389 ohm

$$(Z = 276 \times \log \frac{2S}{D}).$$

We can calculate the hairpin inductors using Eqs 5 and 6 (par 3.7.3.).

1) The 2.6-μH hairpin (reflector loading in the SSB band, director loading in the CW band):

X_L= 62 ohms

$$\ell^\circ = \arctan \frac{X_L}{389} = \arctan \frac{62}{389} = 9.1 \text{ degrees}$$

$$\ell_{cm} = \ell^\circ \times \frac{81.6}{f_{MHz}} = 9.1 \times \frac{81.6}{3.79} = 196 \text{ cm (77 inches)}$$

2) The 5.6-μH hairpin (reflector loading in CW band):

X_L= 123 ohms

$$\ell^\circ = \arctan \frac{123}{389} = 17.5 \text{ degrees}$$

$$\ell_{cm} = \ell^\circ \times \frac{81.6}{f_{MHz}} = 17.5 \times \frac{81.6}{3.51} = 406 \text{ cm (160 inches)}$$

Fig 13-25 shows the loading and switching layout, which is identical for both parasitic elements. The switching has two purposes:
- Switching from SSB to CW band.
- Instantaneous direction reversal.

3.4.6. Remote tuning for optimum F/B.

The radiation patterns are shown in Figs 13-21 and 13-22. Note that the F/B deteriorates quite rapidly in the SSB band below 3.76 MHz.

We can tune the Yagi for a high F/B ratio over quite a wide spectrum by connecting a capacitor in parallel with the hairpin at the center of the reflector element. In practice, this will not be needed on the CW band, where an excellent F/B is obtained from 3.5 to 3.53 MHz. In the phone band, however, adding a variable capacitor across the hairpin of the reflector will allow us to tune the Yagi for an F/B ratio of better than 25 dB at any frequency between 3.68 and 3.8 MHz!

Without the extra capacitance, the F/B is better than 22 dB from 3.76 to 3.8 MHz. With 100 pF in parallel, the F/B is better than 23 dB from 3.73 to 3.78, and with 200 pF in parallel, an F/B of better than 24 dB can be achieved between 3.69 and 3.73 MHz. These are worst-case F/B values over the entire 90-degree wave angle in the back of the Yagi. Fig 13-26 shows the back patterns of the Yagi (on a very much stretched scale—outer ring equals –20 dB referenced to the maximum response) when tuned for maximum F/B using the variable capacitor across the reflector element.

In practice we can mount two transmitting-type 100-pF ceramic capacitors right at the center of the reflector element and switch these capacitors in parallel with the loading hairpin with vacuum relays. Fig 13-25 shows the switching and loading arrangement which must be provided at both parasitic elements.

This arrangement has been successfully implemented by OZ8BV in a 3 element full-size 80 meter Yagi, built along the principles of this Yagi. OZ8BV reports 30 dB F/B over a wide frequency range, tunable by the parallel capacitor across the tuning stub.

3.4.7. Feeding the Yagi.

As we are using split elements for the two parasitic elements, it might seem obvious to try a hairpin feed. The problem with the parasitic capacitance is difficult if not impossible to overcome at both 3.51 and 3.79 MHz. It turned out, however, that it was very simple to design an omega match that would do the job. This also makes it unnecessary to split-insulate the driven element.

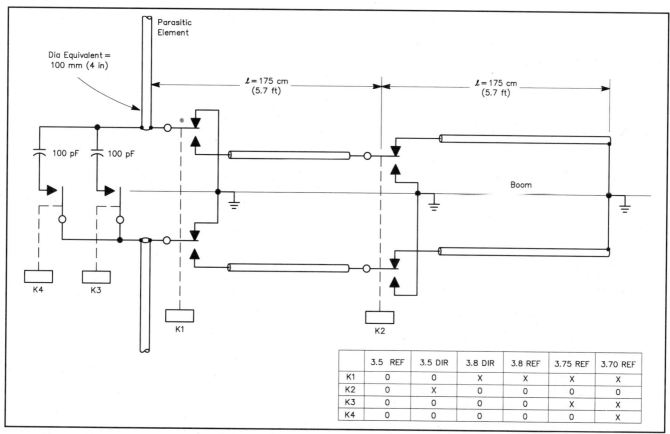

	3.5 REF	3.5 DIR	3.8 DIR	3.8 REF	3.75 REF	3.70 REF
K1	0	0	X	X	X	X
K2	0	X	0	0	0	0
K3	0	0	0	0	X	X
K4	0	0	0	0	0	X

Fig 13-25—Switching harness for the parasitic elements. To make a director at 3.8 MHz the two element halves are strapped. As a reflector element on 3.8 MHz (and as a director element on 3.5 MHz) the short (175 cm) hairpin is used, which has an inductance of 2.6 μH. When operating as a reflector element on 3.5 MHz the extra length of hairpin (making it in total 350 cm long) is switched into the circuit, resulting in a hairpin with an inductance of 5.6 μH.

In our model, which has a constant element diameter of 100 mm (4 in.), the reactive part of the impedances at 3.79 MHz and at 3.51 MHz differ approximately 75 ohms. I dimensioned the driven-element length so that on 3.79 MHz the reactance would be approximately +27 ohms, and –49 ohms at 3.5 MHz. The element was then isolated from its parasitic elements and its resonant frequency was found to be 3.745 MHz. It is interesting to see that our driven element has the same resonant frequency as our reflector for 3.79 MHz and our director for 3.51 MHz. There is no special meaning to this; it only illustrates that the driven-element length does not contribute to the exact radiation pattern of the Yagi. Its exact length will only play a role in designing a matching system for the Yagi. In general the driven element will be between 0.47 and 0.50 wavelength long.

Fig 13-27 shows the matching that was obtained with the GAMMA/OMEGA OPTIMIZER module of the YAGI DESIGN program.

In order to cover both band ends with a smooth and well balanced SWR curve, I decided to use two sets of omega/gamma capacitors, with a single omega rod length. A simple relay can select either set. The schematic with the component values is given in Fig 13-28, as well as the resulting SWR curves, together with the worst-case F/B value. This shows that the Yagi exhibits a well matched SWR and F/B performance over both the DX CW section (3.5 to 3.55 MHz) as well

as the DX SSB section (3.73 to 3.8 MHz), with peak performances centered on 3.79 and 3.51 MHz.

3.4.8. Mechanical design of the elements.

The half-element lengths for our theoretical model, with a constant diameter of 100 mm are:
- Director/reflector: 18.2 m (59.7 ft).
- Driven element: 19.60 m (64.3 ft).

In terms of wavelengths (f = 3.79 MHz) the dimensions of the Yagi are:
- Director/reflector: 0.46 wavelength.
- Driven element: 0.4955 wavelength.
- Spacing: 0.1517 wavelength.

The final elements' lengths, when using a tapering schedule, are much longer than for the constant reference diameter, and can be calculated using the ELEMENT TAPER module of the YAGI DESIGN software. Depending on the exact taper configuration, a full-size reflector will be approximately 42 m (138 ft) long. There are two practical approaches for constructing elements that are that long:
- All tubular construction.
- Tubular tips and lattice construction for central section.

The full-size Yagis that were built by OH1RY, I5NPH and W6MBK use the first approach. The elements are top and side braced to ensure the required structural strength.

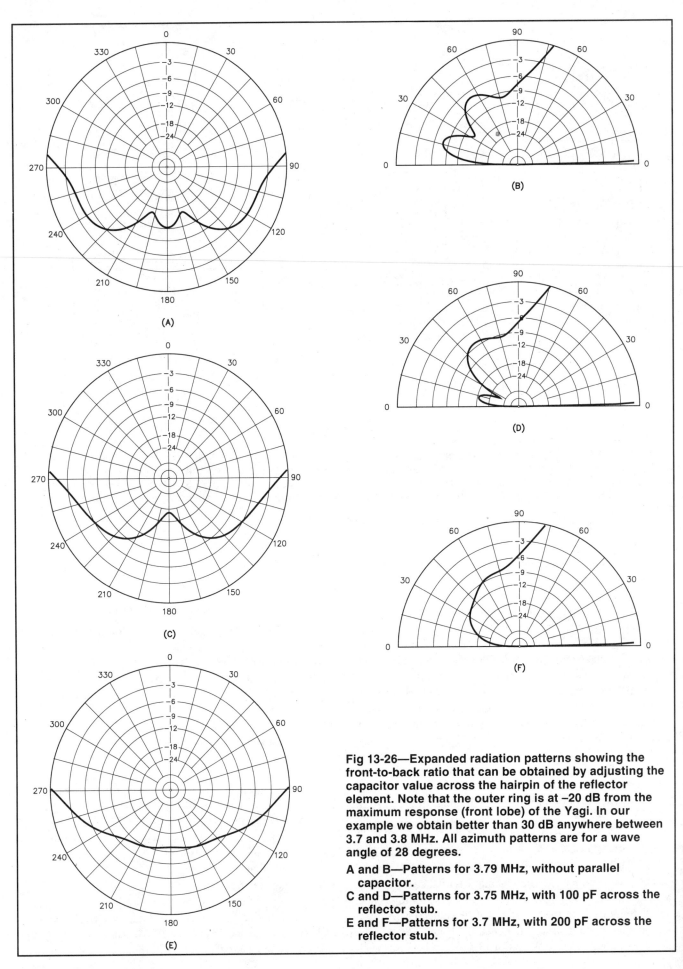

Fig 13-26—Expanded radiation patterns showing the front-to-back ratio that can be obtained by adjusting the capacitor value across the hairpin of the reflector element. Note that the outer ring is at −20 dB from the maximum response (front lobe) of the Yagi. In our example we obtain better than 30 dB anywhere between 3.7 and 3.8 MHz. All azimuth patterns are for a wave angle of 28 degrees.

A and B—Patterns for 3.79 MHz, without parallel capacitor.
C and D—Patterns for 3.75 MHz, with 100 pF across the reflector stub.
E and F—Patterns for 3.7 MHz, with 200 pF across the reflector stub.

```
      DIAMETER DRIVEN ELEMENT =   400        GAMMA WIRE LENGTH = 300.0 mm
      DIAMETER GAMMA ROD =   30                               11.81 inch
      SPACING CENTER TO CENTER =   500       GAMMA CAPACITOR =    252 pF (C1)
                                             OMEGA CAPACITOR = 280.9 pF (C2)
                                             ROD LENGTH = 450.0 cm
      DESIGN FREQUENCY =   3.78 MHz                          177.2 inches

      TUNING RATE = 5  %                      FEEDLINE-Z = 50  ohm
```

─── Press F/C to change tuning rate ───

ANTENNA IMPEDANCE				SWR		MATCHED IMPEDANCE		
FREQ	Real	/	Imag			Real	/	Imag
3.820	17.2	/	37.3	1.99		31.0	/	20.0
3.800	18.6	/	30.1	1.30		39.9	/	6.0
3.790	19.2	/	26.7	1.11		45.0	/	-0.7
3.780	20.4	/	20.1	1.32		58.3	/	-12.4
3.750	23.8	/	14.8	1.62		74.4	/	-17.0
3.740	24.3	/	11.8	1.81		82.8	/	-20.9
3.730	24.7	/	9.0	2.00		91.5	/	-24.0

```
1=DECR.C1 2=INCR.C1   3=DECR.C2   4=INCR.C2   5=DECR.ROD   6=INCR.ROD    Z=CABLE-Z
7=DECR.WIRE   8=INCR.WIRE   C=COURSE   F=FINE  T=TUBE DIMS   S=SAVE   X=EXIT   H=HELP
```

```
      DIAMETER DRIVEN ELEMENT =   400        GAMMA WIRE LENGTH = 300.0 mm
      DIAMETER GAMMA ROD =   30                               11.81 inch
      SPACING CENTER TO CENTER =   500       GAMMA CAPACITOR =    176 pF (C1)
                                             OMEGA CAPACITOR = 262.5 pF (C2)
                                             ROD LENGTH = 450.0 cm
      DESIGN FREQUENCY =   3.55 MHz                          177.2 inches

      TUNING RATE = 5  %                      FEEDLINE-Z = 50  ohm
```

─── Press F/C to change tuning rate ───

ANTENNA IMPEDANCE				SWR		MATCHED IMPEDANCE		
FREQ	Real	/	Imag			Real	/	Imag
3.500	25.3	/	-52.0	1.18		44.1	/	-5.3
3.510	24.8	/	-49.4	1.02		49.8	/	0.8
3.525	23.7	/	-45.6	1.30		59.7	/	10.9
3.550	21.3	/	-38.4	2.04		87.4	/	30.2
3.575	18.7	/	-30.0	3.18		145.1	/	42.3
3.600	16.1	/	-20.8	4.82		240.3	/	-13.5

```
1=DECR.C1 2=INCR.C1   3=DECR.C2   4=INCR.C2   5=DECR.ROD   6=INCR.ROD    Z=CABLE-Z
7=DECR.WIRE   8=INCR.WIRE   C=COURSE   F=FINE  T=TUBE DIMS   S=SAVE   X=EXIT   H=HELP
```

Fig 13-27—Design of the omega match for the 80-meter Yagi. The top table shows the settings for the CW end of the band. The gamma was tuned for 1:1 SWR on
3.51 MHz. The bottom worksheet shows the values for the SSB part of the band. Adjustment was made to cover 3.73 to 3.82 with an SWR of 2:1 or better. The SWR bandwidth (2:1 points) is approximately 100 kHz.

Using the ENTER YOUR OWN DESIGN module of the YAGI DESIGN software, the ELEMENT TAPER module, and the ELEMENT STRENGTH module, we can make the physical design of tubular elements.

Above a certain diameter the use of a lattice construction is more economical than the use of a tubular construction. The lattice construction creates less wind load and weighs much

less. OH6RM (par 3.4.11) uses this approach in his full-size 80-meter designs. Fig 13-29 shows two possible designs where a central lattice section is extended by a 10 m long tapered diameter section.

To keep the weight of the element within practical limits, and in order to obtain the required strength, it may be necessary to guy the central part of the elements toward the boom. In this

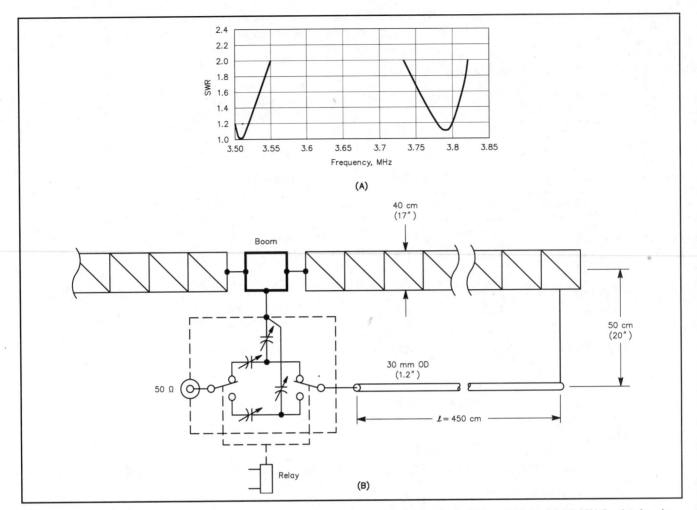

Fig 13-28—At A, SWR curves for the 3-element full-size 80-meter Yagi (optimized for 3.51 and 3.79 MHz), obtained with the omega matching system as shown at B. A single omega rod length was used. Switching from the CW to the SSB portion of the band consists of switching from one set of capacitors (series and parallel) to a second set. This can be done by using vacuum relays.

construction you can calculate the inner section (= the guyed section) using the approach as outlined by Leeson (Ref. 964) for guyed booms. The unguyed section can be calculated using the YAGI DESIGN software.

3.4.9. Building the Yagi.

The 3-element 80-m Yagi described here has been built by H. Lumpe, DJ6JC, who has his own company (WIBI) making commercial radio towers and antenna systems.

DJ6JC designed and constructed an element which is 36.42 m (119.5 ft) long, and which is entirely made as a square tapering lattice construction. At the center (near the boom), the lattice construction measures 42 cm (17 inches) and it tapers to approximately 5 cm (2 inches) at the tips. The lattice-type sections are made of aluminum bars. The sections use bars with an OD of 20 mm (0.8 inch), 15 mm (0.5 inch) and 10 mm (0.4 inch) for the four horizontal members, while bars with an OD of 10 mm (0.4 inch), 8 mm (0.32 inch) and 6 mm (0.24 inch) are used for the oblique members. The weight of the full-size element is only 114 kg (250 lb). This is extremely low, if you compare it to the full-size elements for the 40-meter Yagi which weigh nearly half that much.

This design has an incredible lack of sag over its total length, only 30 cm (1 ft), without any support cables! Fig 13-30 clearly shows that the sag of the full-size 80-meter element is hardly visible to the naked eye.

It is clear that such an element should be okay for all but maybe the strongest hurricane winds. The dimensions and construction of the DJ6JC-built Yagi are shown in Fig 13-31.

The lattice-type elements are connected to the boom by four 2.5 cm (1 inch) thick fiberglass-reinforced plates, in a construction which keeps the parasitic capacitance (to the boom) as low as 64 pF! Fig 13-24 shows how the (horizontal) split element is mounted on the boom (vertical). The fiberglass-reinforced plates are clearly visible.

As there is little, if any information available about the electrical behavior of elements with such an important (and continuous) taper, ON6WU and I decided to check the electrical element length on a test setup.

From earlier modeling, we knew that the director for the SSB band needed to resonate on 4.005 MHz. In this configuration the parasitic element would have no loading coil (hairpin), but the insulated halves would simply be strapped through the contacts of a vacuum relay (see Fig 13-32).

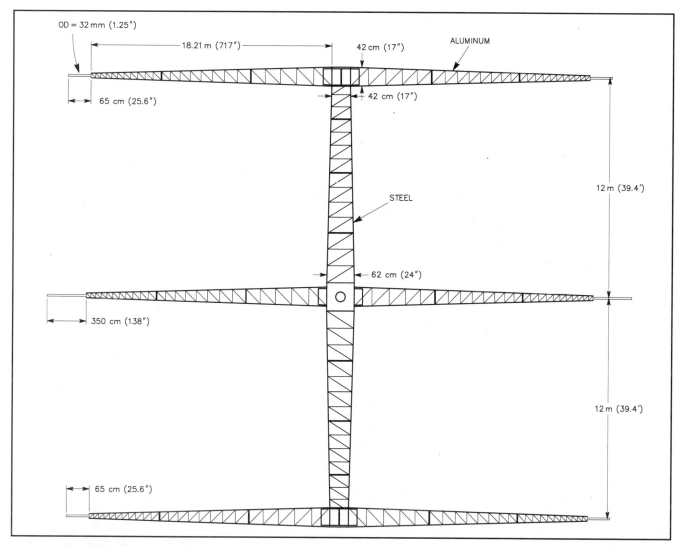

Fig 13-29—Element dimensions for the 80-meter Yagi elements, as used by DJ6JC. The entire element, with the exception of its outer tips (a few feet only), is made as a continuously tapering square-section lattice construction. At the boom the lattice side measures 42 cm (17 inches). This tapers to 5 cm (2 inches) at the tip (18.2 m or 60 ft). Tubular tips (32 mm or 1.25 inches) OD are used to adjust the final element length. The lattice construction is made of solid aluminum bars, and weighs approximately 57 kg (125 lb) for a half element. The total sag is an unbelievable 30 cm (1 ft).

The 36.42 m (119.5 ft) long element was raised to a height of 38 m (½ wavelength) using a hydraulic crane, and the impedance was measured using an HP network analyzer. After we compensated for the 32 pF capacitance (using the SHUNT IMPEDANCE module from the NEW LOW BAND SOFT-WARE) that is in parallel with the impedance bridge, the element turned out to be resonant at 4.090 MHz. Tubular tips with a length of 65 cm (25.6 in.) and with a diameter of 3 cm (1.2 inch OD) were added to the lattice construction to bring the resonant frequency down to 4.050 MHz. Fig 13-33 shows the tubular tip being adjusted to bring the element resonance to 4.005 MHz. Note once again how straight the element is. It is interesting to note that the impedance at resonance was 67 ohms, which corresponds perfectly with the value obtained using ELNEC when modeling an element with an equivalent constant diameter of 100 mm (4 inches) at the same height (1 wavelength) above good ground.

Next we installed a hairpin to bring the resonance down to 3.745 MHz, as required. We had calculated the required hairpin to be 196 cm, but it turned out that a 175 cm (68.9 inch) long line did the trick. The 10% difference is probably due to the inductance of the straps connecting the element to the hairpin.

To bring the resonant frequency of the reflector for CW operation down to 3.465 MHz, we installed a hairpin with a length of 350 cm (137.8 inches).

The driven element was then brought to resonance on 3.745 MHz by extending the lattice section (2 × 18.21 m or 59.75 ft) by 3.5 m (11.5 ft) of aluminum tubing (3.2 cm or 1.25 inch OD). The 3.745-MHz resonant frequency provides a good balance between the positive reactance (at 3.79 MHz) and the negative reactance (at 3.51 MHz), as explained in par 3.4.7.

This procedure of individually checking the resonant frequency of the elements of the Yagi avoids guesswork when

Fig 13-30—The amazing full-size 80-meter element, weighing only 114 kg (250 lb) and good for 160 km/h (106 mi/h) winds. The element is lifted ½ wavelength in the air to make resonant frequency measurements. If you are not sure, no, there are *no* support guys. The totally self-supporting element has a sag of only 30 cm (1 ft). The mechanical design is by H. Lumpe, DJ6JC.

trying to optimize for best performance. It is obvious that checking the resonant frequencies should be done one element at a time; this means without any mutual coupling between elements. This is also how we determined the resonant frequencies of the elements in the model (first, model the Yagi, then isolate the elements to determine their electrical lengths).

Fig 13-34 shows the full-size 80-meter element 38 m

(125 ft) up in the air supported by a hydraulic crane above the place of business of DJ6JC. It is important that the electrical tests are done at the same height where the eventual Yagi will be installed, as well as over the same terrain. It was very instructive to see the resonant frequency of the 36.42 m (119.5 ft) long element change from 3.5 MHz just above ground to over 4.1 MHz at 38 m (125 ft). Between a height of 20 m (66 ft) and 38 m (125 ft), the resonant frequency shifted as much as 200 kHz.

3.4.10. The boom.

The boom for such a large antenna is made of square lattice-type sections, capable of handling the very high boom moment. The moment at the center of the boom (at the mast attachment point) is approximately 7,000 kg-m (550,000 in.-lb) in the vertical plane (weight loading without top-guying) and 4,000 kg-m (250,000 in.-lb) in the vertical plane. This is 25 to 30 times the moments that we encountered with our 40-meter full-size Yagi!

Here again there are two options. You can design the boom of adequate strength without any guying, or you can rely on guy cables for additional strength. I would suggest only to use the guy wires to compensate for the boom sag.

The DJ6JC-designed boom consists of a (square-section) steel lattice construction. Fig 13-24 shows the boom being attached to one of the elements. While the elements are made of aluminum (for weight reasons), each boom half is made of four 3-meter (10 ft) long sections of square-section lattice construction. High-yield-strength steel (solid) bars (not tubes!) are used for the construction. The boom measures 62 cm (24 inches) at the center and tapers to 42 cm (17 inches) at

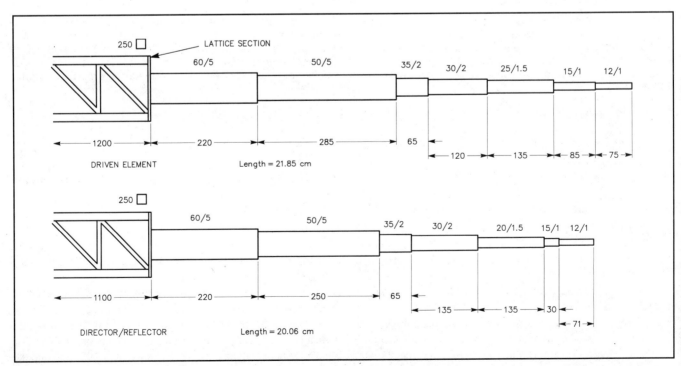

Fig 13-31—Possible layouts for an 80-meter full-size element. In the two examples we see a 10 to 11 m (33 to 36 ft) long tubular tapered section (like a full-size 40-m Yagi element) extending from a lattice tower section. The lattice tower section will likely be top and side braced for added strength as well as to reduce element sag.

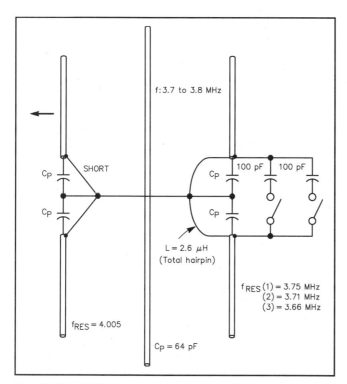

Fig 13-32—Adding a capacitor across the center insulator of the reflector makes it possible to obtain better than 25 dB F/B ratio at any frequency between 3.68 and 3.8 MHz. Having 100 pF in parallel optimizes the F/B between 3.73 and 3.76 MHz, while 200 pF takes care of the range between 3.68 and 3.73 MHz. See text for details.

Fig 13-33—The length of the tubular tip is adjusted to bring the resonance of the element to 4.005 kHz, which is the resonant frequency of the director for 3.8-MHz operation. The element was raised to the operating height (½ wavelength) to do the resonant-frequency measurements. Note the sag of the element, which is really invisible even when looking along the element.

the tips. The total boom weight is approximately 1,500 kg (3,300 lb).

Top guying will be used on the boom only in order to reduce its sag to zero. Side bracing is not necessary with this design.

Including the element-to-boom coupling "satellites," the

Fig 13-34—Eighty-meter full-size dipole element supported 38 m (125 ft) high above the place of business of H. Lumpe (DJ6JC), who is responsible for the outstanding mechanical design of the 80-meter full-size Yagi.

Fig 13-35—Four-element full-size 80-meter Yagi on a 30 m (100 ft) boom. The antenna has been operational at the PJ9M contest QTH on Curacao. This extremely lightweight Yagi is suitable only for use during short periods of contests, and will certainly not withstand high winds.

weight of the 3-element full-size 80-meter Yagi is approximately 1,850 kg (4,000 lb).

Anyone interested in the DJ6JC-made 3-element Yagi can contact the author or H. Lumpe, DJ6JC, Roentgenstrasse 5, D 3013 Barsinghausen, Germany.

3.4.11. The OH6RM full-size 80-meter Yagi.

Fig 13-35 shows the 4-element full-size Yagi designed and made by OH6RM. The boom length is 30 m (100 ft), the weight (only) 400 kg (880 lb). This is 4½ times less than the 3-element design of DJ6JC! The entire Yagi is made of aluminum, including the boom. OH6RM does not specify the wind survival speed of the antenna.

As can be seen from the picture, the center part (18.7 m

or 58.4 ft) of the elements is made of triangular tower sections. The elements are vertically supported by 6-mm-OD (0.25 in.) Kevlar rope. There is no side bracing. The boom is made of triangular lattice tower sections, using 50/43 mm (2.0/1.7 in.) aluminum tubing. The width of the lattice section is 40 cm (15.7 in.). The boom is supported by a single truss wire (7 mm OD steel), from a 2 m (6.5 ft) high truss support tube. This antenna (as well as 40-meter Yagis) are commercially available from KAPASYSTEMS Ky, Touko Kapanen, SF 77980 Itsunmaki, Finland.

All elements are split elements, insulated from the boom, which is handy for making adjustments. The driven element is fed via a 2:1 balun. It is clear that this Yagi will not perform in as high winds as the Yagi built by DJ6JC. The OH6RM Yagi has, however, proved to be an excellent performer in the major contest operations by the OH-gang from PJ9-land. That's where the Yagi got its notoriety. I have done a number of stress calculations on the Finnish design using the dimensions received from OH6RM, and I must say that the design is unlikely to withstand one of the typical Belgian wind storms.

3.4.12. Conclusion.

A project such as the construction of a full-size 3-element Yagi for 80 meters is not a simple task. Very few of the full-size 80-meter Yagis built so far have had a long life. Depending on what wind speed you want the "monster" to be able to survive, an 80-meter Yagi weighs between 400 and 2000 kg (900 - 4500 lb). The material cost is substantial, not to talk about the many hundreds of hours of labor that will go into such a project.

The design and the realization by DJ6JC, as described in this chapter, is thought to be novel in a few ways:
• Instantaneous 180-degree switching with no compromising, combined with instantaneous SSB to CW switching with no compromising.
• Optimum F/B ratio over a wide bandwidth by capacitor-controlled compensation.
• Possibility to tune the matching system to a 1:1 SWR at any frequency in the band by remote control if motor-controlled variable capacitors are used in the omega matching system.
• The full-size self-supporting elements are continuously tapering lattice sections made of aluminum material, showing extreme strength and an unbelievably small sag of only 30 cm (1 ft for a total element length of nearly 40 m (130 ft).
• An element-to-boom mounting system that ensures an extremely low element-to-boom capacitance for the split elements (64 pF per side).

Some of the novel aspects can of course be applied to reduced-size 3-element 80-meter Yagis, such as the KLM 80M-3 Yagi. In this design we use relays to change the lengths of the linear-loading stubs to achieve the instant direction reversal.

3.5 Commercial Low-Band Yagi Antennas

If you consider buying a commercially made low-band Yagi, you know that you will buy a good electrical design. All the commercial Yagis nowadays have been computer optimized from an electrical point of view.

Do not compare gain and F/B figures as claimed by the manufacturers. They are meaningless when not specified exactly how measured. And they are not specified, so they are worthless. We see manufacturers claiming 7 dBd gain without specifying whether this is in free space or over (real?) ground. I consider this as very misleading and almost dishonest. This is why the ARRL does not accept any gain figures in its commercial ads, which was a very wise decision. This, at least in the ads of *QST*, puts an end to the meaningless dB battle.

This section lists the main data of commercial low-band antennas. Claimed gain figures are not given, as none of the consulted manufacturers explains in detail how his gain figures are to be interpreted.

The same accounts for front-to-back data. As the manufacturers do not give a definition of how the F/B is specified, all figures are totally meaningless. Therefore, claimed F/B figures are not listed either.

3.5.1. The 80-meter KLM Yagis.

During the last 15 years, multielement rotatable Yagis with shortened elements have made their appearance. KLM Electronics Inc (PO Box 816, Morgan Hill, CA 95037) is marketing a 2, 3 and formerly a 4-element Yagi, using 70%-length elements and employing the linear-loading principle. Erected at least 30 m (100 ft) up (preferably 40 m or 133 ft), these antennas are really excellent performers.

The 4-element version has a 76-foot (23 m) boom and 90-foot (27.5 m) elements. The linear-loading devices are inserted on the elements approximately 15.8 feet (4.8 m) away from the boom. The loading stubs also serve as mechanical support wires to rig the elements. The stub lengths are adjustable to tune the Yagi, and can be varied depending on the element and the design frequency. A great number of outstanding signals on 80 meters come from KLM Yagis. These antennas have proved to be very good electrical designs.

KLM also has a phone/CW switching option which overcomes the relatively narrow bandwidth (100 to 150 kHz) of this antenna by installing relays which effectively change the length of the linear-loading sections when changing from SSB (3.750 MHz) to CW (3.510 MHz). Fig 13-36 shows the 3-element KLM 80-meter Yagi, topped by a 4-element 40-meter KLM Yagi, as installed at K7EG. Fig 13-37 shows the linear-loading wires, which also serve as horizontal support wires for the elements.

Fig 13-38 shows one of the driven elements of the 4-element KLM Yagi. Note the loading lines which serve as element supports. Side bracing is also used to increase the wind surviving speed.

The KLM specifications quote an antenna weight of 270 lb (122 kg). Compare this with the weight of the earlier described 3-element 40-meter beam which weighs more than twice as much.

A possible problem with antennas of such large dimensions is ice loading. One could insert a lightweight electrical cable made of resistance wire into the elements and feed it from a low voltage source at the top of the tower (via the necessary RF chokes).

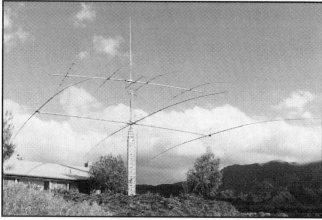

Fig 13-36—Three-element linear-loaded KLM 80-meter Yagi topped by a 4-element linear-loaded 40-meter Yagi at K7EG. The telescoping tower is shown at its full height (top photo), and nests down to a safe height to protect the antennas from high wind during storms (bottom photo).

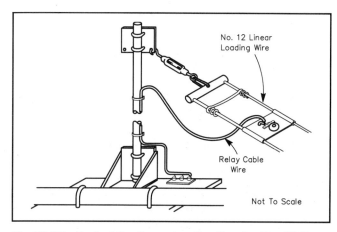

Fig 13-37—End of the linear-loading line for the KLM shortened 80-meter Yagi, showing the relay that makes it possible to shorten the loading line to switch the Yagi from the CW to the SSB part of the band.

Fig 13-38—Close-up view of part of the KLM 80-meter 4-element array. The linear-loading lines that also serve as truss wires for the central part of the elements are clearly visible.

3.5.1.1. *Three-element 80-meter Yagi.*

The latest KLM catalogue no longer lists the 4-element Yagi. The 3-element Yagi mechanical specifications given by the manufacturer are:

Boom length: 60 ft (18.2 m).
Element length 90 ft (27 m).

Bandwidth: 90 kHz (not specified, but assumed as 2:1 SWR bandwidth).[1]
Weight: 120 kg (270 lb).
Wind survival speed: 160 km/h (100 mi/h).
Wind area: 2.8 m² (30 ft²).
Boom diameter: 5 cm (2 inches).

Boom guying: top and side guying with Phyllistran (Kevlar) cable.

The manufacturer's documentation (80M-3, REV 9-9-92) claims that the elements are built to withstand winds in excess of 100 mi/h.

I know it takes approximately 45 kg (100 lb) of 6061-T6 aluminum to make a full-size 40-meter element that will withstand 100 mi/h winds (+30% gusts). I have my doubts that an 80-meter 3-element Yagi, with elements that are 20% longer than for a 40-meter reflector, can be built for a total weight of 120 kg (270 lb), especially as there is no side trussing used on the center part of the elements.

I modeled the elements of the KLM 80M-3 Yagi to assess its wind survival speed. The element mechanical data were taken from the assembly manual of the 80M-3 antenna. The safe wind survival speed turned out to be 90 km/h (56 mi/h), excluding 30% higher gust factor. Fig 13-39 shows the element stress analysis results, which indicate a very unbalanced

design: While sections 2 (2-inch OD) and 3 (1.75-inch OD) are loaded to the limit, the 3 next sections are only loaded to about 60% of their possibilities. The tip section is only loaded 25%. This does not necessarily mean that the element will disintegrate at 90 km/h (56 mi/h), as this assumes that the wind blows at a right angle with respect to the elements. Putting the boom in the wind (perpendicular to the wind direction) will take all the stress off the elements, and provided the side bracing of the boom is well done, it is likely that the Yagi (boom) will survive wind speeds above 90 km/h (56 mi/h). Using the guidelines as explained by Leeson in his book (Ref. 964), the sections 2, 3 and 4 can be reinforced by the double-walling technique to increase the wind survival speed to 77 mi/h. In any case, one should add side guying of the central 3-inch section of the elements. Short boom extensions will be required to do this.

In Fig 13-36 we see the 80-meter KLM Yagi mounted on a telescoping tower at K7EG. Using a motorized telescoping mast and nesting the antenna at minimum height is one way to

```
     7547                      ELEMENT STRESS ANALYSIS                    on4un/on6wu
     SEC#    OD(in)    WT(in)     L(in)   RM(in.lbs)  LMt(lbs.in)  LMv(lbs.in)  CONDIT.
     1       3.000     0.065     191.00    15065.6     17187.7      4400.3       FAIL
     2       2.000     0.058      60.00     5843.7      5754.3      1448.7       SAFE
     3       1.750     0.058      60.00     4418.3      3749.1       940.0       SAFE
     4       1.500     0.058      60.00     3192.2      2253.7       562.0       SAFE
     5       1.250     0.058      60.00     2165.4      1199.8       296.8       SAFE
     6       1.000     0.058      60.00     1337.8       519.3       127.0       SAFE
     7       0.750     0.058      72.00      709.4       143.9        34.7       SAFE
     Velocity=   53.0 Mph                          Wind press.=    6.7 lb/sqft
     Material=  6061-T6        Tens. str. = 35000 psi   Ice thickn.= 0 inch
     Rope     = YES            Ele. weight=  42.5 lbs    El.windload= 121.0 lbs
     Pr. area= 2154 sq.in      Half el.lgt= 563.0 inch   El. sag     = 103.5 inch


     7547                      ELEMENT STRESS ANALYSIS                    on4un/on6wu
     SEC#    OD(in)    WT(in)     L(in)   RM(in.lbs)  LMt(lbs.in)  LMv(lbs.in)  CONDIT.
     1       3.000     0.065     191.00    15065.6     30667.3      5738.9       FAIL
     2       2.000     0.110      60.00    10241.8     10239.8      1846.3       SAFE
     3       1.750     0.110      60.00     7655.9      6580.7      1104.6       SAFE
     4       1.500     0.110      60.00     5447.7      3898.2       600.4       SAFE
     5       1.250     0.058      60.00     2165.4      2057.2       296.8       SAFE
     6       1.000     0.058      60.00     1337.8       891.8       127.0       SAFE
     7       0.750     0.058      72.00      709.4       247.8        34.7       SAFE
     Velocity=   74.0 Mph                          Wind press.=   13.1 lb/sqft
     Material=  6061-T6        Tens. str. = 35000 psi   Ice thickn.= 0 inch
     Rope     = YES            Ele. weight=  52.6 lbs    El.windload= 235.9 lbs
     Pr. area= 2154 sq.in      Half el.lgt= 563.0 inch   El. sag     = 102.8 inch



     If you intend to do a full physical design of a yagi, run each of the yagi
     elements and make a screen dump of the results. You will need the weight data
     as inputs to the BALANCE program.
      1=SPEED   2=GUSTFAC   3=MATER   4=ICE   5=DIM   6=NRUN   7=SECT   H=HELP   X=EXIT
```

Fig 13-39—Wind-survival analysis for the element of a KLM 80-meter Yagi. The unmodified survival wind speed is 54 mi/h (80 km/h) *provided* the inner 3-inch section is side braced. Without side bracing the maximum wind speed is even less. Doubling the wall thickness of sections 2, 3 and 4 increases the maximum wind speed to 74 mi/h (112 km/h), together with side bracing the 3 inch (OD) inner section of the elements. Calculations are done according to EIA/TIA-222-E standard, and exclude any safety factors or modifiers that may be applicable.

protect the antenna from high wind loads that could break the elements in high wind storms.

B. Moeller, OZ8BV, has done a lot of experiments with his 3-element KLM Yagi, and he concludes:

1) After two major disasters it is (unfortunately) proved that the antenna is *not* able to withstand the coastal winds in the mid-south part of Denmark (the elements snapped off right near the boom).

2) The added structural support as shown in Fig 13-40 has proved to be effective for more than two years and many heavy storms. Fig 13-41 shows the fantastic QTH of OZ8BV along the coast in southern Denmark. The base of the 50-meter (166 ft) tower is located just a few meters from the salt water.

3) The exact length of the elements is very critical if optimum F/B ratio is to be achieved. It is also very dependent on the antenna height.

4) A two-year lasting comparison between a ¼-wave vertical over sea water, 90 m (300 ft) offshore with 200 radials in the water, shows that on transmitting the Yagi is always better than or equal to the vertical. The difference is 5 dB on average in favor of the Yagi. On receiving, the signal-to-noise ratio is 20 dB better with the Yagi than with the vertical (that is a *big* difference!).

5) The antenna rotates 360 degrees in 1 minute 15 seconds, and this is felt to be much too slow when you are working VK, PY and Stateside at the same time from Europe.

OZ8BV plans to install an instant direction-switching system as described in par 3.4.

6) B. Moeller, OZ8BV, concludes by saying that if you have the chance or the opportunity to make an 80-meter rotatable Yagi, you should go ahead and do it. He promises you will never forget it!

3.5.1.2. *Two-element 80-meter Yagi.*

The manufacturer claims the same mechanical properties for the 2-element array (100 mi/h wind survival). The same comments apply as for the 3-element Yagi.

Manufacturer specifications:
Boom length: 36 ft (11 m).
Element length: 90 ft (27 m).
Bandwidth: 80 kHz (not specified, but assumed as 2:1 SWR bandwidth).[2]
Weight: 101 kg (225 lb).
Wind survival speed: 160 km/h (100 mi/h).
Wind area: 1.9 m^2 (30 ft^2).
Boom diameter: 5 cm (2 inches).
Boom guying: top guying with Phyllistran (Kevlar) cable.

3.5.1.3. *Rotary 80-meter dipole.*

Manufacturer specifications:
Element length 90 ft (27 m).
Bandwidth: 75 kHz (not specified, but assumed as 2:1 SWR bandwidth).[3]
Weight: 41 kg (90 lb).
Wind survival speed: not specified.
Wind area: 0.9 m^2 (30 ft^2).

3.5.2. The 80-meter Creative Design Yagis.

Creative Design Co, Ltd (4-8 Asanocho Kawasakiku,

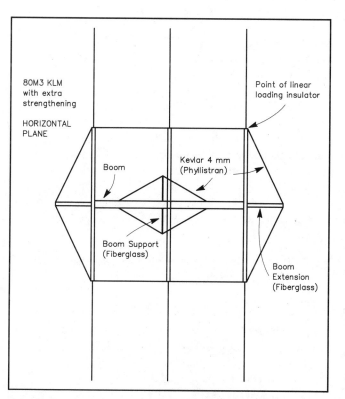

Fig 13-40—After having experienced two major mechanical disasters with his 3-element 80-meter KLM Yagi, OZ8BV added extra guy wires for the elements and rebuilt the element tips using data obtained with the YAGI DESIGN software. Note that the boom extensions, as well as the supports for side-bracing the boom, are made of fiberglass material.

Fig 13-41—This version of the 3-element 80-meter KLM Yagi at OZ8BV has been largely rebuilt to withstand the coastal winds at his seaside QTH in southern Denmark. Fiberglass extensions are visible at the boom tips to provide support for side-guying the elements. The antenna is mounted on top of a 50 m (166 ft) high self-supporting (nontelescoping) tower.

Kawasaki City, Japan) is producing a 2-element reduced-size Yagi for 3.8 MHz (model AFA75-2). Both elements are driven and the spacing is ⅛ wavelength (9 m or 39 ft). Taking into account the velocity factor of the phasing line, the array elements appear to be fed 135 degrees out of phase (like a ZL Special). The elements are 24 meters (88 ft) long (or approximately 62% of full size), and the loading is done with high-Q coils and a small capacitance hat about ⅔ out on the elements. The elements are also loaded at the center with hairpin loading coils, which allows precise matching to the phasing line and the coaxial feed line. The array is fed with 50-ohm coax via a 1:1 balun. Power rating is 4 kW (8 kW PEP), and the total weight is 80 kg (176 lb). The 2:1 SWR bandwidth is slightly over 100 kHz. The specified wind area is 2 m^2 (21.5 ft^2).

3.5.3. 40-meter Cushcraft Yagi.

Probably the most popular reduced-size 40-meter Yagi is the Cushcraft 40-2CD.
Manufacturer specifications:
Boom length: 6.8 m (22.3 ft).
Element length: 13.1 m (43 ft).
2:1 SWR bandwidth: 200 kHz.
Weight: 20 kg (45 lb).
Wind survival speed: 128 km/h (80 mi/h).

Leeson calculated the wind survival speed as 68 mi/h (108 km/h). (Ref. 967). The article also describes how to increase the wind survival speed to 100 mi/h (151 km/h) or 118 mi/h (177 km/h) by using internal boom and element reinforcements.

3.5.4. KLM 40-meter Yagis.

3.5.4.1. *Four-element Yagi.*

Manufacturer specifications:
Boom length: 42 ft (12.8 m).
Element length: 46 ft (14 m).
2:1 SWR bandwidth: Not specified.
Weight: 38 kg (85 lb).
Wind survival speed: Not specified.
Wind area: 1.11 m^2 (12 ft^2).
Boom diameter: Not specified.[4]

3.5.4.2. *Three-element Yagi.*

Manufacturer specifications:
Boom length: 32 ft (9.75 m).
Element length: 46 ft (14 m).
2:1 SWR bandwidth: Not specified.
Weight: 32 kg (70 lb).
Wind survival speed: Not specified.
Wind area: 0.92 m^2 (10 ft^2).
Boom diameter: Not specified.[5]

3.5.4.3. *Two-element Yagi.*

Manufacturer specifications:
Boom length: 16 ft (4.88 m).
Element length: 46 ft (14 m).
2:1 SWR bandwidth: not specified.
Weight: 20 kg (45 lb).
Wind survival speed: Not specified.

Wind area: 0.56 m^2 (6 ft^2).
Boom diameter: Not specified.

3.5.4.4. *Rotatable dipole.*

Manufacturer specifications:
Element length: 46 ft (14 m).
2:1 SWR bandwidth: Not specified.
Weight: 7 kg (15 lb).
Wind survival speed: Not specified.
Wind area: 0.2 m^2 (2 ft^2).

3.5.5. The Hy-Gain 402-BA Yagi.

Manufacturer specifications:
Boom length: 16.1 ft (4.9 m).
Element length: 47.2 ft (14.4 m).
    2:1 SWR bandwidth: 100 kHz.
    Weight: 20 kg (44 lb).
    Wind survival speed: 80 mi/h (128 km/h).
    Wind area: 0.56 m^2 (6 ft^2).
    Hardware: Mostly stainless steel.
    Boom diameter: 5 cm (2 in.).

3.5.6. The Hy-Gain Discoverer 7-2 two-element 40-meter Yagi.

Manufacturer specifications:
Boom length: 22.6 ft (6.9 m).
Element length: 44.8 ft (13.6 m).
2:1 SWR bandwidth: 187 kHz at 18 m (60 ft).
Wind survival speed: 80 mi/h (128 km/h).
Wind area: 0.56 m^2 (6 ft^2).
Weight: 25.3 kg (56.2 lb).
Hardware: Stainless steel.
Boom diameter: 5 cm (2 in.).
Boom supported by two truss wires.

This Yagi makes use of linear loading. The elements are broken up by insulators approximately 3.3 m (11 ft) out from the boom. The linear-loading stub is folded back on itself and mounted along the element toward the boom. Compared to the linear-loading method employed with the "older" 402-BA antenna, this approach has the advantage of producing less loss and a slightly higher radiation resistance. It is similar to the loading technique used by the KLM loaded Yagis for 80 and 40 meters.

3.5.7. The Hy-Gain Discoverer 7-3 three-element 40-meter Yagi.

Manufacturer specifications:
Boom length: 35.2 ft (10.7 m).
Longest element length: 45.6 ft (13.9 m).
2:1 SWR bandwidth: 160 kHz at 18 m (60 ft).
20 dB F/B bandwidth: 40 kHz.
Wind survival speed: 80 mi/h (129 km/h).
Wind area: 0.84 m^2 (9 ft^2).
Weight: 44 kg (98 lb).
Hardware: Stainless steel.
Boom diameter: 5 cm (2 in.).
Boom supported by four truss wires.

The mechanical design is identical to that of the

2-element version described above.

3.6. Wire Yagis

Yagis require a lot of space and electrical height in order to perform well. Excellent results have been obtained with fixed-wire Yagis strung between high apartment buildings. There are few circumstances, however, where supports at the right height and in a favorable direction are available. When using wire elements, it is easy to determine the correct length of the elements using MININEC or any of the MININEC derived programs.

If a folded dipole is used for the driven element, the impedance will probably be between 75 and 100 ohms. In the first case a 75-ohm feed line can be used; in the second case, a 75-ohm quarter-wave transformer will transform the 100 ohms to 50 ohms.

3.7. Vertical Yagis

Fig 13-42 shows a 3-element vertical array built around a quarter-wave vertical. Four cross arms, which support four sloping wires, are mounted at the top of the tower (the quarter-wave vertical). All four sloping wires are dimensioned to act as a director. When used as a reflector, the parasitic element is loaded with a coil at the bottom. The two sloping elements off the side are left floating. This array has a very respectable gain of 4.5 dB over the single vertical over good ground and 60 quarter-wave radials. At the major wave angle the F/B ratio is an impressive 30 dB, as can be seen from the patterns in Fig 13-42.

You can "dip" the sloping wires. Make sure the driven element as well as the other three sloping wires are left floating when dipping a parasitic element. The resonant frequency should be 4.055 MHz. (f_{design} = 3.8 MHz). You can, of course also dip the wires with the loading coil in place in order to find the resonant frequency of the reflector. Again, all other elements must be fully decoupled when dipping the element. The resonant frequency for the reflector element is 3.745 MHz (f_{design} = 3.8 MHz).

Fig 13-43 shows a 160-meter (f_{design} = 1.832 MHz) version of the array. The exact length of the central (driven) element is not critical, but it should be near ¼ wavelength. From the top of the tower, four nylon ropes are sloping away in 90-degree increments. These ropes are used to support four parasitic top-loaded elements that are installed ⅛ wave (20 m or 66 ft) from the central tower.

The example I analyzed uses 23 m (75 ft) long vertical parasitic elements, which are top loaded with a 19.72 m (64.7 ft) long sloping top wire, which is part of the support cable. As the length of the top-loading wire is the same on both sides of the loaded vertical member, there is no horizontally polarized radiation from the top-loading structure.

The four parasitic elements are dimensioned to be resonant at 1.935 MHz. The same procedure as explained above for the 80-meter array can be used to "tune" the parasitic elements. When used as a reflector, the elements are tuned to be resonant at 1.778 MHz. This can be done by installing an inductance of 3.65 µH (reactance = 42 ohms at 1.832 MHz) between the bottom end of the parasitic element and ground. The radiation

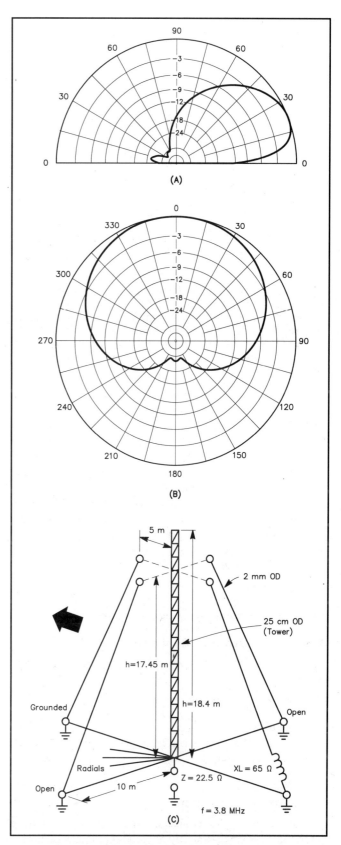

Fig 13-42—Three-element vertical parasitic array, consisting of a central support tower with two support cross-arms mounted at 90 degrees near the top. Two of the sloping wires are left floating, a third one is grounded as a director, and the fourth one is loaded with a coil to act as a reflector. The azimuth pattern at B is taken for a wave angle of 22 degrees.

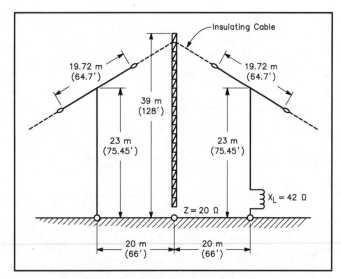

Fig 13-43—This 160-m 3-element parasitic array produces 4.8 dB gain over a single vertical, and better than 25 dB F/B ratio over 30 kHz of the band. With such an array there is no need for Beverage receiving antennas! The drawing shows only two of the four parasitic elements. The two other elements are left floating.

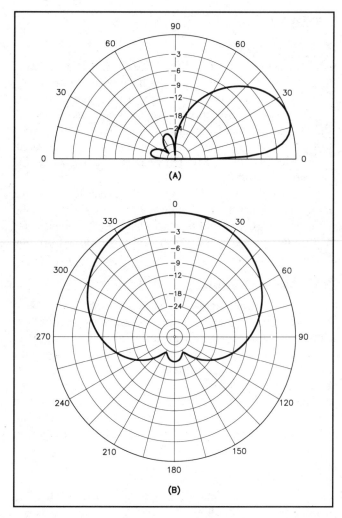

Fig 13-44—Horizontal and vertical radiation patterns of a 3-element vertical parasitic array for 160 meters. The azimuth pattern at B is taken for a wave angle of 20 degrees. Note the perfect radiation pattern and the excellent F/B of the array.

resistance of this array is 20 ohms, and it has a gain of 4.8 dB over the single full-size vertical. Fig 13-44 shows the radiation patterns of this array. The bandwidth behavior is excellent. The array shows a constant gain over more than 50 kHz and better than 25 dB F/B over more than 30 kHz. When tuned for a 1:1 SWR at 1.832 MHz, the SWR will be less than 1.2:1 from 1.820 to 1.850 kHz. This really is a winner antenna, and it requires only one full-size quarter-wave element, plus a lot of real estate to run the sloping support wires and the necessary radials.

The same principle with the sloping support wires and the top-loaded parasitic elements could, of course, be used with the 80-meter version of the 3-element vertical parasitic array.

3.8. Yagi Matching Systems

I will describe three of the most popular matching systems:
• Gamma match.
• Omega match.
• Hairpin match.

The YAGI DESIGN software contains modules which make it possible to design these matching systems with no guesswork.

3.8.1. The gamma match.

In the past, gamma-match systems have often been described in an over-simplifying way. A number of home-builders must have gone half-crazy trying to match one of W2PV's 3-element Yagis with a gamma match. The reason for that is the low radiation resistance, and the fact that the driven-element lengths, as published, are "too long" (positive reactance). The driven element of the 3-element 20-meter W2PV Yagi (which has a high Q factor of 58) has a radiation

resistance of only 13 ohms, and a positive reactance of +18 ohms at the design frequency, with the published radiator dimensions of 0.489661 wavelength (Ref. 957). Yagis with such low radiation resistance, together with a positive reactance (element too long!) cannot be matched with a gamma (or omega) match, unless the driven element is first shortened to introduce the required negative reactance in the feed impedance!

Yagis with a relatively high radiation resistance (25 ohms) or with some amount of negative reactance (slightly short elements), typically –10 ohms, will easily be matched with a whole range of gamma-match element combinations.

Fig 13-45 shows the electrical equivalent of the gamma match. Z_g is the element impedance to be matched. The gamma match will have to match half of the element impedance ($Z_h = Z_g/2$) to the feed-line impedance (50 ohms).

The step-up ratio of a gamma match depends on the dimensions of the physical elements (element diameter, rod diameter and spacing) making up the matching section.

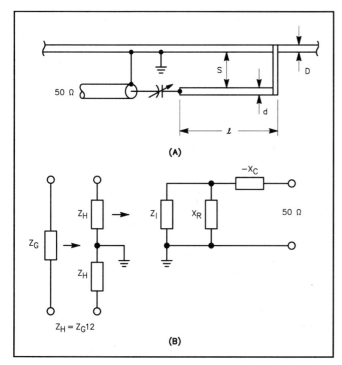

Fig 13-45—Layout and electrical equivalent of the gamma match.

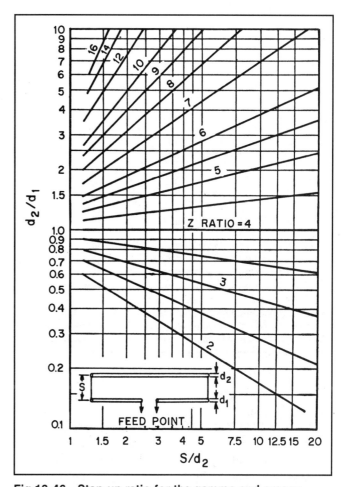

Fig 13-46—Step-up ratio for the gamma and omega match as a function of element diameter (d2), rod diameter (d1) and spacing (S). *(After ARRL Antenna Book)*

Fig 13-46 shows the step-up ratio as a function of the driven-element diameter, the gamma rod diameter and spacing between the two.

The procedure to calculate the elements of a gamma match is as follows:

1) Calculate the step-up ratio (Fig 13-46).

2) Multiply Z_h (half of the radiation resistance) with the step-up ratio (Z_i).

3) Calculate the (inductive) reactance (X_r) of the (shorted) transmission-line length made up by the gamma rod and the driven element. The gamma shorting bar is the shorted end of the transmission line, while the open end of the transmission line is in parallel with half of the feed-point impedance of the Yagi.

4) Calculate the parallel impedance (Z_p) made up by paralleling Z_i and X_r. If the gamma rod has the correct length, then the resistive part of the impedance Z_p will equal 50 ohms. If not, lengthen or shorten the gamma rod until 50 ohms is reached.

5) A capacitor giving a negative reactance of $-X_C$ will have to be connected in series with the gamma rod to tune out the inductive part of the impedance Z_p. This capacitor is the so-called gamma capacitor.

The calculation involves a fair bit of complex mathematics, but software tools have been made available from different sources to solve the gamma match problem. The YAGI DESIGN software addresses the problem in one of its modules (MATCHING SYSTEMS).

In order to illustrate the matching problems evoked above, I have listed the gamma-match element variables in Table 13-6 for a Yagi with R_{rad} = 25 ohms, and in Table 13-7 for a Yagi with R_{rad} = 15 ohms.

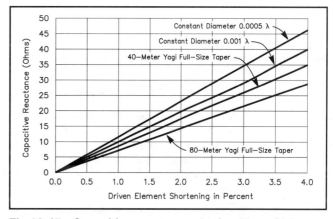

Fig 13-47—Capacitive reactance obtained by various percentages of driven-element shortening. The 40-meter full-size taper is the taper described in Table 13-1; the 80-meter taper is shown in Fig 13-29.

From Table 13-6 it is clear that a Yagi with a radiation resistance of 25 ohms can easily be matched with a wide range of gamma-match parameters, while the exact length of the driven element is not at all critical. It is clear that "short" elements (negative reactance) require a shorter gamma rod and a slightly smaller value of gamma capacitor.

13-6

Table 13-6

Gamma-Match Element Data for a Yagi with a Radiation Resistance of 25 Ohms

Rod d	S	Step up Rat.	−20 ohms L	C	−15 ohms L	C	−10 ohms L	C	−5 ohms L	C	0 ohms L	C	+5 ohms L	C
0.50	5.0	5.28	118	350	123	502	138	614	171	734	231	396	317	734
	4.0	5.42	131	342	135	488	151	592	184	700	255	376	331	700
	3.0	5.65	152	332	155	468	172	562	207	656	267	349	351	654
	2.5	5.83	169	324	172	452	189	540	224	634	285	332	369	624
0.38	5.0	5.87	119	322	121	450	133	536	158	618	203	328	269	618
	4.0	6.08	132	314	133	434	145	514	171	588	216	311	281	584
	3.0	6.43	153	302	154	412	165	482	192	548	238	288	302	558
	2.5	6.71	170	292	169	396	188	462	208	520	255	273	319	520
0.25	5.0	6.75	120	290	119	394	128	458	147	516	181	270	230	516
	4.0	7.07	133	282	131	374	140	430	158	482	192	251	239	482
	3.0	7.62	154	268	151	356	160	408	179	452	213	236	262	452
	2.5	8.06	172	258	167	340	175	398	195	428	230	223	278	428

Design parameters: D = 1.0; Z_{ant} = 25 ohms; Z_{cable} = 50 ohms. The element diameter is normalized as 1. Values are shown for a design frequency of 7.1 MHz. L is the length of the gamma rod in cm, C is the value of the series capacitor in pF. The length of the gamma rod can be converted to inches by dividing the values shown by 2.54.

Table 13-7 tells the story of a high-Q Yagi with a radiation resistance of 15 ohms (similar to the 3-element W2PV or W6SAI Yagis). If such a Yagi is in addition using a "long" driven element (eg, +18 ohms reactance), a match cannot be achieved, not even with a step-up ratio of 15:1. With this type of gamma (step-up = 15), the highest positive reactance that can be accommodated with a radiation resistance of 13 ohms is approximately +12 ohms. In other words, it is simply impossible to match the 13 + j18 ohm impedance of the W2PV 3-element 20-meter Yagi with a gamma match without first reducing the length of the driven element.

The first thing to do when matching a Yagi with a relatively low radiation resistance is to decrease the element length as to introduce, eg, −j15 ohms of capacitive reactance in the driven element impedance. How much shortening is needed (in terms of element length) can be derived from Fig 13-47. From Table 13-7 we learn that an impedance of 15 − j15 ohms can be easily matched with step-up ratios ranging from 5 to 8.

Several Yagis have been built and matched with gamma

13-7

Table 13-7

Gamma Match Element Data for a Yagi with a Radiation Resistance of 15 Ohms

Rod d	S	Step up Rat.	−20 ohms L	C	−15 ohms L	C	−10 ohms L	C	−5 ohms L	C	0 ohms L	C	+5 ohms L	C
0.50	5.0	5.28	93	410	92	586	116	1180	—	—	—	—	—	—
	4.0	5.42	103	400	102	566	121	1074	—	—	—	—	—	—
	3.0	5.65	120	386	117	538	136	948	—	—	—	—	—	—
	2.5	5.83	134	376	131	518	123	874	—	—	—	—	—	—
0.28	5.0	5.87	94	372	91	514	130	860	—	—	—	—	—	—
	4.0	6.08	104	362	101	494	113	996	206	3906	—	—	—	—
	3.0	6.43	121	346	117	466	128	716	208	1680	—	—	—	—
	2.5	6.71	136	334	130	446	140	666	210	1306	—	—	—	—
0.25	5.0	6.75	96	334	91	442	99	660	147	1268			—	—
	4.0	7.07	106	322	101	424	107	614	152	1060	376	1268	—	—
	3.0	7.62	123	304	117	396	122	556	161	864	309	1188	—	—
	2.5	8.06	138	292	131	376	135	518	172	766	295	982	—	—

Design parameters: D = 1.0; Z_{ant} = 15 ohms; Z_{cable} = 50 ohms. The element diameter is normalized as 1. The frequency is 7.1 MHz. C is expressed in pF, L in cm (divide by 2.54 to obtain inches). Note there is a whole range where no match can be obtained. If sufficient negative reactance is provided in the driven element impedance (with element shortening), there will be no problem in matching Yagis even with a low radiation resistance.

```
7547                    YAGI IMPEDANCE MATCHING                    on4un/on6wu

 ------------------------ Gamma match Design ----------------------------
| DESIGN FREQUENCY :    7.10 MHz                                         |
| FEEDLINE IMPEDANCE :  50 ohm.                                          |
| ANTENNA POWER :  1500 WATT.                                            |
| Z-ANT RESISTIVE PART :  28.00 ohm.     -->> STEP UP RATIO =  6.60 <<-- |
| Z-ANT REACTIVE PART :   0.00 ohm.                                      |
| ELEMENT DIAMETER :  6                                                  |
| GAMMA ROD DIAMETER :  2                                                |
| SPACING (CENTER TO CENTER) :  20                                       |
 ------------------------------------------------------------------------

 ------------------------------ Results ---------------------------------
| GAMMA ROD LENGTH : 216.8 cm  OR  85.4 inch.                            |
| SERIES CAPACITOR :  487 pF.                                            |
| VOLTAGE ACROSS SERIES CAPACITOR :  252 Volts.                          |
| CURRENT THROUGH SERIES CAPACITOR :  5.5 Amp.                           |
 ------------------------------------------------------------------------

1=SAVE  2=FREQ  3=Z-CABLE  4=DIMENS  5=MATCH SYS  6=Z-ANT  7=PWR H=HELP X=EXIT
```

```
7547                    YAGI IMPEDANCE MATCHING                    on4un/on6wu

 ------------------------ Gamma match Design ----------------------------
| DESIGN FREQUENCY :    7.10 MHz                                         |
| FEEDLINE IMPEDANCE :  50 ohm.                                          |
| ANTENNA POWER :  1500 WATT.                                            |
| Z-ANT RESISTIVE PART :  28.00 ohm.     -->> STEP UP RATIO =  6.60 <<-- |
| Z-ANT REACTIVE PART : -20.00 ohm.                                      |
| ELEMENT DIAMETER :  6                                                  |
| GAMMA ROD DIAMETER :  2                                                |
| SPACING (CENTER TO CENTER) :  20                                       |
 ------------------------------------------------------------------------

 ------------------------------ Results ---------------------------------
| GAMMA ROD LENGTH : 149.9 cm  OR  59.0 inch.                            |
| SERIES CAPACITOR :  335 pF.                                            |
| VOLTAGE ACROSS SERIES CAPACITOR :  367 Volts.                          |
| CURRENT THROUGH SERIES CAPACITOR :  5.5 Amp.                           |
 ------------------------------------------------------------------------

1=SAVE  2=FREQ  3=Z-CABLE  4=DIMENS  5=MATCH SYS  6=Z-ANT  7=PWR H=HELP X=EXIT
```

Fig 13-48—Screen dump of the design of a gamma match with the YAGI DESIGN software. In the first example I did not shorten the driven element (zero ohms reactance). In the second alternative I introduced –20 ohms, which resulted in a much shorter gamma rod and a series capacitor of smaller value.

systems, calculated as explained above. When the reactance of the driven element at the design frequency was exactly known, the computed rod length as calculated with the above procedure was always right on. In some cases the series capacitor value turned out to be smaller than calculated. This is caused by the stray inductance of the wire connecting the end of the gamma rod with the plastic box containing the gamma capacitor, and the wire between the series capacitor and the coaxial feed line (receptacle). The inductance of such a wire is not at all negligible, especially on the higher frequencies. With a pure coaxial construction, this should not occur. A coaxial gamma rod is made of two concentric tubes, whereby the inner tube is covered by a proper dielectric material (eg, polyethylene tube). The length of the inner tube, as well as the material dielectric and thickness, determine the capacitance of this coaxial capacitor. Make sure to properly seal both ends of the coaxial gamma rod to prevent moisture penetration.

Feeding a symmetric element with an asymmetric feed system has a slight impact on the radiation pattern of the Yagi. The forward pattern is skewed slightly toward the side where the gamma match is attached, but only a few degrees, which is of no practical concern. The more elements the Yagi has, the less the effect is noticeable.

The voltage across the series capacitor is quite small even with high power, but the current rating must be sufficient to carry the current in the feed line without warming up.

For a power of 1500 W, the current through the series capacitor is 5.5 A (in a 50-ohm system) The voltage, depending on the value of the capacitor, will vary between 200 and 400 V in most cases. This means that moderate-spacing air-variable capacitors can be used, although it is advisable to over-rate the capacitors as slight corrosion of the capacitor plates normally caused by the humidity in the enclosure will de-rate the voltage handling of the capacitor.

3.8.1.1. *Designing the gamma match with the Yagi Design software.*

Fig 13-48 shows a screen print of the MATCHING SYSTEMS module. From the prompt line, any of the input data can easily be changed. This is immediately reflected in a different gamma-rod length and gamma capacitor value.

In the first iteration the Yagi feed-point impedance was purely resistive (no reactance). Introducing 20 ohms of negative reactance (shortening the driven element about 2%) results in a shorter gamma rod and a smaller gamma capacitor (second solution).

3.8.2. The omega match.

The omega match is a sophisticated gamma match that uses two capacitors. Tuning of the matching system can be done by adjusting the two capacitors, without having to adjust the rod length.

Fig 13-49 shows the omega match and its electrical equivalent. Comparing it with the gamma electrical equivalent (Fig 13-45) reveals that the extra parallel capacitor, together with the series capacitor, now is part of an L network that follows the original gamma match.

The steps in calculating an omega match are:
1) Calculate the step-up ratio (use Fig 13-46).

Fig 13-50—Motor-driven omega matching unit. The two capacitors with the dc motors and gear box are mounted in line on a piece of insulating substrate material. This can then be slid inside the housing, which is made of stock lengths of PVC water drainage pipe. The PVC pipe is available in a range of diameters, and the pipe can be easily cut to the desired length. The round shape of the housing also has an advantage as far as wind loading is concerned.

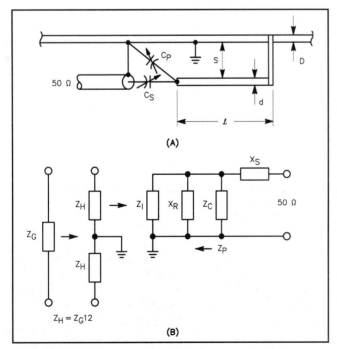

Fig 13-49—Layout and electrical equivalent of the omega match.

2) Multiply Z_h (half of the radiation resistance) with the step-up ratio (Z_i).

3) Decide which omega rod length you will use. Do not use too short a rod, because very high currents will circulate in the low-impedance elements associated with a very short omega rod. As a rule of thumb, use a rod which is ⅔ to ¾ the length of the equivalent gamma rod.

4) Calculate the (inductive) reactance (X_r) of the (shorted) transmission line length made up by the omega rod and the driven element. The omega shorting bar is the shorted end of the transmission line, while the impedance at the open end of the transmission line is in parallel with half of the feed-point impedance of the Yagi.

5) Calculate the parallel impedance (Z_p) made up by paralleling Z_i and X_r. If the omega rod is not too long, then the resistive part of the impedance (Z_p) will be less than 50 ohms.

6) Calculate the impedance resulting from connecting the omega capacitor (Z_C) in parallel with Z_p. Change the value of this capacitor (tune the omega capacitor) until the resistive part of Z_p becomes 50 ohms. For 14.2 MHz and a rod of ⅔ to ¾ the full-size gamma rod length, the value of this capacitor will usually be between 50 and 150 pF.

7) Calculate the value of the (omega) series capacitor required to tune out the inductive reactance of the impedance Z_p (Z_p being 50 + X_s).

Again, the mathematics involved are complex, but the MATCHING section of the YAGI DESIGN software will do the job in a second.

From a practical point of view the omega match is really unbeatable. The ultimate setup consists of a box containing the two capacitors, together with dc motors and gear-reductions. Fig 13-50 shows the interior of such a unit using surplus capacitors and dc motors from a flea market. This system makes the adjustment very easy from the ground, and is the only practical solution when the driven element is located away from the center of the antenna.

The remarks given for the gamma capacitors as to the required current and voltage rating are valid for the omega match as well. The voltage across the omega capacitor is of the same magnitude as the voltage across the gamma capacitor, usually varying between 300 and 400 V, with a current of 2 to 4 A for a power of 1500 W.

3.8.2.1. *Designing the omega match with the YAGI DESIGN software.*

Fig 13-51 shows the screen print from the MATCHING module for an omega-match design. With the omega match you must also enter the rod length. The program will calculate the values of both the parallel (omega) and the series (gamma) capacitors.

3.8.2.2. *Tuning the omega/gamma matching systems.*

The GAMMA/OMEGA TUNING module of the YAGI DESIGN software is a very interesting software modeling tool. It allows you to change all the parameters of the matching system, while observing the effects of varying these parameters on up to 7 different frequencies. Fig 13-52 shows the design of an omega match for one of the designs from the YAGI DESIGN database (no. 10). Note that in the model I have included the parasitic reactance of the wire connecting the rod with the capacitors in the box (in this example the wire was 164 mm (6.5 inches) long. I have adjusted the omega for a 1:1 SWR not in the center of the passband,

```
7547                    YAGI IMPEDANCE MATCHING              on4un/on6wu

 ───────────────────── Omega match Design ─────────────────────
 DESIGN FREQUENCY :    7.10 MHz
 FEEDLINE IMPEDANCE :   50 ohm.
 ANTENNA POWER :  1500 WATT.
 Z-ANT RESISTIVE PART : 28.00 ohm.          ┌──────────────────────────────┐
 Z-ANT REACTIVE PART : -20.00 ohm.          │ -->> STEP UP RATIO =  6.60 <<-- │
 ELEMENT DIAMETER :  6                       └──────────────────────────────┘
 OMEGA ROD DIAMETER :  2
 SPACING (CENTER TO CENTER) :   20


 ───────────────────────── Results ─────────────────────────
 OMEGA ROD LENGTH : 120.0 cm  OR  47.2 inch.
 SERIES CAPACITOR :  335 pF.
 VOLTAGE ACROSS SERIES CAPACITOR :  367 Volts.
 CURRENT THROUGH SERIES CAPACITOR :  5.5 Amp.
 PARALLEL CAPACITOR :  96 pF
 VOLTAGE ACROSS PARALLEL CAPACITOR :  458 Volts.
 CURRENT THROUGH PARALLEL CAPACITOR :  1.95 Amp.

 1=SAVE   2=FREQ   3=Z-CABLE   4=DIMENS   5=MATCH SYS   6=Z-ANT   7=PWR  H=HELP  X=EXIT
```

Fig 13-51—Screen dump for the omega matching design for a 40-meter Yagi with a 28-ohm feed-point impedance. Compare the results with those obtained for the gamma match (Fig 13-48).

```
7547                GAMMA / OMEGA OPTIMIZER PROGRAM              on4un/on6wu
┌──────────────────────────────────────────────────────────────────────────┐
│    ┌──────────────────────────────┐    ┌──────────────────────────────┐   │
│    │ DIAMETER DRIVEN ELEMENT =  6 │    GAMMA WIRE LENGTH = 164.5 mm        │
│      DIAMETER GAMMA ROD    =  2                        6.48 inch           │
│      SPACING CENTER TO CENTER = 20   GAMMA CAPACITOR =   442.6 pF (C1)      │
│                                      OMEGA CAPACITOR = 134.3 pF (C2)        │
│      DESIGN FREQUENCY =  7.05 MHz    ROD LENGTH = 150.0 cm                  │
│                                                 59.1 inches                │
│      TUNING RATE = 1 %               FEEDLINE-Z = 50  ohm                   │
│                   ─── Press F/C to change tuning rate ───                  │
│    ┌─────────────────────────┐  ┌─────────┐  ┌──────────────────────────┐  │
│        ANTENNA IMPEDANCE                        MATCHED IMPEDANCE           │
│      FREQ      Real / Imag       SWR           Real   /   Imag             │
│      6.944    28.8 / -12.6       1.67          83.2   /    4.5             │
│      6.979    29.1 /  -9.0       1.49          74.4   /    2.7             │
│      7.015    28.8 /  -5.3       1.33          66.2   /    1.1             │
│      7.050    28.0 /  -1.4       1.16          58.2   /    0.1             │
│      7.085    26.8 /   2.8       1.00          50.1   /    0.0             │
│      7.121    25.2 /   7.5       1.20          41.8   /    1.0             │
│      7.156    23.4 /  12.5       1.48          34.1   /    3.3             │
│    └─────────────────────────┘  └─────────┘  └──────────────────────────┘  │
│    1=DECR.C1 2=INCR.C1  3=DECR.C2  4=INCR.C2  5=DECR.ROD  6=INCR.ROD  Z=CABLE-Z │
│    7=DECR.WIRE  8=INCR.WIRE  C=COURSE  F=FINE T=TUBE DIMS  S=SAVE  X=EXIT  H=HELP │
└──────────────────────────────────────────────────────────────────────────┘
```

Fig 13-52—Screen print of the omega match as optimized using the **OPTIMIZE GAMMA/OMEGA** module of the **YAGI DESIGN** software. Note the prompt line at the bottom of the screen from where *all* parameters can easily be changed. This is really tweaking the matching system on the computer. "Playing" with the module is most instructive to understand the behavior of gamma and omega matching systems.

but 0.5% above the center frequency.

3.8.3. The hairpin match.

The (center) feed impedance of the driven element of a Yagi (in the neighborhood of 0.5 wavelength. long) consists of a resistive part (the radiation resistance) in series with a reactance. The reactance is positive if the element is "long" and negative if the element is "short." "Long" means longer than the resonant length. A dipole is resonant when the (center fed) feed-point impedance shows zero reactance. In practice, resonance never occurs at a physical length of exactly 0.5 wavelength, but always at a shorter length (see further). With a hairpin matching system we deliberately make the element "short," meaning that the feed-point impedance will be capacitive. Fig 13-53 shows the electrical equivalent of the hairpin matching system.

If we connect an inductor (coil) across the terminals of a "short" driven element, we can now consider the capacitor (the element that is responsible for the capacitance part in the short element feed-point impedance) and the parallel inductor to be the two arms of an L network. This L network can be dimensioned to give a 50-ohm output impedance. In other words, a perfect match can be obtained by shortening the driven element to produce the required capacitive reactance so that, through the parallel combination of the reactive feed-point impedance (negative reactance) and the positive reactance of the inductor, a 50-ohm impedance is obtained. The parallel inductor is normally replaced with a short length of short-circuited open-wire feed line, having the shape of a *hairpin*, and hence the matching system's name.

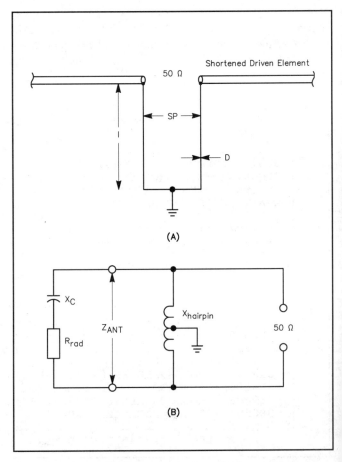

Fig 13-53—Layout and electrical equivalent of the hairpin match.

The resistive part of the impedance of the driven element (radiation resistance) changes only slightly as a function of length if the element length is varied plus or minus 5% around the resonant length. The change in the reactance, however, is quite significant. The rate of change will be greatest with elements having the smallest diameter (see Fig 13-47).

The required hairpin reactance is given by

$$X_{hairpin} = 50 \times \sqrt{\frac{R_{rad}}{50 - R_{rad}}} \qquad \text{(Eq 13-3)}$$

The formula for calculating the size of the shunt reactance depends on the shape of the inductor. There are two common types:
- The hairpin inductor.
- The beta-match inductor.

The hairpin inductor is a short piece of open-wire transmission line. The boom is basically outside the field of the transmission line. This means that the boom is not near the transmission line. In practice the separation between the line and the boom should be at least equal to twice the spacing between the conductors of the transmission line.

The characteristic impedance of such a transmission line is given by

$$Z_C = 276 \times \log \frac{2 \times SP}{D} \qquad \text{(Eq 13-4)}$$

where
   SP = spacing between wires
   D = diameter of the wires

In the so-called beta match, the transmission line is made of two parallel conductors with the boom in between. This is the system used by Hy-Gain.

The characteristic impedance of such a transmission line is given by

$$Z_C = 553 \times \log \frac{2 \times S}{\sqrt{D \times DB}} \qquad \text{(Eq 13-5)}$$

where
   S = spacing of wire to boom center
   D = diameter of wire
   DB = diameter of boom

Z_C is the characteristic impedance of the open wire line made by the two parallel conductors of the hairpin or beta match. The length of the hairpin or beta match is given by

$$\ell^\circ = \arctan \frac{X_{hairpin}}{Z_C} \qquad \text{(Eq 13-6)}$$

where
   ℓ° is expressed in degrees
   arctan is the inverse tangent

To convert to real dimensions (assuming a velocity factor of 0.98 for a transmission line with air dielectric)

$$\ell_{inch} = \ell^\circ \times \frac{32.1}{f} \qquad \text{(Eq 13-7a)}$$

or

$$\ell_{cm} = \ell^\circ \times \frac{81.6}{f} \qquad \text{(Eq 13-7b)}$$

13-8

Table 13-8

Required Capacitive Reactance in Driven Element Impedance and in Hairpin Inductance

R_{rad} ohms	Antenna Reactance (ohms)	Inductance Hairpin (ohms)	Length hairpin (cm) (SS = 10D)	
			3.65 MHz	7.1 MHz
10.0	−20.0	25.0	89	46
12.5	−21.6	28.9	103	53
15.0	−22.9	32.7	117	60
17.5	−23.8	36.7	130	67
20.0	−24.5	40.8	144	74
22.5	−24.9	45.2	160	82
25.0	−25.0	50.0	177	91
27.5	−24.9	55.3	194	100
30.0	−24.5	61.2	216	111

Note: The feed-point impedance is 50 ohms. To obtain the hairpin length in inches, divide values shown by 2.54.

where f = design frequency, MHz

The required driven element reactance is given by

$$X_C = -\frac{R_{rad} \times 50}{X_{hairpin}} \qquad \text{(Eq 13-8)}$$

Table 13-8 shows the required values of capacitive reactance in the driven element as well as the required reactance for a range of radiation resistances. (For a hairpin with S = 10D as in the table, Z = 359 ohms.) The question now is how long the driven element must be to represent the required amount of negative reactance ($-X_C$). Fig 13-47 lists the reactance values obtained with several degrees of element shortening. Although the exact reactance differs for each one of the listed element diameter configurations, one can derive the following formula from the data in Fig 13-47.

$$X_C = -Sh \times A \qquad \text{(Eq 13-9)}$$

where
   Sh = shortening in % versus the resonant length.
   X_C = reactance of the element in ohms
   A = 8.75 (40-meter full-size Yagi) or 7.35 (80-meter full-size Yagi)

This formula is valid for shortening factors of up to 5%.

3.8.3.1. *Design guidelines for a hairpin system.*

Most HF Yagis have a radiation resistance between 20 and 30 ohms. For these Yagis the following rule of thumb applies:
- The required element reactance to obtain a 50-ohm match with a hairpin is approximately −25 ohms (Table 13-8).
- This almost constant reactance value can be translated to an element shortening of approximately 2.8% as compared to the resonant element length for a 40-meter Yagi, and 3.5% for an 80-meter Yagi.
- The value of reactance of the hairpin inductor is equal to 2 times the radiation resistance.

Table 13-9

Hairpin Line Impedance as a Function of Spacing-to-Diameter Ratio

S/D Ratio	Impedance, Ohms
5	193
7.5	325
10	359
15	408
20	442
25	469
30	491
35	510
40	525
45	539
50	552

Table 13-10

Values of Transformed Impedance and SWR for a Range of Driven-Element Impedances

Driven Element Impedance	Hairpin Inductance	Resulting Impedance	SWR, (vs 50 ohms)
20 – j20	40.8 ohms	40 – j0.81	1.25
20 – j24.5	40.8	50 +	1
20 – j25	40.8	51.2 + j0.26	1.02
20 – j30	40.8	64.5 + j5.92	1.32

The length of the hairpin is given by

$$l = \frac{9286 \times R_{rad}}{f \times Z} \qquad \text{(Eq 13-10)}$$

where

   f = design frequency
   Z = impedance of hairpin line (Eq 13-4).
   l = length in cm

To convert to inches, divide the result by 2.54. The impedance of the hairpin line for a range of spacing to wire diameter ratios is shown in Table 13-9.

The real area of concern in designing a hairpin matching system is to have the correct element length that will produce the required amount of capacitive reactance. As we have an open (split) element, we can theoretically measure the impedance, but this is impractical for two reasons:

• The impedance measurement must be done at final installation height.

• The average ham does not have access to measuring equipment that can measure the impedance with the required degree of accuracy. The run-of-the-mill noise bridge will not suffice, and a professional impedance bridge or network analyzer is required.

Let us examine the impact of a driven element that does not have the required degree of capacitive reactance. Table 13-10 shows the values of the transformed impedance and the

Table 13-11

Capacitive Reactance Obtained by various Percentages of Driven-Element Shortening

Shorten Element	Diameter in wavelengths 0.0010527	0.0004736	Light Taper	Heavy Taper
0%	0 ohms	0 ohms	0 ohms	0 ohms
0.5	–4.8	–5.5	–4.6	–4.8
1.0	–9.6	–11.1	–9.1	–9.7
1.5	–14.3	–16.5	–13.6	–14.3
2.0	–19.1	–22.2	–18.2	–19.2
2.5	–23.8	–27.5	–22.7	–23.7
3.0	–28.6	–32.8	–27.2	–28.6
3.5	–33.5	–38.2	–31.7	–33.5
4.0	–38.5	–43.5	–36.2	–38.3

resulting (minimum) SWR if the reactance of the driven element was off +5 ohms and –5 ohms versus the theoretically required value, for an R_{rad} of 20 ohms. An error in reactance of 5 ohms either way is equivalent to an error length of 0.5% (see Table 13-11). In other words, an inaccuracy of 0.5% in element length will deteriorate the minimum SWR value from 1:1 to 1.25 or 1.3:1.

The mounting hardware for a split element will always introduce a certain amount of shunt capacitance at the driven element feed-point. This must be taken into account when designing a hairpin- or beta-match system (see example in par 3.8.3.3).

3.8.3.2. Element loading and a hairpin.

Getting the correct element length that will yield a perfect 50-ohm match in principle requires a very accurate element length. Adjusting the element length while the antenna is in the air is usually not practical.

The length of the driven element that produces zero reactance (at the design frequency) is called the resonant length. This length also depends on the element diameter (in terms of wavelength). If any taper is employed for the construction of the element, the degree of taper will have its influence as well. Finally, the resonant length will differ with every Yagi design. This is caused by the effect of mutual coupling between the elements of the Yagi. For elements with a constant diameter of approximately 0.001 wavelength, the resonant-frequency length will usually be between 0.477 and 0.487 wavelength. The exact value for a given design can be obtained by modeling the Yagi or by obtaining it from a reliable database.

If the exact resonant length is not known, then it is better to make the element somewhat too short (too much negative reactance), whereby the element can be electrically lengthened by loading it in the center with a short piece of transmission line. Adjusting the amount of loading (as a function of how much the element was too short) can usually be done more easily than adjusting the element length (element tips).

The loading is done by using a short length of open-wire line. The short length of line can have the same impedance and configuration (wire diameter and spacing) as used for the

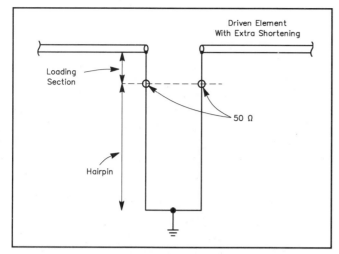

Fig 13-54—Layout of hairpin match combined with element loading, whereby the 50-ohm point is to be found on the hairpin at some distance from the element.

hairpin (usually between 300 and 450 ohms). The layout and the electrical equivalent of this approach is shown in Fig 13-54. The transmission line acts as a loading device between the element feed point and the 50-ohm tap, and as the matching inductor beyond the 50-ohm tap (the hairpin). Another method of changing the electrical length of the driven element is described in par 3.8.3.5., where a parallel capacitor is used to *shorten* the electrical length of the driven element.

Let us examine the impedance of the antenna feed point along a short high-impedance (200 to 450 ohm) transmission line:

- The value of the resistive part will remain almost constant (change negligible).
- The value of the capacitive reactance will decrease by X ohms per degree, where X is given by

$$\frac{X}{degrees} = Z \times 0.017 \qquad \text{(Eq 13-11)}$$

The change in reactance per unit of length is:

$$\frac{X}{cm} = \frac{Z \times f \times 0.204}{1000} \qquad \text{(Eq 13-12a)}$$

$$\frac{X}{inch} = \frac{Z \times f \times 0.5185}{1000} \qquad \text{(Eq 13-12b)}$$

where

    f = frequency, MHz

    Z = characteristic impedance of the line made by the two parallel wires of the hairpin or beta match (see Eq 13-4 and Table 13-9)

Eqs 9 and 10 are valid for line lengths of 4 degrees maximum.

The line length required to achieve a given reactance shift X is given by:

$$L_{cm} = \frac{X \times 4900}{Z \times f} \qquad \text{(Eq 13-13a)}$$

$$L_{inches} = \frac{X \times 1929}{Z \times f} \qquad \text{(Eq 13-13b)}$$

These formulas are valid for values of X of 25 ohms maximum.

Example: Let us assume that we start from a $20 - j30$ ohm impedance, and we need to electrically lengthen the driven element to yield an impedance of $20 - j24.5$ ohms (see Table 13-8). The design frequency is 7.1 MHz.

The required reactance difference is X = 30 − 24.5 = 5.5 ohms. The required 359-ohm line length is

$$L = \frac{5.5 \times 1929}{359 \times 7.1} = 4.16 \text{ inches or } 10.6 \text{ cm}$$

The length of the hairpin section can be determined from Table 13-8 as 111 cm (43.7 inches). This means that we can electrically adjust (load) the element to the required length by adding an extra piece of (hairpin) line. The length of this line will be only a few inches long. In this case the 50-ohm tap will not be at the element but at a short distance on the hairpin line. The length of the hairpin matching inductor will remain the same, but the total transmission-line length will be slightly longer than the matching hairpin itself.

To adjust the entire system, look for the 50-ohm point on the line (move the balun attachment point) while at the same time adjusting the total length of the hairpin. The end of the hairpin (shorting bar) is usually grounded to the boom.

Design Rule of Thumb: The transmission-line loading device can be seen as part of the driven element folded back in the shape of the transmission line. For a 359-ohm transmission line (spacing = 10 × diameter), the length of the loading line will be exactly as long as the length that the element has been shortened. In other words, for every inch of total element length you shorten the driven element, you must add an equivalent inch in loading line. This rule is applicable only for 359-ohm lines and for a maximum length of 406/f cm (160/f inches), where f = design frequency. For other line impedances the calculation as shown above should be followed.

Example:

A driven element is resonant at 7.1 MHz with a length of 2200 cm (866 in.). We want to shorten the total element length by 25 cm (10 in.), and restore resonance by inserting a 359-ohm loading line in the center. The length of the loading line will be approximately 25 cm (10 in.).

3.8.3.3. *Hairpin match design with parasitic element-to-boom capacitance.*

As explained in par 3.4.3., it is virtually impossible to construct a split element without any capacitive coupling to the boom. With tubular elements a "coaxial" construction is often employed, which results in an important parasitic capacitance.

The Hy-Gain Yagis, which use a form of "coaxial" insulating technique to provide a split element for their Yagis, exhibit the following parallel capacitances.

205BA: 27 pF

105BA and 155BA: 10 pF

Let's work out an example for a Yagi designed at 7.1 MHz. We model the driven element to be resonant (zero reactance) at the design frequency (7.1 MHz). Assume the resonant length is 1985 cm (781.5 in.).

The capacitance introduced by the split-element mounting hardware is 300 pF per side (I have measured this with a digital capacitance meter). Do not forget to measure the capacitance without the full element attached (see par 4.3.3.)! The reactance of this capacitor is

$$X_C = \frac{10^6}{2\pi \times 7.1 \times 300} = 75 \text{ ohms}$$

The capacitance across the feed point is 150 pF (2 times 300 in series):

$$X_C = 150 \text{ ohms}$$

Using the SHUNT NETWORK module of the NEW LOW BAND software, we calculate the resulting impedance of this capacitor in parallel with 28 ohms impedance at resonance as

$$Z = 27.1 - j5 \text{ ohms}.$$

The required inductance of the hairpin (using Eq 13-3) will be

$$X_{\text{hairpin}} = 50 \times \sqrt{\frac{R_{\text{rad}}}{50 - R_{\text{rad}}}} = \sqrt{\frac{27.1}{50 - 27.1}} = 54.30 \text{ ohms}$$

Assume we are using a hairpin with two conductors with spacing = $10 \times$ diameter. The impedance of the line is given by Eq 4 as

$$Z_C = 276 \times \log \frac{2 \times SP}{D} = 276 \times \log(20) = 359 \text{ ohms}$$

The length of the hairpin is given by Eq 6 as

$$\ell^\circ = \arctan \frac{X_{\text{hairpin}}}{Z_C} = \arctan \frac{54.3}{359} = 8.6 \text{ degrees}$$

The length in cm is given by Eq 13-7b as

$$\ell_{\text{cm}} = \ell^\circ \times \frac{81.6}{f} = 8.6 \times \frac{81.6}{7.1} = 98.5 \text{ cm (38.8 in.)}$$

For an impedance of 27.1 ohms we need an impedance reactance (using formula [7]) of

$$X_C = -\frac{R_{\text{rad}} \times 50}{X_{\text{hairpin}}} = -\frac{27.1 \times 50}{54.3} = -24.95 \text{ ohms}$$

This means we have to add another 19.95 ohms of negative reactance to our driven element. This can be done by shortening the element approximately 2.2% (see Fig 13-47), which amounts to

$$1985 \times \frac{2.2}{100} = 44 \text{ cm (17 inches) or}$$

22 cm (8.5 inches) on each side.

Instead of shortening the element 20 cm on each side, we can shorten it 40 cm on each side, which will now give us some range to fine-tune the matching system. The 20 cm (8 inches)

we have shortened the driven element on each side will be replaced with an extra length of 20 cm (8 inches) transmission line at the feed point. The 50-ohm point will now be located some 20 cm (8 inches) from the split driven element. The hairpin will extend another 98.5 cm (38.8 inches) beyond this point. Tuning the matching system consists of changing the position of the 50-ohm point on the hairpin as well as changing the length of the hairpin.

If you use "wires" to connect the split driven element to the matching system, you must take the inductance of this short transmission line into account as well.

3.8.3.4. Designing the hairpin match with the YAGI DESIGN software.

Fig 13-55 shows the screen print from the MATCHING SYSTEMS module with the data of the example used in par 3.3.4.3. Note exactly the same results in the bottom part of the screen as those calculated above. From the prompt line you can change any of the input data, which will be immediately reflected in the dimensions of the matching system.

The value of the "parasitic" parallel capacitance (see par 3.8.3.3.) can be specified, and is accounted for during the calculation of the matching system.

3.8.3.5. Using a parallel capacitor to fine-tune a hairpin matching system.

A parallel capacitance (of reasonable value) across the split element only slightly lowers the resistive part of the impedance, while it introduces an appreciable amount of negative reactance.

Example:

A capacitor of 150 pF in parallel with an impedance of $28 + j0$ ohms (at 7.1 MHz) lowers this impedance to $27.1 - j5$ ohms (see example in par 3.8.3.3.). This means that instead of fine tuning the matching system by accurately shortening the driven element in order to obtain the required negative reactance (see Table 13-8), you can use a variable capacitor across the driven element in order to electrically shorten the element. This is a very elegant way of tuning the hairpin matching system "on the nose." The only drawback is that it requires another (vulnerable) component. This method is an alternative fine-tuning method to the configuration where the length of the driven element is altered by using a short length of transmission line as described in par 3.8.3.2.

3.8.4. Selecting a Yagi matching system.

Hairpin or beta matching systems are generally used by manufacturers of commercial Yagis because they are simple and cost effective to reproduce in volume. For the home-builder, things are not quite the same.

Hairpin and Beta Match

Advantages:
• No capacitor required, no box, one less (vulnerable) component.
• Fully symmetric feed system.
• The split element makes it possible to measure the feed-point impedance before matching.

```
┌──────────────── Hairpin match Design ────────────────┐
│ DESIGN FREQUENCY :    7.10 MHz    PARALLEL CAPACITANCE:  150  pF      │
│ FEEDLINE IMPEDANCE :  50 ohm.                                        │
│ Z-ANT RESISTIVE PART :  27.5 ohm.   This Impedance now includes the effect │
│ Z-ANT REACTIVE PART :  -4.0 ohm.    of the parasitic parallel capacitance  │
│ INITIAL DR. ELEMENT HALF LENGTH :  1023.5 cm  OR  402.9 Inches.      │
│ HAIRPIN SPACING :   10                                               │
│ HAIRPIN WIRE DIAMETER :   1                                          │
└──────────────────────────────────────────────────────┘



┌──────────────────── Results ────────────────────┐
│ THE DR. EL. HALF LENGTH MUST BE SHORTENED  21.7 cm   OR    8.5 Inches. │
│ LENGTH OF HAIRPIN : 100.1 cm  OR  39.4 Inches.                        │
│ THE INDUCTANCE OF THE HAIRPIN IS 1.24 µH                              │
└──────────────────────────────────────────────────┘


  1=SAVE   2=FREQ   3=Z-CABLE   4=DIMENS   5=SYST   6=SWR   7=PAR CAP   H=HELP    X=EXIT
```

Fig 13-55—Screen dump of the hairpin matching system as designed with the YAGI DESIGN software.

Disadvantages:
• Length adjustment of driven element required.
• Difficult to adjust at full height unless the modified hairpin system (with the extra loading line) is used.
• No way to adjust if driven element is at a distance from the mast.
• A balun is required.

Gamma and Omega Match

Advantages:
• No length adjustment of driven element required.
• Motor driven capacitors (omega) make remote tuning extremely flexible.
• No split element required (all plumber's delight).
• No risk for insulator breakdown.
• Mechanically much stronger.

Disadvantages:
• Requires box and one or two capacitors.
• Causes very slight asymmetric pattern.

   I use omega matching systems on all my Yagi antennas.

■ 4. QUADS

4.1. Modeling Quad Antennas

   Modeling quad antennas with MININEC or MININEC-based programs requires very special attention. To obtain proper results the number of wire segments should be carefully chosen. Near the corners of the loop, the segments must be short enough not to introduce a significant error in the results. Segments as short as 20 cm (8 inches) must be used on an 80-meter quad to obtain reliable impedance results on multielement loop antennas.

Taper Technique

   If you would break up the entire loop conductor into 20-cm segment lengths, this would mean a very high number of segments, and hence a very long computing time or more pulses than can be handled by the software. To avoid this problem, a conductor can be broken up into a number of (in-line) wires of varying lengths. In our example, the wire closest to the junction is the shortest one (30 cm or 12 inches), and has 1 segment. The next wire has twice that length and also has 1 segment, the third wire again has double the length of the previous wire, etc, until we come to a point where we don't want to make the wires any longer because of accuracy limitations. This last wire can be a "long" one, broken up into different segments of equal length.

   This may all sound difficult, but ELNEC has a special taper function that does all of this automatically. The only thing one must define is the minimum segment length (eg, 20 cm) and the maximum segment length (eg, 200 cm), and whether you want the taper scheme to be applied to both ends of the conductor or to one end only. The program will then divide the conductor into different wires. The tip wires will all have one segment, while the center (or remaining) length will be a long wire divided into different segments. This is illustrated in Fig 13-56. Results of various tapering arrangements are shown in Table 13-12. Using the tapering technique, reliable impedance results can be obtained for quad antennas.

4.2. Two-Element Full-Size 80-Meter Quad with a Parasitic Reflector

   Fig 13-57 shows the configuration of a 2-element 80-meter quad on a 12-m (40 ft) boom, and Fig 13-58 shows the radiation patterns. The optimum antenna height is 35 m

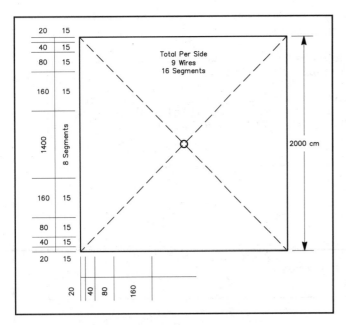

Fig 13-56—Tapering of segment lengths for MININEC analysis. See Table 13-12 for the results with different tapering arrangements. With the segment length taper procedure shown here, the result with a total of just 56 tapered segments is as good as for 240 segments of identical length.

Fig 13-57—Configuration of a 2-element cubical quad antenna designed for 80-meter SSB. Radiation patterns are shown in Fig 13-58. By using a remote tuning system for adjusting the loading of the reflector, the quad can be made to exhibit an F/B of better than 22 dB over the entire operating range. See text for details.

(107 ft) for the center of the quad. Whether you use the square or the diamond shape does not make any difference. The dimensions remain the same, as well as the results. I will describe a diamond-shaped quad, which has the advantage of making it possible to route the feed line and the loading wires along the fiberglass arms.

I designed this quad with two quad loops of identical length. The total circumference for the quad loop is 1.0033 wavelength (for a 2 mm OD conductor or no. 12 wire). The parasitic element is loaded with a coil (or stub) having an

13-12

Table 13-12

Influence of the Number of Sections on the Impedance of a Quad Loop

Taper Arrangement	Calculated Impedance
Nontapered, 4 × 5 segments	$123 - j20$ ohms
Nontapered, 4 × 10 segments	$130 + j44$
Nontapered, 4 × 20 segments	$133 + j78$
Nontapered, 4 × 40 segments	$135 + j95$
Nontapered, 4 × 50 segments	$135 + j97$
Nontapered, 4 × 60 segments	$135 + j98$
32 sections, tapering from 1.0 to 5.0 m	$131 + j85$
56 sections, tapering from 0.4 to 2 m	$134 + j102$
64 sections, tapering from 0.2 to 2 m†	$135 + j104$
104 sections, tapering from 0.2 to 1 m	$135 + j104$

Note: See Fig 13-56 regarding the taper procedure.
†Taper arrangement illustrated in Fig 13-56.

inductive reactance of $+j150$ ohms. The gain is 3.7 dB over a single loop at the same height over the same ground.

In the model I used 3.775 kHz as a central design frequency. This is because the SWR curve rises more sharply on the low side of the design frequency than it does on the high side.

We can optimize the quad by changing the reactance of the loading stub as we change the operating frequency. Figs 13-59 and 13-60 show the gain, F/B and SWR for the 2-element quad with a fixed loading stub (150 ohms) as well as for a design where the loading stub reactance is varied.

To make the antenna instantly reversible in direction, we can run two quarter-wave 75-ohm lines, one to each element. Using the COAX TRANSFORMER/SMITH CHART module from the NEW LOW BAND SOFTWARE we see that a $+j160$-ohm impedance at the end of a quarter-wave-long 75-ohm transmission line (at 3.775 MHz) looks like a $-j35$ ohm impedance. This means that a quarter-wave 75-ohm (RG-11) line terminated in a capacitor having a reactance of -35 ohms is all that we need to tune the parasitic element into a reflector. A switch box mounted at the center of the boom houses the necessary relay switching harness and the required variable capacitor to do the job.

The required optimal loading impedances can be obtained as follows:

3.750 MHz: $X_L = 180$ ohms, C = 1322 pF
3.775 MHz: $X_L = 160$ ohms, C = 1205 pF
3.800 MHz: $X_L = 150$ ohms, C = 1148 pF
3.825 MHz: $X_L = 120$ ohms, C = 931 pF
3.850 MHz: $X_L = 100$ ohms, C = 785 pF

If we tune the reflector for optimum value we will obtain

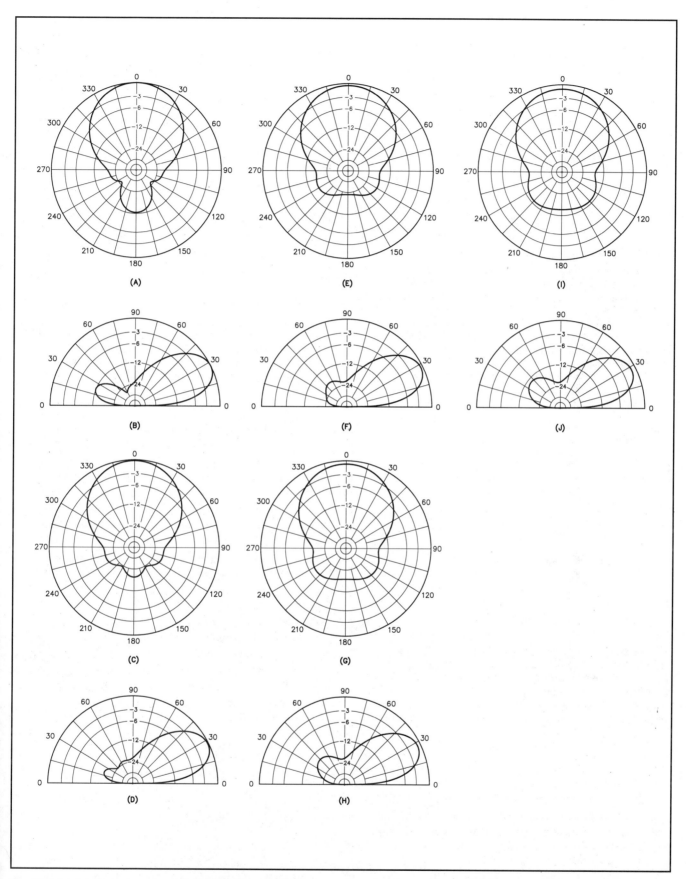

Fig 13-58—Radiation patterns of the 80-meter SSB 2-element cubical quad at various frequencies. The antenna was optimized in the 3.775- to 3.8-MHz range. In that range an F/B of better than 20 dB is obtained. All patterns are plotted to the same scale. Azimuth patterns are taken at an elevation angle of 28 degrees.

A and B—3.75 MHz.   E and F—3.8 MHz.   I and J—3.85 MHz.
C and D—3.775 MHz.   G and H—3.825 MHz.

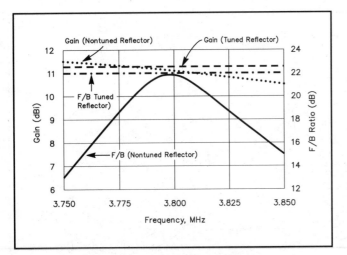

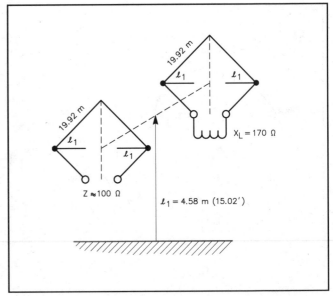

Fig 13-59— Gain and F/B ratio for the 2-element 80-meter quad with fixed reflector tuning, and with adjustable reflector tuning. The antenna is modeled at a height of 35 m over good ground. With fixed tuning the F/B is 20 dB or better over 30 kHz, and the gain drops almost 0.5 dB from the low end to the high end of the operating passband (100 kHz). When the reflector loading is made variable, the gain as well as the F/B remain constant over the entire operating band.

Fig 13-61—Configuration of the 2-element 80-meter cubical quad of Fig 13-57 when loaded to operate in the CW portion of the band. Radiation patterns are shown in Fig 13-62. See text and Fig 13-64 for information on relay switching between SSB and CW.

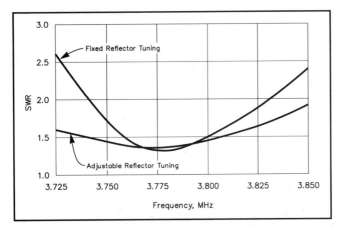

Fig 13-60—SWR curves for the 2-element 80-meter quad. The SWR is plotted versus a nominal input impedance of 100 ohms, which is then matched to a 50-ohm impedance by a quarter-wave 75-ohm line. Note that the variable reflector tuning extends the operating bandwidth considerably toward the lower frequencies.

wires in and out of the circuit. The calculated length for the loading wires to switch the quad from the SSB end of the band (3.775 MHz) to the CW end (3.525 MHz) is 4.58 m (15.03 ft). Note that you are switching at a high-voltage point, which means that a high-voltage relay is essential.

As you will have to run a feed line to the relay on the tip of the spreader, it is likely that the loading wire will capacitively couple to the feed wire. Use small chokes or ferrite beads on the feed wire to decouple it from the loading wires.

Fig 13-61 shows the configuration and Fig 13-62 shows the radiation patterns for the 2-element quad as tuned for the low-end of the band. The patterns are for a fixed reflector-loading reactance of 170 ohms.

As described above, we can optimize the performance by tuning the loading system as we change frequency. Using the same quarter-wave 75-ohm line (cut to be a quarter-wave at 3.775 MHz), we can obtain a constant 22 dB F/B (measured at the main wave angle of 29 degrees) on all frequencies from 3.5 to 3.6 MHz with the following capacitor values at the end of the 75-ohm line:

3.500 MHz: X_L = 180 ohms, C = 1083 pF
3.525 MHz: X_L = 160 ohms, C = 999 pF
3.550 MHz: X_L = 140 ohms, C = 897 pF
3.575 MHz: X_L = 120 ohms, C = 795 pF
3.600 MHz: X_L = 100 ohms, C = 660 pF

The optimized quad has a gain at the low end of 80 meters which is 0.3 dB less than at the high end of the band. When optimized the gain remains constant at 10.8 dBi as modeled at 35 m (117 ft) over good ground.

Fig 13-63 shows the SWR curve of the quad at the CW end of the band, with both a fixed reflector loading (X_L = 170 ohms) and a variable setup as explained above. The switching

better than 22 dB F/B ratio at all frequencies from 3.75 to 3.85 MHz, and the SWR curve will be much flatter than without the tuned reflector (see Figs 13-59 and 13-60).

The quad can also be made switchable from the SSB to the CW end of 80 meters. There are two methods of loading the elements, inductive loading and capacitive loading (see also the chapter on Large Loops). The capacitive method, which I will describe here, is the most simple to realize.

Capacitive Loading

A small single-pole high-voltage (vacuum) relay at the tip of the horizontal fiberglass arms can switch the loading

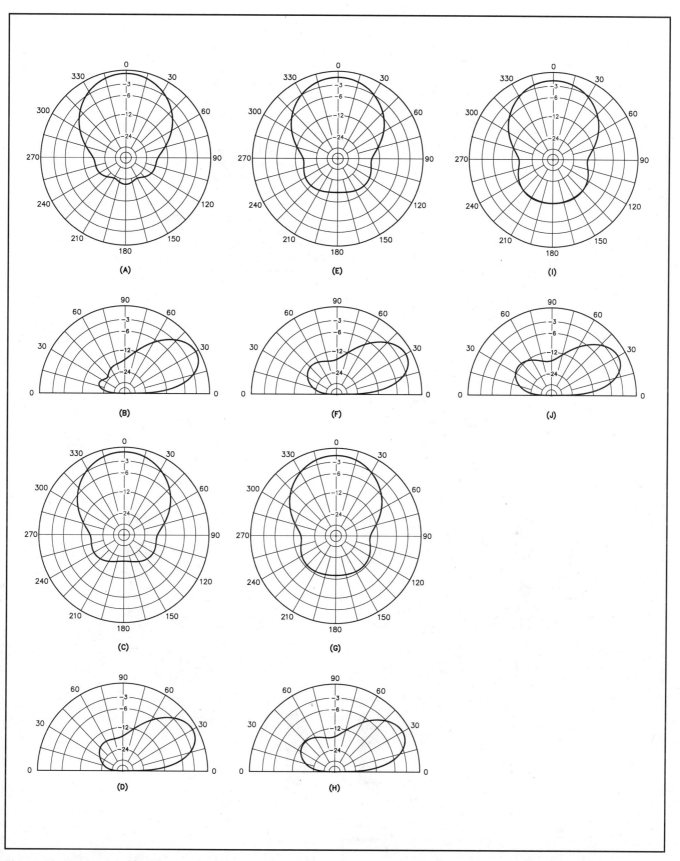

Fig 13-62—Radiation patterns of the 2-element 80-meter quad when capacitively loaded to operate in the CW portion of the band. Azimuth patterns are taken at an elevation angle of 29 degrees. All patterns are plotted to the same scale as the SSB patterns in Fig 13-58. The gain is a fraction of a dB less than at the high-end of the band, but the directional properties are identical. The loading was optimized to yield the best F/B ratio between 3.5 and 3.525 MHz.

A and B—3.5 MHz.   E and F—3.55 MHz.   I and J—3.6 MHz.
C and D—3.525 MHz.   G and H—3.575 MHz.

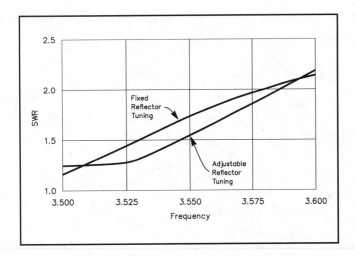

Fig 13-63— (left) SWR curves for the 2-element 80-meter quad as referred to a nominal 100-ohm feed-point impedance. The tuned reflector does not significantly improve the SWR on the high-frequency side of the design frequency. The design was adjusted for the best SWR in the 3.5- to 3.525-MHz region.

Fig 13-64—(below) Feeding and switching method for the 2-element 80-meter quad array. The four high-voltage vacuum relays connect the loading wires to the high-voltage points of the quad, to load the elements to resonance in the CW band. Relay K2 switches directions. The motor-driven variable capacitor (50-1000 pF) is used to tune the reflector for maximum F/B at any part in the CW or phone band. See text for details.

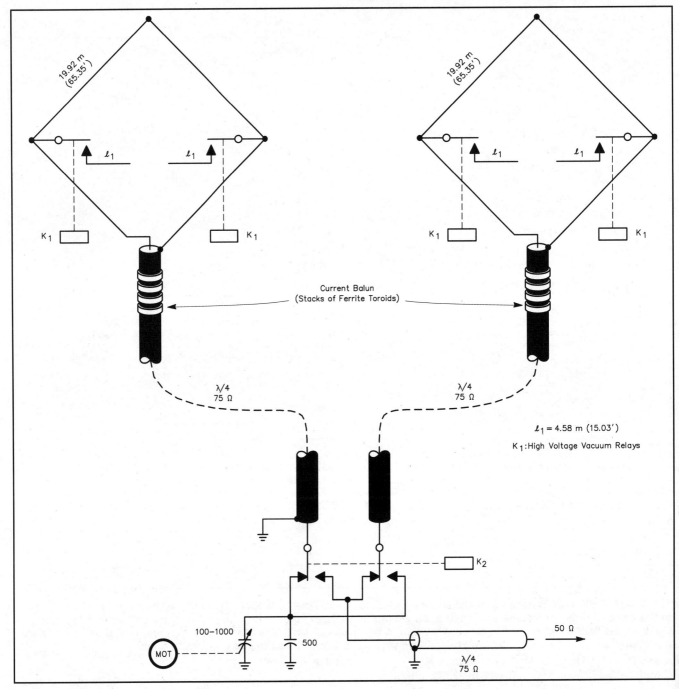

harness for the 2-element quad is shown in Fig 13-64. The tuning capacitor at the end of the 75-ohm line going to the reflector can be made of a 500-pF fixed capacitor in parallel with a 100- to 1000-pF variable capacitor. Note that you need a current balun at both 75-ohm feed lines reaching the loops (a stack of ferrite beads).

It is also possible to design a 2-element quad array with both elements fed. With the dimensions used in the above design, a phase delay of 135 degrees (identical feed current magnitude) yields a gain that is very similar to what is obtained with the parasitic reflector. The F/B may be a little better than with the parasitic array. As the array is not fed in quadrature, the feed arrangement is certainly not simpler than for the parasitic array. The parasitic array is simpler to tune, as the reflector stub (the capacitor value) can be simply adjusted for best F/B.

4.3. Two-element Reduced-Size Quad

D. Courtier-Dutton, G3FPQ, built a reasonably sized 2-element rotatable quad that performs extremely well. The quad side dimensions are 15 m (50 feet), and the elements are loaded as shown in Fig 13-65. The single loop showed a radiation resistance of 50 ohms. Adding a reflector 12 m (40 ft) away from the driven element (0.14 wavelength), dropped the radiation resistance to approximately 30 ohms. The loading wires are spaced 110 cm (3.5 ft) from the vertical loop wires, and are almost as long as the vertical loop wires. The loading wires are trimmed to adjust the resonant frequency of the element. G3FPQ reports a 90-kHz bandwidth from the 2-element quad with the apex at 135 feet. The middle 7 m (24 ft) of the spreaders are made of aluminum tubing, and 3.6 m (12 ft) long tips are made of fiberglass. A front-to-back ratio of up to 30 dB has been reported.

G3FPQ indicates that the length of the reflector element is exactly the same as the length of the driven element, for obtaining the best F/B ratio. This may seem odd, and is certainly not the case for a full-size quad.

4.4. Three-element 80-meter Quad

Fig 13-66 shows the 3-element full-size 80-meter quad at DJ4PT. The boom is 26 m (86 ft) long, and the boom height is 30 m (100 ft). Interlaced on the same boom are 5 elements for a 40-meter quad.

The greatest challenge in building a quad antenna of such proportions is one of mechanical nature. The mechanical design was done by H. Lumpe, DJ6JC, who is a well-known professional tower manufacturer in Germany. The center parts of the quad spreaders are made of aluminum lattice sections that are insulated from the boom and broken up at given intervals as well. The tubular sections are made of fiberglass. The driven element is mounted less than 1 m (3 ft) from the center. This makes it possible to reach the feed point from the tower. In order to be able to reach the lower tips of the two parasitic elements for tuning, a 26 m (87 ft) tower was installed exactly 13 m (43 ft) from the tower. On top of this "small" tower a special platform was installed from where one can easily tune the parasitic elements.

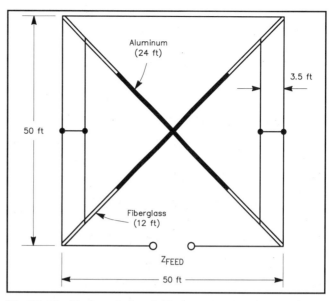

Fig 13-65—Reduced-size 2-element quad designed by D. Courtier-Dutton, G3FPQ. The elements are capacitively loaded as explained in detail in the chapter on large loop antennas.

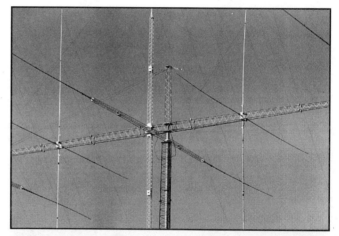

Fig 13-66—This impressive 3-element full-size 80-meter quad, with an interlaced 5-element 40-meter quad on a 26-m (87 ft) long boom sits on top of a self-supporting 30-m (100 ft) tower at DJ4PT. The antenna was built by DJ6JC.

The weight of the quad is approximately 2000 kg (4400 lb). The monster quad is mounted on top of a 30 m (100 ft) self-supporting steel tower, also built by DJ6JC. The rotator is placed at the bottom of the tower, and a 20 cm (8 in.) OD rotating pipe with a 10 mm (0.4 in.) wall takes care of the rotating job.

4.5. Quad or Yagi?

I must admit I have very little first-hand experience with quad antennas. But I can think of a few disadvantages of quad antennas as compared to Yagi antennas:
• They are more critical to model correctly.
• They are three-dimensional; you can't assemble the quad on the ground, and then pick it up with a crane and put it on the tower. You must do a lot of assembly work with the boom way up in the air.
• I always hear of wires that keep breaking.
• It is a non-efficient material user: all the metalwork you put up is not part of the antenna; it is just a support structure.
• As far as electrical performance is concerned, well-tuned quad antennas should (marginally) outperform a Yagi on the same boom length, at least as far as gain is concerned. The difference, being in order of a fraction of a dB to maximum 1 dB, is more of an academic than of a practical nature.

In order to prevent ice build-up on the quad wire, one can feed a current (ac or dc) through the loops. The voltage should be adjusted so as to raise the temperature in the wire just enough to prevent ice loading.

The fact is that the great majority of rotatable arrays on the (low) bands are Yagis. This seems to indicate that the mechanical issues are probably harder to solve with quads than with Yagis.

Notes

[1] KLM makes available a phone/CW switching option that changes the length of the linear loading stubs (see Fig 13-37).
[2] See Note 1.
[3] See Note 1.
[4] KLM makes available a "heavy-duty" boom at extra cost. The catalog does not specify the performance of the "regular-duty" boom nor of the "heavy-duty" boom.
[5] See Note 4.

LITERATURE 14 REVIEW

This literature review lists some 760 reference works, catalogued by subject. The reference numbers are those used in the different chapters of the book. Copies may be obtained directly from the magazines listed at the following addresses:

CQ/Ham Radio: 76 N Broadway, Hicksville NY 11082.
CQ-DL: DARC, Postfach 1155, D3507 Baunatal 1, Germany.
QST: ARRL HQ, 225 Main St, Newington, CT 06111.
Radio Communication: RSGB HQ, Lambda House, Cranborne Rd, Potters Bar, Herts EN6 3JE, England.
For other magazines, contact the author directly
(J. Devoldere, ON4UN, 215 Poelstraat, B9820 Merelbeke, Belgium).
A database program is also available which is designed to handle the literature review. The software is covered in detail in Chapter 4 on software.

■ 1. PROPAGATION

Ref. 100: K. J. Hortenbach et al, "Propagation of Short Waves Over Long Distances: Predictions and Observations," *Telecommunications Journal*, Jun 1979, p 320.

Ref. 101: R. Schetgen - KU7G - ed., *The ARRL Handbook for the Radio Amateur*, ARRL, Newington, CT.

Ref. 102: John Devoldere - ON4UN, "80-Meter DXing," *Communications Technology*, 1978.

Ref. 103: George Jacobs - W3ASK - et al, *The Shortwave Propagation Handbook*,

Ref. 104: Peter Saveskie - W4LGF, *Radio Propagation Handbook*,

Ref. 105: William Orr - W6SAI, *Radio Handbook*,

Ref. 106: Gerald L. Hall - K1TD - ed., *The ARRL Antenna Book*, ARRL - Newington - CT, 1982.

Ref. 107: Wayne Overbeck - N6NB - et al, "Computer Programs for Amateur Radio,"

Ref. 108: Dale Hoppe - K6UA - et al, "The Grayline Method of DXing," *CQ*, Sep 1975, p 27.

Ref. 109: Rod Linkous - W7OM, "Navigating to 80 Meter DX," *CQ*, Jan 1978, p 16.

Ref. 110: Yuri Blanarovich - VE3BMV, "Electromagnetic Wave Propagation By Conduction," *CQ*, Jun 1980, p 44.

Ref. 111: Guenter Schwarzbeck - DL1BU, "Bedeuting des Vertikalen Abstralwinkels von KW-Antennen," *CQ-DL*, Mar 1985, p 130.

Ref. 112: Guenter Schwarzbeck - DL1BU, "Bedeutung des Vertikalen Abstrahlwinkels von KW-Antennen (Part 2)," *CQ-DL*, Apr 1985, p 184.

Ref. 113: Henry Elwell - N4UH, "Calculator-Aided Propagation Predictions," *Ham Radio*, Apr 1979, p 26.

Ref. 114: Donald C. Mead - K4DE, "How to Determine True North for Antenna Orientation," *Ham Radio*, Oct 1980, p 38.

Ref. 115: Henry Elwell - N4UH, "Antenna Geometry for Optimum Performance," *Ham Radio*, May 1982, p 60.

Ref. 116: Stan Gibilisco - W1GV/4, "Radiation of Radio Signals," *Ham Radio*, Jun 1982, p 26.

Ref. 117: Garth Stonehocker - KØRYW, "Forecasting by Computer," *Ham Radio*, Aug 1982, p 80.

Ref. 118: Bradley Wells - KR7L, "Fundamentals of Grayline Propagation," *Ham Radio*, Aug 1984, p 77.

Ref. 119: Van Brollini - NS6N - et al, "DXing by Computer," *Ham Radio*, Aug 1984, p 81.

Ref. 120: Calvin R. Graf - W5LFM - et al, "High-Frequency Atmospheric Noise - Part 2," *QST*, Feb 1972, p 16.

Ref. 121: Jim Kennedy - K6MIO - et al, "D-Layer Absorption During a Solar Eclipse," *QST*, Jul 1972, p 40.

Ref. 122: Edward P. Tilton - W1HDQ, "The DXer's Crystal Ball," *QST*, Jun 1975, p 23.

Ref. 123: Edward P. Tilton - W1HDQ, "The DXer's Crystal Ball - Part II," *QST*, Aug 1975, p 40.

Ref. 124: Paul Argo et al, "Radio Propagation and Solar Activity," *QST*, Feb 1977, p 24.

Ref. 125: Kenneth Johnston - W7LIX - et al, "An Eclipse Study on 80 Meters," *QST*, Jul 1979, p 14.

Ref. 126: V. Kanevsky - UL7GW, "Ionospheric Ducting at HF," *QST*, Sep 1979, p 20.

Ref. 127: Robert B. Rose - K6GKU, "MINIMUF: Simplified MUF-Prediction Program for Microcomputers," *QST*, Dec 1982, p 36.

Ref. 128: Tom Frenaye - K1KI, "The KI Edge," *QST*, Jun 1984, p 54.

Ref. 129: Richard Miller - VE3CIE, "Radio Aurora," *QST*, Jan 1985, p 14.

Ref. 130: Pat Hawker - G3VA, "Technical Topics: Trans-equatorial Supermode Theories," *Radio Communication*, Feb 1972, p 94.

Ref. 131: Pat Hawker - G3VA, "Technical Topics: Whispering Galleries," *Radio Communication*, May 1972, p 306.

Ref. 132: Pat Hawker - G3VA, "Technical Topics: Low Angles for Chordal Hops and TEP," *Radio Communication*, Nov 1972, p 746.

Ref. 133: A. P. A. Ashton - G3XAP, "160M DX from Suburban Sites," *Radio Communication*, Dec 1973, p 842.

Ref. 134: Pat Hawker - G3VA, "Technical Topics: Path Deviations - One-Way Propagation - HF Tropo and LDEs," *Radio Communication*, Oct 1974, p 686.

Ref. 135: Pat Hawker - G3VA, "Fading and the Ionosphere," *Radio Communication*, Mar 1978, p 217.

Ref. 136: Pat Hawker - G3VA, "Technical Topics: When Long-Path is Better," *Radio Communication*, Sep 1979, p 831.

Ref. 137: V. Kanevsky - UL7GW, "DX QSOs," *Radio Communication*, Sep 1979, p 835.

Ref. 138: Pat Hawker - G3VA, "Technical Topics: Chordal Hop and Ionospheric Focusing," *Radio Communication*, Apr 1984, p 315.

■ 2. RECEIVERS

Ref. 200: R. Schetgen - KU7G - ed., *The ARRL Handbook for the Radio Amateur*, ARRL, Newington, CT.

Ref. 201: ON4EG, "Sensibilite des Recepteurs," *CQ-QSO*, Jan 1985.

Ref. 202: ON4EG, "Sensibilite des Recepteurs," *CQ-QSO*, Feb 1985.

Ref. 203: Michael Martin - DJ7JV, "Emfangereingangsteil mit Grossem Dynamik Bereich," *DL-QTC*, Jun 1975.

Ref. 204: R. Schetgen - KU7G - ed, "*The ARRL Handbook for the Radio Amateur*," ARRL, Newington, CT.

Ref. 205: John Devoldere - ON4UN, "80-Meter DX-ing," *Communications Technology*, Jun 1978.

Ref. 206: William Orr - W6SAI, *Radio Handbook*, Howard W. Sams & Co. Inc.

Ref. 207: Robert Sternowsky, "Using Preselectors to Improve HF Performance," *Communications International*, May 1980, p 34.

Ref. 208: John Devoldere - ON4UN, "Improved Performance from the Drake R-4B and T4X-B," *CQ*, Mar 1976, p 37.

Ref. 209: Michael Martin - DJ7VY, "Rauscharmer Oszillator fur Empfaenger mit grossem Dynamikbereich," *CQ-DL*, Dec 1976, p 418.

Ref. 210: Wes Hayward - W7ZOI, "Der Dynamische Bereich eines Empfaengers," *CQ-DL*, Mar 1977, p 93.

Ref. 211: Richard Waxweller - DJ7VD, "Hochfrequenz-Zweitongenerator," *CQ-DL*, Sep 1980, p 412.

Ref. 212: Guenter Schwarzbeck - DL1BU, "Testbericht: NF-Filter Datong FL2," *CQ-DL*, Feb 1981, p 56.

Ref. 213: Guenter Schwarzbeck - DL1BU, "Grosssignalverhalten von Kurzwellenempfaengern," *CQ-DL*, Mar 1981, p 117.

Ref. 214: Walter Flor - OE1LO, "KW-Eingangsteile: Eingangsfilter," *CQ-DL*, Aug 1981, p 373.

Ref. 215: Walter Flor - OE1LO, "IM-feste Verstaerker fuer den KW-bereich," *CQ-DL*, Aug 1981, p 473.

Ref. 216: Walter Flor - OE1LO, "KW-Eingangsteile: Extrem IM-feste selektive Vorverstaerker," *CQ-DL*, Aug 1981, p 376.

Ref. 217: Guenter Schwarzbeck - DL1BU, "Geraeteeigenschaften: Besonderheiten zwischen Testbericht und Praxis," *CQ-DL*, Sep 1982, p 424.

Ref. 218: Erich Vogelsang - DJ2IM, "Grundrmauschen und Dynamiekbereich bei Kurzwellenempfaengern," *CQ-DL*, Sep 1982, p 432.

Ref. 219: Michael Martin - DJ7VY, "Intermodulationsfster Preselector fur 1.5 - 30 MHz," *CQ-DL*, Jul 1984, p 320.

Ref. 220: Ray Moore, "Designing Communication Receivers for Good Strong-Signal Performance," *Ham Radio*, Feb 1973, p 6.

Ref. 221: Wes Hayward - W7ZOI, "Bandpass Filters for Receiver Preselectors," *Ham Radio*, Feb 1975, p 18.

Ref. 222: Ulrich Rohde - DJ2LR, "High Dynamic Range Receiver Input Stages," *Ham Radio*, Oct 1975, p 26.

Ref. 223: James Fisk - W1DTY, "Receiver Noise Figure Sensitivity and Dynamic Range, What The Numbers Mean," *Ham Radio*, Oct 1975, p 8.

Ref. 224: Marvin Gonsior - W6FR, "Improved Selectivity for Collins S-line Receivers," *Ham Radio*, Jun 1976, p 36.

Ref. 225: Howard Berlin - K3NEZ, "Increased Flexibility for MFJ CW Filters," *Ham Radio*, Dec 1976, p 58.

Ref. 226: Ulrich Rohde - DJ2LR, "I-F Amplifier Design," *Ham Radio*, Mar 1977, p 10.

Ref. 227: Alex Burwasser - WB4ZNV, "Reducing Intermodulation Distortion in High-Frequency Receivers," *Ham Radio*, Mar 1977, p 26.

Ref. 228: Wayne C. Ryder - W6URM, "General Coverage Communications Receiver," *Ham Radio*, Nov 1977, p 10.

Ref. 229: R. Sherwood - WB0JGP - et al, "Receivers: Some Problems and Cures," *Ham Radio*, Dec 1977, p 10.

Ref. 230: R. Sherwood - WB0JGP - et al, "New Product Detector for R-4C," *Ham Radio*, Oct 1978, p 94.

Ref. 231: R. Sherwood - WB0JGP - et al, "Audio Amplifier for the Drake R-4C," *Ham Radio*, Apr 1979, p 48.

Ref. 233: James M. Rohler - N0DE, "Biquad Bandpass Filter," *Ham Radio*, Jun 1979, p 70.

Ref. 234: Sidney Kaiser - WB6CTW, "Measuring Receiver Dynamic Range," *Ham Radio*, Nov 1979, p 56.

Ref. 235: Ulrich Rohde - DJ2LR, "Recent Developments in Circuits and Techniques for High Frequency Communications Receivers," *Ham Radio*, Apr 1980, p 20.

Ref. 236: Edward Wetherhold - W3NQN, "High Performance CW Filter," *Ham Radio*, Apr 1981, p 18.

Ref. 237: D. A. Tong - G4GMQ, "Add-On Selectivity for Communication Receivers," *Ham Radio*, Nov 1981, p 41.

Ref. 238: Ulrich Rohde - DJ2LR, "Communication Receivers for the Year 2000: Part 1," *Ham Radio*, Nov 1981, p 12.

Ref. 239: Jan K. Moller - K6FM, "Understanding Performance Data of High-Frequency Receivers," *Ham Radio*, Nov 1981, p 30.

Ref. 240: Ulrich Rohde - DJ2LR, "Communication Receivers for the Year 2000 - Part 2," *Ham Radio*, Dec 1981, p 6.

Ref. 241: Ulrich Rohde - DJ2LR, "Performance Capability of Active Mixers - Part 1," *Ham Radio*, Mar 1982, p 30.

Ref. 242: Ulrich Rohde - DJ2LR, "Performance Capability of Active Mixers - Part 2," *Ham Radio*, Apr 1982, p 38.

Ref. 243: R. W. Johnson - W6MUR, "Bridged T-Filters for Amateur Use," *Ham Radio*, Oct 1982, p 51.

Ref. 244: Cornell Drentea - WB3JZO, "Designing a Modern Receiver," *Ham Radio*, Nov 1983, p 3.

Ref. 245: Edward Wetherhold - W3NQN, "Elliptic Lowpass Audio Filter Design," *Ham Radio*, Jan 1984, p 20.

Ref. 246: J. A. Dyer - G4OBU, "High Frequency Receiver Performance," *Ham Radio*, Feb 1984, p 33.

Ref. 247: E. A. Andrade - WØDAN, "Recent Trends in Receiver Front-End Design," *QST*, Jun 1962, p 17.

Ref. 248: William K. Squires - W2PUL, "A New Approach to Receiver Front-End Design," *QST*, Sep 1963, p 31.

Ref. 249: Byron Goodman - W1DX, "Some Thoughts on Home Receiver Design," *QST*, May 1965, p 11.

Ref. 250: E. H. Conklin - K6KA, "Front-End Receiving Filters," *QST*, Aug 1967, p 14.

Ref. 251: Doug DeMaw - W1CER, "Rejecting Interference from Broadcast Stations," *QST*, Dec 1967, p 35.

Ref. 252: Rudolf Fisher - DL6WD, "An Engineer's Solid-State Ham-Band Receiver," *QST*, Mar 1970, p 11.

Ref. 253: Douglas A. Blakeslee - W1KLK, "An Experimental Receiver for 75-Meter DX Work,"*QST*, Feb 1972, p 41.

Ref. 254: Wes Hayward - W7ZOI, "Defining and Measuring Receiver Dynamic Range," *QST*, Jul 1975, p 15.

Ref. 255: Doug DeMaw - W1FB, "His Eminence: the Receiver," *QST*, Jun 1976, p 27.

Ref. 256: Wes Hayward - W7ZOI, "CER-Verters," *QST*, Jun 1976, p 31.

Ref. 257: Doug DeMaw - W1FB, "Build this Quickie Preamp," *QST*, Apr 1977, p 43.

Ref. 258: Wes Hayward - W7ZOI, "More Thoughts on Receiver Performance Specification," *QST*, Nov 1979, p 48.

Ref. 259: Ulrich Rohde - DJ2LR, "Increasing Receiver Dynamic Range," *QST*, May 1980, p 16.

Ref. 260: Edward Wetherhold - W3NQN, "Modern Design of a CW Filter Using 88- and 44-mH Surplus Inductors," *QST*, Dec 1980, p 14.

Ref. 261: Doug DeMaw - et al, "Modern Receiver Mixers for High Dynamic Range," *QST*, Jan 1981, p 19.

Ref. 262: Wes Hayward - W7ZOI, "A Progressive Communications Receiver," *QST*, Nov 1981, p 11.

Ref. 263: Robert E. Lee - K2TWK, "Build an Audio Filter with Pizzazz," *QST*, Feb 1982, p 18.

Ref. 264: Harold Mitchell - NØARQ, "88-mH Inductors: A Trap," *QST*, Jan 1983, p 38.

Ref. 265: Gerald B. Hull - AK4L/VE1CER, "Filter Systems for Multi-transmitter Amateur Stations," *QST*, Jul 1983, p 28.

Ref. 266: John K. Webb - W1ETC, "High-Pass Filters for Receiving Applications," *QST*, Oct 1983, p 17.

Ref. 267: Doug DeMaw - W1FB, "Receiver Preamps and How to Use Them," *QST*, Apr 1984, p 19.

Ref. 268: Pat Hawker - G3VA, "Trends in H.F. Receiver Front-ends," *Radio Communication*, Sep 1963, p 161.

Ref. 269: D. A. Tong - G4GMQ, "Audio Filters as an Aid to Reception," *Radio Communication*, Feb 1978, p 114.

Ref. 270: John Bazley - G3HCT, "The Datong Multi-Mode Filter FL-2," *Radio Communication*, Aug 1980, p 783.

Ref. 271: Pat Hawker - G3VA, "Technical Topics: More Thoughts On 'Ideal' HF Receivers," *Radio Communication*, Oct 1982, p 861.

Ref. 272: Edward Wetherhold - W3NQN, "Simplified Elliptic Lowpass Filter Design Using Surplus 88-mH Inductors," *Radio Communication*, Apr 1983, p 318.

Ref. 273: P. E. Chadwick - G3RZP, "Dynamic Range; Intermodulation and Phase Noise," *Radio Communication*, Mar 1984, p 223.

Ref. 274: Pat Hawker - G3VA, "Technical Topics: Comparing Receiver Front-Ends," *Radio Communication*, May 1984, p 400.

Ref. 275: Pat Hawker - G3VA, "Technical Topics: Receivers: Numbers Right or Wrong?," *Radio Communication*, Aug 1984, p 677.

Ref. 276: Pat Hawker - G3VA, "Technical Topics: Receivers of Top Performance," *Radio Communication*, Oct 1984, p 858.

Ref. 277: Edward Wetherhold - W3NQN, "A CW Filter for the Radio Amateur Newcomer," *Radio Communication*, Jan 1985, p 26.

Ref. 278: Pat Hawker - G3VA, "Technical Topics: Whither Experimentation?," *Radio Communication*, Mar 1985, p 189.

Ref. 279: Ian White - G3SEK, "Modern VHF/UHF Front End Design—Part 1," *Radio Communication*, Apr 1985, p 264.

Ref. 280: Ian White - G3SEK, "Modern VHF/UHF Front End Design—Part 2," *Radio Communication*, May 1985, p 367.

Ref. 281: Ian White - G3SEK, "Modern VHF/UHF Front End Design—Part 3," *Radio Communication*, Jun 1985, p 445.

Ref. 282: Pat Hawker - G3VA, "Technical Topics: Weak Signal Reception," *Radio Communication*, Jul 1985, p 540.

Ref. 283: D. H. G. Fritsch - GØCKZ, "Active Elliptic Audio Filter Design Using Op-Amps (Part 1)," *Radio Communication*, Feb 1986, p 98.

Ref. 284: Ulrich L. Rohde - KA2WEU/DJ2LR, "Designing a State-of-the-art Receiver," *Ham Radio,* Nov 1987, p 17.

Ref. 285: Robert J. Zavrel - W7SX, "Tomorrow's Receivers," *Ham Radio,* Nov 1987, p 8.

Ref. 286: John Grebenkemper - KI6WX, "Phase Noise and its Effects on Amateur Communications," *QST*, Mar 1988, p 14.

Ref. 287: Zack Lau - KH6CP, "Eliminating AM-Broadcast interference on 160 Meters," *QST*, Apr 1992, p 75.

Ref. 288: Gary Nichols - KD9SV, "Bandpass Filters for 80 and 160 Meters," *QST*, Feb 1989, p 42.

Ref. 289: John Grebenkemper - KI6WX, "Phase Noise and its Effects on Amateur Communications," *QST*, Apr 1988, p 22.

Ref. 290: Dave Hershberger - W9GR, "Low Cost Digital Signal Processing for the Radio Amateur," *QST*, Sep 1992, p 43.

Ref. 291: Bruce C. Hale - KB1MW/7, "An Introduction to Digital Signal Processing," *QST*, Jul 1991, p 35.

Ref. 292: D. DeMaw - W1FB, "Receiver Preamps and How to Use Them," *QST*, Apr 1984, p 19.

Ref. 293: J. Kearman - KR1S, "Audio Filter Roundup," *QST*, Oct 1991, p 36.

Ref. 294: Wes Hayward - W7ZOI, "The Double-tuned Circuit.: An Experimenter's Tutorial," *QST*, Dec 1991, p 29.

Ref. 295: Lew Gordon - K4VX, "Band Pass filters for HF transceivers," *QST*, Sep 1988, p 17

Ref. 296: D. DeMaw - W1FB, "A Diode-switched Bandpass Filter," *QST*, Jan 1991, p 24.

Ref. 297: G. E. Myers - K9GZB, "Diode-switched-filter (corrections and amplifications)," *QST*, Aug 1991, p 41.

■ 3. TRANSMITTERS

Ref. 300: R. Schetgen - KU7G - ed, *"The ARRL Handbook for the Radio Amateur,"* ARRL, Newington, CT.

Ref. 301: Bob Heil - K9EID, "Equalise That Microphone," *CQ-DL*, Apr 1985, p 27.

Ref. 302: John Devoldere - ON4UN, "80-Meter DX-ing," *Communications Technology* Inc, Apr 1978.

Ref. 303: William Orr - W6SAI, *Radio Handbook*, Howard W. Sams & Co.- Inc.

Ref. 304: John Devoldere - ON4UN, "Improved Performance from the Drake R-4B and T4X-B," *CQ*, Mar 1976, p 37.

Ref. 305: John Schultz - W4FA, "An Optimum Speech Filter," *CQ*, Oct 1978, p 22.

Ref. 307: L. McCoy - W1ICP, "The Design Electronics QSK-1500," *CQ*, Apr 1985, p 40.

Ref. 308: Guenter Schwarzbeck - DL1BU, "Geraeteeigenschaften: esonderheiten zwischen Testbericht und Praxis," *CQ-DL*, Sep 1982, p 424.

Ref. 309: Leslie Moxon - G6XN, "Performance of RF Speech Clippers," *Ham Radio*, Nov 1972, p 26.

Ref. 310: Charles Bird - K6HTM, "RF Speech Clipper for SSB," *Ham Radio*, Feb 1973, p 18.

Ref. 311: Henry Elwell - W2MB, "RF Speech Processor," *Ham Radio*, Sep 1973, p 18.

Ref. 312: Barry Kirkwood - ZL1BN, "Principles of Speech Processing," *Ham Radio*, Feb 1975, p 28.

Ref. 313: Timothy Carr - W6IVI, "Speech Processor for the Heath SB-102," *Ham Radio*, Jun 1975, p 38.

Ref. 314: Jim Fisk - W1DTY, "New Audio Speech Processing Technique," *Ham Radio*, Jun 1976, p 30.

Ref. 315: Frank C. Getz - K3PDW, "Logarithmic Speech Processor," *Ham Radio*, Aug 1977, p 48.

Ref. 316: Michael James - W1CBY, "Electronic Bias Switching for the Henry 2K4 and 3KA Linear Amplifiers," *Ham Radio*, Aug 1978, p 75.

Ref. 317: Wesley D. Stewart - N7WS, "Split-Band Speech Processor," *Ham Radio*, Sep 1979, p 12.

Ref. 318: J. R. Sheller - KN8Z, "High Power RF Switching With Pin Diodes," *Ham Radio*, Jan 1985, p 82.

Ref. 319: William Sabin - WØIYH, "R.F. Clippers for S.S.B.," *QST*, Jul 1967, p 13.

Ref. 320: J. A. Bryant - W4UX, "Electronic Bias Switching for RF Power Amplifiers," *QST*, May 1974, p 36.

Ref. 321: Robert Myers - W1FBY, "Quasi-Logarithmic Analog Amplitude Limiter," *QST*, Jul 1974, p 22.

Ref. 322: Hal Collins - W6JES, "SSB Speech Processing Revisited," *QST*, Aug 1976, p 38.

Ref. 323: Bob Heil - K9EID, "Equalize Your Microphone and Be Heard!," *QST*, Jul 1982, p 11.

Ref. 324: R. C. V. Macario - G4ADL - et al, "An Assured Speech Processor," *Radio Communication*, Apr 1978, p 310.

Ref. 325: H. Leerning - G3LLL, "Improving the FT-101," *Radio Communication*, Jun 1979, p 516.

Ref. 326: L. McCoy - W1ICP, "The Design Electronics QSK-1500," *CQ*, Apr 1985, p 40.

Ref. 327: Alfred Trossen - DL6YP, "Die AMTOR-II einheit nach G3PLX," *CQ-DL*, Jul 1983, p 316.

Ref. 328: Alfred Trossen - DL6YP, "Die AMTOR-II einheit nach G3PLX," *CQ-DL*, Aug 1983, p 368.

Ref. 329: J. R. Sheller - KN8Z, "High Power RF Switching With Pin Diodes," *Ham Radio*, Jan 1985, p 82.

Ref. 330: Peter Martinez - G3PLX, "AMTOR: an Improved Error-Free RTTY System," *QST*, Jun 1981, p 25.

Ref. 331: Paul Newland - AD7I, "Z-AMTOR: An Advanced AMTOR Code Converter," *QST*, Feb 1984, p 25.

Ref. 332: Peter Martinez - G3PLX, "AMTOR: an Improved Radio Teleprinter System Using a Microprocessor," *Radio Communication*, Aug 1979, p 714.

Ref. 333: Peter Martinez - G3PLX, "AMTOR the Easy Way," *Radio Communication*, Jun 1980, p 610.

Ref. 334: Jon Towle - WB1DNL, "QSK 1500 High-Power RF Switch," *QST*, Sep 1985, p 39.

Ref. 335: Dr. J. R. Sheller - KN8Z, "What Does 'QSK' Really Mean?," *QST*, Jul 1985, p 31.

Ref. 336: Paul Newland - AD7I, "A User's Guide to AMTOR Operation," *QST*, Oct 1985, p 31.

Ref. 337: W.J. Byron - W7DHD, "Designing an amplifier around the 3CX1200A7," *Ham Radio*, Dec 1978, p 33.

Ref. 338: Richard L. Measures - AG6K, "QSK Modification of the Trio Kenwood TL-922 Amplifier," *Ham Radio*, Mar 1989, p 35.

Ref. 339: Paul A. Johnson - W7KBE, "Homebrewing Equipment - From Parts to Metal Work," *Ham Radio*, Mar 1988, p 26.

Ref. 340: Richard L. Measures - AG6K, "Adding 160-meter Coverage to HF Amplifiers," *QST*, Jan 1989, p 23.

Ref. 341: Safford M. North - KG2M, "Putting the Heath SB-200 on 160 Meters," *QST*, Nov 1987, p 33.

Ref. 342: W.J. Byron - W7DHD, "Design Program for the Grounded-grid 3-500Z," *Ham Radio*, Jun 1988, p 8.

■ 4. EQUIPMENT REVIEW

Ref. 400: Guenter Schwarzbeck - DL1BU, "Testbericht: Transceiver TS820," *CQ-DL*, Apr 1977, p 130.

Ref. 401: Guenter Schwarzbeck - DL1BU, "Testbericht und Beschreibung TS-520S," *CQ-DL*, Feb 1978, p 50.

Ref. 402: Guenter Schwarzbeck - DL1BU, "Testbericht un Messdaten FT-901 DM (receiver section)," *CQ-DL*, Feb 1978, p 438.

Ref. 403: Guenter Schwarzbeck - DL1BU, "Testbericht und Messdaten FT-901 DM (transmitter section)," *CQ-DL*, Nov 1978, p 500.

Ref. 404: Guenter Schwarzbeck - DL1BU, "KW-Empfaenger Drake R-4C mit usatzfiltern," *CQ-DL*, Feb 1979, p 56.

Ref. 405: Guenter Schwarzbeck - DL1BU, "KW Transceiver ICOM IC-701," *CQ-DL*, Feb 1979, p 65.

Ref. 406: Guenter Schwarzbeck - DL1BU, "Testbericht: Vorausbericht FT-ONE," *CQ-DL*, Jan 1982, p 11.

Ref. 407: Guenter Schwarzbeck - DL1BU, "Testbericht und Messwerte IC-730," *CQ-DL*, Mar 1982, p 117.

Ref. 408: Guenter Schwarzbeck - DL1BU, "Testbericht und Messwerte FT-102," *CQ-DL*, Aug 1982, p 387.

Ref. 409: Guenter Schwarzbeck - DL1BU, "Testbericht und Messwerte TS930S," *CQ-DL*, Oct 1982, p 484.

Ref. 410: Peter Hart - G3SJX, "The Trio TS-830 HF Transceiver," *Radio Communication*, Jul 1982, p 576.

Ref. 411: Peter Hart - G3SJX, "The Yaesu Musen FT102 HF Transceiver," *Radio Communication*, Jan 1983, p 32.

Ref. 412: Peter Hart - G3SJX, "The ICOM IC740 HF Transceiver," *Radio Communication*, Nov 1983, p 985.

Ref. 413: Peter Hart - G3SJX, "The Yaesu FT77 HF Transceiver," *Radio Communication*, Jun 1984, p 482.

Ref. 414: Peter Hart - G3SJX, "The Yaesu Musen FT980 HF Transceiver," *Radio Communication*, Sep 1984, p 761.

Ref. 415: Peter Hart - G3SJX, "The Ten-Tec Corsair HF Transceiver," *Radio Communication*, Nov 1984, p 957.

Ref. 416: Peter Hart - G3SJX, "The Yaesu Musen FT757GX HF Transceiver," *Radio Communication*, May 1985, p 351.

Ref. 417: Peter Hart - G3SJX, "The Trio TS430S HF Transceiver," *Radio Communication*, Jun 1985, p 441.

Ref. 418: G. Schwarzbeck - DL1BU, "Yaesu FT-1000 Test Review—Part 1," *CQ-DL*, Mar 1991, p 91.

Ref. 419: G. Schwarzbeck - DL1BU, "Yaesu FT-1000 Test Review—Part 2," *CQ-DL*, Apr 1991, p 215.

Ref. 420: G. Schwarzbeck - DL1BU, "Yaesu FT-1000 Test Review—Part 3," *CQ-DL*, May 1991, p 273.

Ref. 421: G. Shwarzbeck - DL1BU, "TS-850S Test Review," *CQ-DL*, Feb 1991, p 79.

Ref. 422: G. Shwarzbeck - DL1BU, "TS-950 SD test review," *CQ-DL*, Dec 1989, p 750.

Ref. 423: G. Shwarzbeck - DL1BU, "ICOM IC-761 test review," *CQ-DL*, Aug 1988, p 479.

Ref. 424: Peter Hart - G3SJX, "FT-1000 Review," *Radio Communication*, Jun 1991, p 49.

Ref. 425: Peter Hart - G3SJX, "The Yaesu Musen FT767GX HF Transceiver," *Radio Communication*, Jul 1987, p 490.

Ref. 426: Peter Hart - G3SJX, "Kenwood TS-860S transceiver," *Radio Communication*, Mar 1989, p 47.

Ref. 427: Peter Hart - G3SJX, "Yaesu Musen FT-747GX HF Transceiver," *Radio Communication*, May 1989, p 47.

Ref. 428: Peter Hart - G3SJX, "ICOM IC-725 HF Transceiver," *Radio Communication*, Sep 1989, p 56.

Ref. 429: Peter Hart - G3SJX, "Kenwood TS-950S Transceiver Review," *Radio Communication*, Apr 1990, p 35.

Ref. 430: Peter Hart - G3SJX, "ICOM-781 HF Transceiver," *Radio Communication*, Jul 1980, p 52.

Ref. 431: G. Shwarzbeck - DL1BU, "Ten-Tec Paragon 585 test review," *CQ-DL*, May 1988, p 277.

■ 5. OPERATING

Ref. 500: R. Schetgen - KU7G - ed, "*The ARRL Handbook for the Radio Amateur*," ARRL, Newington, CT.

Ref. 501: Erik - SMØAGD, "Split Channel Operation," *CQ-DL*, Apr 1985, p 10.

Ref. 502: John Devoldere - ON4UN, "80-Meter DX-ing," *Communications Technology*, Apr 1987.

Ref. 503: Wayne Overbeck - N6NB, *Computer Programs for Amateur Radio*,

Ref. 504: Rod Linkous - W7OM, "Navigating to 80 Meter DX," *CQ*, Jan 1978, p 16.

Ref. 505: Larry Brockman, "The DX-list Net. What a Mess," *CQ*, May 1979, p 48.

Ref. 506: Wolfgang Roberts - DL7RT, "Wie werde ich DX-er?," *CQ-DL*, Oct 1981, p 493.

Ref. 507: John Lindholm - W1XX, "Is 160 Your Top Band?," *QST*, Aug 1985, p 45.

Ref. 508: V. Kanevsky - UL7GW, "DX QSOs," *Radio Communication*, Sep 1979, p 835.

■ 6. ANTENNAS: GENERAL

Ref. 600: R. Schetgen - KU7G - ed, "*The ARRL Handbook for the Radio Amateur*," ARRL, Newington CT.

Ref. 601: J. J. Wiseman, "How Long is a Piece of Wire," *Electronics and Wireless World*, Apr 1985, p 24.

Ref. 602: William Orr - W6SAI - et al, "Antenna Handbook," Howard W. Sams & Co, Inc,

Ref. 603: Gerald Hall - K1TD - et al, *"The ARRL Antenna Compendium, Volume 1,"* ARRL, Newington, CT,

Ref. 604: Keith Henney, *Radio Engineering Handbook*, 5th ed,

Ref. 605: *Reference Data for Radio Engineers*, Howard W. Sams, 5th Edition,

Ref. 606: John Kraus - W8JK, *Antennas*.

Ref. 607: Joseph Boyer - W6UYH, "The Multi-Band Trap Antenna - Part I," *CQ*, Feb 1977, p 26.

Ref. 608: Joseph Boyer - W6UYH, "The Multi-Band Trap Antenna - Part II," *CQ*, Mar 1977, p 51.

Ref. 609: Bill Salerno - W2ONV, "The W2ONV Delta/Slope Antenna," *CQ*, Aug 1978, p 52.

Ref. 610: Cornelio Nouel - KG5B, "Exploring the Vagaries of Traps," *CQ*, Aug 1984, p 32.

Ref. 611: K. H. Kleine - DL3CI, "Der Verkuerzte Dipol," *CQ-DL*, Jun 1977, p 230.

Ref. 612: Hans Wuertz - DL2FA, "Bis zu Einer S-Stufe mehr auf 80 Meter," *CQ-DL*, Dec 1977, p 475.

Ref. 613: Hans Wuertz - DL2FA, "DX-Antennen mit spiegelenden Flaechen," *CQ-DL*, Aug 1979, p 353.

Ref. 614: Hans Wuertz - DL2FA, "DX-Antennen mit spiegelenden Flaechen," *CQ-DL*, Jan 1980, p 18.

Ref. 615: Willi Nitschke - DJ5DW - et al, "Richtungskarakteristik Fusspunktwiederstand etc von Einelementantennen," *CQ-DL*, Nov 1982, p 535.

Ref. 616: Guenter Schwarzbeck - DL1BU, "Bedeuting des Vertikalen Abstralwinkels von KW-Antennen," *CQ-DL*, Mar 1985, p 130.

Ref. 617: Guenter Schwarzbeck - DL1BU, "Bedeutung des Vertikalen Abstrahlwinkels von KW-antennas (part 2)," *CQ-DL*, Apr 1985, p 184.

Ref. 618: E. Vogelsang - DJ2IM, "Vertikaldiagramme typische Kurzwellenantenne," *CQ-DL*, Jun 1985, p 300.

Ref. 619: John Schultz - W2EEY, "Stub-Switched Vertical Antennas," *Ham Radio*, Jul 1969, p 50.

Ref. 620: Malcolm P. Keown - W5RUB, "Simple Antennas for 80 and 40 Meters," *Ham Radio*, Dec 1972, p 16.

Ref. 621: Earl Whyman - W2HB, "Standing-Wave Ratios," *Ham Radio*, Jul 1973, p 26.

Ref. 622: Robert Baird - W7CSD, "Nonresonant Antenna Impedance Measurements," *Ham Radio*, Apr 1974, p 46.

Ref. 623: H. Glenn Bogel - WA9RQY, "Vertical Radiation Patterns," *Ham Radio*, May 1974, p 58.

Ref. 624: Robert Leo - W7LR, "Optimum Height for Horizontal Antennas," *Ham Radio*, Jun 1974, p 40.

Ref. 625: Bob Fitz - K4JC, "High Performance 80-Meter Antenna," *Ham Radio,* May 1977, p 56.

Ref. 626: Everett S. Brown - K4EF, "New Multiband Longwire Antenna Design," *Ham Radio,* May 1977, p 10.

Ref. 627: William A. Wildenhein - W8YFB, "Solution to the Low-Band Antenna Problem," *Ham Radio,* Jan 1978, p 46.

Ref. 628: John Becker - K9MM, "Lightning Protection," *Ham Radio,* Dec 1978, p 18.

Ref. 629: James Lawson - W2PV, "Part V *Yagi Antenna Design*: Ground or Earth Effects," *Ham Radio,* Oct 1980, p 29.

Ref. 630: Henry G. Elwell - N4UH, "Antenna Geometry for Optimum Performance," *Ham Radio,* May 1982, p 60.

Ref. 631: Randy Rhea - N4HI, "Dipole Antenna over Sloping Ground," *Ham Radio,* May 1982, p 18.

Ref. 632: Bradley Wells - KR7L, "Lightning and Electrical Transient Protection," *Ham Radio,* Dec 1983, p 73.

Ref. 633: R. C. Marshall - G3SBA, "An End-Fed Multiband 8JK," *Ham Radio,* May 1984, p 81.

Ref. 634: David Atkins - W6VX, "Capacitively Loaded High-Performance Dipole," *Ham Radio,* May 1984, p 33.

Ref. 635: David Courtier-Dutton - G3FPQ, "Some Notes on a 7-MHz Linear Loaded Quad," *QST,* Feb 1972, p 14.

Ref. 636: John Kaufmann - WA1CQW - et al, "A Convenient Stub-Tuning System for Quad Antennas," *QST,* May 1975, p 18.

Ref. 637: Hardy Lankskov - W7KAR, "Pattern Factors for Elevated Horizontal Antennas Over Real Earth," *QST,* Nov 1975, p 19.

Ref. 638: Robert Dome - W2WAM, "Impedance of Short Horizontal Dipoles," *QST,* Jan 1976, p 32.

Ref. 639: Donald Belcher - WA4JVE - et al, "Loops vs Dipole Analysis and Discussion," *QST,* Aug 1976, p 34.

Ref. 640: Roger Sparks - W7WKB, "Build this C-T Quad Beam for Reduced Size," *QST,* Apr 1977, p 29.

Ref. 641: Ronald K. Gorski - W9KYZ, "Efficient Short Radiators," *QST,* Apr 1977, p 37.

Ref. 642: Byron Goodman - W1DX, "My Feed Line Tunes My Antenna," *QST,* Apr 1977, p 40.

Ref. 643: Doug DeMaw - W1FB, "The Gentlemen's Band: 160 Meters," *QST,* Oct 1977, p 33.

Ref. 644: David S. Hollander - N7RK, "A Big Signal from a Small Lot," *QST,* Apr 1979, p 32.

Ref. 645: Dana Atchley - W1CF, "Putting the Quarter Wave Sloper to Work on 160," *QST,* Jul 1979, p 19.

Ref. 646: Stan Gibilisco - W1GV, "The Imperfect Antenna System and How it Works," *QST,* Jul 1979, p 24.

Ref. 647: John Belrose - VE2CV, "The Half Sloper," *QST,* May 1980, p 31.

Ref. 648: Larry May - KE6H, "Antenna Modeling Program for the TRS-80," *QST,* Feb 1981, p 15.

Ref. 649: Colin Dickman - ZS6U, "The ZS6U Minishack Special," *QST,* Apr 1981, p 32.

Ref. 650: Doug DeMaw - W1FB, "More Thoughts on the 'Confounded' Half Sloper," *QST,* Oct 1981, p 31.

Ref. 651: John S. Belrose - VE2CV, "The Effect of Supporting Structures on Simple Wire Antennas," *QST,* Dec 1982, p 32.

Ref. 652: Gerald Hall - K1TD, "A Simple Approach to Antenna Impedances," *QST,* Mar 1983, p 16.

Ref. 653: Jerry Hall - K1TD, "The Search for a Simple Broadband 80-Meter Dipole," *QST,* Apr 1983, p 22.

Ref. 654: Charles L. Hutchinson - K8CH, "Getting the Most out of Your Antenna," *QST,* Jul 1983, p 34.

Ref. 655: Doug DeMaw - W1FB, "Building and Using 30-Meter Antennas," *QST,* Oct 1983, p 27.

Ref. 656: James Rautio - AJ3K, "The Effects of Real Ground on Antennas - Part 1," *QST,* Feb 1984, p 15.

Ref. 657: James Rautio - AJ3K, "The Effects of Real Ground on Antennas - Part 2," *QST,* Apr 1984, p 34.

Ref. 658: James Rautio - AJ3K, "The Effect of Real Ground on Antennas - Part 3," *QST,* Jun 1984, p 30.

Ref. 659: Doug DeMaw - W1FB, "Trap for Shunt-Fed Towers," *QST,* Jun 1984, p 40.

Ref. 660: James Rautio - AJ3K, "The Effects of Real Ground on Antennas - Part 4," *QST,* Aug 1984, p 31.

Ref. 661: James Rautio - AJ3K, "The Effects of Real Ground on Antennas - Part 5," *QST,* Nov 1984, p 35.

Ref. 662: Robert C. Sommer - N4UU, "Optimizing Coaxial-Cable Traps," *QST,* Dec 1984, p 37.

Ref. 663: Bob Schetgen - KU7G, "Technical Correspondence" *QST,* Apr 1985, p 51.

Ref. 664: Pat Hawker - G3VA, "Technical Topics: Low Angle Operation," *Radio Communication,* Apr 1971, p 262.

Ref. 665: Pat Hawker - G3VA, "Technical Topics: Low Angle Radiation and Sloping-Ground Sites," *Radio Communication,* May 1972, p 306.

Ref. 666: Pat Hawker - G3VA, "Technical Topics: All Band Terminated Long-Wire," *Radio Communication,* Nov 1972, p 745.

Ref. 667: A.P.A. Ashton - G3XAP, "160M DX from Suburban Sites," *Radio Communication,* Dec 1973, p 842.

Ref. 668: L. A. Moxon - G6XN, "Gains and Losses in HF Aerials - Part 1," *Radio Communication,* Dec 1973, p 834.

Ref. 669: A. Moxon - G6XN, "Gains and Losses in HF Aerials - Part 2," *Radio Communication,* Jan 1974, p 16.

Ref. 670: Pat Hawker - G3VA, "Technical Topics: Thoughts on Inverted-Vs," *Radio Communication,* Sep 1976, p 676.

Ref. 671: A. P. A. Ashton - G3XAP, "The G3XAP Directional Antenna for the Lower Frequencies," *Radio Communication,* Nov 1977, p 858.

Ref. 672: S. J. M. Whitfield - G3IMW, "3.5 MHz DX Antennas for a Town Garden," *Radio Communication,* Aug 1980, p 772.

Ref. 673: Pat Hawker - G3VA, "Technical Topics: Low Profile 1.8 and 3.5 MHz Antennas," *Radio Communication,* Aug 1980, p 792.

Ref. 674: Pat Hawker - G3VA, "Technical Topics: Half Delta Loop - Sloping One-Mast Yagi," *Radio Communication,* Oct 1983, p 892.

Ref. 675: R. Rosen - K2RR, "Secrets of Successful Low Band Operation - Part 1," *Ham Radio,* May 1986, p 16.

Ref. 676: R. Rosen - K2RR, "Secrets of Successful Low Band Operation - Part 2," *Ham Radio,* Jun 1986.

Ref. 677: J. Dietrich - WA0RDX, "Loops and Dipoles: A Comparative Analysis," *QST,* Sep 1985, p 24.

Ref. 678: Roy Lewallen - W7EL, "MININEC: The Other Edge of the Sword," *QST*, Feb 1991, p 18.

Ref. 679: Rich Rosen - K2RR, "Secrets of Successful Low Band Operation," *Ham Radio,* May 1986, p 16

Ref. 680: Yardley Beers - WØJF, "Designing Trap Antennas: a New Approach," *Ham Radio,* Aug 1987, p 60.

Ref. 681: Guenter Schwarzbeck - DL1BU, "Die Antennw und ihre Umgebung," *CQ-DL*, Jan 1988, p 5.

Ref. 682: Maurice C. Hately - GM3HAT, "A No-compromise Multiband Low SWR Dipole," *Ham Radio,* Mar 1987, p 69.

Ref. 683: R. P. Haviland - W4MB, "Design Data for Pipe Masts," *Ham Radio,* Jul 1989, p 38.

Ref. 684: Gary E. O'Neil - N3GO, "Trapping the Mysteries of Trapped Antennas," *Ham Radio,* Oct 1981, p 10.

Ref. 685: J. Belrose VE2CV and P. Bouliane - VE3KLO, "The Off-center-fed Dipole Revisited," *QST*, Aug 1990, p 28.

Ref. 686: John J. Reh - K7KGP, "An Extended Double Zepp Antenna for 12 Meters," *QST*, Dec 1987, p 25.

Ref. 687: James W. Healy - NJ2L, "Feeding Dipole Antennas," *QST*, Jul 1991, p 22.

Ref. 688: Bill Orr, W6SAI, "Antenna Gain," *Ham Radio*, Jan 1990, p 30.

Ref. 689: B. H. Johns - W3JIP, "Coaxial Cable Antenna Traps," *QST*, May 1981, p 15.

7. Vertical Antennas

Ref. 701: Paul Lee - K6TS, *Vertical Antenna Handbook*, CQ Publishing Inc.

Ref. 702: Wait and Pope, "Input Resistance of LF Unipole Aerials," *Wireless Engineer*, May 1955, p 131.

Ref. 703: J. J. Wiseman, "How Long is a Piece of Wire," *Electronics and Wireless World*, Apr 1985, p 24.

Ref. 704: Carl C. Drumeller - W5JJ, "Using Your Tower as an Antenna," *CQ,* Dec 1977, p 75.

Ref. 705: Karl T. Thurber - W8FX, "HF Verticals - Plain And Simple," *CQ,* Sep 1980, p 22.

Ref. 706: John E. Magnusson - WØAGD, "Improving Antenna Performance," *CQ,* Jun 1981, p 32.

Ref. 707: Larry Strain - N7DF, "A 3.5 to 30 MHz Discage Antenna," *CQ,* Apr 1984, p 18.

Ref. 708: Karl Hille - DL1VU, "Optimierte T-Antenne," *CQ-DL*, Jun 1978, p 246.

Ref. 709: Rolf Schick - DL3AO, "Loop - Dipol und Vertikalantennen - Vergleiche und Erfahrungen," *CQ-DL*, Mar 1979, p 115.

Ref. 710: Guenter Schwarzbeck - DL1BU, "DX Antennen fuer 80 und 160 Meter," *CQ-DL*, Apr 1979, p 150.

Ref. 711: Hans Wurtz - DL2FA, "DX-Antennen mit spiegelenden Flaechen," *CQ-DL*, Aug 1979, p 353.

Ref. 712: Hans Wurtz - DL2FA, "DX-Antennen mit spiegelenden Flaechen," *CQ-DL*, Sep 1979, p 400.

Ref. 713: Hans Wurtz - DL2FA, "DX-Antennen mit spiegelenden Flaechen," *CQ-DL*, Jan 1980, p 18.

Ref. 714: Hans Wurtz - DL2FA, "DX-Antennen mit spiegelenden Flaechen," *CQ-DL*, Jun 1980, p 272.

Ref. 715: Hans Wurtz - DL2FA, "DX-Antennen mit spiegelenden Flaechen," *CQ-DL*, Jul 1980, p 311.

Ref. 716: Hans Wurtz - DL2FA, "DX-Antennen mit spiegelenden Flaechen," *CQ-DL*, Feb 1981, p 61.

Ref. 717: Hans Wurtz - DL2FA, "DX-Antennen mit spiegelenden Flaechen," *CQ-DL*, Jul 1981, p 330.

Ref. 718: Guenter Schwarzbeck - DL1BU, "Groundplane und Vertikalantennenf," *CQ-DL*, Sep 1981, p 420.

Ref. 719: Hans Wurtz - DL2FA, "DX-Antennen mit spiegelenden Flaechen," *CQ-DL*, Apr 1983, p 170.

Ref. 720: Hans Wurtz - DL2FA, "DX-Antennen mit spiegelenden Flaechen," *CQ-DL*, May 1983, p 224.

Ref. 721: Hans Wurtz - DL2FA, "Antennen mit spiegelenden Flaechen," *CQ-DL*, Jun 1983, p 278.

Ref. 722: Hans Adolf Rohrbacher - DJ2NN, "Basic Programm zu Berechnungh von Vertikalen Antennen," *CQ-DL*, Jun 1983, p 275.

Ref. 723: Hans Wurtz - DL2FA, "DX-Antennen mit spiegelenden Flaechen," *CQ-DL*, Jul 1983, p 326.

Ref. 724: John Schultz - W2EEY, "Stub-Switched Vertical Antennas," *Ham Radio,* Jul 1969, p 50.

Ref. 725: John True - W4OQ, "The Vertical Radiator," *Ham Radio,* Apr 1973, p 16.

Ref. 726: John True - W4OQ, "Vertical-Tower Antenna System," *Ham Radio,* May 1973, p 56.

Ref. 727: George Smith - W4AEO, "80- and 40-Meter Log Periodic Antennas," *Ham Radio,* Sep 1973, p 44.

Ref. 728: Robert Leo - W7LR, "Vertical Antenna Characteristics," *Ham Radio,* Mar 1974, p 34.

Ref. 729: Robert Leo - W7LR, "Vertical Antenna Radiation Patterns," *Ham Radio,* Apr 1974, p 50.

Ref. 730: Raymond Griese - K6FD, "Improving Vertical Antennas," *Ham Radio,* Dec 1974, p 54.

Ref. 731: Harry Hyder - W7IV, "Large Vertical Antennas," *Ham Radio,* May 1975, p 8.

Ref. 732: John True - W4OQ, "Shunt-Fed Vertical Antennas," *Ham Radio,* May 1975, p 34.

Ref. 733: H. H. Hunter - W8TYX, "Short Vertical for 7 MHz," *Ham Radio,* Jun 1977, p 60.

Ref. 734: Laidacker M. Seaberg - WØNCU, "Multiband Vertical Antenna System," *Ham Radio,* May 1978, p 28.

Ref. 735: Joseph D. Liga - K2INA, "80-Meter Ground Plane Antennas," *Ham Radio,* May 1978, p 48.

Ref. 736: John M. Haerle - WB5IIR, "Folded Umbrella Antenna," *Ham Radio,* May 1979, p 38.

Ref. 737: Paul A. Scholz - W6PYK, "Vertical Antenna for 40 and 75 Meters," *Ham Radio,* Sep 1979, p 44.

Ref. 738: Ed Marriner - W6XM, "Base-Loaded Vertical for 160 Meters," *Ham Radio,* Aug 1980, p 64.

Ref. 739: John S. Belrose - VE2CV, "The Half-Wave Vertical," *Ham Radio,* Sep 1981, p 36.

Ref. 740: Stan Gibilisco - W1GV/4, "Efficiency of Short Antennas," *Ham Radio,* Sep 1982, p 18.

Ref. 741: John S. Belrose - VE2CV, "Top-Loaded Folded Umbrella Vertical Antenna," *Ham Radio,* Sep 1982, p 12.

Ref. 742: W. J. Byron - W7DHD, "Short Vertical Antennas for the Low Bands - Part 1," *Ham Radio,* May 1983, p 36.

Ref. 743: Forrest Gehrke - K2BT, "Vertical Phased Arrays - Part 1," *Ham Radio,* May 1983, p 18.

Ref. 744: John Belrose - VE2CV, "The Grounded Monopole with Elevated Feed," *Ham Radio,* May 1983, p 87.

Ref. 745: Forrest Gehrke - K2BT, "Vertical Phased Arrays - Part 2," *Ham Radio,* Jun 1983, p 24.

Ref. 746: W. J. Byron - W7DHD, "Short Vertical Antennas for the Low Bands - Part 2," *Ham Radio,* Jun 1983, p 17.

Ref. 747: Forrest Gehrke - K2BT, "Vertical Phased Arrays - Part 3," *Ham Radio,* Jul 1983, p 26.

Ref. 748: Forrest Gehrke - K2BT, "Vertical Phased Arrays - Part 4," *Ham Radio,* Oct 1983, p 34.

Ref. 749: Forrest Gehrke - K2BT, "Vertical Phased Arrays - Part 5," *Ham Radio,* Dec 1983, p 59.

Ref. 750: Marc Bacon - WB9VWA, "Verticals Over REAL Ground," *Ham Radio,* Jan 1984, p 35.

Ref. 751: Robert Leo - W7LR, "Remote Controlled 40 - 80 - and 160 Meter Vertical," *Ham Radio,* May 1984, p 38.

Ref. 752: Harry Hyder - W7IV, "Build a Simple Wire Plow," *Ham Radio,* May 1984, p 107.

Ref. 753: Gene Hubbell - W9ERU, "Feeding Grounded Towers as Radiators," *QST*, Jun 1960, p 33.

Ref. 754: Eugene E. Baldwin - WØRUG, "Some Notes on the Care and Feeding of Grounded Verticals," *QST*, Oct 1963, p 45.

Ref. 755: N. H. Davidson - K5JVF, "Flagpole Without a Flag," *QST*, Nov 1964, p 36.

Ref. 756: Jerry Sevick - W2FMI, "The Ground-Image Vertical Antenna," *QST*, Jul 1971, p 16.

Ref. 757: Jerry Sevick - W2FMI, "The W2FMI 20-Meter Vertical Beam," *QST*, Jun 1972, p 14.

Ref. 758: Jerry Sevick - W2FMI, "The W2FMI Ground Mounted Short Vertical Antenna," *QST*, Mar 1973, p 13.

Ref. 759: Jerry Sevick - W2FMI, "A High Performance 20, 40 and 80 Meter Vertical System," *QST*, Dec 1973, p 30.

Ref. 760: Jerry Sevick - W2FMI, "The Constant Impedance Trap Vertical," *QST*, Mar 1974, p 29.

Ref. 761: Barry A. Boothe - W9UCW, "The Minooka Special," *QST*, Dec 1974, p 15.

Ref. 762: Willi Richartz - HB9ADQ, "A Stacked Multiband Vertical for 80-10 Meters," *QST*, Feb 1975, p 44.

Ref. 763: John S. Belrose - VE2CV, "The HF Discone Antenna," *QST*, Jul 1975, p 11.

Ref. 764: Earl Cunningham - W5RTQ, "Shunt Feeding Towers for Operating on the Low Amateur Frequencies," *QST*, Oct 1975, p 22.

Ref. 765: Dennis Kozakoff - W4AZW, "Designing Small Vertical Antennas," *QST*, Aug 1976, p 24.

Ref. 766: Ronald Gorski - W9KYZ, "Efficient Short Radiators," *QST*, Apr 1977, p 37.

Ref. 767: Richard Lodwig - W2KK, "The Inverted-L Antenna," *QST*, Apr 1977, p 32.

Ref. 768: Asa Collins - K6VV, "A Multiband Vertical Radiator," *QST*, Apr 1977, p 22.

Ref. 769: Walter Schultz - K3OQF, "Slant-Wire Feed for Grounded Towers," *QST*, May 1977, p 23.

Ref. 770: Yardley Beers - WØJF, "Optimizing Vertical Antenna Performance," *QST*, Oct 1977, p 15.

Ref. 771: Walter Schultz - K3OQF, "Designing a Vertical Antenna," *QST*, Sep 1978, p 19.

Ref. 772: John S. Belrose - VE2CV, "A Kite Supported 160M (or 80M) Antenna for Portable Application," *QST*, Mar 1981, p 40.

Ref. 773: Wayne Sandford - K3EQ, "A Modest 45 Foot Tall DX Vertical for 160 - 80 - 40 and 30 Meters," *QST*, Sep 1981, p 27.

Ref. 774: Doug DeMaw - W1FB, "Shunt Fed Towers - Some Practical Aspects," *QST*, Oct 1982, p 21.

Ref. 775: John F. Lindholm - W1XX, "The Inverted L Revisited," *QST*, Jan 1983, p 20.

Ref. 776: Carl Eichenauer - W2QIP, "A Top Fed Vertical Antenna for 1.8 MHz. Plus 3," *QST*, Sep 1983, p 25.

Ref. 777: Robert Snyder - KE2S, "Modified Butternut Vertical for 80-Meter Operation," *QST*, Apr 1985, p 50.

Ref. 778: Doug DeMaw - W1FB, "A Remotely Switched Inverted-L Antenna," *QST*, May 1985, p 37.

Ref. 779: Pat Hawker - G3VA, "Technical Topics: Low Angle Operation," *Radio Communication*, Apr 1971, p 262.

Ref. 780: Pat Hawker - G3VA, "Technical Topics: Improving the T Antenna," *Radio Communication*, Sep 1978, p 770.

Ref. 781: J. Bazley - G3HCT, "A 7 MHz Vertical Antenna," *Radio Communication*, Jan 1979, p 26.

Ref. 782: P.J. Horwood - G3FRB, "Feed Impedance of Loaded l/4 Vertical Antennas and the Effects of Earth Systems," *Radio Communication*, Oct 1981, p 911.

Ref. 783: Pat Hawker - G3VA, "Technical Topics: The Inverted Groundplane Family," *Radio Communication*, May 1983, p 424.

Ref. 784: Pat Hawker - G3VA, "Technical Topics: More on Groundplanes," *Radio Communication*, Sep 1983, p 798.

Ref. 785: Pat Hawker - G3VA, "Technical Topics: Sloping One-Mast Yagi," *Radio Communication*, Oct 1983, p 892.

Ref. 786: V. C. Lear - G3TKN, "Gamma Matching Towers and Masts at Lower Frequencies," *Radio Communication*, Mar 1986, p 176.

Ref. 787: B. Wermager - KØEOU, "A Truly Broadband Antenna for 80/75 Meters," *QST*, Apr 1986, p 23.

Ref. 788: Pat Hawker - G3VA, "Technical Topics: Elements of Non-Uniform Cross Section," *Radio Communication*, Jan 1986, p 36.

Ref. 789: Andy Bourassa - WA1LJJ, "Build a Top-hat Vertical Antenna for 80/75 Meters," *CQ,* Aug 1990, p 18.

Ref. 790: Carl C. Drumeller - W5JJ, "Using Your Tower as an Antenna," *CQ,* Dec 1977, p 75.

Ref. 791: Carl Huether - KM1H, "Build a High-performance Extended Bandwidth 160 Meter Vertical," *CQ,* Dec 1986, p 38.

Ref. 792: John Belrose - VE2CV, "More on the Half Sloper," *QST*, Feb 1991, p 39.

Ref. 793: Pat Hawker - G3VA, "The Folded Dipole and Monopole," *Radio Communication*, Jul 1987, p 496.

Ref. 794: C. J. Michaels - W7XC, "Evolution of the Short Top-loaded Vertical," *QST*, Mar 1990, p 26.

Ref. 795: Walter J. Schulz - K3OQF, "Calculating the Input Impedance of a Tapered Vertical," *Ham Radio,* Aug 1985, p 24.

Ref. 796: C. J. Michaels - W7XC, "Some Reflections on Vertical Antennas," *QST*, Jul 1987, p 15.

Ref. 797: C.J. Michaels - W7XC, "Loading Coils for 160 Meter Antennas," *QST*, Apr 1990, p 28.

Ref. 798: D. DeMaw - W1FB, "The 160-meter Antenna Dilemma," *QST*, Nov 1990, p 30.

Ref. 799: Al Christman - KB8I, "Elevated Vertical Antenna Systems Q&A," *QST*, May 1989, p 50.

Ref. 7991: H. Hille - DL1VU, "Vortschritte in der Entwicklung von Vertikalantennen," *CQ-DL*, Oct 1989, p 631.

Ref. 7992: Doug DeMaw - W1FB, "Trap for Shunt-fed Towers," *QST*, Jun 1984, p 40.

Ref. 7993: W. J. Byron - W7DHD, "Ground Mounted Vertical Antennas," *Ham Radio*, Jun 1990, p 11.

Ref. 7994: Dennis N. Monticelli - AE6C, "A Simple Effective Dual-band Inverted-L Antenna," *QST*, Jul 1991, p 38.

Ref. 7995: Walter J. Schultz - K3OQF, "The Folded Wire Fed Top Loaded Grounded Vertical," *Ham Radio*, May 1989, p 32.

Ref. 7996: Gary Nichols - KD9SV and Lynn Gerig - WA9FGR, "Low Band Verticals and How to Feed Them," *CQ*, Aug 1990, p 46.

Ref. 7997: "The phase and magnitude of earth currents near transmitting antennas," *Proceedings IRE*, Vol 23, no. 2, Feb 1935, p 168.

■ 8. ANTENNAS: GROUND SYSTEMS

Ref. 800: Jager, "Effect of Earth's Surface on Antenna Patterns in the Short Wave Range," *Int. Elek. Rundshau*, Aug 1970, p 101.

Ref. 801: G. H. Brown - et al, "Ground Systems as a Factor in Antenna Efficiency," Proceedings IRE, Jun 1937, p 753.

Ref. 802: Abbott, "Design of Optimum Buried RF Ground Systems," Proceedings IRE, Jul 1952, p 846.

Ref. 803: Monteath, "The Effect of Ground Constants of an Earth System on Vertical Aerials," *Proceedings IRE*, Jan 1958, p 292.

Ref. 804: Caid, "Earth Resistivity and Geological Structure," *Electrical Engineering*, Nov 1935, p 1153.

Ref. 805: "Calculated Pattern of a Vertical Antenna With a Finite Radial-Wire Ground System," *Radio Science*, Jan 1973, p 81.

Ref. 806: John E. Magnusson - WØAGD, "Improving Antenna Performance," *CQ*, Jun 1981, p 32.

Ref. 807: "Improving Vertical Antenna Efficiency: A Study of Radial Wire Ground Systems," *CQ*, Apr 1984, p 24.

Ref. 808: Robert Leo - W7LR, "Vertical Antenna Ground System," *Ham Radio*, May 1974, p 30.

Ref. 809: Robert Sherwood - WBØJGP, "Ground Screen - Alternative to Radials," *Ham Radio*, May 1977, p 22.

Ref. 810: Alan M. Christman - WD8CBJ, "Ground Systems for Vertical Antennas," *Ham Radio*, Aug 1979, p 31.

Ref. 811: H. Vance Mosser - K3ZAP, "Installing Radials for Vertical Antennas," *Ham Radio*, Oct 1980, p 56.

Ref. 813: Bradley Wells - KR7L, "Installing Effective Ground Systems," *Ham Radio*, Sep 1983, p 67.

Ref. 814: Marc Bacon - WB9VWA, "Verticals Over REAL Ground," *Ham Radio*, Jan 1984, p 35.

Ref. 815: Harry Hyder - W7IV, "Build a Simple Wire Plow," *Ham Radio*, May 1984, p 107.

Ref. 816: John Stanley - K4ERO/HC1, "Optimum Ground System for Vertical Antennas," *QST*, Dec 1976, p 13.

Ref. 817: Roger Hoestenbach - W5EGS, "Improving Earth Ground Characteristics," *QST*, Dec 1976, p 16.

Ref. 818: Jerry Sevick - W2FMI, "Short Ground Radial Systems for Short Verticals," *QST*, Apr 1978, p 30.

Ref. 819: Jerry Sevick - W2FMI, "Measuring Soil Conductivity," *QST*, Mar 1981, p 38.

Ref. 820: Archibald C. Doty - K8CFU - et al, "Efficient Ground Systems for Vertical Antennas," *QST*, Feb 1983, p 20.

Ref. 821: Brian Edward - N2MF, "Radial Systems for Ground-Mounted Vertical Antennas," *QST*, Jun 1985, p 28.

Ref. 822: Pat Hawker - G3VA, "Technical Topics: Vertical Polarization and Large Earth Screens," *Radio Communication*, Dec 1978, p 1023.

Ref. 823: P. J. Horwood - G3FRB, "Feed Impedance of Loaded ¼ Wave Vertical Antenna Systems," *Radio Communication*, Oct 1981, p 911.

Ref. 824: J. A. Frey - W3ESU, "The Minipoise," *CQ*, Aug 1985, p 30.

Ref. 825: Al Christman - KB8I, "Elevated Vertical Antenna Systems," *QST*, Aug 1988, p 35.

■ 9. ANTENNA ARRAYS

Ref. 900: Bill Guimont - W7KW, "Liftoff on 80 Meters," *CQ*, Oct 1979, p 38.

Ref. 901: Guenter Schwarzbeck - DL1BU, "HB9CV Antenna," *CQ-DL*, Jan 1983, p 10.

Ref. 902: Rudolf Fisher - DL6WD, "Das Monster - eine 2 Element Delta-Loop fuer 3.5 MHz," *CQ-DL*, Jul 1983, p 331.

Ref. 903: G. E. Smith - W4AEO, "Log-Periodic Antennas for 40 Meters," *Ham Radio*, May 1973, p 16.

Ref. 904: G. E. Smith - W4AEO, "80- and 40-Meter Log-Periodic Antennas," *Ham Radio*, Sep 1973, p 44.

Ref. 905: G. E. Smith - W4AEO, "Log-Periodic Antenna Design," *Ham Radio*, May 1975, p 14.

Ref. 906: Jerry Swank - W8HXR, "Phased Vertical Array," *Ham Radio*, May 1975, p 24.

Ref. 907: Henry Keen - W5TRS, "Electrically-Steered Phased Array," *Ham Radio*, May 1975, p 52.

Ref. 908: Gary Jordan - WA6TKT, "Understanding the ZL Special Antenna," *Ham Radio*, May 1976, p 38.

Ref. 909: William Tucker - W4FXE, "Fine Tuning the Phased Vertical Array," *Ham Radio*, May 1977, p 46.

Ref. 910: Paul Kiesel - K7CW, "Seven-Element 40-Meter Quad," *Ham Radio*, Aug 1978, p 30.

Ref. 911: Eugene B. Fuller - W2LU, "Sloping 80-meter Array," *Ham Radio*, May 1979, p 70.

Ref. 912: Harold F. Tolles - W7ITB, "Scaling Antenna Elements," *Ham Radio*, Jul 1979, p 58.

Ref. 913: P. A. Scholz - W6PYK - et al, "Log-Periodic Antenna Design," *Ham Radio*, Dec 1979, p 34.

Ref. 914: James Lawson - W2PV, "Yagi Antenna Design: Experiments Confirm Computer Analysis," *Ham Radio*, Feb 1980, p 19.

Ref. 915: James Lawson - W2PV, "Yagi Antenna Design: Multi-Element Simplistic Beams," *Ham Radio*, Jun 1980, p 33.

Ref. 916: Paul Scholtz - W6PYK - et al, "Log Periodic Fixed-Wire Beams for 75-Meter DX," *Ham Radio*, Mar 1980, p 40.

Ref. 917: George E. Smith - W4AEO, "Log Periodic Fixed-Wire Beams for 40 Meters," *Ham Radio*, Apr 1980, p 26.

Ref. 918: Ed Marriner - W6XM, "Phased Vertical Antenna for 21 MHz," *Ham Radio,* Jun 1980, p 42.

Ref. 919: William M. Kelsey - N8ET, "Three-Element Switchable Quad for 40 Meters," *Ham Radio,* Oct 1980, p 26.

Ref. 920: Patrick McGuire - WB5HGR, "Pattern Calculation for Phased Vertical Arrays," *Ham Radio,* May 1981, p 40.

Ref. 921: Forrest Gehrke - K2BT, "Vertical Phased Arrays - Part 1," *Ham Radio,* May 1983, p 18.

Ref. 922: Forrest Gehrke - K2BT, "Vertical Phased Arrays - Part 2," *Ham Radio,* Jun 1983, p 24.

Ref. 923: Forrest Gehrke - K2BT, "Vertical Phased Arrays - Part 3," *Ham Radio,* Jul 1983, p 26.

Ref. 924: Forrest Gehrke - K2BT, "Vertical Phased Arrays - Part 4," *Ham Radio,* Oct 1983, p 34.

Ref. 925: Forrest Gehrke - K2BT, "Vertical Phased Arrays - Part 5," *Ham Radio,* Dec 1983, p 59.

Ref. 926: R. C. Marshall - G3SBA, "An End Fed Multiband 8JK," *Ham Radio,* May 1984, p 81.

Ref. 927: Forrest Gehrke - K2BT, "Vertical Phased Arrays - Part 6," *Ham Radio,* May 1984, p 45.

Ref. 928: R. R. Schellenbach - W1JF, "The End Fed 8JK - A Switchable Vertical Array," *Ham Radio,* May 1985, p 53.

Ref. 929: Al Christman - KB8I, "Feeding Phased Arrays - an Alternate Method," *Ham Radio,* May 1985, p 58.

Ref. 930: Dana Atchley - W1HKK, "A Switchable Four Element 80-Meter Phased Array," *QST,* Mar 1965, p 48.

Ref. 931: James Lawson - W2PV, "A 75/80-Meter Vertical Antenna Square Array," *QST,* Mar 1971, p 18.

Ref. 932: James Lawson - W2PV, "Simple Arrays of Vertical Antenna Elements," *QST,* May 1971, p 22.

Ref. 933: Gary Elliott - KH6HCM/W7UXP, "Phased Verticals for 40-Meters," *QST,* Apr 1972, p 18.

Ref. 934: Jerry Sevick - W2FMI, "The W2FMI 20-meter Vertical Beam," *QST,* Jun 1972, p 14.

Ref. 935: Robert Myers - W1FBY - et al, "Phased Verticals in a 40-Meter Beam Switching Array," *QST,* Aug 1972, p 36.

Ref. 936: Robert Jones - KH6AD, "A 7-MHz Parasitic Array," *QST,* Nov 1973, p 39.

Ref. 937: J. G. Botts - K4EQJ, "A Four-Element Vertical Beam for 40/15 Meters," *QST,* Jun 1975, p 30.

Ref. 938: Jarda Dvoracek - OK1ATP, "160-Meter DX with a Two-Element Beam," *QST,* Oct 1975, p 20.

Ref. 939: Dana Atchley - W1CF - et al, "360 Degree - Steerable Vertical Phased Arrays," *QST,* Apr 1976, p 27.

Ref. 940: Richard Fenwick - K5RR - et al, "Broadband Steerable Phased Arrays," *QST,* Apr 1977, p 18.

Ref. 941: Dana Atchley - W1CF, "Updating Phased Array Technology," *QST,* Aug 1978, p 22.

Ref. 942: Bob Hickman - WB6ZZJ, "The Poly Tower Phased Array," *QST,* Jan 1981, p 30.

Ref. 943: W. B. Bachelor - AC3K, "Combined Vertical Directivity," *QST,* Feb 1981, p 19.

Ref. 944: Walter J. Schultz - K3OQF, "Vertical Array Analysis," *QST,* Feb 1981, p 22.

Ref. 945: Edward Peter Swynar - VE3CUI, "40 Meters with a Phased Delta Loop," *QST,* May 1984, p 20.

Ref. 946: Riki Kline - 4X4NJ, "Build a 4X Array for 160 Meters," *QST,* Feb 1985, p 21.

Ref. 947: Trygve Tondering - OZ1TD, "Phased Verticals," *Radio Communication*, May 1972, p 294.

Ref. 948: Pat Hawker - G3VA, "Technical Topics: The Half Square Aerial," *Radio Communication*, Jun 1974, p 380.

Ref. 949: J. L. Lawson - W2PV, "Yagi Antenna Design," *Ham Radio,* Jan 1980, p 22.

Ref. 950: J. L. Lawson - W2PV, "Yagi Antenna Design," *Ham Radio,* Feb 1980, p 19.

Ref. 951: J. L. Lawson - W2PV, "Yagi Antenna Design," *Ham Radio,* May 1980, p 18.

Ref. 952: J. L. Lawson - W2PV, "Yagi Antenna Design," *Ham Radio,* Jun 1980, p 33.

Ref. 953: J. L. Lawson - W2PV, "Yagi Antenna Design," *Ham Radio,* Jul 1980, p 18.

Ref. 953: J. L. Lawson - W2PV, "Yagi Antenna Design," *Ham Radio,* Sep 1980, p 37.

Ref. 954: J. L. Lawson - W2PV, "Yagi Antenna Design," *Ham Radio,* Oct 1980, p 29.

Ref. 955: J. L. Lawson - W2PV, "Yagi Antenna Design," *Ham Radio,* Nov 1980, p 22.

Ref. 956: J. L. Lawson - W2PV, "Yagi Antenna Design," *Ham Radio,* Dec 1980, p 30.

Ref. 957: J. L. Lawson - W2PV, *Yagi Antenna Design*, ARRL, Dec 1986

Ref. 958: Dick Weber - K5IU, "Determination of Yagi Wind Loads Using the Cross-flow Principle," *Communications Quarterly*, Apr 1993.

Ref. 959: Roy Lewallen - W7EL, "The Impact of Current Distribution on Array Patterns," *QST,* Jul 1990, p 39.

Ref. 960: Robert H. Mitchell - N5RM, "The Forty Meter Flame Thrower," *CQ,* Dec 1987, p 36.

Ref. 961: Ralph Fowler - N6YC, "The W8JK Antenna," *Ham Radio,* May 1988, p 9.

Ref. 962: Jurgen A Weigl - OE5CWL, "A Shortened 40-meter Four-element Sloping Dipole Array," *Ham Radio,* May 1988, p 74.

Ref. 963: Al Christman - KB8I, "Phase Driven Arrays for the Low Bands," *QST,* May 1992, p 49.

Ref. 964: D. Leeson - W6QHS, *Physical Design of Yagi Antennas*, ARRL, Newington, CT.

Ref. 965: Dick Weber - K5IU, "Vibration Induced Yagi Fatigue Failures," *Ham Radio,* Aug 1989, p 9.

Ref. 966: Dick Weber - K5IU, "Structural Evaluation of Yagi Elements," *Ham Radio,* Dec 1988, p 29.

Ref. 967: Dave Leeson - W6QHS, "Strengthening the Cushcraft 40-2CD," *QST,* Nov 1991, p 36.

Ref. 968: R. Lahlum - W1MK, "Technical Correspondence," *QST,* Mar 1991, p 39.

■ 10. BROADBAND ANTENNAS

Ref. 1000: Larry Strain - N7DF, "3.5 to 30 MHz Discage Antenna," *CQ,* Apr 1984, p 18.

Ref. 1001: F. J. Bauer - W6FPO, "Low SWR Dipole Pairs for 1.8 through 3.5 MHz," *Ham Radio,* Oct 1972, p 42.

Ref. 1002: M. Walter Maxwell - W2DU, "A Revealing Analysis of the Coaxial Dipole Antenna," *Ham Radio,* Jul 1976, p 46.

Ref. 1003: Terry Conboy - N6RY, "Broadband 80-meter Antennas," *Ham Radio,* May 1979, p 44.

Ref. 1004: Mason Logan - K4MT, "Stagger Tuned Dipoles Increase Bandwidth," *Ham Radio,* May 1983, p 22.

Ref. 1005: C. C. Whysall, "The Double Bazooka," *QST,* Jul 1968, p 38.

Ref. 1006: John S. Belrose - VE2CV, "The Discone HF Antenna," *QST,* Jul 1975, p 11.

Ref. 1007: Allen Harbach - WA4DRU, "Broadband 80 Meter Antenna," *QST,* Dec 1980, p 36.

Ref. 1008: Jerry Hall - K1TD, "The Search for a Simple Broadband 80-meter Dipole," *QST,* Apr 1983, p 22.

Ref. 1009: John Grebenkemper - KA3BLO, "Multiband Trap and Parallel HF Dipoles - a Comparison," *QST,* May 1985, p 26.

Ref. 1010: N. H. Sedgwick - G8WV, "Broadband Cage Aerials," *Radio Communication,* May 1965, p 287.

Ref. 1011: Pat Hawker - G3VA, "Technical Topics: Broadband Bazooka Dipole," *Radio Communication,* Aug 1976, p 601.

Ref. 1012: Frank Witt - AI1H, "The Coaxial Resonator Match and the Broadband Dipole," *QST,* Apr 1989, p 22.

Ref. 1013: Frank Witt - AI1H, "Match Bandwidth of Resonant Antenna Systems," *QST,* Oct 1991, p 21.

■ 11. LOOP ANTENNAS

Ref. 1100: William Orr - W6SAI, *All About Cubical Quads,* Radio Publications Inc.

Ref. 1101: Bill Salerno - W2ONV, "The W2ONV Delta/Sloper Antenna," *CQ,* Aug 1978, p 86.

Ref. 1102: Roy A. Neste - W0WFO, "Dissecting Loop Antennas To Find Out What Makes Them Tick," *CQ,* Aug 1984, p 36.

Ref. 1103: Rolf Schick - DL3AO, "Loop - Dipol und Vertikalantennen - Vergleiche und Erfahrungen," *CQ-DL,* Mar 1979, p 115.

Ref. 1104: Guenter Schwarzbeck - DL1BU, "DX Antennen fuer 80 und 160 Meter," *CQ-DL,* Apr 1979, p 150.

Ref. 1105: Gunter Steppert - DK8NG, "Zweielement Delta Loop mit einem Mast," *CQ-DL,* Aug 1980, p 370.

Ref. 1106: Hans Wurtz - DL2FA, "DX-Antennen mit spiegelenden Flaechen," *CQ-DL,* Apr 1981, p 162.

Ref. 1107: Hans Wurtz - DL2FA, "DX-Antennen mit spiegelenden Flaechen," *CQ-DL,* Dec 1981, p 583.

Ref. 1108: Dieter Pelz - DF3IK et al, "Rahmenantenne — keine Wunderantenne," *CQ-DL,* Sep 1982, p 435.

Ref. 1109: Willi Nitschke - DJ5DW - et al, "Richtkarakteristik - Fusspunktwiderstand etc von Einelementantennen," *CQ-DL,* Dec 1982, p 580.

Ref. 1110: Hans Wurtz - DL2FA, "DX-Antennen mit spiegelenden Flaechen," *CQ-DL,* Feb 1983, p 64.

Ref. 1111: Rudolf Fisher - DL6WD, "Das Monster - eine 2-Element Delta-Loop fuer 3.5 MHz," *CQ-DL,* Jul 1983, p 331.

Ref. 1112: John True - W4OQ, "Low Frequency Loop Antennas," *Ham Radio,* Dec 1976, p 18.

Ref. 1113: Paul Kiesel - K7CW, "7-Element 40-Meter Quad," *Ham Radio,* Jul 1978, p 30.

Ref. 1114: Glenn Williman - N2GW, "Delta Loop Array," *Ham Radio,* Jul 1978, p 16.

Ref. 1115: Frank J. Witt - W1DTV, "Top Loaded Delta Loop Antenna," *Ham Radio,* Dec 1978, p 57.

Ref. 1116: George Badger - W6TC, "Compact Loop Antenna for 40 and 80-Meter DX," *Ham Radio,* Oct 1979, p 24.

Ref. 1117: William M. Kesley - N8ET, "Three Element Switchable Quad for 40 Meters," *Ham Radio,* Oct 1980, p 26.

Ref. 1118: Jerrold Swank - W8HXR, "Two Delta Loops Fed in Phase," *Ham Radio,* Aug 1981, p 50.

Ref. 1119: Hasan Schiers - N0AN, "The Half Square Antenna," *Ham Radio,* Dec 1981, p 48.

Ref. 1120: John S. Belrose - VE2CV, "The Half Delta Loop," *Ham Radio,* May 1982, p 37.

Ref. 1121: V.C. Lear - G3TKN, "Reduced Size, Full Performance Corner Fed Delta Loop," *Ham Radio,* Jan 1985, p 67.

Ref. 1122: Lewis Mc Coy - W1ICP, "The Army Loop in Ham Communication," *QST,* Mar 1968, p 17.

Ref. 1123: J. Wessendorp - HB9AGK, "Loop Measurements," *QST,* Nov 1968, p 46.

Ref. 1124: F.N. Van Zant - W2EGH, "160, 75 and 40 Meter Inverted Dipole Delta Loop," *QST,* Jan 1973, p 37.

Ref. 1125: Ben Venster - K3DC, "The Half Square Antenna," *QST,* Mar 1974, p 11.

Ref. 1126: John Kaufmann - WA1CQW et al, "A Convenient Stub Tuning System for Quad Antennas," *QST,* May 1975, p 18.

Ref. 1127: Robert Edlund - W5DS, "The W5DS Hula-Hoop Loop," *QST,* Oct 1975, p 16.

Ref. 1128: Donald Belcher - WA4JVE et al, "Loops vs Dipole Analysis and Discussion," *QST,* Aug 1976, p 34.

Ref. 1129: Roger Sparks - W7WKB, "Build this C-T Quad Beam for Reduced Size," *QST,* Apr 1977, p 29.

Ref. 1130: John S. Belrose - VE2CV, "The Half-Delta Loop: a Critical Analysis and Practical Deployment," *QST,* Sep 1982, p 28.

Ref. 1131: Richard Gray - W9JJV, "The Two Band Delta Loop Antenna," *QST,* Mar 1983, p 36.

Ref. 1132: Edward Peter Swynar - VE3CUI, "40 Meters with a Phased Delta Loop," *QST,* May 1984, p 20.

Ref. 1133: Doug DeMaw - W1FB et al, "The Full-Wave Delta Loop at Low Height," *QST,* Oct 1984, p 24.

Ref. 1134: Pat Hawker - G3VA, "Technical Topics: Another Look at Transmitting Loops," *Radio Communication,* Jun 1971, p 392.

Ref. 1135: Pat Hawker - G3VA, "Technical Topics: Vertically Polarized Loop Elements," *Radio Communication,* Jun 1973, p 404.

Ref. 1136: Laury Mayhead - G3AQC, "Loop Aerials Close to Ground," *Radio Communication,* May 1974, p 298.

Ref. 1137: Pat Hawker - G3VA, "Technical Topics: The Half Square Aerial," *Radio Communication,* Jun 1974, p 380.

Ref. 1138: Pat Hawker - G3VA, "Miniaturized Quad Elements," *Radio Communication,* Mar 1976, p 206.

Ref. 1139: Pat Hawker - G3VA, "Technical Topics: Radiation Resistance of Medium Loops," *Radio Communication,* Feb 1979, p 131.

Ref. 1140: F. Rasvall - SM5AGM, "The Gain of the Quad," *Radio Communication,* Aug 1980, p 784.

Ref. 1141: Pat Hawker - G3VA, "Technical Topics: Polygonal Loop Antennas," *Radio Communication*, Feb 1981.

Ref. 1142: B. Myers - K1GQ, "The W2PV 80-Meter Quad," *Ham Radio,* May 1986, p 56.

Ref. 1143: Bill Orr - W6SAI, "A Two-Band Loop Antenna," *Ham Radio,* Sep 1987, p 57.

Ref. 1144: R. P. Haviland - W4MB, "The Quad Antenna - Part 1," *Ham Radio,* May 1988.

Ref. 1145: R. P. Haviland - W4MB, "The Quad Antenna - Part 2," *Ham Radio,* Jun 1988, p 54.

Ref. 1146: R. P. Haviland W4MB, "The Quad Antenna - part 3," *Ham Radio,* Aug 1988, p 34.

Ref. 1147: C. Drayton Cooper - N4LBJ, "The Bi-Square array," *Ham Radio,* May 1990, p 42.

Ref. 1148: Bill Myers - K1GQ, "Analyzing 80 Meter Delta Loop Arrays," *Ham Radio,* Sep 1986, p 10.

Ref. 1149: Dave Donnelly - K2SS, "Yagi vs. Quad - Part 1," *Ham Radio,* May 1988, p 68.

Ref. 1150: D. DeMaw - W1FB, "A Closer Look at Horizontal Loop Antennas," *QST,* May 1990, p 28.

■ 12. RECEIVING ANTENNAS

Ref. 1200: I. Herliz, "Analysis of Action of Wave Antennas," *AIEE Transactions*, Vol 42, May 1942, p 260.

Ref. 1201: "Diversity Receiving System of RCA Communications for Radio Telegraphy," *AIEE Transactions*, Vol 42, May 1923, p 215.

Ref. 1202: Peterson Beverage, "The Wave Antenna: a New Type of Highly Directive Antenna," *Proc IRE*.

Ref. 1203: Dean Baily, "Receiving System for Long-Wave Transatlantic Radio Telephone," *Proc IRE*, Dec 1928.

Ref. 1204: *Antennas for Reception of Standard Broadcast Signals*, FCC Report, Apr 1958.

Ref. 1205: R. Schetgen - KU7G - ed, *The ARRL Handbook for the Radio Amateur*, ARRL, Newington, CT.

Ref. 1206: Victor Misek - W1WCR, *The Beverage Antenna Handbook,*

Ref. 1207: William Orr - W6SAI, *Radio Handbook*, Howard W. Sams & Co. Inc.

Ref. 1210: Bob Clarke - N1RC, "Six Antennas from Three Wires," 73, Oct 1983, p 10.

Ref. 1211: Davis Harold - W8MTI, "The Wave Antenna," *CQ,* May 1978, p 24.

Ref. 1212: Ulrich Rohde - DJ2LR, "Active Antennas," *CQ,* Dec 1982, p 20.

Ref. 1213: Karl Hille - 9A1VU, "Vom Trafo zum Kurzwellenempgaenger," *CQ-DL*, Mar 1977, p 99.

Ref. 1214: Dieter Pelz - DF3IK et al, "Rahmenantenne - keine Wunderantenne-," *CQ-DL*, Sep 1982, p 435.

Ref. 1215: Hans Wurtz - DL2FA, "Magnetische Antennen," *CQ-DL*, Feb 1983, p 64.

Ref. 1216: Hans Wurtz - DL2FA, "Magnetische Antennen," *CQ-DL*, Apr 1983, p 170.

Ref. 1217: Hans Wurtz - DL2FA, "Elektrisch Magnetische Beam Antennen (EMBA)," *CQ-DL*, Jul 1983, p 326.

Ref. 1218: Guenter Shwarzenbeck - DL1BU, "Rhamen- und Ringantennen," *CQ-DL*, May 1984, p 226.

Ref. 1219: Charles Bird - K6HTM, "160-Meter Loop for Receiving," *Ham Radio,* May 1974, p 46.

Ref. 1220: Ken Cornell - W2IMB, "Loop Antenna Receiving Aid," *Ham Radio,* May 1975, p 66.

Ref. 1221: John True - W4OQ, "Loop Antennas," *Ham Radio,* Dec 1976.

Ref. 1222: Henry Keen - W5TRS, "Selective Receiving Antennas: a Progress Report," *Ham Radio,* May 1978, p 20.

Ref. 1223: Byrd H. Brunemeier - KG6RT, "40-Meter Beverage Antenna," *Ham Radio,* Jul 1979, p 40.

Ref. 1224: David Atkins - W6VX, "Capacitively Loaded Dipole," *Ham Radio,* May 1984, p 33.

Ref. 1225: H. H. Beverage, "A Wave Antenna for 200 Meter Reception," *QST*, Nov 1922, p 7.

Ref. 1226: John Isaacs - W6PZV, "Transmitter Hunting on 75 Meters," *QST*, Jun 1958, p 38.

Ref. 1227: Lewis McCoy - W1ICP, "The Army Loop in Ham Communication," *QST*, Mar 1968, p 17.

Ref. 1228: J. Wessendorp - HB9AGK, "Loop Measurements," *QST*, Nov 1968, p 46.

Ref. 1229: Katashi Nose - KH6IJ, "A 160 Meter Receiving Loop," *QST*, Apr 1975, p 40.

Ref. 1230: Tony Dorbuck - W1YNC, "Radio Direction Finding Techniques," *QST*, Aug 1975, p 30.

Ref. 1231: Robert Edlund - W5DS, "The W5DS Hula-Hoop Loop," *QST*, Oct 1975, p 16.

Ref. 1232: Doug DeMaw - W1FB, "Build this 'Quickie' Preamp," *QST*, Apr 1977, p 43.

Ref. 1233: Larry Boothe - W9UCW, "Weak Signal Reception on 160. Some Antenna Notes," *QST*, Jun 1977, p 35.

Ref. 1234: Doug DeMaw - W1FB, "Low-Noise Receiving Antennas," *QST*, Dec 1977, p 36.

Ref. 1235: Doug DeMaw - W1FB, "Maverick Trackdown," *QST*, Jul 1980, p 22.

Ref. 1236: John Belrose - VE2CE, "Beverage Antennas for Amateur Communications," *QST*, Sep 1981, p 51.

Ref. 1237: H. H. Beverage, "H. H. Beverage on Beverage Antennas," *QST*, Dec 1981, p 55.

Ref. 1238: Doug DeMaw - W1FB et al, "The Classic Beverage Antenna Revisited," *QST*, Jan 1982, p 11.

Ref. 1239: John Webb - W1ETC, "Electrical Null Steering," *QST*, Oct 1982, p 28.

Ref. 1240: John F. Belrose - VE2CV et al, "The Beverage Antenna for Amateur Communications," *QST*, Jan 1983, p 22.

Ref. 1241: Doug DeMaw - W1FB, "Receiver Preamps and How to Use Them," *QST*, Apr 1984, p 19.

Ref. 1242: Pat Hawker - G3VA, "Technical Topics: Beverage Aerials," *Radio Communication*, Oct 1970, p 684.

Ref. 1243: Pat Hawker - G3VA, "Technical Topics: All Band Terminated Longwire," *Radio Communication*, Nov 1972, p 745.

Ref. 1244: Pat Hawker - G3VA, "Technical Topics: A 1.8 MHz Active Frame Aerial," *Radio Communication*, Aug 1976, p 601.

Ref. 1245: Pat Hawker - G3VA, "Technical Topics: Low Noise 1.8/3.5 MHz Receiving Antennas," *Radio Communication*, Apr 1978, p 325.

Ref. 1246: Pat Hawker - G3VA, "Technical Topics: Radiation Resistance of Medium Loops," *Radio Communication*, Feb 1979, p 131.

Ref. 1247: J.A. Lambert - G3FNZ, "A Directional Active Loop Receiving Antenna System," *Radio Communication*, Nov 1982, p 944.

Ref. 1248: R.C. Fenwick - K5RR, "A Loop Array for 160 Meters," *CQ*, Apr 1986, p 25.

Ref. 1249: Mike Crabtree - ABØX, "Some Thoughts on 160 meter receiving antennas for city lots," *CQ*, Jan 1988, p 26.

Ref. 1250: J. Wollweber - DF5PY, "Die Magnetisch Antenne - eine Wunderantenne," *CQ-DL*, Mar 1987, p 149.

Ref. 1251: Gary R. Nichols - KD9SV, "Variable gain 160-meter preamp," *Ham Radio*, Oct 1989, p 46.

Ref. 1252: Robert H. Johns - W3JIP, "How to Build an Indoor Transmitting Loop," *CQ*, Dec 1991, p 30.

Ref. 1253: Robert H. Johns - W3JIP, "How to Build an Indoor Transmitting Loop," *CQ*, Jan 1992, p 42.

Ref. 1254: D. DeMaw - W1FB, "On-Ground Low-Noise Receiving Antennas," *QST*, Apr 1988, p 30.

Ref. 1255: Juergen Schaefer - DL7PE, "Die Rahmantenne - eine Befehlsantenne zum Selbstbau," *CQ-DL*, Jan 1990, p 21.

Ref. 1256: D. DeMaw - W1FB, "Preamplifier for 80 and 160 M Loop and Beverage Antennas," *QST*, Aug 1988, p 22.

Ref. 1257: A. G. Lyner, "The Beverage Antenna: a practical way of assessing the radiation pattern using off-air signals," *BBC RD*, 1991/92.

Ref. 1258: B. H. Brunemeier - KG6RT, "Short Beverage for 40 meters," *HR* July 1979, p 40.

■ 13. TRANSMISSION LINES

Ref. 1300: Wilkinson, "An N-Way Hybrid Power Divider," *IRE Transactions on Microwave*, Jan 1960.

Ref. 1301: R. Schetgen - KU7G, *The ARRL Handbook for the Radio Amateur*, ARRL, Newington, CT.

Ref. 1302: Pat Hawker - G3VA, *Amateur Radio Techniques*, RSGB.

Ref. 1303: Keith Henney, *Radio Engineering Handbook - 5th ed.*

Ref. 1304: *Reference Data for Radio Engineers*, 5th ed, Howard W. Sams & Co. Inc.

Ref. 1305: John Devoldere - ON4UN, "80-Meter DXing," *Communications Technology Inc*, Jan 1979.

Ref. 1306: William Orr - W6SAI, *Radio Handbook*, Howard W. Sams & Co. Inc.

Ref. 1307: Gerald L. Hall - K1TD ed., *The ARRL Antenna Book*, ARRL, Newington, CT.

Ref. 1308: Walter Maxwell - W2DU, "Niedriges SWR aus falschem Grund (Teil 1)," *CQ-DL*, Jan 1976, p 3.

Ref. 1309: Walter Maxwell - W2DU, "Niedriges SWR aus falschem Grund (Teil 2)," *CQ-DL*, Feb 1976, p 47.

Ref. 1310: Walter Maxwell - W2DU, "Niedriges SWR aus falschem Grund (Teil 3)," *CQ-DL*, Jun 1976, p 202.

Ref. 1311: Walter Maxwell - W2DU, "Niedriges SWR aus falschem Grund (Teil 5)," *CQ-DL*, Sep 1976, p 272.

Ref. 1312: Jim Fisk - W1HR, "The Smith Chart," *Ham Radio*, Nov 1970, p 16.

Ref. 1313: Richard Taylor - W1DAX, "N-Way Power Dividers and 3-dB Hybrids," *Ham Radio*, Aug 1972, p 30.

Ref. 1314: Joseph Boyer - W6UYH, "Antenna-Transmission Line Analogy," *Ham Radio*, Apr 1977, p 52.

Ref. 1315: Joseph Boyer - W6UYH, "Antenna-Transmission Line Analogy - Part 2," *Ham Radio*, May 1977, p 29.

Ref. 1316: J. Reisert - W1JR, "Simple and Efficient Broadband Balun," *Ham Radio*, Sep 1978, p 12.

Ref. 1317: Jack M. Schulman - W6EBY, "T-Network Impedance Matching to Coaxial Feedlines," *Ham Radio*, Sep 1978, p 22.

Ref. 1318: Charlie J. Carroll - K1XX, "Matching 75-Ohm CATV Hardline to 50-Ohm Systems," *Ham Radio*, Sep 1978, p 31.

Ref. 1319: John Battle - N4OE, "What is Your SWR?," *Ham Radio*, Nov 1979, p 48.

Ref. 1320: Henry Elwell - N4UH, "Long Transmission Lines for Optimum Antenna Location," *Ham Radio*, Oct 1980, p 12.

Ref. 1321: John W. Frank - WB9TQG, "Measuring Coax Cable Loss with an SWR Meter," *Ham Radio*, May 1981, p 34.

Ref. 1322: Stan Gibilisco - W1GV/4, "How Important is Low SWR?," *Ham Radio*, Aug 1981, p 33.

Ref. 1323: Lewis T. Fitch - W4VRV, "Matching 75-Ohm Hardline to 50-Ohm Systems," *Ham Radio*, Oct 1982, p 43.

Ref. 1324: L. A. Cholewski - K6CRT, "Some Amateur Applications of the Smith Chart," *QST*, Jan 1960, p 28.

Ref. 1325: Walter Maxwell - W2DU, "Another Look at Reflections - Part 1," *QST*, Apr 1973, p 35.

Ref. 1326: Walter Maxwell - W2DU, "Another Look at Reflections - Part 2," *QST*, Jun 1973, p 20.

Ref. 1327: Walter Maxwell - W2DU, "Another Look at Reflections - Part 3," *QST*, Aug 1973, p 36.

Ref. 1328: Walter Maxwell - W2DU, "Another Look at Reflections - Part 4," *QST*, Oct 1973, p 22.

Ref. 1329: Walter Maxwell - W2DU, "Another Look at Reflections - Part 5," *QST*, Apr 1974, p 26.

Ref. 1330: Walter Maxwell - W2DU, "Another Look at Reflections - Part 6," *QST*, Dec 1974, p 11.

Ref. 1331: Gerald Hall - K1PLP, "Transmission-Line Losses," *QST*, Dec 1975, p 48.

Ref. 1332: Walter Maxwell - W2DU, "Another Look at Reflections - Part 7," *QST*, Aug 1976, p 16.

Ref. 1333: Charles Brainard - WA1ZRS, "Coaxial Cable: The Neglected Link," *QST*, Apr 1981, p 28.

Ref. 1334: Crawford MacKeand - WA3ZKZ, "The Smith Chart in BASIC," *QST*, Nov 1984, p 28.

Ref. 1336: R. C. Hills - G3HRH, "Some Reflections on Standing Waves," *Radio Communication*, Jan 1964, p 15.

Ref. 1337: Pat Hawker - G3VA, "Technical Topics: Another Look at SWR," *Radio Communication*, Jun 1974, p 377.

Ref. 1338: Garside - G3MYT, "More on the Smith Chart," *Radio Communication*, Dec 1977, p 934.

Ref. 1339: Pat Hawker - G3VA, "Technical Topics: SWR How Important?," *Radio Communication*, Jan 1982, p 41.

Ref. 1340: Kenneth Parker - G3PKR, "Reflected Power Does Not Mean Lost Power," *Radio Communication*, Jul 1982, p 581.

Ref. 1341: Pat Hawker - G3VA, "Technical Topics: Reflected Power is Real Power," *Radio Communication*, Jun 1983, p 517.

Ref. 1342: H. Ashcroft - G4CCM, "Critical Study of the SWR Meter," *Radio Communication*, Mar 1985, p 186.

Ref. 1343: Walter Maxwell - W2DU, "Niedriges SWR aus falschem Grund (Teil 4)," *CQ-DL*, Aug 1976, p 238.

Ref. 1344: Lew McCoy - W1ICP, "Coax as Tuned Feeders: Is It Practical?," *CQ*, Aug 1989, p 13.

Ref. 1345: Chet Smith - K1CCL, "Simple Coaxial Cable Measurements," *QST*, Sep 1990, p 25.

Ref. 1346: J. Althouse - K6NY, "Using a Noise Bridge to Measure Coaxial Cable Impedance," *QST*, May 1991, p 45.

Ref. 1347: A.E. Popodi - OE2APM/AA3K, "Measuring Transmission Line Parameters," *Ham Radio*, Sep 1988, p 22.

Ref. 1348: Byron Goodman - W1DX, "My Feed Line Tunes My Antenna," *QST*, Nov 1991, p 33.

Ref. 1349: Gary E. Myers - K9CZB, "Solving Transmission Line Problems on Your C64," *Ham Radio*, May 1986, p 74.

■ 14. MATCHING

Ref. 1400: R. Schetgen - KU7G - ed, *The ARRL Handbook for the Radio Amateur*, ARRL, Newington, CT.

Ref. 1401: Harold Tolles - W7ITB, "Gamma-Match Design," *Ham Radio*, May 1973, p 46.

Ref. 1402: Robert Baird - W7CSD, "Antenna Matching Systems," *Ham Radio*, Jul 1973, p 58.

Ref. 1403: Earl Whyman - W2HB, "Standing-Wave Ratios," *Ham Radio*, Jul 1973, p 26.

Ref. 1404: Robert Leo - W7LR, "Designing L-networks," *Ham Radio*, Feb 1974, p 26.

Ref. 1405: G. E. Smith - W4AEO, "Log-Periodic Feed Systems," *Ham Radio*, Oct 1974, p 30.

Ref. 1406: John True - W4OQ, "Shunt-Fed Vertical Antennas," *Ham Radio*, May 1975, p 34.

Ref. 1407: I. L. McNally - K6WX - et al, "Impedance Matching by Graphical Solution," *Ham Radio*, Mar 1978, p 82.

Ref. 1408: Jim Fisk - W1HR, "Transmission-Line Calculations with the Smith Chart," *Ham Radio*, Mar 1978, p 92.

Ref. 1409: Jack M. Schulman - W6EBY, "T-Network Impedance Matching to Coaxial Feed Lines," *Ham Radio*, Sep 1978, p 22.

Ref. 1410: Ernie Franke - WA2EWT, "Appreciating the L Matching Network," *Ham Radio*, Sep 1980, p 27.

Ref. 1411: Robert Leo - W7LR, "Remote-Controlled 40 - 80 - and 160-Meter Vertical," *Ham Radio*, May 1984, p 38.

Ref. 1412: James Sanford - WB4GCS, "Easy Antenna Matching," *Ham Radio*, May 1984, p 67.

Ref. 1413: Chris Bowick - WD4C, "Impedance Matching: A Brief Review," *Ham Radio*, Jun 1984, p 49.

Ref. 1414: Richard Nelson - WBØIKN, "Basic Gamma Matching," *Ham Radio*, Jan 1985, p 29.

Ref. 1415: L. A. Cholewski - K6CRT, "Some Amateur Applications of the Smith Chart," *QST*, Jan 1960, p 28.

Ref. 1416: Gene Hubbell - W9ERU, "Feeding Grounded Towers as Radiators," *QST*, Jun 1960, p 33.

Ref. 1417: J. D. Gooch - W9YRV - et al, "The Hairpin Match," *QST*, Apr 1962, p 11.

Ref. 1418: Eugene E. Baldwin - WØRUG, "Some Notes on the Care and Feeding of Grounded Verticals," *QST*, Oct 1963, p 45.

Ref. 1419: N. H. Davidson - K5JVF, "Flagpole Without a Flag," *QST*, Nov 1964, p 36.

Ref. 1420: Robert Leo - K7KOK, "An Impedance Matching Method," *QST*, Dec 1968, p 24.

Ref. 1421: D. J. Healey - W3PG, "An Examination of the Gamma Match," *QST*, Apr 1969, p 11.

Ref. 1422: Donald Belcher - WA4JVE, "RF Matching Techniques - Design and Example," *QST*, Oct 1972, p 24.

Ref. 1423: James McAlister - WA5EKA, "Simplified Impedance Matching and the Mac Chart," *QST*, Dec 1972, p 33.

Ref. 1424: John Kaufmann - WA1CQW - et al, "A Convenient Stub Tuning System for Quad Antennas," *QST*, May 1975, p 18.

Ref. 1425: Earl Cunningham - W5RTQ, "Shunt Feeding Towers for Operating on the Low Amateur Frequencies," *QST*, Oct 1975, p 22.

Ref. 1426: Doug DeMaw - W1CER, "Another Method of Shunt Feeding Your Tower," *QST*, Oct 1975, p 25.

Ref. 1427: Jerry Sevick - W2FMI, "Simple Broadband Matching Networks," *QST*, Jan 1976, p 20.

Ref. 1428: Walter Schulz - K3OQF, "Slant-Wire Feed for Grounded Towers," *QST*, May 1977, p 23.

Ref. 1429: Bob Pattison - N6RP, "A Graphical Look at the L Network," *QST*, Mar 1979, p 24.

Ref. 1430: Tony Dorbuck - K1FM, "Matching-Network Design," *QST*, Mar 1979, p 26.

Ref. 1431: Herbert Drake Jr. - N6QE, "A Remotely Controlled Antenna-Matching Network," *QST*, Jan 1980, p 32.

Ref. 1432: Doug DeMaw - W1FB, "Ultimate Transmatch Improved," *QST*, Jul 1980, p 39.

Ref. 1433: Colin Dickman - ZS6U, "The ZS6U Minishack Special," *QST*, Apr 1981, p 32.

Ref. 1434: Claude L. Frantz - F5FC/DJØOT, "A New More Versatile Transmatch," *QST*, Jul 1982, p 31.

Ref. 1435: Doug DeMaw - W1FB, "A 'Multipedance' Broadband Transformer," *QST*, Aug 1982, p 39.

Ref. 1436: Don Johnson - W6AAQ, "Mobile Antenna Matching. Automatically!," *QST*, Oct 1982, p 15.

Ref. 1437: Doug DeMaw - W1FB, "Shunt-Fed Towers: Some Practical Aspects," *QST*, Oct 1982, p 21.

Ref. 1438: Crawford MacKaend - WA3ZKZ, "The Smith Chart in BASIC," *QST*, Nov 1984, p 28.

Ref. 1439: J. A. Ewen - G3HGM, "Design of L-Networks for Matching Antennas to Transmitters," *Radio Communication*, Aug 1984, p 663.

Ref. 1440: H. Ashcroft - G4CCM, "Critical Study of the SWR Meter," *Radio Communication*, Mar 1985, p 186.

Ref. 1441: Rober C Cheek - W3VT, "The L-Match," *Ham Radio*, Feb 1989, p 29.

Ref. 1442: W. Orr - W6SAI, "Antenna Matching Systems," *Ham Radio*, Nov 1989, p 54.

Ref. 1443: Will Herzog - K2LB, "Broadband RF Transformers," *Ham Radio,* Jan 1986, p 75.

Ref. 1444: Richard A. Gardner - N1AYW, "Computerizing Smith Chart Network Analysis," *Ham Radio,* Oct 1989, p 10.

Ref. 1445: Joe Carr - K4IPV, "Impedance Matching," *Ham Radio,* Aug 1988, p 27.

Ref. 1446: I. L. McNally - W1CNK, "Graphic Solution of impedance matching problem," *HR,* May 78, p 82.

■ 15. BALUNS

Ref. 1500: J. Schultz - W4FA, "A Selection of Baluns from Palomar Engineers," *CQ,* Apr 1985, p 32.

Ref. 1501: William Orr - W6SAI, "Broadband Antenna Baluns," *Ham Radio,* Jun 1968, p 6.

Ref. 1502: J. Reisert - W1JR, "Simple and Efficient Broadband Balun," *Ham Radio,* Sep 1978, p 12.

Ref. 1503: John J. Nagle - K4KJ, "High Performance Broadband Balun," *Ham Radio,* Feb 1980, p 28.

Ref. 1504: George Badger - W6TC, "A New Class of Coaxial-Line Transformers," *Ham Radio,* Feb 1980, p 12.

Ref. 1505: George Badger - W6TC, "Coaxial-Line Transformers," *Ham Radio,* Mar 1980, p 18.

Ref. 1506: John Nagle - K4KJ, "The Half-Wave Balun: Theory and Application," *Ham Radio,* Sep 1980, p 32.

Ref. 1507: Roy N. Lehner - WA2SON, "A Coreless Balun," *Ham Radio,* May 1981, p 62.

Ref. 1508: John Nagle - K4KJ, "Testing Baluns," Ham Radio, Aug 1983, p 30.

Ref. 1509: Lewis McCoy - W1ICP, "Is a Balun Required?," *QST*, Dec 1968, p 28.

Ref. 1510: R. H. Turrin - W2IMU, "Application of Broadband Balun Transformers," *QST,* Apr 1969, p 42.

Ref. 1511: Bruce Eggers - WA9NEW, "An Analysis of the Balun," *QST,* Apr 1980, p 19.

Ref. 1512: William Fanckboner - W9INN, "Using Baluns in Transmatches with High-Impedance Lines," *QST,* Apr 1981, p 51.

Ref. 1513: Doug DeMaw - W1FB, "A 'Multipedance' Broadband Transformer," *QST,* Aug 1982, p 39.

Ref. 1514: R. G. Titterington - G3ORY, "The FerriteCored Balun Transformer," *Radio Communication,* Mar 1982, p 216.

Ref. 1515: John S. Belrose - VE2CV, "Transforming the Balun," *QST,* Jun 1991, p 30.

Ref. 1516: D. DeMaw - W1FB, "How to build and use Balun Transformers," *QST,* Mar 1987, p 34.

Ref. 1517: J. Sevick - W2FMI, "The 2:1 Unun Matching Transformer," *CQ,* Aug 1992, p 13.

Ref. 1518: J. Sevick - W2FMI, "The 1.5:1 and the 1.33:1 Unun Transformer," *CQ,* Nov 1992, p 26.

Ref. 1519: W. Maxwell - W2DU, "Some aspects of the balun problem," *QST,* Mar 83, p 38.

Ref. 1520: R. Lewallen - W7EL, "Baluns: What they do and how they do it," *ARRL Antenna Compendium, Vol 1,* p 157.

■ 16. ANTENNA MEASURING

Ref. 1600: R. Schetgen - KU7G - ed., *The ARRL Handbook for the Radio Amateur,* ARRL, Newington, CT.

Ref. 1601: John Schultz - W4FA, "The MFJ-202B R.F. Noise Bridge," *CQ,* Aug 1984, p 50.

Ref. 1602: Michael Martin - DJ7YV, "Die HF Stromzange," *CQ-DL,* Dec 1983, p 581.

Ref. 1603: Reginald Brearley - VE2AYU, "Phase-Angle Meter," *Ham Radio,* Apr 1973, p 28.

Ref. 1604: Robert Baird - W7CSD, "Nonresonant Antenna Impedance Measurements," *Ham Radio,* Apr 1974, p 46.

Ref. 1606: John True - W4OQ, "Antenna Measurements," *Ham Radio,* May 1974, p 36.

Ref. 1607: Frank Doting - W6NKU - et al, "Improvements to the RX Noise Bridge," *Ham Radio,* Feb 1977, p 10.

Ref. 1608: Charles Miller - W3WLX, "Gate-Dip Meter," *Ham Radio,* Jun 1977, p 42.

Ref. 1609: Kenneth F. Carr - WØKUS, "Ground Current Measuring on 160 Meters," *Ham Radio,* Jun 1979, p 46.

Ref. 1610: Forrest Gehrke - K2BT, "A Modern Noise Bridge," *Ham Radio,* Mar 1983, p 50.

Ref. 1611: William Vissers - K4KI, "A Sensitive Field Strength Meter," *Ham Radio,* Jan 1985, p 51.

Ref. 1612: Jerry Sevick - W2FMI, "Simple RF Bridges," *QST,* Apr 1975, p 11.

Ref. 1613: David Geiser - WA2ANU, "The Impedance Match Indicator," *QST,* Jul 1980, p 11.

Ref. 1614: Jerry Sevick - W2FMI, "Measuring Soil Conductivity," *QST,* Mar 1981, p 38.

Ref. 1615: Jack Priedigkeit - W6ZGN, "Measuring Impedance with a Reflection-Coefficient Bridge," *QST,* Mar 1983, p 30.

Ref. 1616: Doug DeMaw - W1FB, "Learning to Use Field Strength Meters," *QST,* Mar 1985, p 26.

Ref. 1617: Al Bry - W2MEL, "Beam Antenna Pattern Measurement," *QST,* Mar 1985, p 31.

Ref. 1618: M. R. Irving - G3ZHY, "The 'Peg Antennameter'," *Radio Communication,* May 1972, p 297.

Ref. 1619: Pat Hawker - G3VA, "Technical Topics: Current Probe for Open-Wire Feeders - Wire Antennas - etc.," *Radio Communication,* Nov 1984, p 962.

Ref. 1620: D. DeMaw - W1FB, "A Laboratory Style RX Noise Bridge," *QST,* Dec 1987, p 32.

Ref. 1621: John Belrose - VE2VC, "RX Noise Bridges," *QST,* May 1988, p 34.

Ref. 1622: Andrew S. Griffith - W4ULD, "A Dipper Amplifier for Impedance Bridges," *QST,* Sep 1988, p 24.

Ref. 1623: John Grebenkemper - KI6WX, "Improving and Using R-X Noise Bridges," *QST,* Aug 1989, p 27.

Ref. 1624: D. DeMaw - W1FB, "MFJ-931 Artificial RF Ground," *QST,* Apr 1988, p 40.

INDEX

A

Absorption mechanism: 1-4
Achievement awards: 2-9
Acoustics: 3-14
AKI Special: 9-53
Analog notch filters: 3-8
Antenna tuners: 6-5
Antipodal focusing: 1-9
Antipodes: 1-9, 1-12
Array elements: 11-3
Arrays of Beverages: 7-21
Atmospheric noise: 1-10, 3-2
Attenuation: 6-3
Audio filters: 3-8, 3-9
Aurora: 1-5
Auroral zones: 1-13
Auto-notch filters: 3-8
Average front-to-back: 5-4
Azimuthal projection: 1-12

B

Balun: 5-5, 6-15
Bandwidth: 3-19, 5-6, 8-7, 8-12,
    9-14, 10-13
Base coil loading: 9-22
Base linear loading: 9-22
Base loading: 9-15
Battle Creek Special: 9-41, 9-53
Beacon stations: 2-7
Beat note: 2-4
Beverage: 1-12
Beverage antenna: 1-12, 2-12, 7-1,
    9-53
    Arrays 7-21
    Bi-directional: 7-14
    Construction: 7-20
    Feeding: 7-12
    Feed lines: 7-20
    Ground system: 7-11
    Impedance: 7-9
    Length: 7-3, 7-4
    Matching transformers: 7-17
    Performance: 7-22
    Termination: 7-11
Bi-square: 10-14
Binomial current distribution: .. 11-26

B (Bobtail)

Bobtail Curtain: 12-13
Boom
    Design: 13-10
    Moments: 13-12
    Sag: 13-13
    Strength: 4-4
Breaking stress: 13-3
Broadband matching: 6-16
Buried radials: 9-8, 9-11

C

Calling by numbers: 2-4
Capacitance hat with base
    loading: 9-24
Capacitance-hat loading: 9-22
Capacitive loading: 8-11, 10-10,
    13-54
Cardioid: 11-23
Center loading: 8-9, 9-15
Characteristic impedance: 6-1
Chordal-hop: 1-9
Christman Method: 11-7
Clamps: 13-14
Clarifier: 2-3
Closed-loop antennas: 1-12
Coaxial cable: 6-2
Coaxial-cable trap: 9-39
Coil
    Calculation: 4-2
    Loading: 8-9
    Plus capacitance hat: 9-24
    Value: 8-11
Collinear dipoles: 8-14
Collins Method: 11-11
Combined: 9-17
Compensated ground wires: 7-15
Component: 11-22
Component ratings: 4-2, 6-8
Compressed delta loop: 10-7
Compression or elongation
    strain: 13-3
Computer programs: 4-1
Conductivities: 5-4
Conductor losses: 6-2
Conductor RF resistance: 9-5
Conjugate match: 6-1

C (Contests)

Contests: 2-8
Counterpoise: 7-11
Coupled impedance: 11-4
Critical frequency: 1-2, 1-7
Crooked path: 1-12
Crooked polar paths: 1-14
Cross modulation: 3-5
Cross-flow: 13-4
Current baluns: 6-16
Current-fed T antennas: 9-50
CW: 3-16

D

D-layer activity: 1-3
Database, the: 1-19
Daytime: 1-6
dBc: 3-6
dBd: 5-4
dBi: 5-4
Declination of the sun: 1-5
Definitions of antennas: 5-1, 5-2
Delay line: 11-12
Delta loops: .... 10-1 ff, 10-5
    Dimensions: 10-9
    Impedance: 10-9
    In phase (collinear): 12-12
    Vertically polarized: 10-5
Dielectric constants: 5-4
Dielectric losses: 6-2, 8-6
Digital signal processing: .. 3-9, 3-17,
    3-19
Dipole: .... 5-4, 8-1 ff
    Collinear: 8-14
    Efficiency: 8-5
    Long: 8-12
    Short: 8-8
    Sloping: 8-19
Direction of firing: 11-3
Directivity: 5-2
Distortion products: 3-3
Double Bazooka: 6-16
Drag coefficient: 13-18
Drive impedance: 4-1, 11-4
Drive shaft: 13-19
DSP: 3-9, 3-17, 3-19
Dummy load: 6-3, 6-15

Dummy plate: 13-12
Dusk and dawn: 1-7
DX
    Cluster: 2-8, 2-9
    Edge, The: 1-15
    Information nets: 2-8
    News publications: 2-8
    Window: 2-1
DXing tools: 1-15
DXpedition antennas: 9-53
DXpeditions: . 1-5, 2-2, 2-4, 2-8, 9-11
Dynamic range: 3-4
Dynamic selectivity: 3-7

E
EBS: 3-15
Economical lengths: 13-16
Efficiency: 5-2, 5-5, 7-1, 8-12,
                                 9-5, 9-14
Elastic deformation: 13-3
Elasticity modulus: 13-3
Electrical length: 9-44
Electronic bias switch: 3-15
Element
    Construction: 11-54
    Loading: 13-48
    Sag: 13-8
    Strength: 4-3, 13-5
    Taper: 4-2, 4-3
Elevated radial systems: 9-12
ELNEC: 5-7
Equalizing: 3-13
Equatorial zones: 1-6
Equilateral triangle: 10-6
Equinox period: 1-6
Equipment: .... 3-1 ff
Extended Double Zepp: 8-12, 8-14

F
Far field: 9-6, 9-30
Feed line: 4-4, 6-1
Feed-line cable lengths: 11-18
Filters, notch 3-8
FOT: 1-1, 5-2
Four-Square arrays: 4-2, 11-35
Free space: 5-2
Frequencies: 2-1
Frequency allocation: 2-1, 2-3
Frequency readout: 3-9
Fresnel: 9-30
Front-end filters: 3-9
Front-to-back ratio: 5-4
Full-size 80-m Yagi: 13-21
Full-size 160-m vertical: 9-40

G
Gain: 5-4, 9-29
Gain compression: 3-4
Gamma: 4-4
Gamma and omega matching: 4-2,
                                       9-44
Gamma match: 13-40
Gehrke Method: 11-13
Generic dimensions: 4-3

Geochron: 1-17
Geometric front-to-back: 5-4
Gray line: 1-7, 1-8, 4-1
    Globe: 1-15
    Program: 1-21
Great circle
    Long path: 1-12
    Map: 1-12
    Paths: 1-12
    Short path: 1-12
Ground: 5-3
    Conditions: 8-4
    Losses: 8-6, 9-5
    Plane: 9-8
    Quality: 7-8, 9-2
    Reflection: 5-4
    Rods: 9-11

H
Hail: 1-11
Hairpin: 13-26, 13-48
Hairpin match: 4-2, 4-4, 13-46
Half loop: 10-14
Half-size triangular array: 11-52
Half sloper: 10-17
Half-square antenna: 12-13
HB9CV: 11-23
High-angle signals: 1-7
High-impedance matching
    system: 6-12
Horizontal
    Antennas: 7-30
    Directivity: 5-1, 8-5
    Polarization: 10-2
Horizontally polarized delta
    loop: 10-7
Horizontally polarized element: . 12-1
Hot-switching: 3-17
Hybrid coupler: 11-12

I
Ice loading: 13-17
Impedance measurement: 11-17
Impedance transformer: 6-1
Inductive loading: 10-10
Intermodulation: 3-12
Intermodulation distortion: 3-3
Inverted L: 9-48, 9-53
Inverted V
    Bandwidth: 8-16
    Dipole: 8-15
    Gain: 8-16
    Length: 8-16
    Radiation pattern: 8-16
    Radiation resistance: 8-15
Ionization: 1-1
Ionosphere: 1-1
Ionosphere, heterogeneous: 1-13
Ionospheric tilt: 1-7
Isotropic: 5-2, 5-4

K
Keying waveform: 3-16

L
L network: 4-2, 6-6
Lewallen Method: 11-8
Line stretcher: 4-2
Linear amplifiers: 3-12
Linear loading: 8-11, 9-18
Linear-loaded duo-bander for
    80/160 meters: 9-35
List operations: 2-5
Literature Database Software: 4-5
Loaded loops: 10-10
Loaded tower: 9-43
Loading: 9-17, 11-56
    Coil: 8-10, 9-26
    Methods: 9-29
Local oscillator: 3-5
Location: 1-9, 7-20, 9-51
Long dipoles: 8-12
Long path on 160 meters: 1-12
Long-delayed echoes: 1-9
Loop bandwidth: 10-13
Loop impedances: 10-2
Loss mechanism: 6-2
Losses: 5-6, 8-6, 8-9

M
Magnetic antenna: 7-24
Magnetic disturbances: 1-5
Magnetic disturbances (aurora): 1-10
Mailbox: 2-9
Mast bearings: 13-18
Mast torque: 13-11
Matching: 4-4
Matching systems: 13-40
Material fatigue: 13-17
Material ratings: 13-17
Materials: 13-9, 13-15
Mathematics: 4-1
Mechanical design: 13-2
Microphones: 3-13
MININEC: 5-7
Modeling: .. 5-7, 7-2, 8-22, 9-32, 13-2
    Arrays: 11-3
    Loops: 10-10
    Vertical arrays: 11-5
Modified Lewallen Method: 11-9
Monitor scope: 3-17
Monitoring systems: 3-17
Monopole: 9-1
MUF: 1-1, 5-1
Mutual coupling: 11-3, 11-4
Mutual impedance: 4-1, 5-7, 11-4

N
Near field: 9-6, 9-30
NEC: 5-8
Nets: 2-5
Network measurements: 11-18
Night-time: 1-7
Noise blanker: 3-10
Noise bridges: 11-17
Noise sidebands: 3-5
Non great-circle paths: 1-12
Non-synchronous transformers: . 6-14

Notch filters: 3-8
Null steering: 7-23

O

Omega match: 13-44
Omega system: 4-4, 9-46
Open-wire: 6-2, 6-3

P

Packet radio: 2-8, 2-9
Parallel impedances: 4-2
Parallel losses: 9-5
Parasitic arrays: 13-1
Parasitic capacitance: 13-24
Parasitic elements: 13-1
Passband tuning: 3-6
Pattern switching for: 11-36
Permeability: 7-12
Personal computer programs: 1-19
Personal computers: 4-1
Pileups: 2-4
PIN diode: 3-17
Power: 3-12
Power dissipation: 9-26
Preamplifiers: 7-23
Propagation: .... 1-1 ff, 4-1
     Paths: 1-12
     Programs: 1-19
Pseudo-Brewster angle: 9-2, 9-3

Q

Q factor: 5-6, 5-7, 6-1, 8-12
QRN: 1-10
QSK: 3-13, 3-16
Quad log impedance: 10-2
Quad loops: 10-1
Quadrature-fed arrays: 11-19
Quads: 13-1
     80-m 13-57
Quarter-wave matching sections: . 6-5
Quarter-wave sloper: 10-17
Quarter-wave vertical: 8-21

R

Radial plow: 9-11
Radial system: 9-30
Radials: 7-11, 9-3
Radiation
     Angle: 4-2, 9-29
     Efficiency: 9-6, 9-8
     Patterns: 5-3
     Resistance: .. 5-5, 8-6, 8-8, 8-16,
          9-1, 9-4, 9-6, 9-15, 9-19
Rain: 1-11
Rain static: 7-14
Real cable: 4-1
Real ground: 5-8, 8-3, 9-2
Receiver blocking: 3-4
Receiver noise: 3-2
Receiver specifications: 3-1
Receiving antennas: 5-2, 7-1
Reciprocal mixing
     (VCO noise): 3-5
Reduced-size quad: 13-57

Reflection coefficient: 9-2
Reflection efficiency: 9-9
Reflection losses: 9-8
Refraction: 1-1
Rigidity modulus: 13-3
RIT: 2-3
Rotating mast: 4-5, 13-18
Rotator: 13-19
RX clarifier: 2-3

S

Season: 1-1, 1-5
Selectivity: 3-6
Self impedance: 5-7, 11-4
Sensitivity: 3-1
Series feeding: 11-55
Shape factor: 3-6
Shared band: 2-2
Shear angle: 13-3
Shear section modulus: 13-3
Shear strain: 13-3
Short dipoles: 8-8
Short radials: 9-13
Short verticals: 9-14, 9-20
Shunt fed towers: 9-47
Shunt feeding: 11-55
Shunt/series impedance network: 4-2
Sideband: 3-9
Signal-to-noise ratio: 7-1
Skeds: 2-7
Slant-wire feed system: 9-47
Sloping
     Dipole: 8-19
     Ground: 8-2
     Termination: 7-13
     Vertical array: 11-60
Small loop antennas: 7-24
Smith Chart: 4-1, 6-4
Snake antenna: 7-29
Snow: 1-11
Software: 2-9, 4-1
Special propagation mechanisms: 1-9
Speech processing: 3-14
Split frequency: 2-2
Square loop: 10-2
Stability: 3-9
Standing waves: 6-1, 6-3
Standing-wave ratio: 4-2, 5-5
Static: 3-7
Static selectivity: 3-7
Strength calculations: 13-4
Stress: 13-2
Stub matching: 4-2, 6-10
Sudden ionospheric disturbances
     (SIDs): 1-10
Summer: 1-6
Sunrise/sunset: 2-7, 4-1
     Tables: 1-17
     Times: 1-17, 1-19
Sunspot cycle: 1-1, 1-3
Surge impedance: 5-7
Survey: 2-9
SWR: 4-2, 5-5
SWR bandwidth: 6-1, 8-17, 9-20, 9-38

T

T antenna: 9-50
T-loaded vertical elements: 11-60
T wire: 9-27
T-wire loading: 9-24
Tall verticals: 9-29
Tapering: 8-22
Telescopic fits: 13-16
Terminating resistor: 7-11
Terminator: 1-7
Thermal noise: 3-1
Third-order IMD: 3-3
Third-order intercept point: 3-4
Three elements in phase array: 11-25
Three-band vertical: 9-35
Three-element dipole array: 12-8
Three-element parasitic dipole
     array: 12-9
Time: 1-1
Time of day: 1-1
Top-loaded vertical: 9-35
Top loading: 9-15
Toroidal transformer: 7-12
Toroids: 7-13
Torque balancing: 4-4, 13-11
Tower: 13-18
Transequatorial propagation: 1-6
Transformer: 6-5
Transmission: 7-9
Transmission line: 5-7, 6-3, 6-4
Transmission-line equivalent: 5-6
Transmitters: 3-12
Traps: 9-38, 9-40
Triangular array: 11-49
Tuned circuit equivalent: 5-6
Tuned feeders: 8-8
Tuned open-wire feeders: 6-13
Twilight periods: 1-7
Two-element bidirectional end-fire
     array: 11-27
Two-element delta loop array: ... 12-5
Two-element horizontal parasitic
     array: 12-4
Two elements in phase array: ... 11-25
Two half-waves in phase: 8-12

U

U bolts: 13-15
Unterminated Beverage: 7-14
Unun: 10-10
Unwanted mutual coupling: 11-21
Utilities: 4-5

V

Variable-area: 13-4
VCOs: 3-5
Velocity factor: 7-2
Velocity of propagation: 7-2
Vertical
     Antennas: .... 9-1 ff
     Array: 11-60
     Array feed system: 11-6
     Arrays, modeling: 11-5
     Dipole: 8-18

Vertical, continued
    Dipole radiation pattern: 8-18
    Dipole radiation resistance: 8-19
    Directivity: 5-1
    Full-size 160-m: 9-40
    Polarization: 10-2
    Quarter-wave: 8-21
    Short: 9-14, 9-20
    Three-band: 9-35
    Top-loaded: 9-35
    Yagis: 13-39
Vertically polarized delta loop: .. 10-5
Vibrations: 13-17
Voltage balun: 6-16
Voltage-fed T antennas: 9-50

W
W3PV algorithm: 4-3

W7EL feed system: 4-2
Wave antenna: 7-1
Weight balance: 4-4, 13-11
Whip: 9-28
Whispering-gallery propagation: . 1-9
Wide-band transformers: 6-13
Wind area: 4-4
Wind load: 4-4
Winter: 1-6
Wire connections: 9-32
Wire elements: 11-55
Wire Yagis: 13-39
Wire cage: 8-7
Worst lobe front-to-back: 5-4

X
XIT: 2-3

Y
Yagi design: 4-3
Yagis: .... 13-1 ff
    Full-size 80-m 13-21
    Vertical: 13-39
    Wire 13-39
Year: 1-1
Yield stress: 13-3, 13-17

Z
Zero beat: 2-3, 2-4
ZL Special: 11-12, 12-12

2-element (cardioid): 4-2
2-element horizontal array: 12-4
4-square array: 4-2, 11-35
80-meter quad: 13-57

About the American Radio Relay League

The seed for Amateur Radio was planted in the 1890s, when Guglielmo Marconi began his experiments in wireless telegraphy. Soon he was joined by dozens, then hundreds, of others who were enthusiastic about sending and receiving messages through the air—some with a commercial interest, but others solely out of a love for this new communications medium. The United States government began licensing Amateur Radio operators in 1912.

By 1914, there were thousands of Amateur Radio operators—hams—in the United States. Hiram Percy Maxim, a leading Hartford, Connecticut, inventor and industrialist saw the need for an organization to band together this fledgling group of radio experimenters. In May 1914 he founded the American Radio Relay League (ARRL) to meet that need.

Today ARRL, with more than 170,000 members, is the largest organization of radio amateurs in the United States. The League is a not-for-profit organization that:

- promotes interest in Amateur Radio communications and experimentation
- represents US radio amateurs in legislative matters, and
- maintains fraternalism and a high standard of conduct among Amateur Radio operators.

At League headquarters in the Hartford suburb of Newington, the staff helps serve the needs of members. ARRL is also International Secretariat for the International Amateur Radio Union, which is made up of similar societies in more than 100 countries around the world.

ARRL publishes the monthly journal *QST*, as well as newsletters and many publications covering all aspects of Amateur Radio. Its headquarters station, W1AW, transmits bulletins of interest to radio amateurs and Morse code practice sessions. The League also coordinates an extensive field organization, which includes volunteers who provide technical information for radio amateurs and public-service activities. ARRL also represents US amateurs with the Federal Communications Commission and other government agencies in the US and abroad.

Membership in ARRL means much more than receiving *QST* each month. In addition to the services already described, ARRL offers membership services on a personal level, such as the ARRL Volunteer Examiner Coordinator Program and a QSL bureau.

Full ARRL membership (available only to licensed radio amateurs) gives you a voice in how the affairs of the organization are governed. League policy is set by a Board of Directors (one from each of 15 Divisions). Each year, half of the ARRL Board of Directors stands for election by the full members they represent. The day-to-day operation of ARRL HQ is managed by an Executive Vice President and a Chief Financial Officer.

No matter what aspect of Amateur Radio attracts you, ARRL membership is relevant and important. There would be no Amateur Radio as we know it today were it not for the ARRL. We would be happy to welcome you as a member! (An Amateur Radio license is not required for Associate Membership.) For more information about ARRL and answers to any questions you may have about Amateur Radio, write or call:

ARRL Educational Activities Dept
225 Main Street
Newington CT 06111-1494
(203) 666-1541
Prospective new amateurs call:
800-32-NEW HAM (800-326-3942)

ON4UN NEW LOW BAND SOFTWARE

Price: $50 + $5 for shipping and handling worldwide. MS-DOS format only.

If you have the original version of the LOW BAND SOFTWARE, you are eligible for a $10 price reduction, provided a copy of the registration form that came with the software is sent with your order.

NAME: _____ CALL: _____

ADDRESS: _____

CITY: _____ STATE: _____ ZIP: _____

Send this Order Form with payment to:

George Oliva, K2UO, 5 Windsor Dr, Eatontown NJ 07724, USA, or

John Devoldere, ON4UN, Poelstraat 215, B9820 Merelbeke, Belgium

PAYMENT BY: ☐ Personal check   ☐ Postal order

Make payable to George Oliva (for orders to K2UO) or John Devoldere (for orders to ON4UN)

ON4UN YAGI DESIGN SOFTWARE

Price: $65 + $5 for shipping and handling worldwide. MS-DOS format only.

NAME: _____ CALL: _____

ADDRESS: _____

CITY: _____ STATE: _____ ZIP: _____

Send this Order Form with payment to:

G. Oliva, K2UO, 5 Windsor Dr, Eatontown NJ 07724, USA, or

J. Devoldere, ON4UN, Poelstraat 215, B9820 Merelbeke, Belgium

PAYMENT BY: ☐ Personal check   ☐ Postal order

Make payable to: George Oliva (for orders to K2UO) or John Devoldere (for orders to ON4UN)

LITERATURE DATATABASE SOFTWARE

Price: $20 + $5 for shipping and handling worldwide. MS-DOS format only.

NAME: _____ CALL: _____

ADDRESS: _____

CITY: _____ STATE: _____ ZIP: _____

Send this Order Form with payment to:

G. Oliva, K2UO, 5 Windsor Dr, Eatontown NJ 07724 USA or

J. Devoldere, ON4UN, Poelstraat 215, B9820 Merelbeke, Belgium

PAYMENT BY: ☐ Personal check   ☐ Postal order

Make payable to: George Oliva (for orders to K2UO) or John Devoldere (for orders to ON4UN)

Coils Pg 6-9 AL

FEEDBACK

Please use this form to give us your comments on this book and what you'd like to see in future editions.

Where did you purchase this book? □ From ARRL directly □ From an ARRL dealer

Is there a dealer who carries
ARRL publications within: □ 5 miles □ 15 miles □ 30 miles of your location? □ Not sure.

License class:

□ Novice □ Technician □ Technician with HF privileges □ General □ Advanced □ Extra

Name

_____ Call sign _____

Address _____

City, State/Province, ZIP/Postal Code _____

Daytime Phone (   ) _____ Age _____

If licensed, how long? _____ ARRL member? □ Yes   □ No

Other hobbies _____

_____

Occupation _____

For ARRL use only	LOW
Edition	2 3 4 5 6 7 8 9 10 11 12
Printing	2 3 4 5 6 7 8 9 10 11 12

From _____

_____

_____

EDITOR, LOW-BAND DXING
AMERICAN RADIO RELAY LEAGUE
225 MAIN ST
NEWINGTON CT 06111-1494

please fold and tape